HMH SCIENCE DIMENSIONS®

Chemistry

Teacher Edition

Houghton Mifflin Harcourt

Authors and Reviewers

PROGRAM ADVISORS

Doris Ingram Lewis, PhD
Professor Emerita of Chemistry
Suffolk University
Boston, Massachusetts

Reza M. Mohseni, PhD
Professor of Chemistry/Lab Director
East Tennessee State University
Johnson City, Tennessee

Gary E. Mueller, PhD, PE
Associate Professor
Missouri University of Science &
    Technology
Rolla, Missouri

CLASSROOM REVIEWERS

Max M. Bradbury
Independence High School
Independence, Kansas

Keri Breeding
Southeast of Saline High School
USD 306
Gypsum, Kansas

Steve Harrison
STEM Director
Appleton Area School District
Appleton, Wisconsin

Jennifer A. Karlen
Madison West High School
Madison, Wisconsin

Anne Markos
Holmen High School
Holmen, Wisconsin

Bhavna Rawal
Harmony School of Excellence and
    Houston Community College
Houston, Texas

Jackie Stewart
Quincy Senior High School
Quincy, Illinois

Michelle Tjugum
Madison East High School
Madison, Wisconsin

Michael DiSpezio

Global Educator
North Falmouth, Massachusetts

Michael DiSpezio has authored many HMH instructional programs for Science and Mathematics. He has also authored numerous trade books and multimedia programs on various topics and hosted dozens of studio and location broadcasts for various organizations in the U.S. and worldwide. Most recently, he has been working with educators to provide strategies for implementing the Next Generation Science Standards, particularly the Science and Engineering Practices, Crosscutting Concepts, and the use of Evidence Notebooks. To all his projects, he brings his extensive background in science; his expertise in classroom teaching at the elementary, middle, and high school levels; and his deep experience in producing interactive and engaging instructional materials.

Thomas O'Brien, PhD

Professor, Science Teacher Education & Educational Leadership
Department of Teaching, Learning & Educational Leadership
College of Community & Public Affairs
Binghamton University (State University of New York)
Binghamton, New York

Tom O'Brien has directed the graduate-level science teacher education programs at Binghamton since 1987. His scholarly interests include professional leadership development (e.g., co-principal investigator for NYS and national grants); science curriculum development, as related to STS themes (e.g., original writing team member for the *Chemistry in the Community book*) and 5E Teaching Cycles; and K–12 science teacher education as informed by cognitive learning theory. He is the author of *Brain-Powered Science Teaching & Learning with Discrepant Events* and co-author/co-editor of *Science for the Next Generation: Preparing for the New Standards*.

Bernadine Okoro

STEM Learning Advocate & Consultant
Washington, DC

Bernadine Okoro is a chemical engineer by training and a playwright, novelist, director, and actress by nature. She went from interacting with patents and biotechnology to the K–12 classroom. A 12-year science educator and Albert Einstein Distinguished Fellow, Okoro was one of the original authors of the Next Generation Science Standards. As a member of the Diversity and Equity Team, her focus on Alternative Education, Community Schools, and now Integrating Social-Emotional Learning and Brain-Based Learning into NGSS is a pathway to support underserved groups from elementary school to adult education. An article and book reviewer for NSTA and other educational publishing companies, Okoro currently works as a STEM Learning Advocate & Consultant.

ENGINEERING CONSULTANT

Cary I. Sneider, PhD
Associate Research Professor
Portland State University
Portland, Oregon

LAB SAFETY REVIEWER

Kenneth R. Roy, PhD
Senior Lab Safety Compliance Consultant
National Safety Consultants, LLC
Vernon, Connecticut

EDUCATOR ADVISORY PANEL MEMBERS

Dr. C. Alex Alvarez
Director of STEM and Curriculum
Valdosta City Schools
Valdosta, Georgia

Kerri Angel
Science Teacher
Department Chair
Churchill County School District
Churchill County Middle School
Fallon, Nevada

Regina Brinker
STEM Coordinator
Livermore Valley Joint Unified School District
Livermore, California

Ronald M. Durso, EdS
District Science Supervisor
Fair Lawn Public Schools
Fair Lawn, New Jersey

Cheryl Frye
NGSS/STEM Coordinator
Menifee Union School District
Menifee, California

Brandon A. Gillette, PhD
Middle School Science
The Pembroke Hill School
Kansas City, Missouri

John Labriola
Middle School Science Teacher,
    Science Content Coordinator
Charities Middle School
Wood River Junction, Rhode Island

Gilbert J. Luna
K–12 Science Curriculum Specialist
Vancouver Public Schools
Vancouver, Washington

Jennifer Su Mataele
PreK–12 Technology, STEAM TOSA
Hacienda La Puente Unified School District
Hacienda Heights, California

Shawna Metcalf
Science Teacher Specialist
Glendale Unified School District
Glendale, California

Erica Rose Motamed
Science Teacher
Lake Center Middle School
Santa Fe Springs, California

Monica Murray, EdD
Principal
Bassett Unified School District
La Puente, California

Christie Purdon
K–12 Science Coordinator
Blue Valley School District
Overland Park, Kansas

Stephen J. Rapa
Science Department Chair
Worcester Public Schools
Worcester, Massachusetts

Alison L. Riordan
Science Curriculum Coordinator, K–12
Plymouth Public Schools
Plymouth, Massachusetts

Greta Trittin Smith
Academic Coach—Science
Garvey School District
Rosemead, California

Marsha Veninga
8th Grade Science Teacher
Bloomington Junior High School,
    Bloomington District 87
Bloomington, Illinois

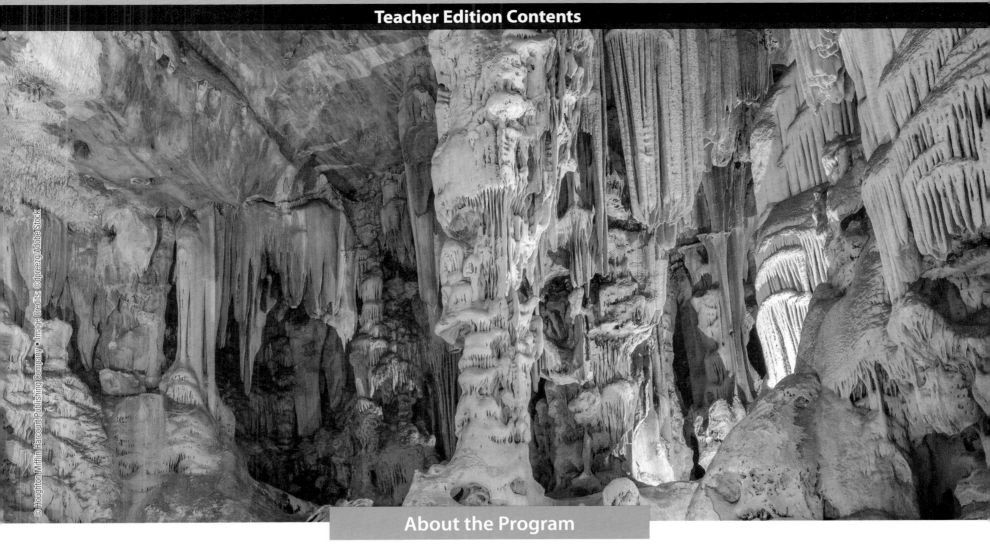

Teacher Edition Contents

© Houghton Mifflin Harcourt Publishing Company • Image Credits: ©dpreezg/Adobe Stock

About the Program

Teacher Edition Contents

Unit 1 Introduction to Chemistry and Engineering

Unit 2 Atoms and Elements

Unit 3 Compounds and Mixtures

Unit 4 Chemical Reactions

Unit 5 Reaction Rates and Equilibrium

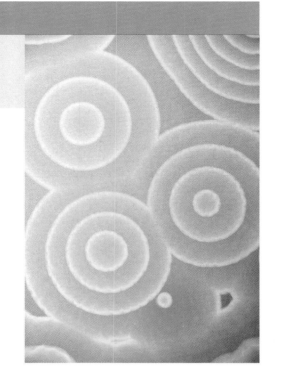

Teacher Resources

Explore Online ▶ Because High School students are accustomed to looking up information online, the Interactive Glossary for *HMH Science Dimensions Chemistry* is provided on *Ed: Your Friend in Learning.*

HMH SCIENCE DIMENSIONS®

Chemistry

Program Overview
GRADES 9–12

Students Are PHENOMENAL

Envision a classroom where students explore real-world phenomena, ask questions, state claims, test their ideas and find resolution through reasoning. With increased demand for science proficiency in the workplace, it has become imperative to develop innovators and problem solvers to fill critical next- generation career roles.

With the program's built-in support and transformed lesson structure, instructors will become facilitators who empower their students to learn through self-directed exploration, analysis, application, and explanation—in short, to think and behave like scientists and engineers.

HMH Science Dimensions Chemistry is more than just a curriculum; it is a vision for developing student scientists.

Built specifically to meet the challenge of the NGSS*, *HMH Science Dimensions* is the complete solution to foster the scientific mind and reach every student.

*Next Generation Science Standards and logo are registered trademarks of Achieve. Neither Achieve nor the lead states and partners that developed the Next Generation Science Standards were involved in the production of, and do not endorse, this product. **T9**

HMH SCIENCE DIMENSIONS®

Chemistry

An **all-new, complete solution** for NGSS: digital, print, and hands-on

What sets HMH Science Dimensions apart?

Active Learning Students make claims, gather evidence and provide reasoning, design and conduct experiments, develop explanations for phenomena, discuss science, and solve problems using the engineering design process.

Engaging Connections Students experience phenomenon-based explorations, real-world storylines, and cross-curricular connections.

Integrated Engineering & STEM Students develop into experts in the engineering design process.

Instructional Support Teachers are supported by online classroom standards, data analyses, digital simulation options, online assessment options, 3D-learning guidance, pacing options, and built-in and in-person professional learning options.

Flexibility Digital, print—with SE available as hardcover or consummable—and professional learning models to fit a full range of needs.

Three-Dimensional Learning made Simple

HMH Science Dimensions Chemistry expertly weaves the Three Dimensions of Learning into each lesson in order to meet the Performance Expectations (PEs). This braided approach takes the burden off you while ensuring a quality 3D-learning experience for your students.

Science and Engineering Practices
Disciplinary Core Ideas
Crosscutting Concepts

Three Dimensions of Learning

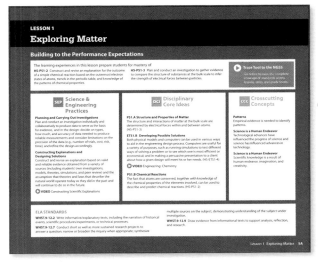

Teacher Edition

Throughout the Teacher Edition, 3D Learning Objectives unpack the Performance Expectations to clearly identify how the **Science and Engineering Practices**, **Crosscutting Concepts**, and **Disciplinary Core Ideas** are put into action.

3D Learning Objective

Students plan and carry out an investigation and describe chemical reactions to determine patterns in the way substances react.

Lessons are designed in the **CER** model to have students make **Claims** about real-world phenomena, do explorations to gather **Evidence,** and apply **Reasoning** to explain a phenomenon. *HMH Science Dimensions Chemistry* has students think like scientists and solve problems like engineers.

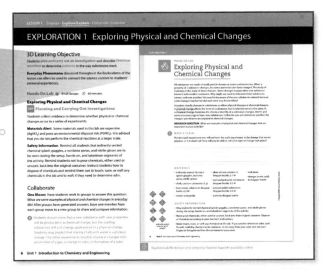

Teacher Edition

*Next Generation Science Standards and logo are registered trademarks of Achieve. Neither Achieve nor the lead states and partners that developed the Next Generation Science Standards were involved in the production of, and do not endorse, this product.

Maximize Instruction with Simplified Planning

Supportive tools and technology give teachers what they need to plan efficiently and effectively. Reclaim valuable time by taking the guesswork out of lesson planning and resource gathering. Between the *HMH Science Dimensions Chemistry* resources and *Ed: Your Friend in Learning* online platform, everything teachers need for their lessons is accessible.

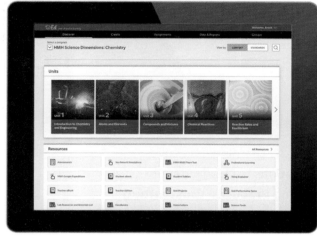

Ed: Your Friend in Learning

Planning is easy with **all-in-one resources**. With Ed's digital lesson planning, you can leverage data and work with digital assessments or with optional printable assessments or assignments as well as assign work to entire classes, multiple classes, or students individually.

Try it now!

Request an online preview at
hmhco.com/ScienceDimensions

HMH Science Dimensions Trace Tool to the NGSS helps you make sense of the standards, understand how they connect and spiral from one grade to another, and identify HMH resources to support your NGSS-based instruction. You can trace the standards by PEs, SEPs, CCCs, or DCIs. When you click on a standard, you can view where in the program that standard is covered.

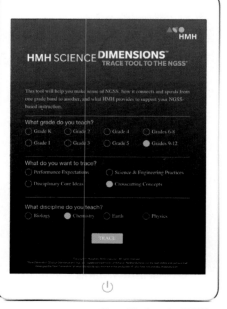

Trace Tool to the NGSS

The NGSS curriculum requires a significantly different approach to how science is being taught in today's classrooms. HMH provides the support you need to make the transition to a student-centered, NGSS style of teaching. With a thoughtfully structured Teacher Edition and professional learning videos built directly into the core curriculum, teachers have more support than ever.

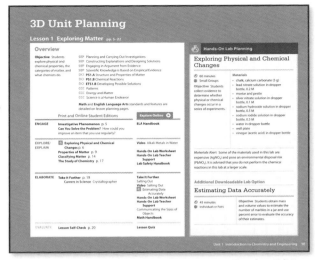

Teacher Edition

The Teacher Edition (online and print) is organized around the familiar **5E instructional model** to ease implementation. This provides a solid foundation upon which to build an NGSS curriculum.

Professional Development Video

Embedded professional learning videos help teachers better prepare for this new approach to science education. Just-in-time videos, featuring our dynamic consulting authors, guide teachers through the key approaches that ensure NGSS success.

Ed: Your Friend in Learning

Grouping tools assist teachers in grouping students based on data that leads to flexibility in making assignments to address specific needs

Assessment to Enhance Instruction for Every Student

At the end of every lesson, students use the evidence they gathered throughout the lesson to explain the **investigative phenomenon** presented at the beginning of the lesson.

Digitally enhanced test items provide greater analysis of student understanding and prep students for state assessments.

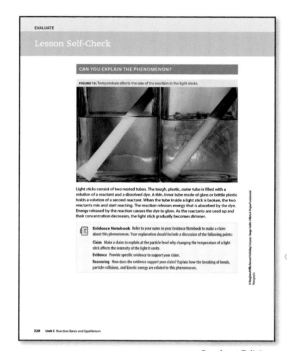

Student Edition

Evidence Notebook prompts encourage students to use evidence gathered to reason out explanations.

Ed: Your Friend in Learning

Assessment Data The Data & Reports feature breaks down how each assessment meets the NGSS and provides data analysis on class and individual progress towards the 3D and Performance Expectations.

Performance-Based Assessments help you ensure that your students can perform the Science and Engineering Practices called for by the NGSS. They also guide students toward making connections across Performance Expectations.

Growing from **Student** to Scientist

As students learn to think like scientists and solve problems like engineers, they need the right supports and guidance. *HMH Science Dimensions Chemistry* lesson design, labs, and activities weave the three dimensions of learning together to have students applying the Science and Engineering Practices to unveil Crosscutting Concepts and explain real-world phenomena.

Beyond learning science as a list of facts, students see the interconnectedness of science topics and recognize patterns across science disciplines.

Every Lesson begins with either **Can You Explain the Phenomenon?** or **Can You Solve the Problem?**—an investigative phenomenon to spark curiosity and motivate students to explore the subsequent learning activities.

Collaboration is an essential part of developing skills for the real world. *HMH Science Dimensions Chemistry* provides ample opportunities for students to participate in groups to complete activities and partner with their peers to discuss their findings.

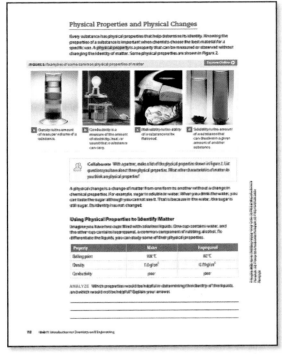

Student Edition

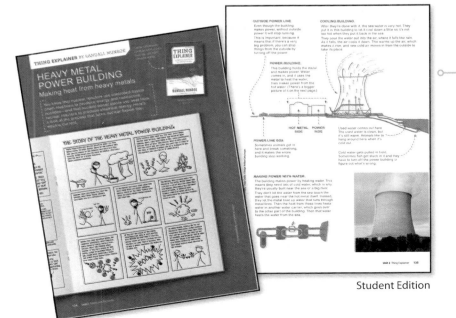

Student Edition

Randall Munroe, author of popular webcomic **xkcd,** former NASA roboticist, and *New York Times* bestselling author of *What If?*, has provided illustrations from his book *Thing Explainer* that are aligned to the curriculum and integrated at point of use in the print and digital editions of *HMH Science Dimensions Chemistry*.

By adding his sense of humor to the drawings and descriptions, Munroe has made "Thing Explainers" succeed in providing a fun way to clarify information students may struggle to grasp. His webcomic style, as seen on **xkcd.com**, engages students and adults alike.

Engage with Meaningful Technology

HMH Science Dimensions Chemistry is a digital-first program. The curriculum leverages the advantages of technology while prioritizing a student-centered learning model.

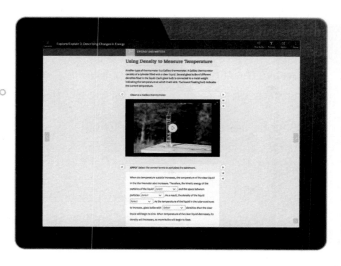

Online lessons are enriched above and beyond the print lessons with educational videos, learning interactivities, and technology-enhanced item choices. Vocabulary is highlighted and clickable, with point-of-use pop-up definitions.

HMH Field Trips
powered by
Google Expeditions

As a Google content partner, HMH has developed unique field trips for **Google Expeditions**. An HMH Teacher Guide provides multiple options for incorporating the Expeditions into your lessons, as well as tips on how to guide and customize the experience.

Experience these **HMH Virtual Field Trips** with your students: Big Cypress National Preserve, Saturn V Rocket at NASA, Volcanoes around the World, and more! Learn more at **hmhco.com/fieldtrips**.

Unique You Solve It simulations provide open-ended opportunities for students to design and run experiments, gather data, and analyze the impact of different variables on a closed system. Students demonstrate problem-solving abilities as described by the NGSS.

Additional Program content can be accessed offline through the accompanying app. This allows for maximum compatibility in 1:1 or **Bring Your Own Device** learning environments or with the wide variety of technology that students have at home.

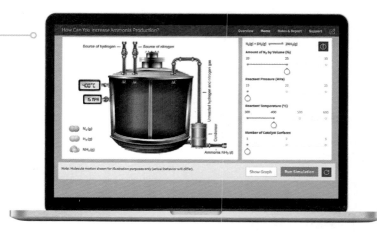

HS-PS1 Matter and its Interactions

		Print and Digital Resources
Performance Expectation	**HS-PS1-1** Use the periodic table as a model to predict the relative properties of elements based on the patterns of electrons in the outermost energy level of atoms.	**Supporting Learning Experiences** Unit 2 Lesson 1 and Hands-On Labs, Crosscutting Concept, pp. 57–82 Lesson 2 and Hands-On Lab, Crosscutting Concept, Engineering, pp. 83–102 Unit 3, Lesson 1 and Hands-On Lab, Crosscutting Concept, pp. 145–168
Science and Engineering Practice	**Developing and Using Models**	
Science and Engineering Practice *Connections to Nature of Science*	**Scientific Investigations Use a Variety of Methods** **Scientific Knowledge is Based on Empirical Evidence** **Scientific Knowledge is Open to Revision in Light of New Evidence**	**Assessment & Performance** *Unit 2* **Project,** pp. 53I–53J, 54 **Performance Task,** p. 138 *Unit 3 You Solve It: Planetary-Rover Materials (digital only)* Assessment Guide and Online Lesson Quizzes Unit Test Middle-of-Year Test End-of-Year Test
Disciplinary Core Idea	**PS1.A Structure and Properties of Matter** Each atom has a charged substructure consisting of a nucleus, which is made of protons and neutrons, surrounded by electrons. The periodic table orders elements horizontally by the number of protons in the atom's nucleus and places those with similar chemical properties in columns. The repeating patterns of this table reflect patterns of outer electron states.	
Crosscutting Concept	**Patterns**	
Crosscutting Concept *Connections to Nature of Science*	**Scientific Knowledge Assumes an Order and Consistency in Natural Systems** **Science is a Human Endeavor**	

Performance Expectation	**HS-PS1-2** Construct and revise an explanation for the outcome of a simple chemical reaction based on the outermost electron states of atoms, trends in the periodic table, and knowledge of the patterns of chemical properties.	**Supporting Learning Experiences** Unit 1, Lesson 1 and Hands-On Lab, pp. 5–22 Unit 3, Lesson 1 and Hands-On Labs, pp. 145–168 Unit 4, Lesson 1 and Hands-On Lab, pp. 231–252
Science and Engineering Practice	**Constructing Explanations and Designing Solutions**	**Assessment & Performance**
Disciplinary Core Idea	**PS1.A Structure and Properties of Matter** The periodic table orders elements horizontally by the number of protons in the atom's nucleus and places those with similar chemical properties in columns. The repeating patterns of this table reflect patterns of outer electron states. **PS1.B Chemical Reactions** The fact that atoms are conserved, together with knowledge of the chemical properties of the elements involved, can be used to describe and predict chemical reactions.	*Unit 3 You Solve It: Planetary-Rover Materials (digital only)* *Unit 4* **Project,** pp. 227I–227J, 228 **Performance Task,** p. 304 Assessment Guide and Online Lesson Quizzes Unit Test ***Performance-Based Assessment*** End-of-Year Test
Crosscutting Concept	**Patterns**	

HS-PS1 Matter and its Interactions continued

		Print and Digital Resources
Performance Expectation	**HS-PS1-3** Plan and conduct an investigation to gather evidence to compare the structure of substances at the bulk scale to infer the strength of electrical forces between particles.	**Supporting Learning Experiences** Unit 1, Lesson 1 and Crosscutting Concept, pp. 5–22 Unit 3 Lesson 1 and Hands-On Labs, Engineering, Guided Research (digital only), pp. 145–168 Lesson 2 and Hands-On Labs, Math Connection, Problem Solving, Guided Research (digital only), pp. 169–194 Lesson 3 and Hands-On Lab (digital only), Engineering Lab, pp. 195–218
Science and Engineering Practice	**Planning and Carrying Out Investigations**	
Science and Engineering Practice *Connections to Nature of Science*	**Scientific Knowledge is Based on Empirical Evidence**	
Disciplinary Core Idea	**PS1.A Structure and Properties of Matter** The structure and interactions of matter at the bulk scale are determined by electrical forces within and between atoms. **PS2.B Types of Interactions** Attraction and repulsion between electric charges at the atomic scale explain the structure, properties, and transformations of matter, as well as the contact forces between material objects. *(secondary)*	**Assessment & Performance** *Unit 1 Performance Task,* p. 50 *Unit 3* 　*Project,* pp. 141J–141K, 142 　*Performance Task,* p. 224 　*You Solve It: Properties of a Substance (digital only)*
Crosscutting Concept	**Patterns**	Assessment Guide and Online
Crosscutting Concept *Connections to Nature of Science*	**Scientific Knowledge Assumes an Order and Consistency in Natural Systems** **Science is a Human Endeavor**	Lesson Quizzes 　Unit Test 　*Performance-Based Assessment* 　End-of-Year Test

Performance Expectation	**HS-PS1-4** Develop a model to illustrate that the release or absorption of energy from a chemical reaction system depends upon the changes in total bond energy.	**Supporting Learning Experiences** Unit 4, Lesson 3 and Engineering Lab, pp. 273–298
Science and Engineering Practice	**Developing and Using Models**	**Assessment & Performance** *Unit 4* 　*Project,* pp. 227I–227J, 228 　*Performance Task,* p. 304
Disciplinary Core Idea	**PS1.A Structure and Properties of Matter** A stable molecule has less energy than the same set of atoms separated; one must provide at least this energy in order to take the molecule apart. **PS1.B Chemical Reactions** Chemical processes, their rates, and whether or not energy is stored or released can be understood in terms of the collisions of molecules and the rearrangements of atoms into new molecules, with consequent changes in the sum of all bond energies in the set of molecules that are matched by changes in kinetic energy.	*You Solve It: Diesel (digital only)* 　Assessment Guide and Online 　Lesson Quizzes 　Unit Test 　*Performance-Based Assessment* 　End-of-Year Test
Crosscutting Concept	**Energy and Matter**	

HS-PS1 Matter and its Interactions

Performance Expectation	**HS-PS1-5** Apply scientific principles and evidence to provide an explanation about the effects of changing the temperature or concentration of the reacting particles on the rate at which a reaction occurs.
Science and Engineering Practice	**Constructing Explanations and Designing Solutions**
Disciplinary Core Idea	**PS1.B Chemical Reactions** Chemical processes, their rates, and whether or not energy is stored or released can be understood in terms of the collisions of molecules and the rearrangements of atoms into new molecules, with consequent changes in the sum of all bond energies in the set of molecules that are matched by changes in kinetic energy.
Crosscutting Concept	**Patterns**

Supporting Learning Experiences
Unit 5
Lesson 1 and Hands-On Lab, Crosscutting Concept, Problem Solving, Math Connection, pp. 311–330
Lesson 2 and Data Analysis, Hands-On Lab, pp. 331–358

Assessment & Performance
Unit 5 Performance Task, p. 386

Assessment Guide and Online
  Lesson Quizzes
  Unit Test
  End-of-Year Test

Performance Expectation	**HS-PS1-6** Refine the design of a chemical system by specifying a change in conditions that would produce increased amounts of products at equilibrium.
Science and Engineering Practice	**Constructing Explanations and Designing Solutions**
Disciplinary Core Idea	**PS1.B Chemical Reactions** In many situations, a dynamic and condition-dependent balance between a reaction and the reverse reaction determines the numbers of all types of molecules present. **ETS1.C Optimizing the Design Solution** Criteria may need to be broken down into simpler ones that can be approached systematically, and decisions about the priority of certain criteria over others (trade-offs) may be needed. (secondary)
Crosscutting Concept	**Stability and Change**

Supporting Learning Experiences
Unit 5
Lesson 2 and Data Analysis, Crosscutting Concept, pp. 331–358
Lesson 3 and Hands-On Lab, Guided Research (digital only), pp. 359–380

Assessment & Performance
Unit 5
  Project, pp. 307J–307K, 308
  Performance Task, p. 386
  You Solve It: Ammonia Production (digital only)

Assessment Guide and Online
  Lesson Quizzes
  Unit Test
  Performance-Based Assessment
  End-of-Year Test

HS-PS1 Matter and its Interactions continued

		Print and Digital Resources
Performance Expectation	**HS-PS1-7** Use mathematical representations to support the claim and atoms, and therefore mass, are conserved during a chemical reaction.	**Supporting Learning Experiences** Unit 4 Lesson 1 and Hands-On Labs, Problem Solving, Crosscutting Concept, pp. 231–252 Lesson 2 and Problem Solving, Engineering, Hands-On Lab, pp. 253–272
Science and Engineering Practice	**Using Mathematical and Computational Thinking**	
Science and Engineering Practice *Connections to Nature of Science*	**Scientific Investigations Use a Variety of Methods** **Scientific Knowledge is Based on Empirical Evidence** **Scientific Knowledge is Open to Revision in Light of New Evidence** **Science Models, Laws, Mechanisms, and Theories Explain Natural Phenomena**	**Assessment & Performance** *Unit 4 Project,* pp. 227I–227J, 228
Disciplinary Core Idea	**PS1.B Growth and Development of Organisms** The fact that atoms are conserved, together with knowledge of the chemical properties of the elements involved, can be used to describe and predict chemical reactions.	Assessment Guide and Online Lesson Quizzes Unit Test End-of-Year Test
Crosscutting Concept	**Energy and Matter**	
Crosscutting Concept *Connections to Nature of Science*	**Scientific Knowledge Assumes an Order and Consistency in Natural Systems** **Science is a Human Endeavor** **Science Addresses Questions About the Natural and Material World**	

Performance Expectation	**HS-PS1-8** Develop models to illustrate the changes in the composition of the nucleus of the atom and the energy released during the processes of fission, fusion, and radioactive decay.	**Supporting Learning Experiences** Unit 2, Lesson 3 and Crosscutting Concept, Hands-On Lab, Hands-On Lab (digital only), pp. 103–128
Science and Engineering Practice	**Developing and Using Models**	
Disciplinary Core Idea	**PS1.C Nuclear Processes** Nuclear processes, including fusion, fission, and radioactive decays of unstable nuclei, involve release or absorption of energy. The total number of neutrons plus protons does not change in any nuclear process.	**Assessment & Performance** *Unit 2 Project,* pp. 53I–53J, 54 Assessment Guide and Online Lesson Quizzes Unit Test *Performance-Based Assessment* Middle-of-Year Test
Crosscutting Concept	**Energy and Matter**	
Crosscutting Concept *Connections to Nature of Science*	**Scientific Knowledge Assumes an Order and Consistency in Natural Systems**	

HS-PS2 Motion and Stability: Forces and Interactions

		Print and Digital Resources
Performance Expectation	**HS-PS2-6** Communicate scientific and technical information about why the molecular-level structure is important in the functioning of designed materials.	**Supporting Learning Experiences** Unit 3, Lesson 3 and Engineering Lab, Engineering, Guided Research (digital only), Careers in Engineering (digital only), pp. 195–218
Science and Engineering Practice	**Obtaining, Evaluating, and Communicating Information**	
Disciplinary Core Idea	**PS2.B Types of Interactions** Attraction and repulsion between electric charges at the atomic scale explain the structure, properties, and transformations of matter, as well as the contact forces between material objects.	**Assessment & Performance** ***Unit 3*** ***Project,*** pp. 141J–141K, 142 ***Performance Task,*** p. 224
Crosscutting Concept	**Structure and Function**	Assessment Guide and Online Lesson Quizzes Unit Test ***Performance-Based Assessment*** End-of-Year Test

HS-PS3 Energy

		Print and Digital Resources
Performance Expectation	**HS-PS3-4** Plan and conduct an investigation to provide evidence that the transfer of thermal energy when two components of different temperature are combined within a closed system results in a more uniform energy distribution among the components in the system (second law of thermodynamics).	**Supporting Learning Experiences** Unit 4, Lesson 3 and Hands-On Labs, Engineering Lab (digital only), pp. 273–298
Science and Engineering Practice	**Planning and Carrying Out Investigations**	**Assessment & Performance** ***Unit 4 Performance Task,*** p. 304
Disciplinary Core Idea	**PS3.B Conservation of Energy and Energy Transfer** Energy cannot be created or destroyed, but it can be transported from one place to another and transferred between systems. Uncontrolled systems always evolve toward more stable states—that is, toward more uniform energy distribution (e.g., water flows downhill, objects hotter than their surrounding environment cool down). **PS3.D Energy in Chemical Processes** Although energy cannot be destroyed, it can be converted to less useful forms—for example, to thermal energy in the surrounding environment.	Assessment Guide and Online Lesson Quizzes Unit Test End-of-Year Test
Crosscutting Concept	**Systems and System Models**	

HS-ETS1 Engineering Design

Print and Digital Resources

Performance Expectation	**HS-ETS1-1** Analyze a major global challenge to specify qualitative and quantitative criteria and constraints for solutions that account for societal needs and wants.
Science and Engineering Practice	**Asking Questions and Defining Problems**
Disciplinary Core Idea	**ETS1.A Defining and Delimiting Engineering Problems** Criteria and constraints also include satisfying any requirements set by society, such as taking issues of risk mitigation into account, and they should be quantified to the extent possible and stated in such a way that one can tell if a given design meets them. Humanity faces major global challenges today, such as the need for supplies of clean water and food or for energy sources that minimize pollution, which can be addressed through engineering. These global challenges also may have manifestations in local communities.
Crosscutting Concept *Connections to Engineering, Technology, and Applications of Science*	**Influence of Science, Engineering, and Technology on Society and the Natural World**
Crosscutting Concept *Connections to Nature of Science*	**Science Addresses Questions About the Natural and Material World**

Supporting Learning Experiences

Unit 1, Lesson 2 and Crosscutting Concept, pp. 23–44

Unit 2, Lesson 3, pp. 103–128

Unit 3, Lesson 2 and Language Arts, pp. 169–194

Unit 4, Lesson 3 and Engineering Lab, pp. 273–298

Assessment & Performance

Unit 1 Project, pp. 1H–1I, 2

Unit 4

   Project, pp. 227I–227J, 228

   You Solve It: Diesel (digital only)

Unit 5 You Solve It: Design a Battery (digital only)

   Assessment Guide and Online

     Lesson Quizzes

     Unit Test

     Middle-of-Year Test

     End-of-Year Test

HS-ETS1 Engineering Design

Performance Expectation	**HS-ETS1-2** Design a solution to a complex real-world problem by breaking it down into smaller, more manageable problems that can be solved through engineering.
Science and Engineering Practice	**Constructing Explanations and Designing Solutions**
Disciplinary Core Idea	**ETS1.C Optimizing the Design Solution** Criteria may need to be broken down into simpler ones that can be approached systematically, and decisions about the priority of certain criteria over others (trade-offs) may be needed.

Supporting Learning Experiences
Unit 3, Lesson 3 and Engineering, Engineering Lab, Careers in Engineering (digital only), pp. 195–218

Assessment & Performance
Unit 3
   Project, pp. 141J-141K, 142
   Performance Task, p. 224
Unit 4 Project, pp. 227I-227J, 228
Unit 5
   Project, pp. 307J-307K, 308
   You Solve It: Design a Battery (digital only)

   Assessment Guide and Online
      Lesson Quizzes
      Unit Test
      Performance-Based Assessment
      End-of-Year Test

HS-ETS1 **Engineering Design** continued

		Print and Digital Resources
Performance Expectation	**HS-ETS1-3** Evaluate a solution to a complex real-world problem based on prioritized criteria and tradeoffs that account for a range of constraints, including cost, safety, reliability, and aesthetics, as well as possible social, cultural, and environmental impacts.	**Supporting Learning Experiences** Unit 1, Lesson 2 and Engineering, Engineering Lab, Crosscutting Concept, pp. 23–44 Unit 2, Lesson 3, pp. 103–128
Science and Engineering Practice	**Constructing Explanations and Designing Solutions**	Unit 3, Lesson 3 and Engineering Lab, pp. 195–218 Unit 4, Lesson 3 and Engineering Lab, pp. 273–298
Disciplinary Core Idea	**ETS1.B Developing Possible Solutions** When evaluating solutions, it is important to take into account a range of constraints, including cost, safety, reliability, and aesthetics, and to consider social, cultural, and environmental impacts.	Unit 5 Lesson 2 and Crosscutting Concept, Engineering, pp. 331–358
Crosscutting Concept *Connections to Engineering, Technology, and Applications of Science*	**Influence of Science, Engineering, and Technology on Society and the Natural World**	Lesson 3 and Engineering Lab, Crosscutting Concept, Guided Research (digital only), pp. 359–380

Crosscutting Concept *Connections to Nature of Science*	**Science Addresses Questions About the Natural and Material World**	**Assessment & Performance**
		Unit 1 Project, pp. 1H–1I, 2
		Unit 3
		  Project, pp. 141J-141K, 142
		  Performance Task, p. 224
		Unit 4
		  Performance Task, p. 304
		  You Solve It: Diesel (digital only)
		Unit 5 Project, pp. 307J-307K, 308
		
		Assessment Guide and Online
		  Lesson Quizzes
		  Unit Test
		  Performance-Based Assessment
		  Middle-of-Year Test
		  End-of-Year Test

HS-ETS1 Engineering Design

Performance Expectation	**HS-ETS1-4** Use a computer simulation to model the impact of proposed solutions to a complex real-world problem with numerous criteria and constraints on interactions within and between systems relevant to the problem.
Science and Engineering Practice	**Using Mathematical and Computational Thinking**
Disciplinary Core Idea	**ETS1.B Developing Possible Solutions** Both physical models and computers can be used in various ways to aid in the engineering design process. Computers are useful for a variety of purposes, such as running simulations to test different ways of solving a problem or to see which one is most efficient or economical; and in making a persuasive presentation to a client about how a given design will meet his or her needs.
Crosscutting Concept	**Systems and System Models**

Supporting Learning Experiences

Unit 1, Lesson 2 and Engineering Lab (digital only), pp. 23–44

Unit 4, Lesson 3 and Engineering Lab, pp. 273–298

Unit 5, Lesson 1 and Crosscutting Concept, Engineering Lab (digital only), pp. 311–330

Assessment & Performance

Unit 3

   You Solve It: Planetary-Rover Materials (digital only)

   You Solve It: Properties of a Substance (digital only)

Unit 5 You Solve It: Design a Battery (digital only)

   Assessment Guide and Online

     Lesson Quizzes

     Unit Test

     End-of-Year Test

The following pacing guide shows one possible approach, labeled Comprehensive Path, to completing the curriculum in 180 days of instructional time.

However, **HMH Science Dimensions**® was built for flexibility. The approach in the Comprehensive Path may not fit every situation. If you find that more time is needed for some units, you can indicate this in the Custom Pacing column. Consult the Adjusted Path column for the units you

haven't taught yet to identify possible ways to accelerate them so you still cover the entire curriculum in 180 days. A Detailed Pacing Guide is available on Ed: Your Friend in Learning.

The lessons and activities in this guide are referenced in both print and online editions. Therefore, the guide may be used by those working solely with the Interactive Online Edition, those working solely with the printed edition, or those who use selections from both in a hybrid approach.

In the tables, 1 = 45 minutes of instruction.

	Comprehensive Path Allotted Time	Adjusted Path Allotted Time	Custom Pacing
Unit 1 Introduction to Chemistry and Engineering			
Unit Project	3	3	
Lesson 1 Exploring Matter	9	6	
Lesson 2 Chemistry and the Engineering Design Process	11	8	
Unit 1 Practice and Review	1	1	
Unit 1 Assessment–choose from the following options:	4	3	
• Unit 1 Performance Task (3) • Unit 1 Test, Assessment Guide (1) • Performance-Based Assessment, Assessment Guide (variable)			
Total for Unit 1	**28**	**21**	

	Comprehensive Path Allotted Time	Adjusted Path Allotted Time	Custom Pacing
Unit 2 Atoms and Elements			
Unit Project	3	3	
Lesson 1 Modeling Atomic Structure	11	9	
Lesson 2 Investigating Patterns in the Periodic Table	9	6	
Lesson 3 Analyzing Nuclear Reactions	9	7	
Unit 2 Practice and Review	1	1	
Unit 2 Assessment–choose from the following options:	4	3	
• Unit 2 Performance Task (2) • Unit 2 Test, Assessment Guide (1) • Performance-Based Assessment, Assessment Guide (variable)			
Total for Unit 2	**37**	**29**	

	Comprehensive Path Allotted Time	Adjusted Path Allotted Time	Custom Pacing
Unit 3 Compounds and Mixtures			
Unit Project	3	3	
Lesson 1 Investigating Chemical Compounds	9	7	
Lesson 2 Analyzing the Properties of Compounds and Solutions	10	9	
Lesson 3 Engineering Materials	10	9	
You Solve It: Which Planetary-Rover Materials are Suitable?	1	*Optional*	
You Solve It: How Can You Change the Properties of a Substance?	1	*Optional*	
Unit 3 Practice and Review	1	1	
Unit 3 Assessment–choose from the following options:	4	3	
• Unit 3 Performance Task (3) • Unit 3 Test, Assessment Guide (1) • Performance-Based Assessment, Assessment Guide (variable)			
Total for Unit 3	**39**	**32**	

	Comprehensive Path Allotted Time	Adjusted Path Allotted Time	Custom Pacing
Unit 4 Chemical Reactions			
Unit Project	3	3	
Lesson 1 Observing and Modeling Chemical Reactions	8	7	
Lesson 2 Analyzing Chemical Reactions	8	6	
Lesson 3 Investigating Energy in Chemical Reactions	10	10	
You Solve It: Why Use Diesel?	1	*Optional*	
Unit 4 Practice and Review	1	1	
Unit 4 Assessment—choose from the following options:	4	3	
• Unit 4 Performance Task (3) • Unit 4 Test, Assessment Guide (1) • Performance-Based Assessment, Assessment Guide (variable)			
Total for Unit 4	**35**	**30**	

Pacing Guide

	Comprehensive Path Allotted Time	Adjusted Path Allotted Time	Custom Pacing
Unit 5 Reaction Rates and Equilibrium			
Unit Project	3	3	
Lesson 1 Investigating Reaction Rates	10	8	
Lesson 2 Exploring Chemical Equilibrium	11	9	
Lesson 3 Analyzing Chemical Systems	10	8	
You Solve It: How Can You Design a Battery?	1	*Optional*	
You Solve It: How Can You Increase Ammonia Production?	1	*Optional*	
Unit 5 Practice and Review	1	1	
Unit 5 Assessment–choose from the following options:	4	3	
• Unit 5 Performance Task (2) • Unit 5 Test, Assessment Guide (1) • Performance-Based Assessment, Assessment Guide (variable)			
Total for Unit 5	**41**	**32**	

Teacher Notes

By Thomas O'Brien

We live in a time that challenges citizens to integrate **scientific literacy** and **mathematical numeracy** to *model, make sense of, and solve quantitative problems arising in everyday life, society, and the workplace* (CCSS Mathematics). As "next generation" science teachers, we need to teach our students to think beyond the limitations of the "useful fiction" of separate subject silos for science and math. We can integrate teaching these two subjects by focusing on the following leverage points for interdisciplinary connections:

1. NGSS Dimension 1: The eight Science & Engineering Practices overlap with the eight CCCS Mathematical Practices.

2. NGSS Dimension 2: The seven Crosscutting Concepts serve as the big-picture conceptual themes that apply equally well to mathematics courses.

3. Hands-on explorations that use real-world problems, driving questions, materials, models, and data collection and analysis fit equally well into science and mathematics classes.

The NGSS call for the reintegration of these two subjects harkens back to the natural philosophy of Archimedes (287–212 BCE), the ancient Greek scientist-mathematician-engineer who literally and figuratively saw his work as a "lever to move the world." Galileo (1564–1642), Archimedes' intellectual "grandson," argued that "The universe is a grand book of philosophy. The book lies continuously open to man's gaze, yet none can hope to comprehend it who has not first mastered the language and characters in which it has been written. This language is mathematics."

> **"The transition to the era of modern science was catalyzed by the close synergy between the physical sciences and mathematics."**

In fact, the transition to the era of modern science was catalyzed by the close synergy between the physical sciences and mathematics. The systematic measurement, manipulation, analysis, interpretation, and representation of quantitative data enabled the discovery of universal patterns and principles in nature. Or, as Isaac Newton (1642–1727) put it, "The latest authors, like the most ancient, strove to subordinate the phenomena of nature to the laws of mathematics."

More recently, the *School Science & Mathematics* journal was founded in 1901 to promote interdisciplinary collaboration across the K–college curricular continuum. Consider the domain of chemistry as a representative case. Chemistry topics such as the law of conservation of matter and energy, the gas laws, the periodic table, stoichiometry, thermodynamics, chemical kinetics, solubility, equilibrium and redox reactions, and environmental pollution all demonstrate that *mathematics matters* and *chemistry counts* in community contexts and careers well beyond school textbooks and tests.

Let's consider a specific, concrete example of how the NGSS Crosscutting Concepts of system models and scale, proportion, and quantity can be featured in interdisciplinary, hands-on explorations that focus on metric measurements and powers of ten across the sciences.

> **Manipulative Models Matter** Physical models can be made with a meterstick, twelve one-meter-long dowel rods, eight (3 cm^3) wooden blocks with a hole cut in the center of each of the six faces (to be used as connectors for the dowel rods), standard cubic decimeters (1 L box), cubic centimeters (or sugar cubes as an approximate model), and individual crystals of table salt (as an approximate model for a cubic millimeter). The latter are interesting to have students examine with magnifying lenses.

With the meter (= 10 dm = 100 cm = 1000 mm) as the metric base unit of length, one can easily visualize the power of ten scales of 10^1, 10^2, 10^3, and 10^4 (i.e.,10 one-meter-long dowel rods laid end-to-end would contain 10 000 mm).

Four one-meter-long dowel rods (and four connector cubes) can be used to construct a square with a surface area of 1 m^2 (= 100 dm^2 = 10 000 cm^2 = 1 000 000 mm^2). One million (10^6) salt crystals could fit into this two-dimensional square.

We can "next gen" this flat model by going three dimensional. Two separate square meters can be connected with four vertical dowel rods to form a cubic meter.

> 1 m^3 = 10 dm × 10 dm × 10 dm = 10^3 dm^3 **(thousand)**
>
> 1 m^3 = 100 cm × 100 cm × 100 cm = 10^6 cm^3 **(million and parts per million)**
>
> 1 m^3 = 1000 mm × 1000 mm × 1000 mm = 10^9 mm^3 **(billion and parts per billion)**

Have three students hold (one each), a model of a cubic millimeter (one salt crystal), centimeter, and decimeter and have them step into the cubic meter to get an insider's perspective on 3D mathematical modeling, scientific notation, and powers of ten!

Scales of Science: Magnitudes Matter

Now, let's see how these powers-of-ten mathematical models help us appreciate some key "far out" scientific facts and principles across multiple science disciplines.

Astronomy and Physics

Textbook images and 3D models of even our own solar system misrepresent relative sizes and distances. Challenge students to see how our "local" Earth-moon system could be modeled to the correct scale in a classroom and even in a textbook. Beyond this, space science is truly "far out," and textbook images are "forced to lie." Distances are measured in light-years based on the 3.0×10^5 km/s speed of light. When we look at stars beyond the sun, we truly look back in time! Similarly, standard textbook images of the electromagnetic spectrum have to be drawn on a nonlinear scale given the 10^{-13} (gamma rays) to 10^2 (AM radio) meter range in wavelengths.

Biology

Earth's biosphere contains about 30×10^6 known species that range in size from viruses ($20\text{–}250 \times 10^{-9}$ meters) to typical prokaryotic cells ($1\text{–}10 \times 10^{-6}$ m) to typical eukaryotic cells ($10\text{–}100 \times 10^{-6}$ meters) to the 31-meter length of blue whales. Challenge students to explain (1) how textbook visual representations "lie" when they do not include the magnification or scale and (2) the mathematical plausibility of the claim that the human body contains more bacteria than human cells. Similarly, the need for cell organelles and multicellularity (in eukaryotes) can be explained with the surface area–to-volume ratios and relative diffusion rates of different-sized cubes. Textbook-induced misconceptions also occur at the macroscopic level when students lack a sense of millions and billions when it comes to the populations of nations and the world and the scale of human resource consumption and pollution production.

> **"No human investigation can be called scientific if it cannot be demonstrated mathematically."**
>
> —Leonardo da Vinci

Chemistry

A 22.4 L cubic box (with 28.2 cm edges) filled with any gas (at STP) contains Avogadro's number (6.02×10^{23}) of particles. This large number of particles and the low density of gases relate to the nanometer (10^{-9} m) scale of atoms and molecules and the large distances between molecules in a gas. Similarly, measurements of nuclear and atomic radii and volume calculations can be used to assess the mathematical plausibility of the "far out" claim that most of the atom is empty space.

Geology

Earth is 4.5×10^9 years old, with geological periods measured in millions of years ago. Consider that a kilometer contains one million (10^6) millimeters and how the mm^3-to-m^3 model can be used to visualize the idea of a billion. Alternatively, Earth's evolutionary timeline requires linear scale models at least the length of toilet paper rolls (if not football fields). In textbooks, these scales can be represented only on nonlinear scales that tend to mislead students and grossly underrepresent the almost unbelievable scale of "deep time."

In summary, mathematics is essential to understand the immense powers-of-ten scale of the universe. But more broadly, mathematical principles and practices are essential tools for scientists who seek to discover the cosmos (order/unity) in the diversity and seeming chaos of the universe. Or as Leonardo da Vinci (1452–1519) so aptly put it: "No human investigation can be called scientific if it cannot be demonstrated mathematically." Consider modeling for your students how they can "make friends with mathematics" by your collaboration with mathematics teachers to create **TEAMS** in which **T**ogether **E**veryone **A**chieves **M**ore **S**ynergy.

References

O'Brien, T. (2011). Activity 17: Metric Measurements, Magnitudes and Mathematics; pp. 201–220 in *More Brain-Powered Science: Teaching and Learning with Discrepant Events*. Arlington, VA: NSTA Press.

O'Brien, T. (2018, May 21). *Metric Measurements, Magnitudes, and Mathematics Matter in the Science of Scale*. Houghton Mifflin Harcourt/HMH-Sponsored National Webinar.

Teacher Notes

Cary I. Sneider, PhD

Change is rarely welcomed with open arms. A few weeks ago I was helping a colleague facilitate a team of teacher-leaders develop a district plan to implement the Next Generation Science Standards (NGSS). During a break, two of the teachers asked to speak with me. They were upset and nearly in tears. One of the teachers explained that they had spent the past 20 years developing the best possible science program for their school. The kids and parents loved it. The principal was proud of what they had accomplished. But now they would be asked to start all over because they would be assigned to teach science units they had never taught before.

It helped that the district leaders were listening and willing to consider some changes that these teachers recommended, although the leaders were quite firm about implementing the NGSS. It was also helpful for these teachers to learn that they would be helping other teachers by sharing the great ideas and resources that they had developed for their own students, so their creativity and hard work wouldn't be wasted. Even more important, I believe, was the gradual realization, over the next couple of days, that the profound changes called for by the NGSS

were not simply a change in when different science topics would be taught but rather a change in how they would be taught—in ways that these excellent teacher-leaders valued and had established with their own students.

> **"... the profound changes called for by the NGSS were not simply a change in when different science topics would be taught but rather a change in how they would be taught."**

What follows is a brief summary of the ways that the NGSS is similar to but also different from science as it has been taught for the past 20 years. I won't compare it to "traditional" science education because the method of having students read and answer questions at the end of the chapter is (thankfully) rarely done these days. But the changes called for by the NGSS can be surprising, even for teachers who are comfortable with a hands-on inquiry approach that has come to characterize the best of science teaching. And I'll admit some of these changes have been hard for me to get used to after nearly 50 years as a science educator and as a member of the NGSS writing team.

Disciplinary Core Ideas

With respect to the Disciplinary Core Ideas (what we used to call the "content") of the new standards, at least 80% are unchanged. Students still need to learn about Newton's laws of motion and the periodic table of elements. Some topics in the Earth and space sciences have been updated—such as by the addition of a greater focus on human impacts on the environment—so that topics that many teachers introduced as a way to enrich the curriculum with contemporary issues are now mainstream.

Crosscutting Concepts

Crosscutting Concepts also should be familiar to teachers who appreciate the nature of scientific thinking. The purpose of these seven concepts is to help students see the commonalities among the science and engineering fields. They include the idea that patterns we observe in nature are clues to some underlying process. For example, the monthly pattern of moon phases can best be understood in terms of systems and system models by manipulating a model of the Earth-sun-moon system. The Crosscutting Concept of cause and effect grows from our human instinct to know why things occur as they do, and the concepts of energy and matter are fundamental to all fields of science and engineering. The Crosscutting Concept of structure and function is useful in understanding how the structure of molecules affects the macroscopic behavior of a substance, as well as understanding how the structure of an organ enables it to carry out its function in the body. As students mature, they are more able to study the world by applying the concepts of scale, proportion, and quantity. And finally, the need to explain stability and change is at the

> **"Technology in the NGSS is portrayed as the application of science to the development of various products, processes, and systems to meet human needs . . ."**

root of our conservation laws in physics, chemical reactions in chemistry, and the theory of evolution in biology. By introducing these Crosscutting Concepts at appropriate times, teachers can help their students gain perspective on the study of various topics in science and see how they all—in a very important sense—reflect the same scientific way of thinking.

Emphasizing Technology and Engineering

Despite these similarities, the NGSS is very different from what has come before. One way it differs from prior standards is in the prominent role of technology and engineering. Although the idea that students should learn about technology and engineering has been around since the beginning of the standards movement[1], they have rarely been woven into the natural sciences as they are in the NGSS. Technology in

[1] American Association for the Advancement of Science. (1990). *Project 2061: Science for all Americans*. London: Oxford University Press.

the NGSS is portrayed as the application of science to the development of various products, processes, and systems to meet human needs, such as the application of wave phenomena to communication technologies. Engineering is positioned both as a core idea about defining and solving problems and as a means of applying the natural sciences to a wide variety of issues of both societal and environmental importance. And along with engineering comes a new set of skills for students to learn, such as defining problems by identifying criteria and constraints, applying tradeoffs to find the best acceptable solution, and learning to appreciate failure as a valuable aspect of the iterative design process.

Science and Engineering Practices

Some of the practices of science and engineering in the NGSS will be familiar to teachers, and some will seem quite different. What is especially different is that all of these practices are useful for scientific inquiry and engineering design. Table 1 illustrates why they are called practices of science and engineering.

It has taken me some time to fully appreciate what it means to help students develop skills in using these practices because most of my career has focused on teaching concepts. I empathized with the two teachers to whom I referred in my opening paragraph because I've been in a similar position. My favorite subject is astronomy, and I've developed some really effective ways for students to use models so they can understand phenomena such as moon phases and seasons. I hated to give those methods up! But if students are to learn to develop and use models, then they are the ones who need to figure out how to use

models to explain the phenomena. Telling them how to use the models just doesn't cut it. I should add that it's fine to illustrate how to use a model so they can learn how it's done, but at some point the students need to pick up the pieces as a means for figuring out why the moon goes through phases and how phases are different from eclipses. Another way to think about this is to consider who is doing the science. If the teacher is doing all of the explaining and asking all of the questions, the teacher—not the student—is doing the science.

Performance Expectations

Perhaps the most unusual aspect of the NGSS is the way these three dimensions are assembled—in single statements called Performance Expectations (PEs). They are called that because the NGSS is a set of assessment

> **"Perhaps the most unusual aspect of the NGSS is the way these three dimensions are assembled—in single statements called Performance Expectations."**

Table 1. Science and Engineering Practices

Practices	Science	Engineering
1. Asking Questions and Defining Problems	A basic practice of science is to ask questions about the world that can be answered by gathering data.	Engineering begins by defining a problem in terms of criteria for a successful solution and constraints or limits.
2. Developing and Using Models	Science often involves the construction and use of models to help answer questions about natural phenomena.	Engineering makes use of models to analyze existing systems or to test possible solutions to a new problem.
3. Planning and Carrying Out Investigations	Scientific investigation can be controlled experiments to test predictions, attempts to identify correlations, or taxonomic identifications of species.	Engineers use investigations both to gain data essential for their design and to test the designs they develop.
4. Analyzing and Interpreting Data	Scientific investigations generally produce data that must be analyzed in order to derive meaning.	Engineers analyze and interpret data to determine how well each meets specific design criteria.
5. Using Mathematics and Computational Thinking	In science, mathematics and computers are used for a range of tasks, from constructing models to analyzing data, as well as expressing relationships between variables.	In engineering, mathematics and computers are integral parts of the engineering design process.
6. Constructing Explanations and Designing Solutions	The goal of science is to explain phenomena in the natural world.	The goal of engineering is to solve meaningful problems.
7. Engaging in Argument From Evidence	In science, reasoning, argument, and participating actively in a community of peers are essential for finding explanations for natural phenomena.	In engineering, reasoning and argument are essential for finding the best possible solutions to problems.
8. Obtaining, Evaluating, and Communicating Information	A major practice of science is to communicate ideas and results of scientific inquiry and to obtain and evaluate findings reported by others.	Engineering needs to start by finding out how similar problems have been solved in the past and by communicating ideas clearly and persuasively.

> **"The NGSS describes which practices students of various ages are expected to use in order to demonstrate their understanding of a specific core idea and Crosscutting Concept. "**

standards. That is, they describe what students should be able to do at the end of instruction—not just what they know, but what they can do with what they know. That means achievement of these standards cannot be assessed with a multiple-choice test alone. Performance assessments of some sort will be necessary. The challenge for curriculum developers and teachers is to figure out what experiences they can provide so that their students will be able to meet these Performance Expectations not just at the end of class, but several months or even years later.

If all this seems daunting, keep in mind that the NGSS requires students to learn fewer core ideas than prior standards do so that teachers have time to teach those

that remain in depth. When our writing team circulated drafts for public comment, we were told that there were too many standards to reasonably expect students to learn; so, in the final round we cut the number of standards by one third. We did not "cheat" by combining standards—we actually cut the number of core ideas.

Another major advantage of the NGSS is that the standards are specific. I recall a project a few years ago, when I was helping to facilitate a team of teachers and other instructional leaders in the state of Washington to revise the state's standards. The Director of Science and I were meeting groups at various locations in the state to gather feedback on a draft. I recall one teacher who stood up to complain that the state test had questions that were impossible to anticipate because the standards were too vague. "Just tell us what the tests will be about," he said, "and we can help our students succeed!" The Next Generation Science Standards will not be subject to that objection. The NGSS describes which practices students of various ages are expected to use in order to demonstrate their understanding of a specific core idea and Crosscutting Concept. Each PE is followed by an additional clarification of the specific experiences that are referred to in the PE and also a list of performances that would not be assessed at that grade level.

So, to sum up: The great majority of core ideas in the NGSS are the same core ideas we've been teaching for years, with the addition of a few updates, especially related to societal and environmental issues. Although Crosscutting Concepts may sound new, they represent well-known features of scientific thinking. A new feature of the NGSS is that technology and engineering are woven deeply into the fabric of the document so that students are expected to develop skills that are quite new to most science teachers. And finally, the core ideas are fewer in number than prior standards in order to allow teachers more time to teach to mastery. The standards are also more specific to enable students to have greater success on tests by making it easier to align curriculum, instruction, and assessment. These last qualities alone are a reason for science teachers to cheer the NGSS.

Building an NGSS Curriculum

It's especially important for curriculum developers to keep in mind that the NGSS is sparse for a reason and to avoid including lessons just because they were there before and teachers expected to see them. Studies that have attempted to explain why U.S. students do poorly on international examinations have faulted textbooks in this country for being "a mile wide and an inch deep."[2] In light of that finding, I've been very impressed with the new *HMH Science Dimensions* textbook series. As a consulting author I've been pleased to see it develop as an entirely new curriculum that sticks to the PEs at each grade level, with rich science content and activities involving practices and core ideas but without extraneous material that would take up valuable instructional time.

It's hard to say what impact the NGSS will have, but I'm hopeful. For the past two years I've worked with middle school teachers in one school district in Oregon, which was one of the first states to adopt the NGSS. The teachers were given the task of designing units to match the sequence of PEs that their state recommended. I asked the teachers who had the most experience teaching a unit to design it for the district, even if they were not going to be teaching it in the fall. Initially some of the teachers protested having to spend a week during the summer preparing lessons they would not be teaching. One veteran teacher saved the day by saying, "Let's think of this as a barn raising. We'll all pitch in to help one group of teachers, and later they'll pitch in to help us."

Change is rarely embraced, but in the long run it has the advantage of keeping us on our toes. Science teachers are among the most creative people I know. With the support of their school and district leaders I know they will rise to the challenge, even if it means giving up some of their most treasured lessons. Their students will certainly be the beneficiaries of renewed instructional ideas and materials, especially as those students become the ones doing the science in the classroom.

> **"Science teachers are among the most creative people I know. With the support of their school and district leaders I know they will rise to the challenge."**

[2]Schmidt, W. H., McKnight, C., & Raizen, S. (Eds.). (1997). A splintered vision: An investigation of U.S. science and mathematics education (Vol. 1). Dordrecht, The Netherlands: Kluwer Academic Publishers.

by Michael A. DiSpezio

In **HMH Science Dimensions** you'll discover references to a brand-new type of tool—the Evidence Notebook—designed to support and reinforce the three-dimensional learning so central to NGSS pedagogy. *Evidence Notebook* may be a new term to you. So, how does it differ from a traditional lab notebook or science journal? Great question. As you are about to discover, the Evidence Notebook is a critical part of an NGSS approach to effective science education.

Think back to science notebooks that you maintained throughout your student experience. There's a good chance that these were a linear chronology of your learning accomplishments. In the earlier grades, they were bound records of classroom experience. For the most part, these entries were limited to lab observations; data collection tables; and answers to specific, prepackaged questions. By the time you reached middle school, the role of the lab notebook often segued into worksheet-and-lab-report repository.

Typically, all notebooks were organized in the same manner. There was little opportunity for individuality, personal voice, or indication of a student's interests. Often, they were used as summative assessment based on the expected homogenization of entries.

With the Next Generation Science Standards' revolutionary approach to pedagogy, the role and organization of what had been a record-keeping device has evolved. No longer a landscape on which to record prescriptive responses, the Evidence Notebook assumes the role of conceptual "scratch-pad." Like computer RAM, this is where the higher processing occurs.

With this evolution to a much more interactive role for the Evidence Notebook, let's examine the nuts and bolts of creating and maintaining it. The first thing to consider is that the notebook is student-directed. Remember, it's primarily for the students—not for you! With that in mind, it is organized according to each student's learning style, personal interests, questions, observations, and interactions with the three dimensions of science.

Using evidence notebooks, students can

- assume an increased role and responsibility for their own learning
- direct or create their own learning path by recording, selecting, and pursuing questions of interest
- organize their thinking
- record and analyze observations
- compare/contrast passive information to higher-level thinking and critical analysis
- better commit ideas to long-term memory through the writing process
- perfect language skills in an authentic learning experience
- communicate understanding and competency
- record and evaluate evidence both from within the classroom and outside of the classroom in a Claims/Evidence/Reasoning model

Evidence Notebook

Beyond the Classroom Walls

The Evidence Notebook travels both literally and figuratively beyond the physical school boundary. Not limited to recording classroom experiences and prescribed assignments, it assumes the role of an interactive diary. Students record relevant thoughts and observations of the world around them in their notebooks. For example, if studying runoff, they might write about or photograph neighborhood gullies or storm-drainage systems. Entries can then be examined in a context of active learning using these meaningful examples from the students' immediate world.

Spreading It Out

One way in which students might organize their notebooks is based upon right- and left-side pages of a spread. The left side of the page spread might incorporate the higher-level thinking process associated with an investigation. The posed question, evolving thoughts, and critical-thinking analysis would form this page's content. The facing right-hand page might include more of the prescribed and quantitative thought processes, such as steps, data collection, and observations.

Claims/Evidence/Reasoning Connection

Claims/Evidence/Reasoning, or CER for short, is a strategy for getting students to go beyond memorization and construct explanations. The Evidence Notebook is the ideal landscape on which to address all three of the CER components. First, students can record and further distill their claims into testable hypotheses. Then, based upon a student-directed investigation, they can collect and record data as evidence. Finally, the students can illustrate the logic they used in arriving at a reasoned explanation.

Evidence for Assessment

Don't overlook the role that the Evidence Notebook can play in formative assessment. By reviewing student notebooks, the instructor gains insight into each student's qualitative thinking. The instructor can then offer targeted feedback to help students improve their Evidence Notebook's organization and entries.

"The Evidence Notebook travels both literally and figuratively beyond the physical school boundary."

From Data to Thinking About Data

As you know, "thinking about one's thinking" is a key element to successful learning. However, prior to Evidence Notebooks, students lacked a classroom tool adapted to metacognition. Now, within Evidence Notebooks, students can record and analyze their thinking processes. By reflecting on how best they learn, they can assume more control of personal learning. Not only does this awareness result in richer understanding, but it also evolves the organization and content of the Evidence Notebook to its most effective design.

Organizing the Evidence Notebook

By now, perhaps you are wondering what makes up the specific content and organization of an effective Evidence Notebook. The definitive answer is, "It depends." That's because it varies from student to student. Although all notebooks should have a sequential format, the nature of each notebook's specific content and organization depends upon individual learning styles.

That said, effective Evidence Notebooks may include

- student interests and related questions

- a record of prior knowledge

- evidence collected from student-directed explorations

- short essays that address concepts and a student's personal thinking process

- graphic organizers such as concept maps and Venn diagrams

- drawings and embedded digital photographs

- observations that go beyond the classroom's physical boundaries

- reflections on understanding

- thinking and processes that address claims, evidence, and reasoning

21st Century Tools

Exploit the technology! As the installed base of tablets and PCs broadens, there are increasing opportunities for creating electronic Evidence Notebooks. Strategies in **HMH Science Dimensions** print and electronic student editions offer the opportunity for open-ended student input. Students can also construct an Evidence Notebook using appropriate apps and software. In addition to accepting written input, electronic versions can include embedded media such as digital photos, video clips, and sound files.

Dynamic, Not Static

Unlike its traditional counterpart, the Evidence Notebook is not a static record. It is a work in progress on which understanding is continually constructed. Students update its content on a daily basis, not just around investigations and lab reports. So remind students to keep it current and use it as a foundation on which to construct understanding.

How *HMH Science Dimensions* Supports an Evidence Notebook

Throughout both the Electronic Student Edition and the student text of **HMH Science Dimensions** are Evidence-Notebook writing prompts. They are designed to introduce and reinforce the skills that you've just read about. But these should be considered only the beginning. Let your imagination run wild, but most of all, encourage your students to use this important tool in ways that foster their own learning and understanding of science and engineering and their connections to everyday life.

By Marjorie Frank

A s educators, we often think in terms of disciplines: I teach English. I'm a science teacher. I'm a math coach. While these may be useful distinctions, they obscure an important consideration: Our brain has no such distinctions.

The Brain and Learning

No special region of the brain is active during science class and inactive during English or math. Or, vice versa. Yet, we often operate as if it were. Most science teachers don't focus deeply on reading or writing skills; English and math teachers aren't greatly concerned with science concepts. Yet, the cognitive processes in all these—and other— disciplines are pretty much the same. We just talk about them differently . . . and sometimes, we don't even do that. For example, citing evidence to support a claim is central to science. Explaining how an author uses evidence to support particular points is central to English language study. How different are these phenomena, really?

Which Standards?

Here's a short activity to test this idea. The sentences below are from science and English language arts standards. Except for giveaway words such as science and nonfiction, which I've deleted, the standards are reproduced here verbatim. See if you can tell which are science standards and which are ELA standards. [Answers are at the end of this article.]

1. Obtain information using various texts, text features (e.g. headings, tables of contents, glossaries, electronic menus, icons), and other media that will be useful in answering a question.

2. Ask questions based on observations to find more information. . . .

3. Write arguments to support claims . . . using valid reasoning and relevant and sufficient evidence.

4. Construct an argument with evidence to support a claim.

5. Ask questions to clear up any confusion. . . .

6. Know and use various text features (e.g. headings, tables of contents, glossaries, electronic menus, icons) to locate key facts or information. . . .

7. Obtain and combine information from books and/or other reliable media to explain phenomena or solutions . . . to a design problem.

8. Integrate information from several texts on the same topic. . . .

This confluence of interdisciplinary realities is embodied in the Next Generation Science Standards.

Curriculum Crossover in NGSS

Released in April 2013, the Next Generation Science Standards are, I believe, the only standards to date that recognize and embrace the natural crossover of disciplines. If you were to print the standards, each page would include a set of Science and Engineering Practices, a set of Disciplinary Core Ideas, a set of Crosscutting Concepts, and sets of ELA and Mathematics standards, formalizing what is true naturally—they all work together.

> **"Much of the time, you may be engaging in cross-disciplinary practices without even realizing it. "**

Much of the time, you may be engaging in cross-disciplinary practices without even realizing it. In English class, your students participate in exchanges that require close reading of a text. They cite evidence from the reading to support their responses to questions. Is this really different from asking students to cite evidence in support of a science claim? In science class, your students communicate solutions to a design problem via posters or verbal presentations. Is this all that different from reporting on a topic or engaging in collaborative discussions? Perhaps the expression "a distinction without a difference" applies here.

If your students are doing science, and I do mean doing science, they are likely to be engaging in crossover English language arts skills coincidentally.

HMH Science Dimensions takes the coincidence out of the crossover.

HMH Science Dimensions and Integrated Learning

The instructional design and lesson plans of the student-facing materials for all levels of *HMH Science Dimensions* facilitate English language arts in ways that are both subtle and explicit. Prompts throughout a lesson lead learners to collaborate, ask questions, summarize, explain, and analyze. Frequent opportunities connected to students' Evidence Notebooks integrate writing into the process. You need only scroll through a digital lesson or page through the print to find evidence of these approaches.

Something else you'll find in the teacher materials is a system of icons and headings that identify an extensive structure of online handbooks containing tips and strategies for developing science, math, and language arts skills. Some of the language skills that receive attention include asking and answering questions, doing research, collaborating, using visuals, and describing problems.

For the youngest learners there is a robust feature in the student-facing materials called Read, Write, Share! Here, children are guided to practice asking and answering questions, collaborating, drawing, writing, and presenting ideas to others. And throughout the teacher-facing materials you will find suggestions for collaboration, a quintessentially language-based endeavor.

For older learners you'll find a lesson feature called Language SmArts in Grades 6–8 and Language Arts Connection in Grades 9–12. These are activities that integrate language arts skills into the science learning process. Some activities appear in the student-facing materials; others appear only in the teacher-facing components. Examples of activities include those connected to making inferences, conducting research, and using visuals in multimedia displays, among others. In all cases, they represent another way in which **HMH Science Dimensions** helps facilitate the alignment of English language arts and the Next Generation Science Standards.

In the end, if your goal is to help learners draw upon their full complement of natural abilities to gain ownership of science, you can relax knowing that you've come to the right place: **HMH Science Dimensions**.

Language Arts Connection

"... all levels of *HMH Science Dimensions* facilitate English language arts in ways that are both subtle and explicit."

Answers:

1. NGSS standard; **2.** NGSS standard; **3.** English language arts standard; **4.** NGSS standard; **5.** English language arts standard; **6.** English language arts standard; **7.** NGSS standard; **8.** English language arts standard.

by Michael R. Heithaus, PhD

Improving STEM education at every level—from K–12 through university—is a national priority. Distinction in STEM fields is critical to ensuring the ability of the United States to compete in international markets and actualize intellectual goals, and jobs in STEM fields are projected to grow at higher rates than in other professions. Yet at the university and career levels, there is seemingly not enough interest or achievement in STEM fields. How we prepare students for college and career is a growing concern. The Next Generation Science Standards are built to ensure readiness.

What is college and career readiness?

At the simplest level, being college-ready means that students are able to succeed in college classes without remediation. Being career-ready means that graduates are prepared to obtain and succeed in entry-level positions. Sounds simple, but as STEM fields evolve and change, so do requirements related to content-area knowledge. For that reason, NGSS and **HMH Science Dimensions** focus on students demonstrating that they have mastered important skills more than specific knowledge or facts. Through formative assessments, evidence notebooks, and summative assessments, including critical performance-based assessments, teachers are supplied with the tools they need to understand student performance. Strategies throughout this Teacher Edition provide means of addressing many deficiencies.

When students have mastered skills and understand the underlying connections between STEM fields and other curriculum areas, they will not only have the background knowledge they need but also be prepared to fill in gaps in their understanding independently, without the need for remediation or extensive on-the-job training. And although college and career readiness might seem like qualities for students to master in high school, NGSS brings a greater coherence across grade levels: students from primary grades through high school have the opportunity to work on these skills and learn to apply them in everyday life.

According to the NGSS, career- and college-ready students should be able to

- make sense of the world and approach novel problems, phenomena, and information using a blend of Science and Engineering Practices, Disciplinary Core Ideas, and Crosscutting Concepts

- use valid research strategies

- be self-directed in planning, monitoring, and evaluation

- flexibly apply knowledge across disciplines (through continued exploration of Science and Engineering Practices, Crosscutting Concepts, and Disciplinary Core Ideas)

Not included in this list are some other skills that students should master to succeed in today's college classroom and workplace. First, students need to be

- comfortable working in diverse groups and with peers with different perspectives

- able to support their claims with logical arguments while being respectful and constructive in dealing with those who don't agree

- able to think critically and creatively

- able to communicate effectively in multiple settings and via diverse media

New teaching methods and a new role for teachers

The new focus on skills rather than content knowledge alone has led to big changes, backed by research, in how we teach science at universities and in K–12 classrooms. We know that active learning from student-centered activities that include group work and problem solving enhance student success.

There is no question that implementing NGSS requires teachers to shift both what and how they teach. For much of the instruction, the teacher's role in the classroom is different. Because NGSS integrates the practices of science and engineering with content-area knowledge, there is an increasing focus on students being scientists in the discovery process and leading their own investigations. Does this mean teachers are less important? Not by a long shot. In fact, teachers are probably more important than ever! It will take a bit of work to adapt your course to active learning and to integrate NGSS-style learning, but believe me, it will be worth it for you and your students.

Some things to keep in mind:

- Think about questions. Asking the right questions can be critical to getting students on—or back to—the right track to discovering material for themselves and making connections between concepts that are critical to NGSS. Pose questions to get students to think deeply about the nature and strength of evidence used to support a claim.

- Facilitate team learning. Science and engineering are all about teams, and students need to be comfortable working in groups with peers. Team learning can help students at very different levels benefit from the same course of investigation. I have found that strong students gain better mastery of concepts when they help students who are having trouble. On the flip side, some students actually learn better from a peer than a teacher! Pay attention to group dynamics, but facilitate cooperative teams wherever you can.

- Moderate discussions and peer critiques purposefully.

> **"There is no question that implementing NGSS requires teachers to shift both what and how they teach. For much of the instruction, the teacher's role in the classroom is different."**

- Remember that NGSS can help improve math skills. Throughout **HMH Science Dimensions**, you'll find opportunities to practice age- and discipline-appropriate math practices to support science investigations and learning. Find ways to bring math into investigations. Math is critical to science and engineering, and science and engineering can make math more accessible and exciting to students!

- Help students make connections continuously. The **HMH Science Dimensions** Teacher Edition provides many strategies to assist students in making those connections. There is plenty of evidence that multiple opportunities to associate pieces of information in different contexts facilitate retention. NGSS is built so that particular standards can be blended with others and integrated throughout a year and across grade levels. Online resources facilitate this blending—and you will find them already integrated in HMH Science Dimensions!

- Collaborate! Whether you teach kindergarten or college, you are not alone in applying NGSS innovations in science education. When you talk to your colleagues and look online for best ideas and practices, you are serving as a role model for your students.

As you move into teaching NGSS and preparing students for college and career, look for the many strategies and opportunities for assessment embedded in both the student-facing materials and the teacher materials of your **HMH Science Dimensions** program. These will facilitate implementation of best practices in NGSS pedagogy. Even if your students won't be entering STEM fields, solid science education at this point will help students prepare for the coming years by inculcating the critical thinking skills necessary for science literacy and making informed, reasonable, evidence-backed decisions in all facets of life.

"Whether you teach kindergarten or college, you are not alone in applying NGSS innovations in science education."

STEM

By Marjorie Frank

Questions. As teachers, we tend to think of ourselves as Keepers of the Questions. They are the reins we use to guide our students' learning. We write them. We ask them. We analyze them. We ponder them. Are our questions authentic enough? Do they necessitate a high enough level of thinking? Elicit a great enough depth of knowledge? A complex enough response? An inspired reaction?

Dozens of articles, years of research, and miles of neural pathways have been devoted to matters such as these. Only more recently have we given thought to the people asking the questions. And its corollary, are we the best people to be doing the asking? And if not us, who?

It turns out the answer may be easier, and more obvious, than expected.

When students do the asking, the questions are authentic. They tend to tap into high levels of thinking, considerable depth of knowledge, and complex responses . . . just as their questions did when they were youngsters.

Like all very young children, your students were once relentless questioners, asking a hundred or so questions every day: Where does the water go when you flush the toilet? How can birds stay up in the air? Why is the sky blue? You know the drill.

Research shows, however, that once children start school, the number of questions they ask decreases dramatically. It coincides in many cases, with decreasing engagement in learning. Returning, or at least sharing, the reins of questioning with your students rekindles their sense of ownership and enthusiasm for learning—which, in turn, can deliver much improved learning outcomes.

> **❝As teachers, we tend to think of ourselves as Keepers of the Questions. They are the reins we use to guide our students' learning. ❞**

Here are some ideas for making it happen.

Step one is to set the scene by creating an emotionally safe environment. Initially, your students may not be accustomed to being the ones to ask the questions. Their first attempts may be tentative, halting, unsure. They need to feel their efforts are respected and accepted, not judged, edited, or revised. This is true for learners who are sailing along as well as for those who are struggling. Everyone needs to feel her or his questions have value. You want to encourage your students to use their imaginations and do what they do naturally—ask questions.

Step two is to come up with a prompt that gets the ball rolling. The prompt can be an intriguing visual. A short video. A discrepant event. A brief reading. A demonstration. A thought-provoking phrase.

The prompt should be clear; it should trigger thinking; it should stimulate; but it need not be exotic. A list of extreme weather events is a possibility. A statement such as "Copernicus changed the way we see the world" is a possibility. Here are some examples of visuals that can work.

Step three is to divide students into groups of three or four and lay down the "rules."

1. Write as many questions as you can.

2. No discussing or judging.

3. No editing or revising.

4. No answering questions.

When first using this process, you may want to post the rules in the room so everyone can refer to them.

> **"... encourage your students to use their imaginations and do what they do naturally— ask questions "**

Step four is to let go. Tell students they have ten minutes to write questions according to the "rules." At first, you can expect students to try to get you to give examples ("Tell us what you want.") or ask you to comment on their questions ("Is this what you mean?"). Your job is to resist these efforts and repeatedly return the reins to them.

The way your students are going to gain confidence in themselves and regain their questioning strength is just to do it—not to ask questions that please you or satisfy some secret criteria they may think you have in mind. They need to embrace the freedom of it.

This process is helpful at many points in a lesson, such as at the start of a new topic, a new unit, or a new investigation. Suggestions for cultivating students' questions appear throughout this Teacher Edition. When students are asking the questions, very often they feel it's their job to find the answers.

As a separate matter, and at a separate time, the youngest children and language learners may benefit initially from scaffolding. Having children finish sentences like "I wonder what/when/why/where/how/who_____." is one kind of scaffold. Generating questions from stems is another: What's the difference between _____ and _____? How does ____work? Why does _____ happen? When does _____ change? Where does _____go?

As students gain practice in asking questions, they'll become more comfortable with it.

After students have a list of questions, they can number them and share them with the class. The entire class can engage in the exercise of analyzing, improving, and prioritizing questions. They involve taking action, sharing, and reflecting on what's been learned. Then you have a roster of student questions that can be checked off as you progress through a lesson. Questions that don't get answered can become writing prompts or possibilities for additional investigation for gifted or highly engaged, motivated students. But you can't get there until you first let go of the reins and share them with your students.

Where does _____go?

Why does _____ change?

Why does _____ happen?

How does ____work?

For more information on cultivating student questions, do an online search for The Right Question Institute, where you will find resources, templates, and advice from the foremost researchers on questions and question formulation.

By Bernadine Okoro

The diverse and changing population of the United States shows steady increases in low-income students, immigrant families, and English Learners. As these children and youth enter the classroom, they bring with them from their home communities a wide array of skills and abilities, experiences and perspectives, and cultural and linguistic resources. As student diversity increases, the learning experiences for all become enriched. Teachers are charged with the need to deliver high-quality science instruction as well as to provide curriculum resources and support to ensure that all students succeed in the science classroom.

Supporting All Learners

Each student enters the classroom with individual needs that require different forms of support and present a range of challenges; however, many common classroom strategies can be used to support all learners. The following tips use the most up-to-date research about support for each student population.

"As student diversity increases, the learning experiences for all become enriched."

Students from Low-Income Families

When working with students living in poverty, some effective forms of support are:

- Teach with confidence.
- Establish consistent high expectations and practices.
- Integrate reading and literacy support into the science curriculum.
- Use data to inform instruction.
- Restructure time and space for more flexibility in responding to questions.

Students Below Grade Level

When dealing with students who are working below grade level, the following support has been shown to be effective:

- Make it relevant by personalizing science content for individual interests and asking questions that highlight science in the students' world.

- Break down assignments into smaller, more manageable tasks.

- Use Socratic seminars for science—guide without telling by formulating questioning strategies to get students engaged from the beginning.

- Use guided practice protocols, for example, "I Do, We Do, You Do."

- Use thinking routines by performing an online search for "thinking routines" or "thinking maps" to discover a wide array of resources to assist you in bringing these research-based strategies into your classroom.

Students from Foster Families

Foster youth face an array of challenges that in turn present challenges to most teachers. Do the following to best support these students:

- Explore the student's academic history to find out about academic status, strengths, and challenges.

- Find out who the student's educational decision maker is—resource parents, foster parents, kinship caregivers, adoptive parents, etc.—and invite them to work with you in evaluating the student's current level of achievement and setting reasonable goals for the academic year.

- Structure materials and tasks in the classroom to help the student achieve success, even if academics are a problem. Provide structure and predictability in the classroom through classroom norms and routines.

- Respect the student's right to privacy. Other teachers or children do not need to know about the child's foster care status. One of the biggest challenges for a teacher with foster youth in the classroom is negotiating confidentiality and determining how to address confidential issues appropriately.

- Encourage students to participate in extracurricular activities and other special school events that allow them to widen their circle of friends and help make the school a source of stability for students.

Students from Migrant Families

As with foster youth, though for different reasons, environmental stability and a sense of belonging are a challenge to children from migrant worker families. Support should emphasize and strengthen the sense of stability and the ability of students to succeed, even in constantly changing circumstances.

- Welcome students and families by creating a positive environment that models respect for differences and allows for sharing experiences and values.

- Encourage academic success by exposing students to rigor and holding students to high expectations.

- Encourage future educational participation by encouraging students to continue their schooling whenever possible.

Female Students

In the past, girls and young women were often discouraged from pursuing science or math. Classrooms have changed, but sometimes older thought patterns can recur and be a source of discouragement. To combat these attitudes, do the following:

- Expose young girls to STEM early and equally.

- Make sure students understand that effort and persistence rather than natural ability are the reason for success in STEM fields.

- Praise effort, evidence, and reasoning rather than correct answers.

- Assist girls and young women in developing confidence, positive self-perceptions, and self-efficacy in STEM endeavors.

- Encourage participation in special programs, and support learning opportunities in the community.

- Use student-centered teaching methods within a safe classroom climate.

- Emphasize process and not just product.

- Serve as a mentor.

> **"Make sure students understand that effort and persistence rather than natural ability are the reason for success in STEM fields."**

- Use equitable student participation practices.

- Expose students to historical and contemporary role models of women in STEM through stories, posters, films, speakers, class assignments, etc.

Find strategies that work with multiple groups, and combine these general strategies to target combinations of different populations that may exist in your classroom. Incorporating these strategies into your instructional practices as you implement the NGSS will ensure success for all students in your science classroom.

HMH Science Dimensions™ and the EQuIP Rubric

The **EQuIP Rubric** is an instrument for evaluating a curriculum's conformance with the contours of an authentic NGSS program. As such, one needs to bear in mind the known limitations and proper usages of the rubric:

- The rubric is intended to be applied to lessons or units, not to entire curricula.

- The rubric itself indicates that it is unlikely that a single lesson will lead to mastery of a Performance Expectation. High-Quality Units may do so.

- The evaluation process is intended to be done in a group, not by an individual.

- The rubric requires familiarity with the Performance Expectation and its supporting Dimensions of Learning. The **HMH Science Dimensions Trace Tool to the NGSS** can help provide this orientation.

Throughout the **HMH Science Dimensions Teacher Edition,** you will find features to help you orient toward the critical dimensions of the EQuIP Rubric. Using the book, you are well beyond the evaluation phase of considering a program, but these features will demonstrate the best practices of NGSS summarized by the evaluation instrument. Highlights of critical EQuIP Rubric evaluation points are summarized in the reduced pages you see here.

UNIT PLANNING PAGES

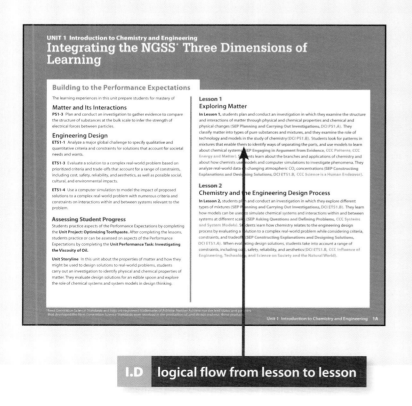

I.D logical flow from lesson to lesson

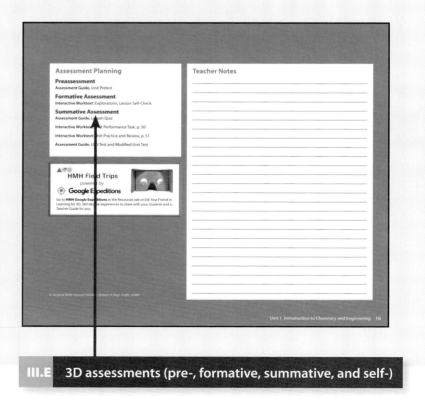

III.E 3D assessments (pre-, formative, summative, and self-)

LESSON PLANNING PAGES

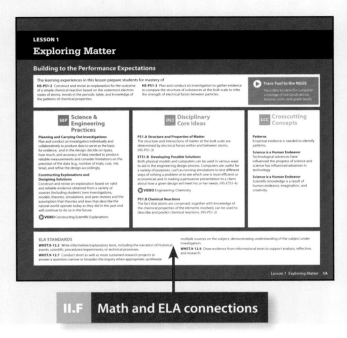

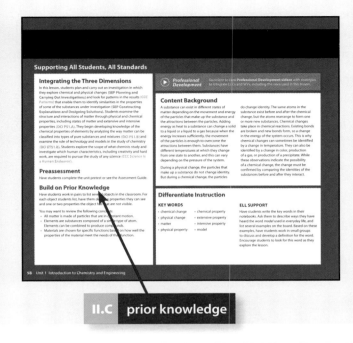

II.F Math and ELA connections

II.C prior knowledge

LESSON OPENER PAGES

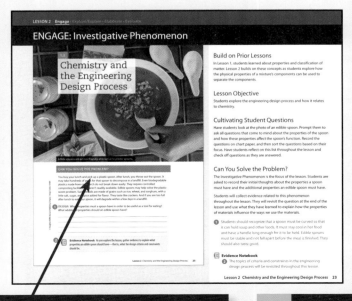

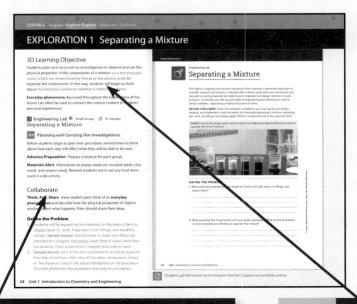

II.A authentic and meaningful scenarios

II.B collaborative opportunities to express ideas and respond

I.B.i–iii 3D learning

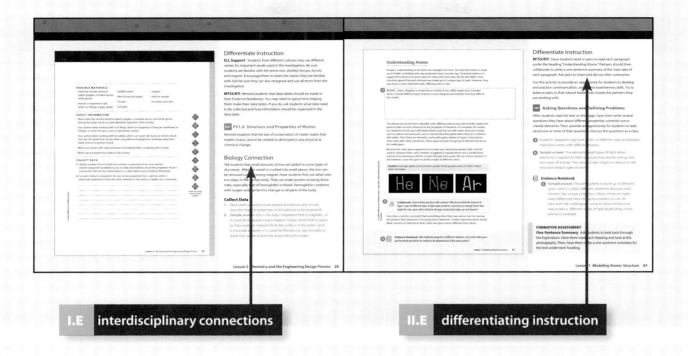

I.E interdisciplinary connections

II.E differentiating instruction

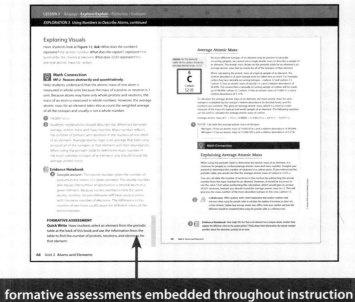

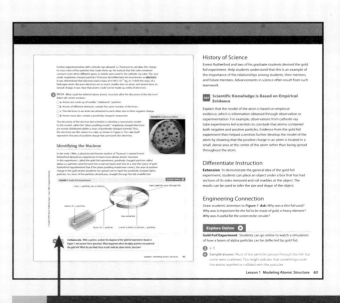

III.B formative assessments embedded throughout instruction

II.D scientifically accurate and grade-appropriate content

LESSON AND UNIT CLOSER PAGES

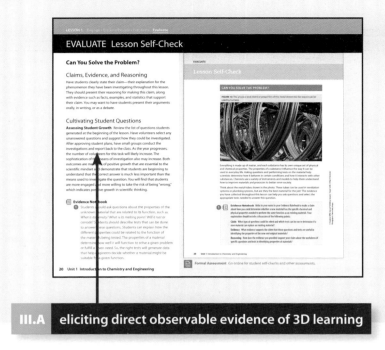

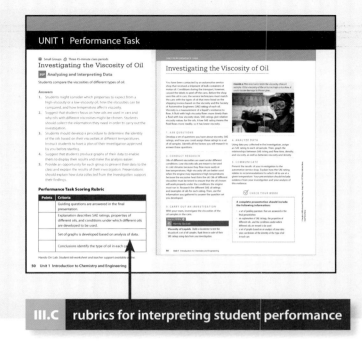

III.A eliciting direct observable evidence of 3D learning

III.C rubrics for interpreting student performance

UNIT INTERLEAF PAGES

II.A developing connections

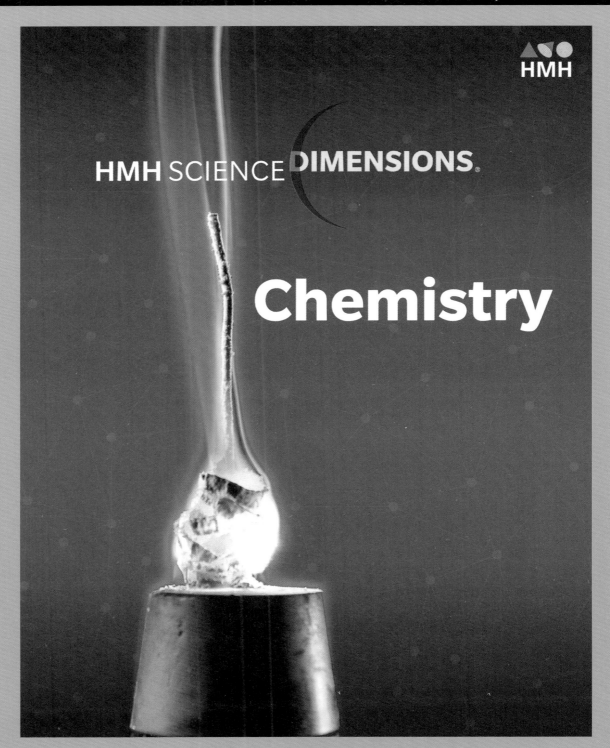

HMH SCIENCE DIMENSIONS®

Chemistry

Empirical Evidence

For CER arguments in science and engineering, evidence presented must be empirical evidence. Ask students which of the following statements is based on empirical evidence.

- Many people agree that the most popular pet is a dog. no

- Arabic is harder to learn than Chinese. no

- According to a survey of more than 5,000 people, the world's top three favorite foods are rice, pasta, and meat. yes

SEP **Engaging in Argument from Evidence**

Students construct an argument based on a short experiment or on their experience or observations.

Getting Students Started To prepare students for this activity, encourage them to discuss what they already know about the world that is based on evidence.

Ask: *What do you know about the world based on evidence you have observed in your daily life?*

Sample answer: It takes longer for my hair to dry in cold weather than it does in warm weather.

Claims, Evidence, and Reasoning

You likely use claims, evidence, and reasoning in your daily life—perhaps without even being aware of it. Suppose you leave a notebook behind in the cafeteria. When you return later, you see a number of similar notebooks on the counter. You say, "I left my notebook here earlier," and pick up one of them.

The cafeteria worker says, "Are you sure that one is yours? They all look pretty much alike."

You say, "Yes, my initials are right here on the cover." To confirm the fact, you open the notebook to show your full name inside. You also present your student ID to prove that it's your name.

This encounter is a claims-evidence-reasoning interaction. You claimed the notebook was yours, and you showed evidence to prove your point.

CLAIM
A *claim* is your position on an issue or problem. It answers the question, "What do you know?"

EVIDENCE
Evidence is any data related to your claim that answer the question, "How do you know that?" These data may be from your own experiments and observations, reports by scientists or engineers, or other reliable sources. Scientific knowledge is based on *empirical evidence*, or evidence that is derived from observation or experiment. As you read about science, perform lab activities, engage in class discussions, and write explanations, you will need to cite evidence to support your claims.

REASONING
Reasoning is the use of logical, analytical thought to form conclusions or inferences. It answers the question, "Why does your evidence support your claim?" Reasoning may involve citing a scientific law or principle that helps explain the relationship between the evidence and the claim.

Scientists use claims, evidence, and reasoning—or *argumentation*—for many purposes: to explain, to persuade, to convince, to predict, to demonstrate, and to prove things. When scientists publish the results of their investigations, they must be prepared to defend their conclusions if they are challenged by other scientists.

Here is an example of a claims-evidence-reasoning argument.

CLAIM: Ice melts faster in the sun than it does in the shade.

EVIDENCE: We placed two ice cubes of the same size in identical plastic dishes. We placed one dish on a wooden bench in the sun and placed the other on a different part of the same bench in the shade. The ice cube in the sun melted in 14 minutes and 32 seconds. The ice cube in the shade melted in 18 minutes and 15 seconds.

REASONING: We designed the investigation so that the only variable in the setup was whether the ice cubes were in the shade or in the sun. Because the ice cube in the sun melted almost 4 minutes faster, this is sufficient evidence to support the claim that ice melts faster in the sun than it does in the shade.

Construct your own argument below by recording a claim, evidence, and reasoning. With your teacher's permission, you can do an investigation to answer a question you have about how the world works, or you can construct your argument based on observations you have already made about the world.

CLAIM	
EVIDENCE	
REASONING	

For more information on claims, evidence, and reasoning, see the online **English Language Arts Handbook**.

History of Science

Claims, Evidence, and Reasoning In ancient Greece, Aristotle and the natural philosophers who followed him established a set of widely held assumptions about the natural world and how it functioned. Answers to specific questions had to fit these assumptions. One assumption was that the sun and other stars and planets revolve around Earth. In the 17th century, a new scientific method started with data and observations, from which an explanation was derived. Experimentation was used to test assumptions.

Answers

Sample Answer:

Claim: I go faster on my bike coasting down a high hill compared with a short hill.

Evidence: There are two hills on my way to school—one at 15th Street and one at Kirkwood Drive. The Kirkwood Drive hill is about twice as high as the 15th Street hill. Both hills are about the same steepness. If I stop at the top of each one and ride my bike without pedaling down the hills, I end up going much faster at the bottom of Kirkwood Drive than I do at 15th Street.

Reasoning: The evidence that I go faster coasting down Kirkwood Drive than I do coasting down 15th Street shows that a higher hill leads to a faster bike speed. Because I start with no motion at the top of each hill, the only factor that is different is the height of the hill. This could be because gravity is pulling me down for a longer time on the higher hill.

Some students may know that they have more potential energy at the top of a higher hill than at the top of a shorter hill.

Introducing the Evidence Notebook

You may wish to use these Student Edition pages to introduce students to the Evidence Notebook and familiarize them with the types of Evidence Notebook prompts they will encounter throughout the lessons of **HMH Science Dimensions Chemistry**. These prompts enable students to regularly interact with the concepts and phenomena they are learning about.

Notebook Format

It is up to you, as the teacher, to determine the format that you wish students to use, whether it be a paper notebook or some form of digital notebook. In addition to recording their thoughts and reflections in writing, students may also use drawings, graphic organizers, and other visual tools in their notebooks.

Beyond the Classroom

The use of Evidence Notebooks is certainly not limited to just responding to the prompts provided in the lessons. Encourage students to use this important tool in ways that foster their own learning and understanding of science and engineering and their connections to everyday life. For example, the Evidence Notebook is a great place for students to generate their own questions and to record relevant thoughts and observations of the world around them.

Using Your Evidence Notebook

Throughout the units and lessons of **HMH Science Dimensions Chemistry**, you will see notebook icons that highlight important places for you to stop and reflect. These Evidence Notebook prompts signal opportunities for you to record observations and evidence, analyze data, and make explanations for phenomena.

The Evidence Notebook is your location to gather evidence and record your thinking as you make your way through each lesson. Your teacher may determine a specific format for you to use, such as a digital or paper notebook. Whatever the format, you will record here the evidence you gather throughout the lesson to support your response to the Can You Explain the Phenomenon?/Can You Solve the Problem? challenge. You will also record significant information from the lesson to use as a study tool and to build your own study guide at the end of the lesson.

The following pages from the first lesson in the book will familiarize you with the main types of Evidence Notebook prompts you will see throughout the course.

Make Your Own Study Guide

At the end of each lesson, students have an opportunity to create a study guide that helps them organize and visualize the important information from the lesson. Their study guide should focus on the main ideas from the lesson and tie multiple ideas together. Students can create an outline, a concept map, graphic organizer, or other representation.

Evidence for Assessment

While the Evidence Notebook is first and foremost for the student, it can also play an important role in formative assessment. By reviewing student notebooks periodically, you can gain insight into each student's thinking and level of understanding. By providing targeted feedback, you can also support students in making the Evidence Notebook a more effective tool for learning.

Provides general direction about the evidence to collect related to this phenomenon as you explore the lesson.

Provides a point-of-use opportunity to address the unit project or lesson phenomena.

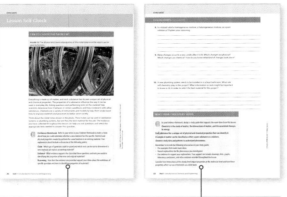

Prompts you to synthesize information from evidence, analysis, models, and other information gathered over the course of an Exploration.

At the end of each lesson, you will also be prompted to use the notes from your Evidence Notebook to construct an explanation and to make your own study guide for the main ideas from the lesson.

Engineering Design Connection

Students might wonder why the Mars Climate Orbiter was designed using two different systems of measurement. Explain that while the scientists at NASA were conducting their work using SI, other engineers in the United States, such as those who developed the problematic program for Lockheed Martin, were using standard measurements. Ask: Why might engineers lag in adopting the SI system if it is already used by most scientists? The lag is related to requirements of existing hardware. Where existing machinery is mostly tooled for standard sizes, it is difficult to adopt a completely different set of measurements.

Language Arts Connection

Explain the difference between *dimension* and *unit*. Be sure students understand that a dimension refers to a physical quantity such as length or mass. A unit represents the numerical measurement of a dimension. Then ask students to generate examples that include both a dimension and a unit, such as "a length of 10 meters" or "a mass of 2.5 kilograms."

History of Science

The metric system—the forerunner of SI—was first used in France in the late 1700s, around the time of the French Revolution. The revolutionaries embraced the system and wanted to standardize the number of days per month as 30, which is divisible by 10. There was even a movement to increase the number of days per week from seven to ten. Have interested students do research to learn more about methods of measurement and their impact on science.

1 Sample answer: To calculate the volume of the cube, you measure the length of one edge and multiply both the number and the unit of the measurement times itself three times. The base unit for measuring length in SI is the meter, so one unit for volume would be cubic meters, or m^3.

Working with Measurement

FIGURE 1: An artist's rendition of the Mars Climate Orbiter

Clear communication is important for scientific investigation. In 1999, a miscommunication about units of measurement had devastating consequences for NASA's Mars Climate Orbiter, shown in Figure 1. Part of the landing system was programmed to transmit information in one unit of measurement, and the intended receiving component was programmed to receive information in a different unit of measurement. The resulting miscalculation caused the Orbiter to pass too close to Mars and to disintegrate in the planet's atmosphere. The mathematical mistake cost $125 million, and no data were collected.

Standardization of Units

In 1960, scientists established a standard set of units based on the metric system called the *Système International d'Unités* (French for the International System of Units), or SI.

Derived Units and Other Accepted Units

SI has seven base units to describe physical quantities that have key importance in scientific measurements.

Measure	Base unit
Length	meter (m)
Mass	kilogram (kg)
Time	second (s)
Temperature	kelvin (K)
Quantity	mole (mol)
Electric Current	ampere (A)
Luminous Intensity	candela (cd)

ANALYZE Notice that volume is not one of the measures assigned a base unit. Think about how you would calculate the volume of an object such as a cube. Which of the base units in the table could you use to measure volume? Give an example of the units associated with volume based on one of the base units in SI.

_____

_____

_____

_____

In SI, many units are derived from the base units. For example, when describing how fast something is moving, the base units for length and time are combined to give a rate of meters per second, m/s. Some derived units are named. For example, the unit of force is called the newton (N), which is equal to 1 kg·m/s^2.

Liquid volume is commonly measured in liters (L). Though not officially an SI unit, the liter is an accepted unit of measure in SI. Similarly, degree Celsius is an accepted unit to use when measuring temperature. Figure 2 shows the relationship between Kelvin, Celsius, and Fahrenheit temperature scales.

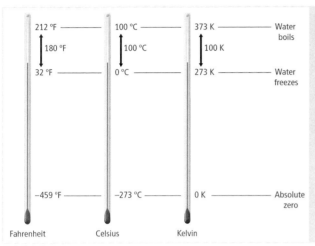

212 °F ——— 100 °C ——— 373 K ——— Water boils

180 °F   100 °C   100 K

32 °F ——— 0 °C ——— 273 K ——— Water freezes

−459 °F ——— −273 °C ——— 0 K ——— Absolute zero

Fahrenheit   Celsius   Kelvin

FIGURE 2: A diagram showing the relationships between the Kelvin, Celsius, and Fahrenheit temperature scales, with respect to three key temperatures. Any temperature in one of the scales can be converted to a temperature in the other scales. Though Fahrenheit is common in some parts of the world, it is not an accepted unit for scientific measurement.

Unit Prefixes

The diameter of a single atom ranges from about 0.1 to 0.3 nanometers (nm). If you measure something with a meterstick, you may report its length in centimeters (cm). The distance between two cities may be measured in kilometers (km). By appending a prefix such as kilo- or centi- onto a base unit, it is easier to report measurements for large or small quantities. SI has 20 accepted prefixes that change the magnitude of a unit by a power of 10. For example, 1 kilometer is equal to 1000 meters, and 1 millisecond is equal to 0.001 second.

To convert from the original unit to the modified unit, multiply or divide by the appropriate power of 10 or simply move the decimal the corresponding number of places. For example, to convert from grams to kilograms, divide the number of grams by 1000 or move the decimal three places to the left. Fill in places with zeros if needed. Only one prefix at a time may be appended to a unit.

Factor	Prefix (symbol)
10^{-24}	yocto (y)
10^{-21}	zepto (z)
10^{-18}	atto (a)
10^{-15}	femto (f)
10^{-12}	pico (p)
10^{-9}	nano (n)
10^{-6}	micro (μ)
10^{-3}	milli (m)
10^{-2}	centi (c)
10^{-1}	deci (d)

Factor	Prefix (symbol)
10^{1}	deka (da)
10^{2}	hecto (h)
10^{3}	kilo (k)
10^{6}	mega (M)
10^{9}	giga (G)
10^{12}	tera (T)
10^{15}	peta (P)
10^{18}	exa (E)
10^{21}	zetta (Z)
10^{24}	yotta (Y)

SOLVE Write the correct quantity for each conversion.

1. 38 000 kg = _____ g   **3.** 4.3 ms = _____ s

2. 6.5 m = _____ mm   **4.** 0.02 km = _____ cm

Differentiate Instruction

MTSS/RTI Encourage students to work collaboratively to make a reference list of units for themselves. Ask them to list *meter, kilogram,* and *second* at the top of a piece of a paper. Provide them with the tools to measure each of these values (a meterstick, a balance, and a stopwatch). Have them find three things in the classroom that are about one meter in length, three things that have masses of about one kilogram, and three events that are approximately one second in duration. Students should then have an idea of what these units represent. Discuss why the focus was on these particular units, and have students describe how these units are used in both chemistry and physics.

Extension Students likely already know that the prefix *kilo-* stands for 1000, *mega-* stands for 1 million, and *giga-* stands for 1 billion.

Practice working with these units. Ask students to write the RAM and storage capacity of their own computer or a school computer in bytes. Sample answer: 2 x 10^9 bytes of RAM, 2.56 × 10^{11} storage capacity. Ask how many watts a 20 megawatt power station supplies. 20 million watts How many watts does a 300 milliwatt bulb use? 0.3 watts

Solve

1. 38 000 000

2. 6500

3. 0.0043

4. 2000

Math Connection

Model for students how to convert a number into scientific notation. Write a six-digit number on the board and start with the marker at the decimal point. Show students how they can easily count the number of digits to the left as they "jump" over them to get to the spot between the first two digits. The number of jumps gives the exponent for the ten. For numbers 10 or greater, the exponent is positive.

Conversely, for numbers less than 1, the marker "jumps" to the right, and the exponent on the 10 is a negative number. If the number is greater than or equal to 1 but less than 10, the marker does not move, and there is no need to write the number in scientific notation using an exponent of 0 on the 10.

1 4.967×10^{15}

5 120 000 000 000

1.59×10^{-13}

0.000 000 000 000 000 000 000 000 000 9109

Magnitude and Scientific Notation

Imagine you are measuring the mass of an electron or the distance from Earth to the sun. Without some handy shortcuts, you would have to write out a lot of zeros. For example, the mass of an electron is 0. 000 000 000 000 000 000 000 000 000 9109 kg. The distance from Earth to the sun is 149 600 000 000 m.

When measurements are very small or very large, scientists may report a measurement using scientific notation, which is based on powers of 10, or *magnitude*. Scientific notation is written in the form $m \times 10^n$, where the magnitude is $1 \leq m < 10$, and n is an integer.

In scientific notation, the mass of an electron may be written as 9.109×10^{-31} kg, and the average distance from Earth to the sun is about 1.496×10^{11} m. Adding a prefix to a unit is similar to using scientific notation. For example, 1 milligram (mg) = 1×10^{-3} gram (g). Note that negative powers of 10 represent smaller numbers, and positive powers of 10 represent larger numbers. Use the order of magnitude to estimate and help check your work. For example, if you are trying to calculate the mass of a molecule, you know your answer should be small, so it should be on the order of 10^{-23} g rather than 10^{23} g.

To convert a number from scientific notation to decimal form, follow the rules of multiplication and exponents to multiply the number as usual. To convert a number from decimal form to scientific notation, perform the following steps:

1. Determine m by moving the decimal point in the original number to the left or right so that only one nonzero digit remains to the left of the decimal point.

2. Determine n by counting the number of places you moved the decimal point in the first step. If you moved the decimal point to the right, n is negative. If you moved the decimal to the left, n is positive.

1 **EVALUATE** Use your knowledge of multiplication and exponents to rewrite the following numbers in either decimal notation or scientific notation.

Decimal notation	Scientific notation
5280	5.28×10^3
4 967 000 000 000 000	
	5.12×10^{12}
0. 000 000 000 000 159	
	9.109×10^{-31}

When it comes to very small or very large numbers, scientific notation reduces errors due to miscounting the number of digits. Numbers written in scientific notation all require approximately the same amount of space regardless of magnitude, making it easier to compare the magnitude of values by looking at the power of 10 in the number. For example, consider the distances 1.5×10^6 m, 3.4×10^6 m, and 9.5×10^{-3} m. The first two distances have the same magnitude, 10^6, and are much larger than the magnitude of the third distance, 10^{-3}. If you add these three distances, the third distance will have little effect on the final sum, even though the leading coefficient 9.5 is larger than the other two coefficients.

2 **SOLVE** A measurement may be reported in many different ways. The diameter of Earth is approximately 12 700 km. Match the quantities shown with the appropriate units to show other ways that Earth's diameter may be written.

$$1.27 \times 10^4 \qquad 1.27 \times 10^7 \qquad 1.27 \times 10^{10} \qquad 12.7$$

| _____ Mm | _____ km | _____ m | _____ mm |

Many calculators and software programs can display results in scientific notation. The letter E is used in place of the multiplication. For example, the number 1.689×10^{-15} may be displayed as 1.689E–15 or 1.689e–15. Refer to a calculator's manual to see how to enter numbers in scientific notation and how to configure the calculator to display numbers in scientific notation.

Accuracy and Precision

The tools that scientists use to measure affect how accurately and precisely the measurement can be made. The terms *accuracy* and *precision* are often used interchangeably in everyday conversation. In science, however, these terms have different meanings. *Accuracy* is the closeness of a measurement to the correct or accepted value of the quantity measured. *Precision* is the closeness of a set of measurements of the same quantity made in the same way. Precision may also refer to the number of gradations on a measurement device.

If a balance displayed values that were two grams more than the true mass every time you used it, the balance would be precise but not accurate. Its readings are wrong, but they are consistent. Imagine you have two digital scales and a known 2 kg mass. You use the 2 kg mass to determine how accurate and precise the two scales are. You place the 2 kg mass on each scale 4 different times and record the values shown in the table.

In this example, the accuracy of each measurement on scale A varies widely, though, if averaged, the average value is close to the accepted value. The measurements are also not very precise. Scale B gives more precise measurements, but it is still inaccurate. The ideal measuring tool would be both precise and accurate.

Scale A measurements	Scale B measurements
1999 g	2005 g
2005 g	2004 g
2008 g	2005 g
1994 g	2005 g

3 **ANALYZE** Below each image, state whether the points on the target are *accurate* or *not accurate,* and whether they are *precise* or *not precise*.

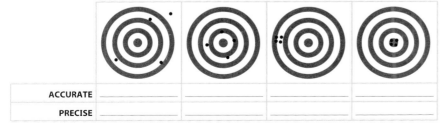

| ACCURATE | | | | |
| PRECISE | | | | |

Preconception Alert

The term *precision* is often misunderstood as meaning the same thing as *accuracy*. Make sure students understand what precision is, and take time to reinforce the concept throughout the course.

Differentiate Instruction

MTSS/RTI The terms *accuracy* and *precision* may be difficult for some students to fully understand. For students who are kinesthetic learners, you may want to play a quick game of "pin the tail on the donkey." Game pieces can be made and stuck onto the image of the donkey using tape to avoid having blindfolded students handle pins. Discuss how well students did in terms of accuracy and precision.

Exploring Visuals

Examples of Accuracy and Precision Ask students to identify which targets in the diagram correspond to the following examples of error. Say: The readings on a digital thermometer are never the same, but they are off by only 0.01°C. Target 2 A speedometer on a racecar consistently gives measurements that are the same as the actual speed of the car. Target 4 A scale gives measurements that are sometimes too high, sometimes too low, and never the same from one day to another. Target 1 The lines on a graduated cylinder give the amounts that are always one milliliter less than the actual volume. Target 3

2 12.7
1.27×10^4
1.27×10^7
1.27×10^{10}

3 first target: not accurate, not precise
second target: accurate, not precise
third target: not accurate, precise
fourth target: accurate and precise

Collaborate

Divide the class into groups of three or four. Provide each group with a set of objects and a metric ruler. Each group should have the same objects, but the rulers should vary somewhat in precision. Have the groups measure the lengths of the objects and compare their measurements with those of other groups. Ask them to note any trends in the measurements related to the precision of the rulers.

1 The amount of acceptable error in a measurement depends on the size of the measurement and the application. Compared with the volume of the swimming pool, 1 mL is a small amount of error. Additionally, the volume of the swimming pool is not something that needs to be carefully controlled for safety reasons. Compared with the volume of medicine, a 1-mL error is large. And a mistake in dosage could be dangerous.

2 To precisely measure 29 mL, you would need a tool capable of measuring with a precision of 1 mL or smaller. The graduated cylinder has increments marked every 2 mL, which means you would be able to estimate a measurement to the nearest mL. Therefore, the graduated cylinder would be the best choice for this measurement.

Describing Accuracy

Consider the following two measurements: the amount of water in a swimming pool and the amount of medicine being administered to a patient. The swimming pool has a volume of 3.75×10^8 mL, and the medicine has a volume of 5.00 mL. Both measurements are 1 mL more than the true volume.

1 ARGUE All measurements have some error. How do you determine the acceptable level of accuracy for a measurement? Use the measurements of the swimming pool volume and medicine volume to support your claim.

_____

_____

_____

_____

Measuring Precisely

Different pieces of equipment allow for measurements with different levels of precision. Digital measuring devices may specify precision by the smallest digit presented. In the scale example earlier, the scales may be said to have a precision of 1 g, because that is the smallest increment the scales can report (though, as the example shows, that is not their true precision).

FIGURE 3: Left to right, the name and smallest increment marked on each piece of equipment: graduated cylinder (2 mL), Erlenmeyer flask (25 mL), beaker (10 mL).

For analog devices, the precision is related to how many measuring increments or graduations the device has. For example, a graduated cylinder with 0.1 mL increments allows for more-precise measurements than a graduated cylinder with 1 mL increments. The smallest division on the equipment indicates how precisely you can make a measurement using the equipment.

It is appropriate to estimate a value that is 1/10 the size of the smallest division on a measurement tool. If using equipment that clearly indicates the tenths place, you could record a value with an estimated digit in the hundredths place. For example, if a volume appeared to be between 36.2 and 36.3 mL on a graduated cylinder with 0.1 mL increments, the volume could be recorded as 36.25 mL. The 5 in the hundredths place is the estimated digit.

2 EXPLAIN Which of the pieces of equipment shown in Figure 3 would be the most appropriate for precisely measuring 29 mL of liquid? Explain your reasoning, citing evidence related to the divisions on each tool and the concept of an estimated digit.

_____

_____

_____

_____

Significant Figures

When manipulating and reporting measurements, it is important to know the precision with which the measurements were made. For example, you use a scale with a precision of 0.1 kg to measure the mass of an object three times. The results are 8.5 kg, 8.6 kg, and 8.5 kg. You average the three measurements and get 8.533 333 33 kg on the calculator. If you report the mass as 8.533 333 33 kg this indicates that you measured the mass much more precisely than you really did.

One way to maintain the precision of a measurement is to use significant figures. The *significant figures* in a measurement are all of the digits known with certainty, plus the first uncertain or estimated digit. Recall that the 5 in the hundredths place of the graduated cylinder measurement of 36.25 mL was an estimated digit. The measurement of 36.25 mL has 4 significant figures. The table below shows the rules for identifying significant figures in a measurement. Writing a number in scientific notation can help you see which digits are significant.

Digit	Rule	Examples
1, 2, 3, 4, 5, 6, 7, 8, or 9	Significant	275 m: three significant figures 42.35 mL: four significant figures
0 between nonzero digits (captive zeros)	Significant	40.7 °C: three significant figures 87 009 g: five significant figures
0 before nonzero digits (leading zeros)	Not significant	0.095 807 cm: five significant figures
0 at the end of a number without decimal point (trailing zeros)	Not significant	2000 kg: 1 significant figure, unless otherwise specified
0 at the end of a number with a decimal point (trailing zeros)	Significant	2000. s: four significant figures 25.00 mA: four significant figures

When a calculation is completed, you will often need to round the value to the correct number of significant figures for the problem. If the digit after the place you are rounding to is a 5 or higher, you round up. For example, 27.15 cm rounds to 27.2 cm. But 27.14 cm rounds to 27.1 cm.

3 SOLVE A calculator displays the number 50 238.450 124. Round this number as described for each row of the table.

Round to . . .	Rounded value
thousandths place	
tenths place	
3 significant figures	
1 significant figure, in scientific notation	
4 significant figures, in scientific notation	

© Houghton Mifflin Harcourt Publishing Company

Collaborate

Write ten numbers on the board in two columns. After each number, write the number of digits to which the number is to be rounded. Divide students into pairs. One student should round the numbers in the first column and the second student should round the numbers in the second column. Have each student justify their answers to their partner.

3 50 238.450
50 238.5
50 200
5×10^4
5.024×10^4

Preconception Alert

Some common mistakes students make when working with significant figures are

1. reporting all of the digits given in the calculator readout instead of rounding;

2. not including significant zeros that fall to the right of the decimal point, at the end of a number, for example, 2.2560;

3. reporting all leading zeros as significant, for example, 0.005. This number has only one significant figure, 5.

Referencing these common mistakes made in significant figures, ask students if they can draw any "real-world" analogies to them.

Example: Students may draw the comparison between using all the numbers in a calculator display to answering a question with the correct but also unnecessary or misleading information.

Math Connection

For answers to problems in this interactive worktext involving both types of calculations (multiplication/division and addition/subtraction), all calculations were carried out and then rounded at the end. The more commonly used method is to use all available figures, both significant and insignificant, during intermediate calculations and to round to the correct number of significant figures only when reporting the final result. If an intermediate calculation needs to be reported, it should be rounded for only reporting purposes. The rounded number should not be used in any further calculations. Significant digits in calculations are important only when reporting a number. Be sure to explain to students which method you want them to follow.

1 tenths place, hundredths place, tenths place

2 3, 4, 3

Mathematical Operations and Significant Figures

Calculators do not account for significant figures, so you must properly manage the precision of reported results. The following sections describe some standard rules that should be used when calculating with measured values to ensure that significant figures are manipulated in a uniform way. If performing a multistep problem, keep track of which figures are significant as you work, but do not round until your final answer. Check with your teacher in case they have any different rules for operations with measurements.

Adding and Subtracting Significant Figures

When adding or subtracting measured values, the resulting number can have no more precision than any of the numbers used in the calculation. Perform the addition or subtraction and then round the result to the appropriate decimal place.

1 **ANALYZE** In the right column identify the decimal place, such as *tenths place*, with the most precision for each measurement and the precision of the resulting sum.

	Measured/Calculated value	Most-precise place
Length one	25.1 cm	
Length two	2.05 cm	
Sum	27.2 cm	

Multiplying and Dividing Significant Figures

When multiplying or dividing measured values, the resulting number can have no more significant figures than any of the factors, divisors, or dividends. Perform the multiplication or division, and then round.

2 **ANALYZE** In the right column, write the number of significant figures for each measurement and the resulting quotient.

	Measured/Calculated value	Significant figures
Mass	3.05 g	
Volume	8.470 mL	
Density = mass / volume	0.360 g/mL	

Conversion Factors and Counting Numbers

Some quantities—counted numbers, defined values and conversion factors—are considered exact numbers. These quantities have no uncertainty and therefore have infinite significant figures. These quantities do not affect the uncertainty of a calculation. For example, there are exactly 100 cm in 1 m. A measure of 460.8 cm will convert to 4.608 m. Both the original measurement and the converted measurement have 4 significant figures.

Combined Operations

When performing a multistep problem, identify the measurement with the least significant figures before you begin your calculations. The order of operations matters. If the measurement 25.1 m is subtracted from 26.1 m, the result of 1.0 m has 2 significant figures. If this result is then divided by 0.512 s, the result of 1.953125 m/s would need to be rounded to 2 significant figures, 2.0 m/s, even though the original measurements had 3 significant figures.

3 **SOLVE** To calculate the rate at which an object moves you subtract Position A, 5.20 m, from Position B, 102.10 m, and then divide by the time it took to move between positions, 4.81 s. Using the rules presented here, what should the final answer be?

○ **a.** 20 m/s   ○ **b.** 20. m/s   ○ **c.** 20.1 m/s   ○ **d.** 20.15 m/s

Dimensional Analysis

It is common to convert units within SI or from non-SI units to SI units. Dimensional analysis is a method that helps you apply conversion factors to convert between units. *Conversion factors* are ratios relating the value of one unit of measure to another. In dimensional analysis, the conversion factors are applied such that when you multiply, all of the units except for the desired units cancel out. For example, a length of 1 foot is equivalent to 0.3048 meters.

$$1 \text{ ft} = 0.3048 \text{ m}$$

This conversion factor may be written as:

$$\frac{1 \text{ ft}}{0.3048 \text{ m}} \quad \text{or} \quad \frac{0.3048 \text{ m}}{1 \text{ ft}}$$

depending on whether you want to convert from feet to meters or meters to feet. To convert a measurement of 3.1 feet to meters, you would do the following:

$$3.1 \text{ ft} \times \left(\frac{0.3048 \text{ m}}{1 \text{ ft}} \right) = 0.94 \text{ m}$$

Notice that the final quantity has 2 significant figures because the original measurement had 2 significant figures; significant figure rules apply during dimensional analysis.

Dimensional analysis may involve multiple conversion factors, so special care must be taken to ensure the conversion factors are placed appropriately. This may be more challenging if you are converting a ratio such as speed.

4 **SOLVE** Use the following equivalent values to convert the measurement 55 mi/h into m/s. Make sure to write each conversion factor such that units will cancel when you multiply, leaving only the desired units.

   1 mi = 5280 ft   1 ft = 0.3048 m   1 h = 3600 s

_____ m/s

Differentiate Instruction

Extension Provide students with problems that involve both converting units and performing calculations to arrive at an answer with the correct number of significant figures. For example, ask students to add 10.8 cm and 102 mm or to divide 274.1 grams by 0.025 L to get the density in g/mL.

Earth Science Connection

Tell students that an example of a simple conversion factor that is not exact is the conversion of time from days to years. Because the year is defined by one revolution of Earth around the sun, it is not an exact value. We generally use 365 days for a year, but a year has 365.24 days if five significant figures are used.

Reinforce the concept of conversion factors for dimensional analysis by reminding students that any number divided by itself is 1.

Ask: What is the quantity represented by the following fractions:

$\frac{3}{3}$; $\frac{12 \text{ eggs}}{1 \text{ dozen eggs}}$; $\frac{1 \text{ m}}{100 \text{ cm}}$? 1; 1; 1

Explain to students that those fractions are called conversion factors. They can be used to convert the units used in an equation, but any time you multiply a number by 1, the answer is the same number. Likewise, a conversion factor does not change the actual amounts.

3 c

4 25 m/s

▶ **Lab Safety Handbook**

Additional resources to support safe practices in the lab and in the field can be found in the *Lab Safety Handbook*.

Safety in the Lab

Concern for safety begins before any activity in the classroom and before students enter the lab. Be sure to familiarize yourself with federal, state, and local safety regulations. It is your responsibility to provide students with a safe working environment. Post the student safety guidelines and dress code in a prominent place in the room. PPE should include eye protection, nonlatex gloves, and nonlatex aprons. In all labs involving chemicals, indirectly vented chemical splash goggles are required.

Facilities Make sure all equipment is in good working order before school begins, and plan a regular schedule of inspection for the school year. Inspect all safety equipment, such as the fume hood, eyewash station, emergency shower, fire extinguishers, and smoke detectors.

Waste Disposal Review federal, state, and local regulations for disposal and recycling of chemical and biological waste. Make sure the school has the proper container for storage and the necessary means for removal.

First Aid Have a first aid kit available for minor injuries, with antiseptics, bandages, ointments, tape, and gauze pads. Post in the lab a list of phone numbers including your number, poison control, and local police and fire departments. Be prepared to document any incident.

Lab Safety

Before you work in the laboratory, read these safety rules. Ask your teacher to explain any rules that you do not completely understand. Refer to these rules later on if you have questions about safety in the science classroom.

Personal Protective Equipment (PPE)

• PPE includes eye protection, nitrile or nonlatex gloves, and nonlatex aprons. In all labs involving chemicals, indirectly vented chemical splash goggles are required.

• Wear the required PPE during the setup, hands-on, and takedown segments of the activity.

Dress Code

• Secure any article of clothing—such as a loose sweater or a scarf—that hangs down and may touch a flame, chemical, or piece of equipment.

• Wear closed-toe shoes.

• Tie back long hair or hair that hangs in front of your eyes.

• Acrylic fingernails are very flammable and should not be worn when using a flame.

Directions

• Observe all safety icons.

• Know where the fire extinguisher, fire blanket, shower, and eyewash station are located in your classroom or lab, and know how to use them in an emergency.

• Read all directions, and make sure that you understand them before starting the activity.

• Do not begin any investigation or touch any equipment until your teacher has told you to start.

• Never experiment on your own. If you want to try a procedure that the directions do not call for, ask your teacher for permission first.

• If you are hurt or injured in any way, tell your teacher immediately.

Chemical Safety

• If you get a chemical in your eye, use the eyewash station immediately. Flush the eye a minimum of 15 minutes.

• If you get a hazardous chemical on your skin or clothes, use the emergency shower for a minimum of 15 minutes.

• Never touch, taste, or sniff any chemicals in the lab. If you need to determine odor, waft. To waft, hold the chemical in its container 15 cm away from your nose, and use your fingers to bring fumes from the container to your nose.

• Take only the amount of chemical you need for the investigation. If you get too much, ask your teacher how to dispose of the excess. Do not return unused chemicals to the storage container; this can cause contamination.

• When diluting acid with water, always add acid to water. Never add water to an acid.

Heating and Fire Safety

• Keep your work area neat, clean, and free of materials.

• Never reach over a flame or heat source.

• Never heat a substance or an object in a closed container.

- Use oven mitts, clamps, tongs, or a test tube holder to hold heated items.

- Do not throw hot substances into the trash. Wait for them to cool, and dispose of them in the container provided by your teacher.

Electrical Safety

- Never use lamps or other electrical equipment with frayed cords or plugs with a missing ground prong.

- Make sure no cord is lying on the floor where someone can trip over it.

- Do not let a cord hang over the side of a counter or table so that the equipment can easily be pulled or knocked to the floor.

- Never let cords hang into sinks or other places where water can be found.

- Only use a Ground Fault Interrupter (GFI) protected circuit receptacle.

Glassware and Sharp-Object Safety

- Use only clean glassware that is free of chips and cracks.

- Use knives and other cutting instruments carefully. Always wear eye protection, and cut away from yourself.

Animal Safety

- Never hurt an animal.

- Wear gloves when handling animals or preserved specimens.

- Specimens for dissection should be properly mounted and supported.

Cleanup

- Follow your teacher's instructions for the disposal or storage of supplies.

- Clean your work area and pick up anything that has dropped to the floor.

- Wash your hands with soap and water after completing the activity.

Safety in the Field

- Be sure you understand the goal of your fieldwork and the proper way to carry out the investigation before you begin fieldwork.

- Do not approach or touch wild animals. Do not touch plants unless instructed by your teacher to do so. Leave natural areas as you found them.

- Use proper accident procedures, and let your teacher know about a hazard in the environment or an accident immediately, even if the hazard or accident seems minor.

Chemical Safety

Make sure you have Safety Data Sheets for all chemicals in your storeroom, including household items such as bleach. Check for shelf-life dates of purchase on existing stock. Generally, chemicals should not be stored longer than two years. Organize stock so that incompatible reagents, such as acids and bases, are stored separately.

Electrical Safety

Make sure that electrical outlets are protected with ground fault interrupters. Familiarize yourself with the location of the master shutoff valves and switches for the lab.

Animal Safety

Live animals to be used in investigations should be kept separate from other lab materials and from students. Refer to federal, state, and local laws and regulations regarding the acquisition, handling, and care of animals. Future care or disposal of animals must be considered before making any acquisition. Remind students that animals used for an investigation must be handled in a humane way, with every effort to minimize harm. Students should wear gloves and wash their hands thoroughly after handling the animals.

Safety in the Field

If you plan to conduct any fieldwork, be sure that activities fall within the school's guidelines for outside activities and additional supervision. Visit the site ahead of time to assess the potential for hazards and also to address any accommodations needed for special needs students. Make sure all student permission forms are turned in the day before the trip. Go over assignments and protocols for the handling and use of equipment. Make sure to bring a first aid kit.

Safety Symbols

Safety symbols appear in the instructions for labs and activities to emphasize important notes of caution. Make sure students learn what these symbols represent and understand the appropriate precautions to take.

At the beginning of the school year, and before students conduct their first investigation, go over the safety symbols, safety regulations, and dress code for the lab. Show students where the information is posted, point out fire exits and alarms, and discuss fire evacuation procedures. Discuss the safety equipment in the lab—how it works and when it is appropriate to use.

Safety Symbols

Safety is the priority in the science classroom. In all of the activities in this textbook, safety symbols are used to alert you to materials, procedures, or situations that could be potentially hazardous if the safety guidelines are not followed. Learn what you need to do when you see these icons, and read all lab procedures before coming to the lab so you are prepared. Always ask your teacher if you have questions.

 ANIMALS Never injure an animal. Follow your teacher's instructions for handling specific animals or preserved specimens. Wash your hands with soap and water after handling animals or preserved specimens.

 APRON Wear a nonlatex apron at all times in the lab as directed. Stand whenever possible to avoid spilling in your lap.

 BREAKAGE Use caution when handling items that may break, such as glassware and thermometers. Always store test tubes in a test tube rack.

 CHEMICALS Always wear indirectly vented chemical splash goggles when working with chemicals. Stand whenever possible when working with chemicals to avoid spilling on your lap. Tell your teacher immediately if you spill chemicals on yourself, the table, or the floor. Never taste any substance or chemical in the lab. Always wash your hands with soap and water after working with chemicals.

 DISPOSAL Follow your teacher's instructions for disposing of all waste materials, including chemicals, specimens, or broken glass.

 ELECTRIC Keep electrical cords away from water to avoid shock. Do not use cords with frayed edges or plugs with a missing ground prong. Unplug all equipment when done. Only use GFI protected electrical receptacles.

 FIRE Put on safety goggles before lighting flames. Remove loose clothing and tie back hair. Never leave a lit object unattended. Extinguish flames as soon as you finish heating.

 FUMES Always work in a well-ventilated area. Do not inhale or sniff fumes; instead, use your fingers to bring fumes from the container to your nose.

 GLOVES Always wear gloves to protect your skin from possible injury when working with substances that may be harmful or when working with animals.

 HAND WASHING Wash your hands with soap and water after working with soil, chemicals, animals, or preserved specimens.

 HEATING Wear indirectly vented chemical splash goggles, and never leave any substance while it is being heated. Use tongs or appropriate insulated holders when handling heated objects. Point any materials being heated away from you and others. Place hot objects such as test tubes in test tube racks while cooling.

 PLANTS Do not eat any part of a plant. Do not pick any wild plant unless your teacher instructs you to do so. Wash your hands with soap and water after handling any plant.

 SAFETY GOGGLES Always wear indirectly vented chemical splash goggles when working with chemicals, heating any substance, or using a sharp object or any material that could fly up and injure you or others.

 SHARP OBJECTS Use scissors, knives, or razor tools with care. Wear goggles when cutting something. Always cut away from yourself.

 SLIP HAZARD Immediately pick up any items dropped on the floor, and wipe up any spilled water or other liquid so it does not become a slip/fall hazard. Tell your teacher immediately if you spill chemicals.

Integrating the NGSS* Three Dimensions of Learning

Building to the Performance Expectations

The learning experiences in this unit prepare students for mastery of

Matter and Its Interactions

PS1-3 Plan and conduct an investigation to gather evidence to compare the structure of substances at the bulk scale to infer the strength of electrical forces between particles.

Engineering Design

ETS1-1 Analyze a major global challenge to specify qualitative and quantitative criteria and constraints for solutions that account for societal needs and wants.

ETS1-3 Evaluate a solution to a complex real-world problem based on prioritized criteria and trade-offs that account for a range of constraints, including cost, safety, reliability, and aesthetics, as well as possible social, cultural, and environmental impacts.

ETS1-4 Use a computer simulation to model the impact of proposed solutions to a complex real-world problem with numerous criteria and constraints on interactions within and between systems relevant to the problem.

Assessing Student Progress

Students practice aspects of the Performance Expectations by completing the **Unit Project: Optimizing Toothpaste.** After completing the lessons, students practice or can be assessed on aspects of the Performance Expectations by completing the **Unit Performance Task: Investigating the Viscosity of Oil.**

Unit Storyline In this unit about the properties of matter and how they might be used to design solutions to real-world problems, students carry out an investigation to identify physical and chemical properties of matter. They evaluate design solutions for an edible spoon and explore the role of chemical systems and system models in design thinking.

Lesson 1
Exploring Matter

In Lesson 1, students plan and conduct an investigation in which they examine the structure and interactions of matter through physical and chemical properties and chemical and physical changes **(SEP Planning and Carrying Out Investigations, DCI PS1.A).** They classify matter into types of pure substances and mixtures, and they examine the role of technology and models in the study of chemistry **(DCI PS1.B).** Students look for patterns in mixtures that enable them to identify ways of separating the parts, and use models to learn about chemical systems **(SEP Engaging in Argument from Evidence, CCC Patterns, CCC Energy and Matter).** Students learn about the branches and applications of chemistry and about how chemists use models and computer simulations to investigate phenomena. They analyze real-world data on changing atmospheric CO_2 concentrations **(SEP Constructing Explanations and Designing Solutions, DCI ETS1.B, CCC Science is a Human Endeavor).**

Lesson 2
Chemistry and the Engineering Design Process

In Lesson 2, students plan and conduct an investigation in which they explore different types of mixtures **(SEP Planning and Carrying Out Investigations, DCI ETS1.B).** They learn how models can be used to simulate chemical systems and interactions within and between systems at different scales **(SEP Asking Questions and Defining Problems, CCC Systems and System Models).** Students learn how chemistry relates to the engineering design process by evaluating a solution to a complex real-world problem while considering criteria, constraints, and tradeoffs **(SEP Constructing Explanations and Designing Solutions, DCI ETS1.A).** When evaluating design solutions, students take into account a range of constraints, including cost, safety, reliability, and aesthetics **(DCI ETS1.B, CCC Influence of Engineering, Technology, and Science on Society and the Natural World).**

NGSS across This Unit

Next Generation Science Standards	Unit Project	Lesson 1	Lesson 2	Unit Performance Task
SEP Asking Questions and Defining Problems	•		•	
SEP Planning and Carrying Out Investigations	•	•		•
SEP Constructing Explanations and Designing Solutions	•	•	•	
SEP Using Mathematics and Computational Thinking		•	•	
SEP Engaging in Argument from Evidence		•		
DCI **PS1.A** Structure and Properties of Matter		•	•	•
DCI **ETS1.A** Defining and Delimiting Engineering Problems	•		•	
DCI **ETS1.B** Developing Possible Solutions	•	•	•	
CCC Influence of Engineering, Technology, and Science on Society and the Natural World	•		•	
CCC Patterns		•	•	•

NGSS across the Grades

Middle School

MS-PS1-2 Analyze and interpret data on the properties of substances before and after the substances interact to determine if a chemical reaction has occurred.

MS-ETS1-1 Define the criteria and constraints of a design problem with sufficient precision to ensure a successful solution, taking into account relevant scientific principles and potential impacts on people and the natural environment that may limit possible solutions.

MS-ETS1-2 Evaluate competing design solutions using a systematic process to determine how well they meet the criteria and constraints of the problem.

Grades 9–12

HS-PS1-2
HS-PS1-3
HS-ETS1-1
HS-ETS1-3
HS-ETS1-4

▶ **Trace Tool to the NGSS** Go online to view the complete coverage of standards across lessons and units.

Differentiate Instruction

Differentiate with Technology

Open Chemistry Database
Students can use an online chemical database to learn about the ingredients in toothpastes. Have students search the database using the term *dentifrice*, which means "a paste or powder for cleaning teeth."

Virtual Field Trip
Locate a chemical plant, materials safety organization, or car manufacturing plant in your area to arrange a virtual field trip with a materials scientist using a video chat application. In advance, encourage students to generate a list of questions they would like answered about the chemical and physical properties of materials.

Biosphere 2
Choose an online video to help students learn more about Biosphere 2. For example, you might show students a TED Talk by one of the scientists who lived in the habitat for an extended period of time.

Key Word Support

Key Words
physical
    change *Lesson 1*
chemical
    change *Lesson 1*
matter *Lesson 1*
physical
    property *Lesson 1*
chemical
    property *Lesson 1*
extensive
    property *Lesson 1*
intensive
    property *Lesson 1*
model *Lesson 1*
engineering design
    process *Lesson 2*
criterion *Lesson 2*
constraint *Lesson 2*
tradeoff *Lesson 2*
system *Lesson 2*

Reinforcing Key Words
Have students work in pairs to make a graphic organizer for the key words in this lesson. Each pair of students should make a four-column table. In the first column, students should list the key words. For each of the words, students should write a sentence containing the key word in the second column. In the third column, have students write a definition of the term in their own words. In the fourth column, students should draw a picture that will help them remember the meaning of each word.

Academic Vocabulary
Discuss with students the difference in how the word *matter* is used in everyday language and how it is used in science. If students need extra help, guide a class discussion in which volunteers say sentences that use the word in everyday language or in science language. Have students give examples of each use of the word.

English Language Learners
Students may struggle with the difference between *criteria* and *constraints*. Apply the terms to a real-world solution to emphasize the difference. For example, have students identify design criteria and constraints for a new cold medicine. Criteria might include that the new medicine relieve symptoms consistently in 90% or more of test subjects and that it can be taken orally. Constraints might include that it cannot require ingredients from outside the country of production, it must not cause disturbing side effects, and the cost to the consumer cannot be more than the cost of other popular cold medicines. Emphasize that both criteria and constraints must be met for a design solution to be considered successful.

ELL
ELL teaching strategies in this unit include

Lesson 1 p. 12
Lesson 2 pp. 25, 32, 40

MTSS/RTI
Strategies for students who need extra support in this unit include

Lesson 1 p. 14
Lesson 2 p. 25

Extension
Strategies for students who have mastered core content in this unit include

Lesson 2 pp. 38, 40

Making Connections

Connections to Community

Use these opportunities for informal science learning to provide local context and to extend and enhance unit concepts.

At Home
CHEMICAL AND PHYSICAL CHANGES IN THE KITCHEN Have students work in small groups to generate a list of physical and chemical changes that occur in a kitchen. Then have students conduct research about innovative technologies or methods that facilitate these changes. For example, students might research the use of liquid nitrogen to quickly freeze foods (physical change) or *sous vide* pouches that cook foods slowly (chemical change) and help them retain more moisture. *Use with Lesson 1.*

In the Community
REMOVING POLLUTANTS FROM SMOKESTACKS Smokestacks, which can tower high above factories, are a significant source of pollutants, including carbon dioxide. Carbon emissions contribute to climate change, so engineers have designed technologies to remove pollutants from factory output gases before they leave the smokestack. Have students work in pairs to research how components of the gaseous mixture leaving a smokestack can be separated in order to keep the air clean. *Use with Lesson 2.*

Culture
MATERIAL CULTURE Have partners conduct research about *material culture*, which is the creation, use, and trade of materials and objects, as well as the impact they have on human behaviors, norms, and rituals. Remind students that understanding the human use of materials is an important part of archaeology and anthropology. Ask students to identify what materials they think might "define" their generation and how they are used in society. Then have them research the source or manufacturer of the materials. What are the physical and chemical properties of the material that make it useful to humans? *Use with Lessons 1 and 2.*

Home Letters Use these letters to engage family members with unit concepts.

Collaborate

Opportunities for students to work collaboratively in this unit:

Accessing Prior Knowledge p. 9

Discussion pp. 30, 37

Graffiti p. 13

One Moves p. 6

Think-Pair-Share pp. 24, 35

Connections to Other Disciplines

Opportunities to connect to other content areas in this unit:

Language Arts Connection pp. 19, 29, 33, 41

Engineering Design Connection p. 33

Environmental Science Connection p. 31

Math Connection pp. 10, 32, 38

3D Unit Planning

Lesson 1 Exploring Matter pp. 5–22

Overview

Objective Students explore physical and chemical properties, the categories of matter, and what chemists do.

SEP Planning and Carrying Out Investigations
SEP Constructing Explanations and Designing Solutions
SEP Engaging in Argument from Evidence
SEP Scientific Knowledge is Based on Empirical Evidence
DCI **PS1.A** Structure and Properties of Matter
DCI **PS1.B** Chemical Reactions
DCI **ETS1.B** Developing Possible Solutions
CCC Patterns
CCC Energy and Matter
CCC Science is a Human Endeavor

Math and **English Language Arts** standards and features are detailed on lesson planning pages.

Print and **Online** Student Editions	**Explore Online**
ENGAGE	
Investigative Phenomenon p. 5	**ELA Handbook**
Can You Solve the Problem? How could you improve an item that you use regularly?	
EXPLORE/ EXPLAIN	
Exploring Physical and Chemical Changes p. 6	**Video** Alkali Metals in Water
Properties of Matter p. 9	**Hands-On Lab Worksheet**
Classifying Matter p. 14	**Hands-On Lab Teacher Support**
The Study of Chemistry p. 17	**Lab Safety Handbook**
ELABORATE	
Take It Further p. 19	**Take It Further**
Careers in Science Crystallographer	Salting Out
	Video Salting Out
	Estimating Data Accurately
	Hands-On Lab Worksheet
	Hands-On Lab Teacher Support
	Communicating the Sizes of Objects
	Math Handbook
EVALUATE	
Lesson Self-Check p. 20	**Lesson Quiz**

Hands-On Lab Planning

Exploring Physical and Chemical Changes

🕐 60 minutes
👥 Small Groups

Objective Students collect evidence to determine whether physical or chemical changes occur in a series of experiments.

Materials
- chalk, calcium carbonate (5 g)
- lead nitrate solution in dropper bottle, 0.2 M
- mortar and pestle
- silver nitrate solution in dropper bottle, 0.1 M
- sodium hydroxide solution in dropper bottle, 0.5 M
- sodium iodide solution in dropper bottle, 0.5 M
- water in dropper bottle
- well plate
- vinegar (acetic acid) in dropper bottle

Materials Alert Some of the materials used in this lab are expensive ($AgNO_3$) and pose an environmental disposal risk ($PbNO_3$). It is advised that you do not perform the chemical reactions in this lab at a larger scale.

Additional Downloadable Lab Option

Estimating Data Accurately

🕐 45 minutes
👥 Individuals or Pairs

Objective Students obtain mass and volume values to estimate the number of marbles in a jar and use percent error to evaluate the accuracy of their estimates.

3D Unit Planning, continued

Lesson 2 Chemistry and the Engineering Design Process pp. 23–44

Overview

Objective Students explore the engineering design process and how it relates to chemistry.

SEP Asking Questions and Defining Problems
SEP Constructing Explanations and Designing Solutions
SEP Planning and Carrying Out Investigations
DCI **PS1.A** Structure and Properties of Matter
DCI **ETS1.A** Defining and Delimiting Engineering Problems
DCI **ETS1.B** Developing Possible Solutions
CCC Influence of Engineering, Technology, and Science on Society and the Natural World
CCC Systems and System Models
CCC Energy and Matter
CCC Science Addresses Questions About the Natural and Material World

Math and **English Language Arts** standards and features are detailed on lesson planning pages.

Print and **Online** Student Editions

Explore Online

	Print and Online Student Editions	Explore Online
ENGAGE	**Investigative Phenomenon** p. 23 **Can You Solve the Problem?** What properties must a spoon have in order to be useful as a tool for eating? What additional properties should an edible spoon have?	**ELA Handbook**
EXPLORE/ EXPLAIN	**Separating a Mixture** p. 24 **The Engineering Design Process** p. 28 Considering Tradeoffs Process Design **Systems and Models** p. 34 **Case Study: Biosphere 2** p. 37	**Math Handbook** **3D Model** Carbon Nanotube **Engineering Lab Worksheet** **Engineering Lab Teacher Support** **Lab Safety Handbook**
ELABORATE	**Take It Further** Multiscale Modeling p. 40	Correlation vs. Causation Food Technologist Modeling a System **Engineering Lab Worksheet**
EVALUATE	**Lesson Self-Check** p. 42	**Lesson Quiz**

Hands-On Lab Planning

Separating a Mixture

🕐 45 minutes
👥 Small Groups

Objective Students observe physical properties of the components of a mixture and separate the mixture based on their observations.

Materials
- components (salt, sand, iron filings, poppy seeds)
- distilled water
- filter funnel and paper
- forceps
- hot plate
- magnet
- mixture sample
- test tubes and rack

Advance Preparation Prepare the mixtures of salt, sand, iron filings, and poppy seeds for each group, and have the components available for students to test individually.

Additional Downloadable Lab Option

Modeling a System

🕐 90 minutes
👥 Individuals or Pairs

Objective Students identify a system and then create a model of the system and revise it based on a consideration of tradeoffs.

Assessment Planning

Preassessment
Assessment Guide, Unit Pretest

Formative Assessment
Interactive Worktext: Explorations, Lesson Self-Check

Summative Assessment
Assessment Guide, Lesson Quiz

Interactive Worktext: Unit Performance Task, p. 50

Interactive Worktext: Unit Practice and Review, p. 51

Assessment Guide, Unit Test and Modified Unit Test

HMH Field Trips
powered by

Google Expeditions

Go to **HMH Google Expeditions** in the Resources tab on Ed: Your Friend in Learning for 3D, 360-degree experiences to share with your students and a Teacher Guide for you.

Teacher Notes

_____
_____
_____
_____
_____
_____
_____
_____
_____
_____
_____
_____
_____
_____
_____
_____
_____
_____
_____
_____
_____
_____

Unit Project

Overview and Planning

Optimizing Toothpaste

3D Learning Objective

Students perform an engineering design project in which they design, test, and optimize homemade toothpaste.

Students design and produce a homemade toothpaste. They test its cleaning capability by using it to clean a coffee-stained tile that serves as a model for teeth. Based on these results, students then optimize their design by adjusting the toothpaste ingredients.

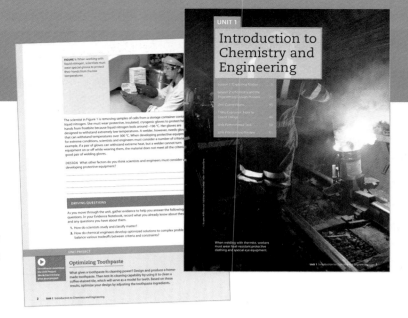

NGSS Focus

This project supports building student mastery of **Performance Expectations HS-ETS1-1** and **HS-ETS1-3.** Students will design a homemade toothpaste by first analyzing the real-world problem of a need for toothpaste and then breaking the problem down into smaller, more manageable problems that can be solved through engineering. Students will test the toothpaste and optimize the design by altering the ingredients to increase its whitening power.

Science and Engineering Practices
- Planning and Carrying Out Investigations
- Asking Questions and Defining Problems
- Constructing Explanations and Designing Solutions
- Obtaining, Evaluating, and Communicating Information

Disciplinary Core Ideas
- **ETS1.A** Defining and Delimiting Engineering Problems
- **ETS1.B** Developing Possible Solutions
- **ETS1.C** Optimizing the Design Solution

Crosscutting Concepts
- Influence of Engineering, Technology, and Science on Society and the Natural World

Classroom Management

👥 Small Groups

⏱ Three 45-minute class periods

Suggested Materials
- See the procedure for detailed materials list for the lab.
- To reduce the number of toothbrushes required for this activity, have students use the same brush for each test. Have students rinse and dry their toothbrush after completing each test and before beginning the next one. Toothbrushes can also be shared between class periods.
- If the classroom budget does not allow for the purchase of multiple ceramic tiles for each group, have students divide each tile into quadrants using masking tape. Then they can run each test in one section.

Safety
- Remind students not to eat any food items used in a lab activity.

Suggested Resources
- **American Dental Association:** describes common ingredients in toothpaste, identifies those that are often allergens, and lists special considerations for toothpaste ingredients for small children
- Local dentists and orthodontists as well as national health organizations

▶ Go Online

- Go online to download the teacher version of the student worksheet for this unit project, which includes additional questions, sample answers, and additional scaffolding to help students use evidence and reasoning to support their claims.

Introducing the Project

Prepare students for their investigation by asking the following questions:
- **What type of toothpaste do you use at home?**
- **What ingredients are in your toothpaste, and what is the function of each ingredient?**
- **Are there some ingredients in toothpaste that are controversial?**

Student Deliverables

A **student worksheet** is available to help students in planning and completing the project. Students can turn in their worksheets, or they can be assessed on a final lab report, the toothpaste they produce, and/or final presentations explaining their project. Evidence Notebook prompts throughout the unit refer to the Unit Project to help keep its connection to the investigative phenomenon present in students' minds.

Students should document the steps they take in designing, testing, and optimizing their toothpaste by taking photos or drawing pictures. Students can use the images at the end of the project to explain how they applied the engineering design process.

Scoring Rubric for Unit Project	
	The worksheet and presentation describe observations and measurements used to determine whether the data support their claims.
	The plan follows simulated brushing recommendations that follow guidelines for daily brushing.
	The plan has a way of qualitatively or quantitatively measuring the cleaning capability of each toothpaste formulation, such as using digital photos and time-based observations.
	An optimized toothpaste formulation is developed, tested, and compared with the original toothpaste formulations to evaluate cleaning capabilities.

Guiding Students on Project Planning

Once students understand the project goals and their deliverables, the next step is for students to plan the initial design for their toothpaste and develop a method for testing it. To help students think about these tasks, consider asking:

- **How will you test the cleaning power of the initial toothpaste recipe?**
  Remind students that their testing procedures will need to compare the initial and optimized recipes. Students may consider different types of qualitative and quantitative data they can collect. For example, they may generate a cleaning scale from 1 to 5 to analyze the cleaning power. They may also take pictures to visually compare the results of the two recipes.

- **What are possible ways that the toothpaste recipe could be optimized to increase cleaning power?**
  Students may suggest increasing the amount of cleaning agent in the toothpaste, increasing the foaming agent in the toothpaste, or introducing a new abrasive to remove stains. Students should make claims explaining why they think their design change will increase the cleaning power of the toothpaste and how they will determine success.

Be sure to review and approve project plans before students begin. The Unit Project Worksheet can be used for formal approval.

Differentiate Instruction

MTSS/RTI Have groups make a two-column list of materials they will use in their toothpaste. Beside each ingredient, have them list its function. Guide students in discussing and determining the functions. Be alert to the possibility that some students may have poorly formed or colored teeth and may feel self-conscious discussing these topics. Avoid situations in which students may be teased about their appearance.

Extension Bring in several brands of commercially available toothpaste. Have students plan and conduct an investigation in which they compare the properties of their toothpaste with the properties of the commercial brands and identify several desirable properties of the commercial brands that their toothpaste does not have. Properties might include foaming ability, color, creaminess, abrasiveness, pH, and a viscosity that allows it to sit well on a toothbrush. Have students determine methods and attempt to alter their toothpaste so that it has those properties.

Teacher Notes

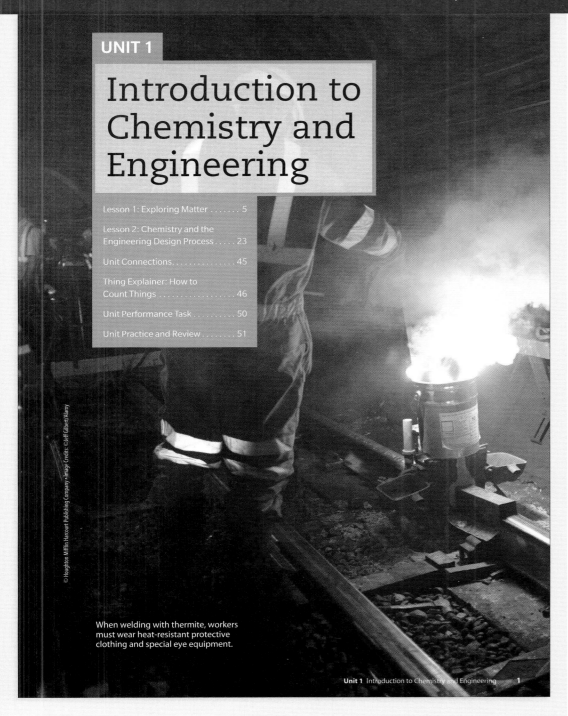

UNIT 1

Introduction to Chemistry and Engineering

When welding with thermite, workers
must wear heat-resistant protective
clothing and special eye equipment.

The learning experiences in this unit prepare students for the mastery of

Performance Expectations

HS-PS1-2 Construct and revise an explanation for the outcome of a simple chemical reaction based on the outermost electron states of atoms, trends in the periodic table, and knowledge of the patterns of chemical properties.

HS-PS1-3 Plan and conduct an investigation to gather evidence to compare the structure of substances at the bulk scale to infer the strength of electrical forces between particles.

HS-ETS1-1 Analyze a major global challenge to specify qualitative and quantitative criteria and constraints for solutions that account for societal needs and wants.

HS-ETS1-3 Evaluate a solution to a complex real-world problem based on prioritized criteria and trade-offs that account for a range of constraints, including cost, safety, reliability, and aesthetics, as well as possible social, cultural, and environmental impacts.

HS-ETS1-4 Use a computer simulation to model the impact of proposed solutions to a complex real-world problem with numerous criteria and constraints on interactions within and between systems relevant to the problem.

Explore Online

In addition to the print resources, the following resources are available online to support this unit.

Lesson 1 Exploring Matter
  • Interactive Online Student Edition
  • Lesson Quiz
Lesson 2 Chemistry and the Engineering Design Process
  • Interactive Online Student Edition
  • Lesson Quiz
Unit Performance Task
Unit Test

Unit Prerequisite Knowledge

Students should understand these concepts before starting the unit:

- Matter can be described by its properties. It can be measured and observed to determine its properties. Heating or cooling matter can change its physical state as well as its temperature.
- A substance can be broken down into smaller parts, which may have properties different from those of the original substance.
- Systems can be defined in terms of matter and energy.

Collaborate

Driving Questions Have partners discuss their initial thoughts about the Driving Questions for this unit before you discuss the questions as a class. Encourage students to record the questions and their initial responses in their Evidence Notebook, where they can revise and add to their answers as they work through the unit.

Anchoring Phenomenon

Project Based Learning

Optimizing Toothpaste

SEP Asking Questions and Defining Problems

An anchoring phenomenon connects student learning across the lessons in a unit. The Unit Project serves as an anchoring phenomenon as students use what they learn about matter in Lesson 1 and the engineering design process in Lesson 2 to design and test a homemade toothpaste.

Tips on Cultivating Questions Bring in several tubes of toothpaste in their original boxes, and give students time to make comparisons. Prompt them to ask questions about each one's unique characteristics.

1 **Sample answer:** Scientists and engineers must consider the materials used in the equipment. For example, the gloves the welder is wearing should not catch fire easily or react with any commonly used chemicals. Equipment designers must also consider material costs vs. benefits and whether the equipment should be disposable or durable enough to be used many times.

FIGURE 1: When working with liquid nitrogen, scientists must wear special gloves to protect their hands from the low temperatures.

The scientist in Figure 1 is removing samples of cells from a storage container containing liquid nitrogen. She must wear protective, insulated, cryogenic gloves to protect her hands from frostbite because liquid nitrogen boils around −196 °C. Her gloves are designed to withstand extremely low temperatures. A welder, however, needs gloves that can withstand temperatures over 300 °C. When developing protective equipment for extreme conditions, scientists and engineers must consider a number of criteria. For example, if a pair of gloves can withstand extreme heat, but a welder cannot turn equipment on or off while wearing them, the material does not meet all the criteria for a good pair of welding gloves.

1 **DESIGN** What other factors do you think scientists and engineers must consider when developing protective equipment?

_____

_____

_____

_____

DRIVING QUESTIONS

As you move through the unit, gather evidence to help you answer the following questions. In your Evidence Notebook, record what you already know about these topics and any questions you have about them.

1. How do scientists study and classify matter?
2. How do chemical engineers develop optimized solutions to complex problems that balance various tradeoffs between criteria and constraints?

UNIT PROJECT

Go online to download the Unit Project Worksheet to help plan your project.

Optimizing Toothpaste

What gives a toothpaste its cleaning power? Design and produce a home-made toothpaste. Then test its cleaning capability by using it to clean a coffee-stained tile, which will serve as a model for teeth. Based on these results, optimize your design by adjusting the toothpaste ingredients.

Language Development

Use the lessons in this unit to complete the chart and expand your understanding of the science concepts.

TERM: physical property

Definition	Example

Similar Term	Phrase

TERM: chemical property

Definition	Example

Similar Term	Phrase

TERM: model

Definition	Example

Similar Term	Phrase

TERM: system

Definition	Example

Similar Term	Phrase

© Houghton Mifflin Harcourt Publishing Company

Language Development

The summary chart graphic organizer allows students to practice using unit vocabulary to convey meaning and to communicate clearly. The chart shown, which is continued on the next page, may not include every unit vocabulary term.

Using the Chart As you encounter a highlighted vocabulary term within the unit, direct students to fill in the corresponding boxes in the summary chart. Students should always fill in the Definition box, but they need not fill in all others. Students can write a cognate from their home language in the Similar Term box. Students whose home language is English can fill in a synonym or word with the same root (such as *atomic* for the word *atom*). Accept all reasonable answers.

If desired, hand out to students a blank summary chart. Provide the starting words or have students select their own from the list of unit vocabulary. Work with students to complete the charts for each word. You may also ask students to work in pairs and then share and compare their work with that of their classmates.

Students can explore all vocabulary terms in the Online Glossary. A multilingual glossary is also available online.

SAMPLE ANSWERS

physical property: a characteristic of a substance that does not involve a chemical change; color or boiling point; propiedad física; Melting point is a physical property.

chemical property: a property of matter that describes a substance's ability to participate in chemical reactions; some metals reacting violently when exposed to air; propiedad química; Reactivity with oxygen is a chemical property.

model: a pattern, plan, representation, or description designed to show the structure or workings of an object, system, or concept; a solar system mobile; modelo; Electron dot diagrams model valence states of atoms.

system: a set of interacting, interrelated, or interdependent components that form a complex whole; a computer; sistema; Forming a compound in a chemical manufacturing plant is an example of a system of interacting parts.

SAMPLE ANSWERS

engineering design process: a series of steps that engineers use to come up with a solution to a problem; a pharmaceutical company develops, tests, and optimizes a new pain-reliever medicine; proceso de diseño de ingeniería; The engineering design process may be used to develop solutions to global climate change.

criterion (plural criteria): a standard that can be used to judge the desirability of a solution; in engineering design, criteria are often determined when defining a problem; an adhesive must not dissolve easily in water; criterio; A criterion for chemical paint thinners is the ability to dissolve oil-based paint.

constraint: a restriction or limitation; in engineering design, a limitation that a design or solution must stay within, often determined when defining a problem; a satellite must fit within the payload space of a spaceship; restricción; Available materials are typically constraints of a design solution.

tradeoff: the giving up of one thing in return for another, often applied to the engineering design process; higher cost in return for better performance; intercambio; Engineers must accept tradeoffs related to costs, materials, and performance.

TERM: engineering design process

Definition	Example

Similar Term	Phrase

TERM: criterion (plural criteria)

Definition	Example

Similar Term	Phrase

TERM: constraint

Definition	Example

Similar Term	Phrase

TERM: tradeoff

Definition	Example

Similar Term	Phrase

LESSON 1
Exploring Matter

Building to the Performance Expectations

The learning experiences in this lesson prepare students for mastery of

HS-PS1-2 Construct and revise an explanation for the outcome of a simple chemical reaction based on the outermost electron states of atoms, trends in the periodic table, and knowledge of the patterns of chemical properties.

HS-PS1-3 Plan and conduct an investigation to gather evidence to compare the structure of substances at the bulk scale to infer the strength of electrical forces between particles.

 Trace Tool to the NGSS

Go online to view the complete coverage of standards across lessons, units, and grade levels.

 **Science & Engineering Practices**

Planning and Carrying Out Investigations
Plan and conduct an investigation individually and collaboratively to produce data to serve as the basis for evidence, and in the design: decide on types, how much, and accuracy of data needed to produce reliable measurements and consider limitations on the precision of the data (e.g., number of trials, cost, risk, time), and refine the design accordingly.

Constructing Explanations and Designing Solutions
Construct and revise an explanation based on valid and reliable evidence obtained from a variety of sources (including students' own investigations, models, theories, simulations, and peer review) and the assumption that theories and laws that describe the natural world operate today as they did in the past and will continue to do so in the future.

 VIDEO Constructing Scientific Explanations

 **Disciplinary Core Ideas**

PS1.A Structure and Properties of Matter
The structure and interactions of matter at the bulk scale are determined by electrical forces within and between atoms. (HS-PS1-3)

ETS1.B Developing Possible Solutions
Both physical models and computers can be used in various ways to aid in the engineering design process. Computers are useful for a variety of purposes, such as running simulations to test different ways of solving a problem or to see which one is most efficient or economical; and in making a persuasive presentation to a client about how a given design will meet his or her needs. (HS-ETS1-4)

VIDEO Engineering: Chemistry

PS1.B Chemical Reactions
The fact that atoms are conserved, together with knowledge of the chemical properties of the elements involved, can be used to describe and predict chemical reactions. (HS-PS1-2)

 **Crosscutting Concepts**

Patterns
Empirical evidence is needed to identify patterns.

Science is a Human Endeavor
Technological advances have influenced the progress of science and science has influenced advances in technology.

Science is a Human Endeavor
Scientific knowledge is a result of human endeavor, imagination, and creativity.

ELA STANDARDS

WHST.9-12.2 Write informative/explanatory texts, including the narration of historical events, scientific procedures/experiments, or technical processes.

WHST.9-12.7 Conduct short as well as more sustained research projects to answer a question; narrow or broaden the inquiry when appropriate; synthesize multiple sources on the subject, demonstrating understanding of the subject under investigation.

WHST.9-12.9 Draw evidence from informational texts to support analysis, reflection, and research.

Supporting All Students, All Standards

Integrating the Three Dimensions

In this lesson, students plan and carry out an investigation in which they explore chemical and physical changes **(SEP Planning and Carrying Out Investigations)** and look for patterns in the results **(CCC Patterns)** that enable them to identify similarities in the properties of some of the substances under investigation **(SEP Constructing Explanations and Designing Solutions).** Students examine the structure and interactions of matter through physical and chemical properties, including states of matter and extensive and intensive properties **(DCI PS1.A).** They begin developing knowledge of the chemical properties of elements by analyzing the way matter can be classified into types of pure substances and mixtures **(DCI PS1.B)** and examine the role of technology and models in the study of chemistry **(DCI ETS1.B).** Students explore the scope of what chemists study and investigate which human characteristics, including creativity and hard work, are required to pursue the study of any science **(CCC Science is a Human Endeavor).**

Preassessment

Have students complete the unit pretest or see the Assessment Guide.

Build on Prior Knowledge

Have students work in pairs to list several objects in the classroom. For each object students list, have them describe properties they can see and one or two properties the object has that are not visible.

You may want to review the following concepts:
- All matter is made of particles that are in constant motion.
- Elements are substances composed of a single type of atom. Elements can be combined to produce compounds.
- Materials are chosen for specific functions based on how well the properties of the material meet the needs of that function.

 Professional Development Go online to view **Professional Development videos** with strategies to integrate CCCs and SEPs, including the ones used in this lesson.

Content Background

A substance can exist in different states of matter depending on the movement and energy of the particles that make up the substance and the attractions between the particles. Adding energy as heat to a substance can change a solid to a liquid or a liquid to a gas because when the energy increases sufficiently, the movement of the particles is enough to overcome the attractions between them. Substances have different temperatures at which they change from one state to another, and this can vary depending on the pressure of the system.

During a physical change, the particles that make up a substance do not change identity. But during a chemical change, the particles do change identity. The same atoms in the substance exist before and after the chemical change, but the atoms rearrange to form one or more new substances. Chemical changes take place in chemical reactions. Existing bonds are broken and new bonds form, so a change in the energy of the system occurs. This is why chemical changes can sometimes be identified by a change in temperature. They can also be identified by a change in color, production of a gas, or production of a precipitate. While these observations indicate the possibility of a chemical change, the change must be confirmed by comparing the identities of the substances before and after they interact.

Differentiate Instruction

KEY WORDS

- chemical change
- physical change
- matter
- physical property
- chemical property
- extensive property
- intensive property
- model

ELL SUPPORT

Have students write the key words in their notebooks. Ask them to describe ways they have heard the word *model* used in everyday life, and list several examples on the board. Based on these examples, have students work in small groups to discuss and develop a definition for the word. Encourage students to look for this word as they explore the lesson.

ENGAGE: Investigative Phenomenon

1.1
Exploring Matter

A worker inspects metal tubing.

CAN YOU SOLVE THE PROBLEM?

People develop new technologies, including new materials, to address problems or offer better solutions to existing ones. For decades, plumbing pipes in buildings were made of metal tubing, such as galvanized steel or copper. More recently, plastic pipes have started to replace metal pipes because plastic pipes are cheaper, easier to work with, and do not corrode over time. However, compared to metal pipes, plastic pipes are not as heat resistant, not as strong, and are less environmentally friendly. There are many factors to consider when trying to replace an existing material with a new material.

1 **EXPLAIN** How could you improve an item that you use regularly?

_____

_____

_____

_____

2 **Evidence Notebook** As you explore the lesson, gather evidence to explain what questions scientists could ask and what tests they could run if they wanted to use a new material in place of an existing one, such as using plastic pipes instead of metal ones.

Lesson 1 Exploring Matter **5**

Lesson Objective

Students explore physical and chemical properties, the categories of matter, and what chemists do.

Cultivating Student Questions

Have students look at the photo of metal tubing. Prompt them to ask all questions that come to mind about how to describe the properties and uses of the tubing. Record the questions on chart paper, and then sort the questions based on their focus. With students, narrow the questions down to ones that directly relate to the learning objective. Have students reflect on this list throughout the lesson and check off questions as they are answered.

Can You Solve the Problem?

The Investigative Phenomenon is the focus of the lesson. Students are asked to record their initial thoughts about the properties of materials that make up items they use regularly. Encourage students to name everyday items, such as electronic devices, clothing, tools, building materials, and musical instruments, and to consider the materials they are made of, the properties of those materials, and how those items could be improved. Students will collect evidence related to this phenomenon throughout the lesson. They will revisit the question at the end of the lesson and use what they have learned to explain whether a new material could perform the same function as an existing material.

1 Students may mention making cell phones or computers smaller or lighter, or making a bridge stronger. Students should focus on properties of an existing item that can be enhanced.

Evidence Notebook

2 The topic of the properties of matter and how those properties influence the way we use materials will be revisited throughout this lesson. Students should collect information about how to identify physical and chemical properties of a substance and how those data can be used to determine whether a new material is a suitable replacement for an existing one.

Lesson 1 Exploring Matter 5

EXPLORATION 1 Exploring Physical and Chemical Changes

3D Learning Objective

Students **plan and carry out an investigation** and describe **chemical reactions** to determine **patterns** in the way substances react.

Everyday Phenomena discussed throughout the Explorations of the lesson can often be used to connect the science content to students' personal experiences.

Hands-On Lab 👥 Small Groups ⏱ 60 minutes

Exploring Physical and Chemical Changes

SEP **Planning and Carrying Out Investigations**

Students collect evidence to determine whether physical or chemical changes occur in a series of experiments.

Materials Alert Some materials used in this lab are expensive ($AgNO_3$) and pose an environmental disposal risk ($PbNO_3$). It is advised that you do not perform the chemical reactions at a larger scale.

Safety Information Remind all students that indirectly vented chemical splash goggles, a nonlatex apron, and nitrile gloves are to be worn during the setup, hands-on, and takedown segments of the activity. Remind students not to pour chemicals, either used or unused, back into the original container. Instruct students how to dispose of chemicals and remind them not to touch, taste, or sniff any chemicals in the lab and to waft if they need to determine odor.

Collaborate

One Moves Ask students groups: *What are some examples of physical and chemical changes in everyday life?* Have one member from each group move to a new group to share and compare information.

1 Students should claim that a new substance with new properties will be produced in a chemical change, but the starting substances will just change appearance in a physical change. Students may predict that mixing chalk with water is a physical change. The other experiments result in chemical changes with production of a gas, a change in color, or formation of a solid.

Hands-On Lab

Exploring Physical and Chemical Changes

All substances are made of small particles known as atoms and molecules. When a property of a substance changes, its atoms and molecules have changed. The study of chemistry is the study of these changes. Some changes happen when one substance interacts with another substance. Why might we need to determine how substances interact with one another? We need to be aware of the way substances interact because some changes may be harmful and some may be beneficial.

Scientists classify changes in substances as either physical changes or chemical changes. A physical change affects the form of a substance, but its identity remains the same. In a chemical change, however, the chemical identity of a substance changes. Atoms and molecules rearrange to form new substances. In this lab, you will determine whether the changes you observe are physical or chemical changes.

RESEARCH QUESTION What are examples of physical and chemical changes that are important in your daily life?

1 **MAKE A CLAIM**

Preview each experiment you will perform. For each experiment, is the change that occurs physical, or is it chemical? How will you be able to tell what type of change took place?

_____

_____

_____

_____

MATERIALS

- indirectly vented chemical splash goggles, nonlatex apron, nitrile gloves
- chalk, calcium carbonate (5 g)
- lead nitrate solution in dropper bottle, 0.2 M
- mortar and pestle
- silver nitrate solution in dropper bottle, 0.1 M
- sodium hydroxide solution in dropper bottle, 0.5 M
- sodium iodide solution in dropper bottle, 0.5 M
- water in dropper bottle
- well plate
- vinegar (acetic acid) in dropper bottle

indirectly vented
chemical splash
goggles

SAFETY INFORMATION

- Wear indirectly vented chemical splash goggles, a nonlatex apron, and nitrile gloves during the setup, hands-on, and takedown segments of the activity.
- Never pour chemicals, either used or unused, back into their original container. Dispose of chemicals according to your teacher's instructions.
- Never touch, taste, or sniff any chemicals in the lab. If you need to determine odor, waft. To waft, hold the chemical in its container 15 cm away from your nose, and use your fingers to bring fumes from the container to your nose.

6   **Unit 1** Introduction to Chemistry and Engineering

 Student Lab Worksheet and complete Teacher Support available online.

© Houghton Mifflin Harcourt Publishing Company

PLAN THE INVESTIGATION

In your Evidence Notebook, develop a procedure to safely combine each pair of materials listed below. Use five drops of each solution. In your procedure, consider how much of each solid you will need given this constraint. Have your teacher approve your procedure and safety plan before you start.

1. water and crushed chalk

2. vinegar and crushed chalk

3. silver nitrate solution and sodium hydroxide solution

4. silver nitrate solution and sodium iodide solution

5. lead nitrate solution and sodium iodide solution

6. sodium hydroxide solution and sodium iodide solution

Follow your teacher's instructions for disposal of the chemicals in your well plate. Wash and dry the well plate.

COLLECT DATA

In your Evidence Notebook, develop a matrix-style table to record the properties of each material before and after it was combined, as well as any evidence that a physical or chemical change took place once the materials were combined.

ANALYZE

1. Which of the changes you observed indicated a physical change, and which indicated a chemical change?

_____

_____

_____

2. What are some limitations of this experiment? How could you revise your procedure to improve the results?

_____

_____

_____

_____

3. Sketch the difference between a physical change and a chemical change.

SEP Planning and Carrying Out Investigations

If students need extra guidance in developing their procedures, provide a model for the first experiment, as follows: *Place 5 g of chalk in a well, and add five drops of water.* Make sure their procedures demonstrate reasonable observations of safety. Encourage students to add the chalk and the sodium hydroxide solution to the well before adding drops of the more acidic solutions.

DCI PS1.B Chemical Reactions

Ask students what happens in a chemical reaction. Elicit responses that describe how atoms are rearranged but never destroyed in a chemical reaction. Encourage students to let this guide their approach to their sketches.

Analyze

1. A physical change occurred when water dissolved the crushed chalk. A physical change can be indicated by a change in shape or state of matter. Combinations 2 through 5 showed evidence of a chemical change. A chemical change can be indicated by the formation of a precipitate, the formation of bubbles (not caused by boiling or the release of gas from a mixture such as a carbonated beverage), or a color change. Some chemical changes are not obvious, and it must be determined whether a new substance formed. There was no evidence of a chemical or a physical change when sodium hydroxide and sodium iodide were mixed.

2. Students may suggest that they were limited by the amount of material they could use in their test, by the number of trials they were able to perform, and by which substances they were allowed to combine. Students may suggest that they could improve their procedure by running additional trials or by using different combinations of materials.

3. Sketch should show that in a physical change, the substances change form but do not form a new substance. Students may draw the chalk particles starting out as a solid and then dissolving in the liquid, but the chalk particles are still present and unchanged. In a chemical change, a new substance is formed. Students may draw lead nitrate particles and sodium iodide particles, both of which are in clear, colorless liquids, forming a new substance that is a yellow precipitate.

ccc Patterns

Demonstrate the following examples of **everyday phenomena,** and ask students to identify whether it is a physical or a chemical change: ripping paper into two pieces (physical), burning paper (chemical), stirring salt into water (physical), adding an effervescent antacid to water (chemical). *Ask: What evidence can you use to determine if a change is chemical or physical?* Physical changes are sometimes reversible. Chemical changes alter the identity of the material.

Construct an Explanation

1. Physical changes do not involve the rearrangement of atoms to form new substances. Chemical changes involve the rearrangement of atoms, and new substances are produced.

2. **Sample answer:** Some of the materials were similar. For example, silver nitrate and lead nitrate were both tested with sodium iodide. Both tests resulted in a chemical change, so silver nitrate and lead nitrate have similar chemical properties.

1 Evidence of a chemical change can be a change in color, odor, or temperature, the formation of a solid precipitate, or the formation of a gas. Indicators of a physical change include changes in shape, size, and states of matter. Students should list whether they think a physical or chemical change occurred and use evidence from their observations to support their claims. They should use this evidence to explain which type of change they observed.

Evidence Notebook

2 Observing changes can yield data about whether a new material has properties that are similar to an existing material. Physical changes provide details about physical properties, such as density and boiling point. Chemical changes offer insight about chemical properties, which describe how a material does or does not react to form new substances.

FORMATIVE ASSESSMENT

One-Sentence Summary Ask students to look back through the Exploration and review their notes for the Hands-On Lab. Then have them write a one-sentence summary describing chemical and physical changes.

CONSTRUCT AN EXPLANATION

1. Explain the difference between a physical change and a chemical change on a molecular level.

_____

_____

2. Based on the materials you used and the results of your experiments, what patterns do you see? Which materials do you think have similar properties? Explain your reasoning.

_____

_____

_____

_____

1 DRAW CONCLUSIONS

Write a conclusion that addresses each of the points below.

Claim How were you able to determine whether a physical or chemical change occurred in each experiment?

Evidence What evidence from your investigation supports your claim?

Reasoning Explain how the evidence you gave supports your claim. Describe, in detail, the connections between the evidence you cited and the argument you are making.

_____

_____

_____

_____

_____

_____

_____

_____

_____

_____

_____

_____

2 **Evidence Notebook** Consider the differences between chemical and physical changes. How could you use physical and chemical changes to determine if a new material can be used in the same way as an existing material?

EXPLORATION 2 Properties of Matter

EXPLORATION 2

Properties of Matter

Everything around you—your desk, your chair, and even the people—are all made of matter. Even things you cannot see, such as air, are made of matter. Matter is anything that takes up space and has mass. The mass of an object is the amount of matter the object contains. Although all things are made of matter, the kind and amount of matter in each object usually varies.

FIGURE 1: A ball of clay is manipulated into different shapes in each of the images below.

3 **ANALYZE** Do the amounts of mass and matter in Figure 1 change as the size and shape of the clay ball is changed? Explain your reasoning.

_____

_____

_____

The law of conservation of matter, or the law of conservation of mass, states that matter cannot be created or destroyed in either physical or chemical changes. During a chemical reaction, substances interact with each other to form new substances. The starting substances are the reactants; the new substances formed are the products. The reactant particles are rearranged to form the product particles in such a way that no atoms are lost and no atoms are added. Because no atoms are gained or lost during the chemical reaction, the total mass of the substances involved remains the same.

Now consider a spoonful of sodium chloride, also known as table salt. Sodium chloride is made when an atom of sodium bonds to an atom of chlorine. The spoonful of sodium chloride has a specific mass. You can change the total mass by adding salt to the spoon or removing salt from the spoon.

4 **EXPLAIN** You pour a spoonful of salt into a glass of water. Explain what happens to the mass of the salt and the mass of the water.

_____

_____

3D Learning Objective

Students explore **chemical reactions** by analyzing physical and chemical properties and changes. They examine **energy and matter** by modeling water molecules in different states of matter and **engage in argument from evidence** using physical and chemical properties to identify materials. Students categorize the **structure and properties of matter** according to whether or not these are dependent on the quantities of matter present.

Collaborate

Accessing Prior Knowledge Have students work in small groups to discuss what they already know about the properties of the materials around them in the classroom. Have them make a list of five materials and a description of their properties.

CCC **Energy and Matter**

Help students understand the law of conservation of mass by referring to the photos in **Figure 1.** *Ask: Has any matter left the table on which the modeling clay is sitting?* Encourage students to imagine an invisible boundary around the system into which matter does not enter or exit. Challenge them to connect the law of conservation of mass to examples of **everyday phenomena.**

Ask: How does the law of conservation of mass apply to liquid water that turns to ice? The number of water molecules does not change, so the mass is the same before and after freezing.

3 Students should recognize that even though the shape of the object has been changed in the first two views, the mass, and therefore the amount of matter in the object, are the same. In the third view, each individual clay ball has less mass and therefore less matter than the original, but the total mass and matter are conserved.

4 The mass of the water and the mass of the salt remain the same. Even though the water dissolves the salt, the water is still water, and the salt is still salt.

Exploring Visuals

Comparing Physical Properties In **Figure 2,** students observe four examples of physical properties. ***Ask:*** *Which of these properties could you use to distinguish between a plastic bar and a copper bar?* You could use malleability to identify copper. *Which two of these properties could you use to distinguish between oil and water?* You could use density and solubility to distinguish between oil and water, because oil is less dense, and many substances are soluble in water that are not soluble in oil.

Explore Online

Encourage students to go online to view an image gallery with more information about these and other physical properties of matter.

Math Connection

Density Explain to students that the density of water at 4 °C is 1.000 g/cm³. ***Ask:*** *What is the mass of 1000 cm³ of water?* 1.000 kg Tell students that 1 cm³ equals 1 mL. *What is the mass of 1.000 L of water?* 1.000 kg *What is the mass of 1.00 L of isopropanol?* 790 g **(MP.2)**

Preconception Alert

Water Vapor Students may mistakenly identify visible mist as water vapor. Emphasize that water vapor is an invisible gas. ***Ask:*** *What is the phase of water seen in mist?* Mist is made of tiny droplets of liquid water. *How might the presence of mist indicate the presence of water vapor?* The droplets in mist may form when water vapor in the air condenses into liquid water.

1 The physical properties shown in **Figure 2** are density, conductivity, malleability, and solubility. Questions will vary but might include asking how the properties of a substance can be used to identify it. Students may list other physical properties, such as odor, texture, color, viscosity, and magnetism.

2 Students should indicate that boiling point and density would be helpful because these differ for the two liquids. Both water and isopropanol are poor conductors, so conductivity would not help students distinguish between the two liquids.

Physical Properties and Physical Changes

Every substance has physical properties that help determine its identity. Knowing the properties of a substance is important when chemists choose the best material for a specific use. A **physical property** is a property that can be measured or observed without changing the identity of matter. Some physical properties are shown in Figure 2.

FIGURE 2: Examples of some common physical properties of matter

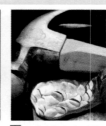

a Density is the amount of mass per volume of a substance.

b Conductivity is a measure of the amount of electricity, heat, or sound that a substance can carry.

c Malleability is the ability of a substance to be flattened.

d Solubility is the amount of a substance that can dissolve in a given amount of another substance.

1 **Collaborate** With a partner, make a list of the physical properties shown in Figure 2. List questions you have about these physical properties. What other characteristics of matter do you think are physical properties?

A physical change is a change of matter from one form to another without a change in chemical properties. For example, sugar is soluble in water. When you drink the water, you can taste the sugar although you cannot see it. That is because in the water, the sugar is still sugar. Its identity has not changed.

Using Physical Properties to Identify Matter

Imagine you have two cups filled with colorless liquids. One cup contains water, and the other cup contains isopropanol, a common component of rubbing alcohol. To differentiate the liquids, you can study some of their physical properties.

Property	Water	Isopropanol
Boiling point	100 °C	82 °C
Density	1.0 g/cm³	0.79 g/cm³
Conductivity	poor	poor

2 **ANALYZE** Which properties would be helpful in determining the identity of the liquids, and which would not be helpful? Explain your answer.

_____

_____

_____

States of Matter

States of matter—solid, liquid, gas, or plasma—are the common forms in which matter exists in the universe. When a substance goes from one state of matter to another, the process is called a *change in state*. During a change in state, the physical properties of a substance change, but the chemical composition does not. When water in the form of ice melts, it looks different on the macroscopic scale, but its chemical composition has not changed on the molecular scale.

FIGURE 3: Water changes state from solid (ice) to liquid (liquid water) to gas (water vapor).

3 ASK What questions could you ask about the arrangement of particles in the states of matter shown in Figure 3?

_____

_____

The particles in a solid are packed very closely together in a rigid, orderly arrangement. They are held together by the attractive forces that act between all particles of matter. Solids, therefore, have fixed volumes and shapes. In the solid state, particles cannot break away from their fixed position; they can only vibrate in place.

The particles that make up a liquid move more rapidly than those in a solid do. This causes the particles in the liquid to overcome some of the attractive forces between them, and the particles can slide freely around each other.

The particles of a gas are very far apart and move rapidly compared to particles in solids or liquids. At these distances, the attractive forces between gas particles have a lesser effect than they have on particles in liquids and solids. In general, the volume of a liquid or solid increases greatly when it forms a gas. However, the density of the gaseous state of most substances is approximately one-thousandth the density of the liquid state.

Plasma is a gas in which the particles have so much energy that they become electrically charged. Plasma is the most common state of matter in the universe, with more than 99.99% of observable matter in the universe being plasma. Most of the matter of the sun is plasma. Stars and lightning are also examples of plasma. However, this state is not experienced in the physical and chemical changes we encounter every day on Earth.

4 MODEL Draw a diagram of the arrangement of water molecules when water is a solid, a liquid, and a gas.

SEP Developing and Using Models

On the board, have students develop a model that explains the effect on particle motion and energy when a substance changes from a solid to a liquid to a gas. Draw students' attention to the description of the different states of matter on this page. Emphasize that there are large distances between particles in the gaseous state, making it impractical to show the same scale as in models of solids and liquids.

CCC Energy and Matter

Ask: *How do you think the law of conservation of matter applies as a substance changes from a liquid to a solid?* The change occurs because energy is removed from the system. Although the behavior and movement of the particles change, the same type and number of particles exist in the solid as in the liquid.

DCI PS1.A Structure and Properties of Matter

Emphasize to students that a substance is held together by attraction between its particles. As thermal energy is added, the motion between the particles increases. The temperature at which a phase change occurs depends in large part on the force of attraction between the particles.

3 Students may ask whether, how, and why the arrangement of particles changes as ice becomes liquid water and liquid water becomes water vapor when heated to certain temperatures. The particles of water are gaining energy from the heat source, moving more rapidly, and spreading farther apart. Some are escaping into the air as water vapor. The particles in the ice cube are also gaining energy and moving faster. They break out of their rigid arrangement and begin to flow as a liquid.

4 Students should draw water molecules that are close together and in an ordered arrangement when in a solid state. The molecules are far apart and less ordered in a gaseous state. Water molecules will be close together in the liquid state but not as ordered as they are when in a solid state. Students may indicate the ability of water molecules to move around each other in the liquid and gaseous states.

CCC Energy and Matter

Explain to students that the coldest parts of Earth do not go below about 180 K, but the average temperature of the universe is about 3 K. **Ask:** *Where would scientists likely find BEC particles?* Scientists would likely find BEC particles in outer space, far from any star.

Explore Online

Encourage students to go online to view videos of three different alkali metals reacting with water.

Differentiate Instruction

ELL Support Students encountering chemical reactions for the first time might find the terms *reactant* and *product* unfamiliar. Scaffold the components for writing chemical equations by showing how these terms are used with a reaction arrow. Write the terms on the board, and draw a reaction arrow connecting them. Explain that the arrow indicates that a chemical reaction has occurred. Emphasize that in a chemical reaction, the bonds between particles are broken and rearranged. The only way to reverse the results would be to go through another chemical reaction.

History of Science

In the early 1800s chemists began isolating and identifying some of the alkali metal elements. Have interested students research the discovery of one of the alkali metals.

1 Students should recognize that matter in a BEC has the least amount of energy of all states of matter. Instead of moving as separate particles, some of the particles clump together and move as a system. Because their energy is so low, their movement is very slow.

2 Melting a piece of metal is a physical change because the identity of the metal does not change. Burning a piece of coal and cooking an egg are both chemical changes because the atoms are rearranged and new substances form.

Energy and Matter

Bose-Einstein Condensate

A fifth state of matter, a Bose-Einstein condensate (BEC), was identified by scientists in 1995. In this state, extremely cold particles just above absolute zero (−273 °C or 0 K) barely move. BEC particles have so little energy that they clump and behave as a single particle. Satyendra Nath Bose and Albert Einstein predicted the BEC in the 1920s, but the technology needed to produce the matter did not exist until 1995.

1 **Collaborate** With a partner, discuss how the matter in a BEC is different from other states of matter.

Chemical Properties and Chemical Changes

A chemical property is a property that can be determined by attempting to change the identity of a substance, but it cannot be determined simply by observing the substance. Rather, a change (or lack of a change) in a substance must be observed during or after a chemical reaction.

FIGURE 4: The alkali metals lithium, sodium, and potassium react with water.   **Explore Online** ▶

a lithium   **b** sodium   **c** potassium

In a chemical change, the particles of a substance are rearranged, resulting in a change in chemical composition. Figure 4 shows three metals—lithium, sodium, and potassium—each reacting with water. The products of the reactions include hydrogen gas, which can burn if the reactions take place in the presence of oxygen. The reactivity of alkali metals with water is a chemical property. This property cannot be observed until the metal and water react and both the metal and the water change identity in the process. Rusting is also a chemical change. Iron oxide, or rust, forms when iron is exposed to water and oxygen. Understanding the chemical properties of matter is critical for safety when using materials such as the rechargeable lithium batteries found in laptop computers.

2 **ANALYZE** Classify each statement as describing a chemical or a physical change. Explain your reasoning.

A piece of metal melts. _____

A piece of coal burns. _____

An egg cooks on a stove. _____

Using Chemical Properties to Identify Matter

Chemical properties can also be used to identify a substance and they determine which kinds of materials a substance will react with. An example of a chemical property is flammability, or the ability of a substance to catch on fire. Water is not flammable, but isopropanol is. Another chemical property, reactivity, describes how likely a substance is to undergo a chemical reaction. Acidity is another chemical property. Some strong acids, such as hydrochloric acid, are highly corrosive.

3 EVALUATE You have two samples of gray powder, both of which are flammable. Are these powders the same substance? Explain your reasoning.

_____

_____

_____

Extensive and Intensive Properties

Scientists describe properties of matter as extensive and intensive. An extensive property depends directly on the amount of the substance present. An intensive property is one that does not depend on the amount of the substance present. For any particular substance, any amount of the substance has the same value for any intensive property.

4 APPLY Classify each statement as an extensive or an intensive property.

A pot of boiling water has more energy than a cup of boiling water.   extensive | intensive

A big piece of metal melts at the same temperature as a small piece.   extensive | intensive

Copper wire conducts electricity.   extensive | intensive

As seen in Figure 5, if you put a 12-ounce can of regular cola and a 12-ounce can of diet cola in a tub of water, you will notice the regular cola sinks and the diet cola floats. The sweetener in diet cola is hundreds of times sweeter per unit volume than the sugar in regular cola.

5 EXPLAIN Why does the can of diet cola float in water but the can of regular cola does not? Consider mass and density in your explanation.

_____

_____

_____

FIGURE 5: Cans of regular cola and diet cola behave differently in water.

6 **Collaborate** With a partner, list the extensive and intensive properties described in the cola experiment. Which properties would change and which would stay the same if you ran the experiment using 7.5-ounce cans instead?

7 **Evidence Notebook** Which physical and chemical properties would allow you to determine if a new material can replace an existing material? For example, what properties must a plastic pipe have in order to perform the same function as a metal pipe?

Collaborate

Graffiti Have students work in groups. Give each group a large piece of paper and felt pens of different colors. Ask students to generate ideas about extensive and intensive properties in the form of graffiti.

3 Students should indicate that not enough information is given to determine if the two powders are the same substance. Two different substances often have a few similar physical or chemical properties. Further testing is needed to identify more of their physical and chemical properties.

4 extensive, intensive, intensive

5 The diet sweetener is hundreds of times sweeter per unit volume than the sugar in regular cola, so a smaller mass of sweetener is needed in the diet cola to produce the amount of sweetness the sugar produces in regular cola. Therefore, the regular soda is denser because it contains more dissolved matter per volume.

6 Density is an intensive property because both the aluminum can and the cola have their own unique, constant densities regardless of whether a large can or a small can is used. Volume and mass are extensive properties. If a smaller can is used, density stays the same, but volume and mass decrease.

Evidence Notebook

7 Students should note that certain physical properties, such as color and texture, may not be helpful because they might be the same for different materials but do not determine function. Other physical properties, such as hardness and melting point, would be more useful. Some chemical properties, such as the tendency to rust, are also important.

FORMATIVE ASSESSMENT

Have students choose an object in the classroom. Ask them to identify one physical property, one chemical property, one extensive property, and one intensive property of the object. ***Ask:*** *Were you able to see both the physical and chemical properties? Why or why not?* The physical property was visible, but the chemical property was not. *How did you know whether to classify a property you observed as extensive or intensive?* An extensive property depends on the amount of the substance present.

EXPLORATION 3 Classifying Matter

3D Learning Objective

Students use the structure and properties of matter to classify pure substances and mixtures. They **engage in argument from evidence** to identify patterns in the classification of matter.

SEP Engaging in Argument from Evidence

Show students a black water-soluble marker. Tell them it has been claimed that the ink in most black markers is a mixture of three to five different colors. **Ask:** *How can we prove that the ink in this marker is made of different colors?* Paper chromatography can be used. Demonstrate by placing a solid line across a strip of paper towel suspended over a glass of water.

Differentiate Instruction

MTSS/RTI Read aloud the sentences on the student page about different techniques for separating mixtures. Then slowly repeat the name of each technique: *filtration, centrifugation, chromatography.* Help students determine the root word that corresponds to each technique: *filter, centrifuge,* and *chroma.* Guide students in using the names during a discussion of each technique.

1 Air is considered a mixture because it contains several elements and compounds. In decreasing order these are nitrogen, oxygen, argon, carbon dioxide, and also much smaller concentrations of other gases.

2 Students should consider the various items found in a sample of soil, such as rocks, leaves, and dirt particles. Students should design a way to separate these components based on their size. Students could design a filtration system or a series of sieves.

Classifying Matter

Matter can be classified as either a mixture or a pure substance. For example, distilled water is a pure substance but salt water is a mixture. Every sample of distilled water has the same composition and the same chemical and physical properties. However, salt water may contain varying amounts of salt dissolved in water. The resulting salt water solutions have some properties that are the same and some that differ.

1 APPLY Is air considered a pure substance or a mixture? Explain your reasoning.

_____

_____

Mixtures

A mixture is a blend of two or more pure substances, each of which retains its own identity, although the mixture may have different properties than the individual components. Some mixtures are homogeneous, meaning they have a uniform composition throughout. Sugar water is an example of a homogeneous mixture. Mixtures that are not uniform throughout, such as a bowl of mixed nuts, are heterogeneous.

2 DESIGN You pick up a handful of soil from the ground. Design a way to separate all the components found in the soil sample.

_____

_____

FIGURE 6: Physical properties can be used to separate mixtures into their components.

a Filtration separates based on particle size.   **b** Centrifugation separates based on density.   **c** Chromatography separates based on the nature of the pigment.

Mixtures can be separated by physical means, some of which are shown in Figure 6. These methods take advantage of different physical properties of the components. For example, filtration uses a filter to catch large particles while allowing smaller particles to pass through. Centrifugation separates particles from a mixture by spinning the mixture at a high speed. Chromatography separates mixtures based on their different relative attractions to a medium, such as paper, and a solvent, such as water.

Pure Substances

A pure substance is made up of a single element or compound so it is always homogeneous. Because a pure substance has a fixed composition it cannot be separated by physical means. The 92 naturally occurring elements cannot be broken down into simpler substances by chemical or physical means. The iron and the sulfur shown in Figure 7 are elements. Both of these elements have their own unique set of physical and chemical properties. Iron and sulfur can chemically combine, or bond, to form the compound iron(II) sulfide, which has a completely different set of characteristic physical and chemical properties compared to the elements that make it up.

FIGURE 7: Iron(II) sulfide (right) is composed of iron (left) and sulfur (center).

3 **Collaborate** Talk with a partner about the properties you observe for each substance shown in Figure 7. Do you think the formation of iron(II) sulfide is an example of a chemical or physical change? Explain your reasoning.

Pure substances that are compounds can decompose, or break down, during a chemical change. For example, water can be broken down by electrolysis. Pure water has the molecular formula H_2O. It contains two hydrogen atoms bonded to a single oxygen atom. During electrolysis, an electric current is used to split water.

Thermal decomposition is another way that some pure substances can be broken down. At extreme temperatures, the bonds holding a compound together might break, causing a compound to decompose into simpler substances.

4 **MODEL** Draw a sketch of what you think happens when water is split by electrolysis.

Table sugar, also called *sucrose*, is a carbohydrate found in sugar cane, sugar beets, and many processed foods. Sucrose is made up of two sugars, glucose and fructose, joined together. Unlike some other compounds, sucrose does not melt when exposed to extreme temperatures. As seen in Figure 8, when sucrose is heated to 186 °C, it decomposes into glucose and fructose. These sugars then undergo further reactions that cause the sugar to turn brown. The browning of sugar is also known as *caramelization*.

FIGURE 8: Sucrose can be broken down when exposed to high temperatures.

5 **INFER** Would the composition of sucrose purified from sugar cane differ from the composition of sucrose purified from sugar beets? Explain your reasoning.

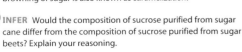

© Houghton Mifflin Harcourt Publishing Company • Image Credits: (tr) ©Martyn F Chillmaid/Science Source; (b) ©Charles D. Winters/Science Source

---

Tell students that elemental iron has magnetic properties but not when it is in a compound with sulfur. **Ask:** *If iron and sulfur interact, what test could you use to determine that the result is a new compound and not a mixture?* Magnetism—the iron in a mixture would still be magnetic, but the iron-sulfur compound would not be. Help students connect this concept to **everyday phenomena** by explaining that dietary iron can be extracted from crushed corn flakes using a magnet. **Ask:** *Is the extract elemental iron, or is it a compound containing iron?* If it is magnetic, it is most likely elemental iron.

Collaborate

Gallery Walk Fill some clear containers with samples of mixtures and other containers with samples of pure substances. Place each container at a different, numbered station around the room. Have pairs of students silently rotate through the stations, recording which samples they think are mixtures and which they think are pure substances. When all pairs have rotated through all stations, have each pair choose another pair with which to share and compare their findings. Allow several minutes for them to share, and then ask groups to revisit those stations they decided were mixtures. This time, have them record which samples they think are homogeneous and which they think are heterogeneous.

When all groups have recorded their findings, write the numbers of the stations on the board. Have one student from each group write their findings for each station beside the corresponding number. Go through the list, and ask other students to raise their hands if they have different answers. Call on one or two students per item to explain the reasoning they used to arrive at their conclusion.

3 Students should discuss physical properties, such as state of matter, color, and magnetism. The formation of iron(II) sulfide is a chemical change because a chemical reaction occurs between the reactants iron and sulfur to form a new substance, iron(II) sulfide.

4 Students should draw water molecules being split into hydrogen gas and oxygen gas.

5 The composition would be the same. The source of the sucrose does not matter because it was purified and is a pure substance.

Have students carefully examine the flow chart in **Figure 9**. Have them use the chart to classify examples in the classroom. Ask students where atoms and molecules would fit into this scheme.

Career Connection

A flow chart uses only a few words to convey complex processes. Challenge students to research careers that rely heavily on flow charts. Have students share examples of flow charts used in each area.

1 Apple juice and salt water are homogeneous mixtures. Fruit salad and juice with ice cubes are heterogeneous mixtures. CO_2 and CH_4 are compounds. He and N_2 are elements.

2 **Sample answer:** A fruit salad is a heterogeneous mixture because it is made up of different types of fruit and is not uniform. Carbon is an element because it cannot be broken down into simpler components. Methane is a compound because it has a certain number of carbon and hydrogen atoms and can be broken down.

Evidence Notebook

3 When testing a new material, you should ask if the material is a pure substance or a mixture. If the sample is a mixture, the combination of the substances that make it up can be in different ratios, so each possible ratio in the mixture would need to be considered and tested. For a pure substance, the test would only need to be run on one sample because all samples have the same physical and chemical properties.

FORMATIVE ASSESSMENT

Have students write *mixture* on one side of a note card and *pure substance* on the other side. Then quickly give students a series of examples, such as milk, ice, pond water, diamond, vinegar, baking soda, and oxygen. Have them raise their cards to show their understanding of these as mixtures and pure substances.

Ask: Which of these examples is an element, a compound, a homogeneous mixture, and heterogeneous mixture? element: diamond, oxygen; compound: ice, baking soda; homogeneous mixture: milk, vinegar; heterogeneous mixture: pond water

---

When looking at a sample it can be difficult to determine if it is a mixture or a pure substance. It can be even more tricky to determine if a mixture is homogeneous or heterogeneous, or if a pure substance is an element or a compound. These classifications can be organized in a flow chart, such as the one shown in Figure 9.

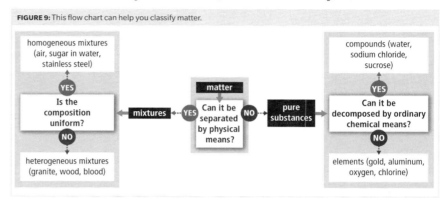

FIGURE 9: This flow chart can help you classify matter.

1 **ANALYZE** Use the chart in Figure 9 to categorize each material in the list below as either a homogeneous mixture, a heterogeneous mixture, a compound, or an element. Write your own examples in the final row.

salt water   fruit salad   methane (CH_4)   nitrogen (N_2)

carbon dioxide (CO_2)   juice with ice cubes   apple juice   helium (He)

Homogeneous Mixture	Heterogeneous Mixture	Compound	Element

2 **EXPLAIN** Choose three items from the table, and explain why you classified them the way you did.

_____

_____

_____

_____

3 **Evidence Notebook** Consider the differences between a sample of a pure substance and a sample of a mixture. When testing the properties of a new material, what questions should you ask and what considerations need to be made regarding the samples?

EXPLORATION 4 The Study of Chemistry

EXPLORATION 4

The Study of Chemistry

Have you ever wondered how new materials are identified or how you can determine how those materials can be used? Studying a material's physical and chemical properties is an important step. Comparing a material's properties to those of other materials can help identify ways a material can be used. These are just some things a chemist may do.

What Is Chemistry?

Chemistry is one branch of science. Science develops explanations based on observation and experimentation. So, scientific knowledge is based on empirical evidence, and it also requires creativity, imagination, and hard work. Science and technology often influence each other. Science aids in the development of technology, and new technology allows for more scientific knowledge to be acquired.

Examples of chemistry and the work chemists do are all around you. Chemistry studies the composition, structure, and properties of matter. Chemistry also examines the interactions and changes that matter undergoes along with the energy changes that accompany these processes. Chemistry deals with questions such as: How can we make matter more resistant to chemical changes? How can we make manufacturing and energy production more efficient and environmentally friendly?

4 **Evidence Notebook** How is chemistry involved in developing new toothpaste recipes? How can you use this information when making your own toothpaste in your unit project?

Chemists cannot identify all of a substance's properties just by looking at a sample. They need tools to make observations and take measurements. Chemists also develop and use models to study the behavior of matter. A *model* is a pattern, representation, or description designed to show the structure or workings of an object, system, or concept. Some models help chemists understand phenomena and make predictions about future events. Models may be conceptual, visual, 3D physical objects, mathematical, or graphical. A computer simulation is a type of model that is useful when trying to identify possible solutions because they show how various materials will react in specific conditions.

5 APPLY What are the benefits and limitations of physical models and computer models?

_____

_____

_____

The chemist in Figure 10 is using a computer model to analyze the structure of a molecule. She may also use other tools to study the elements in the molecule and the purity of her sample. Creative thinking is also important when solving problems.

6 **Collaborate** Discuss with your peers how reliable tools, technology, careful planning of experiments, and recording data are important to chemists.

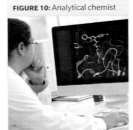

FIGURE 10: Analytical chemist

© Houghton Mifflin Harcourt Publishing Company • Image Credits: ©Javier Larrea/age fotostock

3D Learning Objective

Students evaluate models for **developing possible solutions** in the field of chemistry. They observe that science is a human endeavor often dependent on technology. They examine how technology can be used in **constructing explanations and designing solutions.**

SEP **Developing and Using Models**

Point out that the emergence of computers in research significantly influenced scientists' ability to produce and use models of chemical structures. Have student groups research how three-dimensional models are used in an area of chemistry, and give a short presentation to the class demonstrating a model and explaining its use.

Evidence Notebook

4 This Evidence Notebook question refers to the Unit Project. Chemistry is important in developing toothpastes because certain elements and compounds must be present in order to kill microorganisms in the mouth, clean the teeth, and freshen breath. Many toothpastes also whiten teeth and prevent tooth decay. To do these things, certain chemical reactions must occur and be safe for the human body.

5 Physical models can be held and manipulated but cannot show how a molecule or substance will react in a given situation. When specific information is known about a molecule or system, chemists can run a computer simulation to see how a molecule might react under certain conditions. Also, computer models may require reliable technology, Internet connection, and software.

6 Students should discuss the need for careful planning of experiments to ensure that an experiment will collect the type of data needed to answer the research question. Recording data is essential to making claims about a phenomenon to the scientific community. While careful planning and recording data are important, data acquired from an experiment using unreliable tools and techniques are not useful because they come from an untrustworthy source. Reliable, accurate, and reproducible data can only be collected with careful, systematic testing.

DCI ESS3.D Global Climate Change

Dr. Keeling began collecting data on atmospheric CO_2 in 1958. Have interested students research what motivated him to track this trend.

CCC Patterns

Have students use **Figure 11 to** explore the role CO_2 plays in Earth's carbon cycle. Have them research the carbon cycle, and call on volunteers to diagram its components on the board. ***Ask:*** *What is the source of the additional CO_2 in the atmosphere? Explain.* The source is the burning of fossil fuel and other human activities, such as raising livestock.

1 Students should describe the up-and-down pattern of the data in the Keeling Curve. They should see that there is one peak and one low spot for every year. They can see this by counting the number of peaks in a given 10-year span on the *x*-axis. Students should also see the general increase in atmospheric CO2 levels and might notice the steeper increase in carbon dioxide concentration in recent years.

2 Students' reports should show the patterns of fluctuations in the Keeling Curve. They could include a smaller part of the curve so that the pattern over several years is apparent, showing which months have higher CO2 and which months have lower CO2 concentrations. Student reports should identify the cause of the seasonal fluctuations as the change in the amount of photosynthesis happening at different times of the year.

Evidence Notebook

3 Students should think about the benefits and drawbacks of each type of model. A chemist could run a computer simulation that shows what happens when each material is produced and when each is discarded.

FORMATIVE ASSESSMENT

One-Sentence Summary Ask students to write a sentence answering this question: *Why are models important in chemistry?*

Patterns

Analyzing Atmospheric CO_2

The burning of fossil fuels is a chemical change that releases carbon dioxide, CO_2, into the atmosphere. Other human activities, such as raising livestock, also add CO_2 and methane, CH_4, to the atmosphere. Chemists analyze the composition of the atmosphere to see how these human activities affect the atmosphere and the entire Earth system. The first step in understanding these effects is to gather empirical evidence that shows the patterns of change in components of the Earth system such as the atmosphere.

Monthly Average Carbon Dioxide Concentration

FIGURE 11: Dr. C. D. Keeling began collecting and analyzing air samples in 1958. The Keeling Curve shows atmospheric CO_2 concentrations in samples taken at the Mauna Loa Observatory in Hawaii.

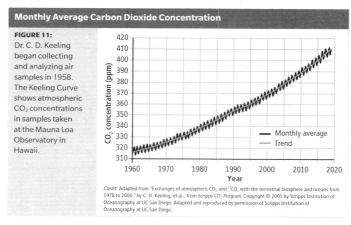

Credit: Adapted from "Exchanges of atmospheric CO_2 and $^{13}CO_2$ with the terrestrial biosphere and oceans from 1978 to 2000." by C. D. Keeling, et al., from *Scripps CO₂ Program*, Copyright © 2001 by Scripps Institution of Oceanography at UC San Diego. Adapted and reproduced by permission of Scripps Institution of Oceanography at UC San Diego.

ANALYZE What two patterns do you see in the graph shown in Figure 11?

Early in Dr. Keeling's career, he discovered that the concentration of CO_2 in the atmosphere was relatively constant regardless of where he was sampling, as long as the samples were taken in areas away from sources or sinks of CO_2, such as cities. So, the air samples from Mauna Loa are considered to be representative of Earth's atmosphere.

Language Arts Connection Research the seasonal fluctuations in the Keeling Curve. Write a report that explains the relationship of the data set to the burning of fossil fuels and other processes in the Earth system. Use multiple sources of information, such as models, peer reviewed journals, and scientific theories, and include diagrams and images in your report.

Evidence Notebook How can a chemist model the environmental impacts of making a new material compared to an existing one? For example, plastic pipes may not rust like metal ones, but they may release toxic chemicals as they degrade. How can a model help compare the materials?

TAKE IT FURTHER Careers in Science

Careers in Science

Crystallographer

Crystallographers study the structure and properties of crystals. A crystal is a homogeneous solid that contains a specific compound with particles in a consistent and ordered arrangement. Crystallographers explore the arrangement of atoms and the forces that hold the atoms together in a crystal. Modeling the structure of a compound helps scientists understand how it interacts with other compounds and how the compound could possibly be modified to alter its properties.

X-ray crystallography is a technique in which a crystal is placed on a platform, and an x-ray beam is directed toward it. Electrons within the crystal deflect the beam so that an image is produced on a screen. The pattern and intensity of the x-rays that hit the screen can be interpreted to reveal the structure of the crystal. The crystallographers can analyze the image to determine the size of particles within the crystal and the distances between them.

Large biomolecules, such as proteins and nucleic acids, do not normally have a crystalline structure, but crystallographers can work with highly concentrated solutions of the substances to grow small crystals. Once the crystals form, the crystallographers use x-ray diffraction to produce models of their molecular structures. The crystallographers may use other instrumentation in their investigations as well, such as robots that help grow crystals and a detector that captures and displays the diffraction image in a form that can be stored digitally.

X-ray crystallography is also used to determine the structure of viruses. An individual virus particle is so tiny that a light microscope is not powerful enough to view it. Knowing the structure of a virus is critical to figuring out how it infects organisms, and this knowledge can help in the development of treatments to prevent infection.

FIGURE 12: Crystallographers work in government agencies, universities, and industrial laboratories.

 Chemistry in Your Community Research a discovery made using crystallography that has benefited your community. A community can be a group of people who live in the same region or who share similar beliefs and norms. For example, you may research a molecule whose structure helped scientists understand an important reaction within the human body or a compound that was engineered to treat a genetic disease. Consider some of the following to guide your research:

• Why was the molecule chosen for study?

• How was the molecule crystallized?

• What are important features about the molecule's structure?

• How did knowing the structure of the molecule benefit your community?

Use multiple and different types of sources to help you write a magazine article about the discovery and its importance to your community. Be sure to include a relevant image in your article that illustrates your findings.

| SALTING OUT | ESTIMATING DATA ACCURATELY | COMMUNICATING THE SIZES OF OBJECTS | Go online to choose one of these other paths. |

Collaborate

You may choose to assign this activity or direct students to the Interactive Online Student Edition, where they can choose from all available paths. These activities can be assigned individually, to pairs, or to small groups.

History of Science

Linus Pauling and Rosalind Franklin used crystallography to accomplish ground-breaking work on the three-dimensional structure of proteins and nucleic acids. Have students prepare a brief report that summarizes the role of crystallography in Pauling's work and the subsequent work by Franklin that led to the discovery of the structure of DNA. Challenge students to describe how these findings changed the field of biochemistry.

Language Arts Connection

Students use multiple sources for research and then write a magazine article about a beneficial discovery. Have them refer to the online **English Language Arts Handbook** for tips on synthesizing information from multiple sources. (WHST.9-12.7)

Explore Online ▶

Salting Out

Students learn how the salting out process can be used to purify substances using differences in solubility that result from differences in ionic attractions.

Estimating Data Accurately

Students obtain mass and volume values to estimate the number of marbles in a jar and use percent error to evaluate their accuracy.

Communicating the Sizes of Objects

Students explore how scientists describe things that are very large or tiny. They research the vast range in sizes of objects in the universe.

EVALUATE Lesson Self-Check

Can You Solve the Problem?

Claims, Evidence, and Reasoning

Have students clearly state their claim—their explanation for the phenomenon they have been investigating throughout this lesson. They should present their reasoning for making this claim, along with evidence such as facts, examples, and statistics that support their claim. You may want to have students present their arguments orally, in writing, or as a debate.

Cultivating Student Questions

Assessing Student Growth Review the list of questions students generated at the beginning of the lesson. Have volunteers select any unanswered questions and suggest how they could be investigated. After approving student plans, have small groups conduct the investigations and report back to the class. As the year progresses, the number of volunteers for this task will likely increase. The sophistication of the means of investigation also may increase. Both outcomes are measures of positive growth that are essential to the scientific mindset and demonstrate that students are beginning to understand that the correct answer is much less important than the means used to investigate the question. You will find that students are more engaged and more willing to take the risk of being "wrong," which indicates positive growth in scientific thinking.

 Evidence Notebook

1 Students should ask questions about the properties of the unknown material that are related to its function, such as *What is its density? What is its melting point? Will it rust or corrode?* Students should describe tests that can be done to answer these questions. Students can explain how the different properties could be related to the function of the materials being tested. The properties of a material determine how well it will function to solve a given problem or fulfill a given need. So, the right tests will generate data that help engineers decide whether a material might be suitable for a given function.

Lesson Self-Check

CAN YOU SOLVE THE PROBLEM?

FIGURE 13: The physical and chemical properties of this metal determine the ways it can be used by humans.

Everything is made up of matter, and each substance has its own unique set of physical and chemical properties. The properties of a substance influence the way it can be used in everyday life. Asking questions and performing tests on the material help scientists determine how it behaves in certain conditions and how it interacts with other substances. Chemists use a variety of instruments and models to help them understand how to improve materials and processes to better serve society.

Think about the metal tubes shown in the photo. These tubes can be used in ventilation systems or plumbing systems, but are they the best material for the job? The evidence you have collected throughout this lesson can help you ask questions and select the appropriate tests needed to answer this question.

1 **Evidence Notebook** Refer to your notes in your Evidence Notebook to make a claim about how you could determine whether a new material has the specific chemical and physical properties needed to perform the same function as an existing material. Your explanation should include a discussion of the following points:

Claim What type of questions could be asked and which tests can be run to determine if a new material can replace an existing material?

Evidence What evidence supports the claim that these questions and tests are useful in identifying the properties of the new and original materials?

Reasoning How does the evidence you provided support your claim about the usefulness of specific questions and tests in identifying properties of materials?

 Formal Assessment Go online for student self-checks and other assessments.

Name _____ Date _____

Check Your Understanding

1. Which statement best defines matter?
   ○ **a.** Matter is anything that is a solid at room temperature.
   ○ **b.** Matter is anything that takes up space and has mass.
   ○ **c.** Matter is any substance that reacts with another substance.
   ○ **d.** Matter is any substance that contains carbon.

2. Select the correct terms to complete the statement about physical and chemical changes.

   When electricity passes through liquid water, two gases form. This is an example of a physical | chemical change because the identity of the substance changed | stayed the same.

   When liquid water loses energy, a change in state | chemical identity occurs. This is an example of a chemical | physical change.

3. Match the description of particle motion to the correct state of matter.

Particles are packed very close together in a relatively fixed arrangement; has definite volume and shape. ○	○ liquid
Particles are close together but can move past one another; has a definite volume but an indefinite shape. ○	○ plasma
Particles are far apart and move very rapidly; has neither definite volume nor definite shape. ○	○ solid
Particles have a large amount of energy, and they become electrically charged. ○	○ gas

4. Select the correct terms to complete the statement about intensive and extensive properties.

   An intensive | extensive physical property can be used to help identify a substance because it changes | does not change with the amount of matter present. An intensive | extensive property cannot be used to help identify a substance because it changes | does not change with the amount of the substance present.

5. Choose the projects most likely to be worked on by a chemist. Select all correct answers.
   ☐ **a.** studying the structure of an enzyme
   ☐ **b.** analyzing the components of petroleum
   ☐ **c.** analyzing the velocity of planets
   ☐ **d.** observing the behavior of farm animals
   ☐ **e.** building a computer model for producing antacids

6. Chemists have identified three new forms of alternative fuel. If the chemists want to predict how each fuel would affect the environment and change the efficiency of the car, what type of model should they use?
   ○ **a.** 3D model
   ○ **b.** mathematical model
   ○ **c.** computer simulation
   ○ **d.** visual model

7. Categorize each substance as a pure substance or a mixture.

   | air | aluminum | carbon dioxide |
   | table salt | soil | wood |

Pure Substance	Mixture

Answers

1. b
2. chemical, changed, state, physical
3. Particles are packed very close—solid, Particles are close together—liquid, Particles are far apart—gas, Particles have a large amount of energy—plasma
4. intensive, does not change, extensive, changes
5. a, b, e
6. c
7. pure substance: table salt, aluminum, carbon dioxide; mixture: air, soil, wood

Answers

8. A tossed salad is a heterogeneous mixture. Student answers should show an understanding of a mixture and the difference between a homogeneous mixture and a heterogeneous mixture. In addition, students should recognize that a salad is not a pure substance because it does not have a fixed composition.

9. Students should be able to distinguish between a physical change of state and a chemical change in which a new substance is formed. **Sample answer:** The melting of wax is a change of state from solid to liquid, which is a physical change. The burning of the wax and burning of the wick are chemical changes in which the carbon in the wax combines with oxygen to produce a new substance, carbon dioxide.

10. Students should mention that chemistry is the study of matter and how matter interacts with other matter. Therefore, chemistry is important in identifying which physical and chemical properties would be useful for a material to have if it is being used as part of a plumbing system. The material should be able to carry hot and cold water. The material should not corrode when exposed to water for long periods of time. An antimicrobial material would be beneficial. Tests should be done to determine the malleability and strength of the material. It is also important to determine whether the material is conductive and whether it degrades when exposed to water and air.

Make Your Own Study Guide

Have students create a study guide that helps them organize and visualize the important information from this lesson. Their study guide should focus on the main ideas from the lesson and tie multiple ideas together. Students can make an outline, a concept map, a graphic organizer, or another representation.

EVALUATE

CHECKPOINTS (continued)

8. Is a tossed salad a homogeneous mixture, a heterogeneous mixture, or a pure substance? Explain your reasoning.

_____

_____

_____

_____

9. Many changes occur to a wax candle after it is lit. Which changes are physical? Which changes are chemical? How do you know what kind of changes took place?

_____

_____

_____

_____

10. A new plumbing system needs to be installed in a school bathroom. What role will chemistry play in this project? What information or tests might be important to know or do in order to select the best material for this project?

_____

_____

_____

_____

MAKE YOUR OWN STUDY GUIDE

 In your Evidence Notebook, design a study guide that supports the main ideas from this lesson:

Chemistry is the study of matter, the interactions of matter, and the associated changes in energy.

Each substance has a unique set of physical and chemical properties that can identify it.

A sample of matter can be classified as either a pure substance or a mixture.

Chemists study data and patterns to understand phenomena.

Remember to include the following information in your study guide:
- Use examples that model main ideas.
- Record explanations for the phenomena you investigated.
- Use evidence to support your explanations. Your support can include drawings, data, graphs, laboratory conclusions, and other evidence recorded throughout the lesson.

Consider how interactions at the atomic level impact properties at the bulk scale and how these properties affect our use of materials on a daily basis.

Chemistry and the Engineering Design Process

Building to the Performance Expectations

The learning experiences in this lesson prepare students for mastery of

HS-ETS1-1 Analyze a major global challenge to specify qualitative and quantitative criteria and constraints for solutions that account for societal needs and wants.

HS-ETS1-3 Evaluate a solution to a complex real-world problem based on prioritized criteria and trade-offs that account for a range of constraints, including cost, safety, reliability, and aesthetics, as well as possible social, cultural, and environmental impacts.

 Trace Tool to the NGSS

Go online to view the complete coverage of standards across lessons, units, and grade levels.

 SEP Science & Engineering Practices

Asking Questions and Defining Problems
Analyze complex real-world problems by specifying criteria and constraints for successful solutions.

▶ **VIDEO** Asking Questions and Defining Problems

Constructing Explanations and Designing Solutions
Evaluate a solution to a complex real-world problem, based on scientific knowledge, student-generated sources of evidence, prioritized criteria, and tradeoff considerations.

Using Mathematics and Computational Thinking
Use mathematical models and/or computer simulations to predict the effects of a design solution on systems and/or the interactions between systems.

 **Disciplinary Core Ideas**

ETS1.A Defining and Delimiting Engineering Problems
Criteria and constraints also include satisfying any requirements set by society, such as taking issues of risk mitigation into account, and they should be quantified to the extent possible and stated in such a way that one can tell if a given design meets them. (HS-ETS1-1)

ETS1.B Developing Possible Solutions
When evaluating solutions, it is important to take into account a range of constraints, including cost, safety, reliability and aesthetics and to consider social, cultural and environmental impacts. (HS-ETS1-3)

ETS1.B Developing Possible Solutions
Both physical models and computers can be used in various ways to aid in the engineering design process. Computers are useful for a variety of purposes, such as running simulations to test different ways of solving a problem or to see which one is most efficient or economical; and in making a persuasive presentation to a client about how a given design will meet his or her needs. (HS-ETS1-4)

▶ **VIDEO** Engineering: Chemistry

 **CCC Crosscutting Concepts**

Influence of Engineering, Technology, and Science on Society and the Natural World
New technologies can have deep impacts on society and the environment, including some that were not anticipated. Analysis of costs and benefits is a critical aspect of decisions about technology.

Systems and System Models
Models (e.g., physical, mathematical, computer models) can be used to simulate systems and interactions—including energy, matter, and information flows—within and between systems at different scales.

▶ **VIDEO** System Models

Energy and Matter
Changes of energy and matter in a system can be described in terms of energy and matter flows into, out of, and within that system.

ELA STANDARDS

RST.11-12.7 Integrate and evaluate multiple sources of information presented in diverse formats and media (e.g., quantitative data, video, multimedia) in order to address a question or solve a problem.

RST.11-12.9 Synthesize information from a range of sources (e.g., texts, experiments, simulations) into a coherent understanding of a process, phenomenon, or concept, resolving conflicting information when possible.

Supporting All Students, All Standards

Integrating the Three Dimensions

In this lesson, students conduct an investigation in which they plan and implement a solution for separating a mixture **(SEP Planning and Carrying Out Investigations, SEP Constructing Explanations and Designing Solutions)**. When defining a problem and evaluating solutions, students take into account a range of constraints, including cost, safety, reliability, and aesthetics **(DCI ETS1.A, DCI ETS1.B)**. Students use models to simulate systems and interactions within and between systems at different scales **(CCC Systems and System Models)**. Finally, they investigate a case study and construct explanations about chemical processes in a model biosphere **(SEP Constructing Explanations and Designing Solutions, DCI ETS1.B)**.

Preassessment

Have students complete the unit pretest or see the Assessment Guide.

Build on Prior Knowledge

Have students work in pairs to list several things they eat or drink. For each food or drink students list, have them describe whether the item is a mixture or a pure substance, and have them explain their choices.

You may want to review the following concepts:
- Matter can change state when energy is added or removed.
- Mixtures can be separated into their component substances by physical means.
- Scientists ask questions about phenomena and systematically investigate the phenomena in order to develop explanations based on evidence. Engineers define problems and work systematically to develop solutions to problems.
- Systems are defined by humans to make the study of phenomena or problems easier.

Professional Development Go online to view **Professional Development videos** with strategies to integrate CCCs and SEPs, including the ones used in this lesson.

Content Background

When two substances are mixed together and do not react chemically, a mixture forms. The components of a mixture can be separated by physical means, and each component keeps its own physical properties. In addition, the proportion of each component can vary.

Mixtures can be either homogeneous or heterogeneous. The particles in a homogeneous mixture are distributed evenly throughout the mixture. All samples taken from a homogeneous mixture are identical. The particles in a heterogeneous mixture are not evenly distributed, so samples will vary.

Some mixtures can be classified as solutions, colloids, or suspensions. The classification depends on the particle size of the substances. A solution is a homogeneous mixture in which tiny particles of one component, the solute, are dissolved in another component, the solvent. Because the particle size of the solute is so small, the solute particles do not settle out.

Colloids are heterogeneous mixtures in which particles between 1 and 1000 nm in size are evenly suspended in another medium. The particles will not settle out because they are too small. Suspensions are also heterogeneous mixtures. In a suspension, particles larger than about 1000 nm are suspended in a medium. The particles are large enough that they will eventually settle out.

Differentiate Instruction

KEY WORDS
- engineering design process
- criteria
- constraint
- tradeoff
- system
- energy

ELL SUPPORT

Have students write the key terms in their notebooks. Ask them to describe ways they have heard the word *system* used in everyday life, and list several examples on the board. Based on these examples, have students work in small groups to discuss and develop a definition for the word. Encourage students to look for this word as they explore the lesson.

ENGAGE: Investigative Phenomenon

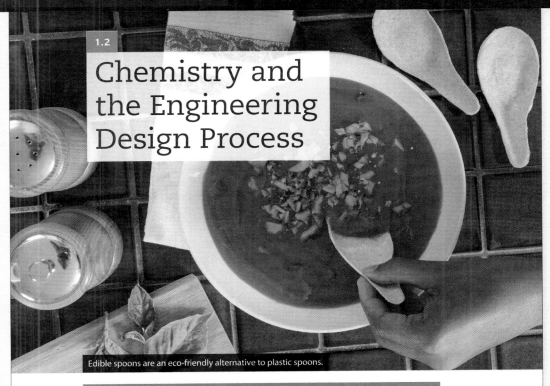

1.2

Chemistry and the Engineering Design Process

Edible spoons are an eco-friendly alternative to plastic spoons.

CAN YOU SOLVE THE PROBLEM?

You buy your lunch and pick up a plastic spoon. After lunch, you throw out the spoon. It may take hundreds of years for that spoon to decompose in a landfill. Even biodegradable plastics made from cornstarch do not break down easily. They require controlled composting facilities that aren't readily available. Edible spoons may help solve the plastic-waste problem. Such utensils are made of grains such as rice, wheat, and sorghum, with a little salt, sugar, and spice added for flavor. They taste like crackers. And if you are too full after lunch to eat your spoon, it will degrade within a few days in a landfill.

1 DESIGN What properties must a spoon have in order to be useful as a tool for eating? What additional properties should an edible spoon have?

_____

_____

_____

_____

2 **Evidence Notebook** As you explore the lesson, gather evidence to explain what properties an edible spoon should have—that is, what the design criteria and constraints should be.

Build on Prior Lessons

In Lesson 1, students learned about properties and classification of matter. Lesson 2 builds on these concepts as students explore how the physical properties of a mixture's components can be used to separate the components.

Lesson Objective

Students explore the engineering design process and how it relates to chemistry.

Cultivating Student Questions

Have students look at the photo of an edible spoon. Prompt them to ask all questions that come to mind about the properties of the spoon and how these properties affect the spoon's function. Record the questions on chart paper, and then sort the questions based on their focus. Have students reflect on this list throughout the lesson and check off questions as they are answered.

Can You Solve the Problem?

The Investigative Phenomenon is the focus of the lesson. Students are asked to record their initial thoughts about the properties a spoon must have and the additional properties an edible spoon must have.

Students will collect evidence related to this phenomenon throughout the lesson. They will revisit the question at the end of the lesson and use what they have learned to explain how the properties of materials influence the ways we use the materials.

1 Students should recognize that a spoon must be curved so that it can hold soup and other foods. It must stay cool in hot food and have a handle long enough for it to be held. Edible spoons must be stable and not fall apart before the meal is finished. They should also taste good.

Evidence Notebook

2 The topics of criteria and constraints in the engineering design process will be revisited throughout this lesson.

Lesson 2 Chemistry and the Engineering Design Process   23

EXPLORATION 1   Separating a Mixture

3D Learning Objective

Students **plan and carry out an investigation** to observe and use the physical properties of the components of a mixture **on a macroscopic scale, which are determined by forces at the atomic scale,** to separate the components. In this way, students will begin to think about **the empirical evidence needed to identify patterns.**

Everyday phenomena discussed throughout the Explorations of the lesson can often be used to connect the science content to students' personal experiences.

Engineering Lab 👬 Small Groups 🕐 45 minutes
Separating a Mixture

SEP **Planning and Carrying Out Investigations**

Before students begin to plan their procedure, remind them to think about how each step will affect what they will be able to do next.

Advance Preparation Prepare a mixture for each group.

Materials Alert Alternatives to poppy seeds are mustard seeds, chia seeds, and sesame seeds. Remind students not to eat any food items used in a lab activity.

Collaborate

Think, Pair, Share Have student pairs think of an **everyday phenomenon** and describe how the physical properties of objects involved affect what happens. Pairs should share their ideas.

Define the Problem

1. Students will be separating the materials on the basis of density (poppy seeds vs. sand), magnetism (iron filings), and solubility (of salt). **Sample answer:** Salt dissolves in water, iron filings are attracted to a magnet, and poppy seeds float in water. Sand does not dissolve, is not attracted to a magnet, and sinks in water.

2. **Sample answer:** Each of the four components would be separate from the other three, with none of the other components mixed in. The materials used in the lab are limitations on the procedure. The time allotted for the separation also may be a limitation.

Engineering Lab
Separating a Mixture

The ability to separate and recover substances from mixtures is extremely important in scientific research and industry. Chemists often need to work with pure substances, but naturally occurring materials are seldom pure. Engineers can design solutions to such problems. In this lab, you will use principles of engineering and chemistry to solve a similar problem—separating a mixture of common items.

DESIGN CHALLENGE Given the materials available to you, how would you design, develop, and implement a safe procedure for physically separating a mixture containing salt, sand, iron filings, and poppy seeds? All four components are in dry, granular form.

FIGURE 1: Sand, salt, poppy seeds, and iron filings have different properties that can be used to separate them from a mixture.

DEFINE THE PROBLEM

1. What physical properties do you observe or know of in salt, sand, iron filings, and poppy seeds?

_____

_____

_____

2. What would be the characteristics of a successful separation? What are the limitations on any procedure you develop to separate this mixture?

_____

_____

_____

_____

 Student Lab Worksheet and complete Teacher Support are available online.

POSSIBLE MATERIALS

- indirectly vented chemical splash goggles, nonlatex apron, nitrile gloves
- mixture components (salt, sand, iron filings, poppy seeds)
- distilled water
- filter funnel and paper
- forceps
- hot plate
- magnet
- mixture sample
- test tubes and rack

SAFETY INFORMATION

- Wear indirectly vented chemical splash goggles, a nonlatex apron, and nitrile gloves during the setup, hands-on, and takedown segments of the activity.

- Use caution when working with iron filings, which are hazardous if they are swallowed or inhaled, or enter the eyes, nose, or other body cavities.

- Use caution when working with hot plates, which can cause skin burns or electric shock. Use only GFI-protected circuits when using electrical equipment, and keep away from water sources to prevent shock.

- Wash your hands with soap and water immediately after completing this activity.

- Never eat any food items used in a lab activity.

COLLECT DATA

1. Obtain samples of each of the four mixture components from your teacher. Use the equipment available to you to make observations about the properties of each component. Record your observations in a data table in your Evidence Notebook.

2. For each mixture component, list one or two properties that could be useful in physically separating it from the other materials in the mixture. Explain your reasoning.

indirectly vented chemical splash goggles

© Houghton Mifflin Harcourt Publishing Company

Differentiate Instruction

ELL Support   Students from different cultures may use different names for important words used in the investigation. Be sure students are familiar with the terms *iron, distilled, forceps, funnel,* and *magnet.* Encourage them to share the names they are familiar with, but be sure they can also recognize and use all terms from the investigation.

MTSS/RTI   Remind students that data tables should be made in their Evidence Notebooks. You may need to spend time helping them make their data tables. If you do, ask students what data need to be collected and how information should be organized in the data table.

DCI PS1.A Structure and Properties of Matter

Remind students that the law of conservation of matter states that matter (mass) cannot be created or destroyed in any physical or chemical change.

Biology Connection

Tell students that small amounts of iron are added to some types of dry cereal. After the cereal is crushed into small pieces, the iron can be removed using a strong magnet. Have students find out what roles iron plays in the human body. They can make posters showing these roles, especially that of hemoglobin in blood. Hemoglobin combines with oxygen and carries this vital gas to all parts of the body.

Collect Data

1. Data tables should include empirical evidence and should describe physical properties of all materials to be separated.

2. **Sample answer:** Iron is the only component that is magnetic, so it could be removed using a magnet. Poppy seeds float in water, so they could be removed from the surface of the water. Sand is insoluble in water, so it could be filtered out. Salt dissolves in water but can be isolated by evaporating the water.

CCC Patterns

Ask students what empirical evidence they would have to observe and collect for them to see a pattern in physical properties.

Test

1. **Sample answer:** I would first remove the iron filings from the mixture using a magnet. I would then add water to the mixture and skim the poppy seeds off the surface of the water. I would then filter out the sand using filter paper in a funnel. The salt would still be dissolved in the remaining liquid. I could heat the water to evaporate it, leaving the salt behind.

Optimize

1. **Sample answer:** Removing the iron filings with a magnet was easy and effective. After I added water to the mixture, I used a piece of filter paper to skim the poppy seeds off the surface of the solution and scrape them into a container. Using filter paper to skim off the poppy seeds was messy and took several tries. I then filtered out the sand using a funnel lined with filter paper. The liquid that remained was evaporated by heating it on a hot plate. Salt was left after all the water evaporated.

2. **Sample answer:** For the poppy seeds, I could try to pour some of the liquid through a filter, being careful not to stir up the sand so it is not removed with the poppy seeds. The filtered liquid would have to be returned to the mixture because salt is dissolved in it.

3. **Sample answer:** I was able to remove all the poppy seeds by carefully pouring the mixture through filter paper without stirring up the sand.

Analyze

1. **Sample answer:** I considered different ways to use the materials and the order in which to separate the materials. Pouring the mixture through a filter to remove the poppy seeds was an improvement, but if I were to do this again, I would try holding a second piece of filter paper over all but the spout of the beaker to help keep the sand separate from the poppy seeds.

TEST

1. Now that you have described the properties of each material, develop a procedure and a safety plan in your Evidence Notebook explaining how you will isolate each material in the mixture, and in what order. You may wish to include a sketch of your setup. Make sure your teacher approves your procedure and safety plan before proceeding.

2. When your procedure, safety plan, and materials are approved, begin your experiment.

OPTIMIZE

1. Summarize the results of your procedure. How well did it work for each component?

2. Describe changes you could make to improve the procedure.

3. If you have time, test the revised, optimized procedure after it is approved by your teacher. Describe the results.

ANALYZE

1. What factors did you consider when optimizing the procedure? Did your changes improve the procedure? What would you change if you were to repeat the experiment again?

2. Name the specific physical property of each component that enabled you to separate the component from the rest of the mixture, and explain how it was useful. Use evidence from your data to support your answers.

_____

_____

_____

_____

_____

_____

_____

1 **EXTEND**

How could you separate each of the following two-component mixtures?

Mixture	Separation method
Aluminum filings and iron filings	
Sand and finely ground polystyrene foam	
Alcohol and water	

2 **Evidence Notebook** An edible spoon is made from a mixture of substances. What properties should the substances have so the spoon can be used to stir or consume liquids?

DCI **PS1.A Structure and Properties of Matter**

Point out to students that whether something floats or sinks in another substance is not a property intrinsic to that material but instead depends on the difference between the densities of the two substances. Oil floats on water, for example, but alcohol floats on oil.

Analyze (continued)

2. **Sample answer:** Sand is denser than water. Iron filings are magnetic. Salt dissolves in water. Poppy seeds float. The iron filings can be removed from the mixture first by using a magnet. When the substances were mixed in water, the poppy seeds could be removed because they float. The sand could be filtered out of the saltwater solution using filter paper. The salt was left behind after I evaporated the water.

1 Accept all reasonable answers, as students may not know that aluminum is not magnetic or that alcohol evaporates at a lower temperature than water. Aluminum filings and iron filings could be separated using a magnet. Sand and finely ground polystyrene foam could be separated by adding water and checking for flotation. Alcohol and water could be separated by heating (alcohol boils at a lower temperature than water does).

 Evidence Notebook

2 **Sample answer:** All substances used in the mixture should be able to hold together and not dissolve in the liquid.

FORMATIVE ASSESSMENT

3-Minute Pause Have students pause to consider the concepts applied in the lab. Have them respond to the following prompts.

I became more aware of . . .

I didn't realize that . . .

I still don't understand . . .

Have volunteers share their responses with the class.

EXPLORATION 2 The Engineering Design Process

3D Learning Objective

Students **analyze and evaluate complex real-world problems.** They **take into account a range of constraints** for successful solutions and **analyze costs and benefits** in making decisions about technology.

Exploring Visuals

Have students look at the diagram in **Figure 2.**

Ask: *What is the starting point for the engineering design process chart?* Identify the want/need.

Ask: *What are the three main parts of the process? How does the diagram show these parts?* The three main parts are defining the problem, designing solutions, and optimizing solutions. The chart shows these three main parts as heads at the top of each column.

Ask: *What do the red dashed lines under each circled NO indicate?* The red dashed lines indicate that you should repeat certain steps if the result is not sufficient.

Ask: *What do the green dashed lines under each circled YES indicate?* The green dashed lines indicate that you should continue to follow the process because your plan for a solution is succeeding.

SEP Constructing Explanations and Designing Solutions

Have students look at the first box in the diagram and read through the three steps. Point out that part of conducting research and considering previous solutions involves applying experiences with similar problems. The process frequently is a collaboration in which many people give their ideas and share their professional opinions.

The Engineering Design Process

Think about the last time you had to deal with an unexpected event: maybe you were running late for school, or you had an extra chore or errand to do. How did you solve the problem? It is likely that you used a process similar to the ones engineers use, even if you were not aware of it. Humans are natural problem solvers. Engineers formalize the process of solving problems in order to work as efficiently and effectively as possible. Their work goes hand in hand with the work of scientists.

Solving Problems Step by Step

Science is the study of phenomena. Scientists ask questions and carry out investigations in order to explain phenomena. Engineering is the study of problems. Engineers use a series of steps, called the engineering design process, in order to solve problems.

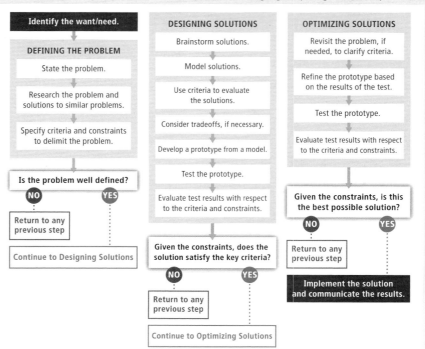

FIGURE 2: The engineering design process is a set of steps that lead to designing or improving a solution to a problem.

1 **Collaborate** With a partner, think of a process or tool you use at school. What need does it address? Are there other possible solutions?

The engineering design process is used to develop or improve technology to solve problems. *Technology* is any tool, machine, process, or system designed to address a problem or need. Figure 3 shows one way technology can help to model or test solutions.

FIGURE 3: This engineer is using a touchscreen device to work with a 3D model of a complex system.

2 **APPLY** How might a computer-based technology help you design a solution?

_____

_____

_____

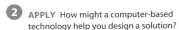
Influence of Engineering, Technology, and Science on Society and the Natural World

Chemical Engineering

Chemical engineering is the application of chemistry to solve real-world, relevant problems. Chemical engineers aim to develop products or chemical processes that are efficient, environmentally sound, safe, and cost-effective. They may develop new materials or design new equipment for a production process. Often, chemical engineers are responsible for planning, designing, and optimizing processes at plants that manufacture chemicals for use in a wide range of industries.

3 **ASK** Think of ways that technologies such as telephones, televisions, light bulbs, computers, or food packaging have changed since an adult you know was a child. What were some impacts of the changes? Were all the impacts positive?

_____

_____

_____

The advancement of science and technology may provide better solutions with fewer risks to human health and environmental integrity. But today's solutions may lead to unanticipated problems tomorrow. Developing and improving products and processes is at the heart of chemical engineering.

4 **Evidence Notebook** The engineering design process is iterative, meaning some or all of its steps may be repeated. What does the iterative nature of the engineering design process tell you about your unit project goal of optimizing a toothpaste?

© Houghton Mifflin Harcourt Publishing Company • Image Credits: ©Iain Masterton/Alamy Stock Photo

DCI **ETS1.A Defining and Delimiting Engineering Problems**

Draw students' attention to the words *delimit* and *prototype*. Explain that *delimit* means to set a boundary. A *prototype* is a model of a solution to a problem that can be tested to provide guidance about how well that solution would work. Engage students in a discussion during which they have to use both terms. Present a scenario that is a simple problem to be solved. Guide students in applying the terms as they discuss ways to solve the problem. ***Ask***: *How can you delimit this problem? What would a prototype look like?*

Language Arts Connection

Have students conduct a short research project to find out the method used to include stripes in toothpaste. Then, have them write a short paragraph explaining the process. Remind students to look at several sources for information and to be sure to assess the reliability of each source. (RST.11-12.7, WHST.11-12.8)

1 **Sample answer:** We use the bell to signal when it's time to go to the next class. This addresses the need for everyone to be aware of the time no matter where they are in the building. Other solutions could be a different type of sound or flashing lights, but that might not work for students who are outdoors .

2 **Sample answer:** I could use a computer to create a graph to understand trends in data, to create presentations or documents to describe or define a problem, to research similar solutions, or to make a visual model of different solutions.

3 **Sample answer:** Telephones have changed by becoming portable, battery-powered, and useful for many tasks besides talking to someone who isn't in the same place. This has made them useful in a broader range of situations. However, it has also led to pollution from electronics and metal mines.

Evidence Notebook

4 This Evidence Notebook question refers to the Unit Project. Students should recognize that all steps of the engineering design process can be repeated and that a final product could be optimized further at some point in the future.

Collaborate

Discussion Before students answer the Apply question, have them work in small groups to discuss the meanings of *criterion* and *constraint*. Then have students apply the engineering design process to one of the following **everyday phenomena.** Have each group make a list of several design problems and include criteria and constraints for each problem.

- A city wants to construct bicycle paths alongside several roadways.
- A local group wants to make a dog park.
- A drama class needs to construct background scenes for a play.

Preconception Alert

Students often think that they can solve a problem before they completely understand the problem's criteria and constraints. Have students think of an **everyday phenomenon,** such as completing an assignment, and a problem they may have had in dealing with the phenomenon. Ask how they solved the problem. Were they able to solve the problem before completely understanding it?

SEP Constructing Explanations and Designing Solutions

Emphasize to students that a proposed solution to a design problem is almost never the same as the final design. The process of designing a solution involves taking into account many factors before proposing a solution. The solution often goes through several cycles of testing and iterative improvements before a final design is chosen.

1 Accept all reasonable answers. **Sample answer:** A good taste, a certain consistency, and a certain level of abrasiveness could be criteria.

2 criterion, constraint, constraint, criterion, criterion

Defining the Problem

Imagine one of your classmates walks in one day and makes an announcement: "We need a solution!" How would you respond? To design a solution, engineers must establish what the problem is and what need or want the solution should address. Next, they identify the groups affected by the problem, relevant scientific issues, and possible impacts on the environment and society. Once this is done, they can identify the main components of the problem, including what contributes to the problem and what is affected by it.

Identifying criteria helps engineers further define the problem by giving them a set of goals for the solution. Criteria are the features that a successful solution should have—that is, criteria are the "wants" that the solution will fulfill. Criteria (or a *criterion*) can include many factors. For example, imagine a team of engineers is developing a new toothpaste that has a blue, mint-flavored stripe. They would need to consider several possible criteria.

1 **APPLY** The blue, mint-flavored stripe is an example of a design criterion for the toothpaste. What other criteria might this design have?

_____

_____

_____

_____

After engineers define the problem, they delimit the problem. *Delimiting* is the process of determining the constraints of the solution. Constraints are the limitations of a design. They are sometimes, but not always, provided by a client. These constraints may relate to considerations such as cost, weight, safety, available resources and technologies, and time. Any solution that does not meet the constraints of the design is generally not considered. In the toothpaste example, some constraints the client might impose include a maximum cost, a blue stripe that does not "bleed" into the white toothpaste, a specific thickness for the toothpaste, or a tube with a specific design.

2 **ANALYZE** The client told the engineering team that they want production costs for the new toothpaste (with the blue stripe) to be the same as for the old toothpaste. They want to continue to use the same design for the tube, which is made of plastic. Consider whether each of the following statements represents a criterion or a constraint for this engineering problem.

	criterion	constraint
The blue stripe should be a particular shade of blue.		_____
Adding the blue stripe must not exceed a certain cost.		_____
The chemicals in the blue stripe must not react with plastic.		_____
The toothpaste foam should be white or light blue.		_____
The toothpaste should taste like peppermint, not spearmint.		_____

Designing Solutions

After defining and delimiting the problem, engineers work in teams to brainstorm solutions. Potential solutions are evaluated against criteria and constraints. Teams then test the top ideas, often with the help of models or simulations. They evaluate the results of that testing, again using the criteria and constraints as a guide.

 Engineering

Considering Tradeoffs

It is not always possible for a solution to fulfill every criterion within the given constraints. In such cases, engineers may need to decide which criteria are most important, and whether the drawbacks of a given design outweigh its benefits. A tradeoff is an exchange of one thing for another. Engineers may give up one criterion if doing so enables them to keep another or avoid a potential risk. For example, the blue, minty stripe might reduce the amount of foam the toothpaste produces when used. Engineers must then decide whether that tradeoff is worthwhile.

FIGURE 4: Even a new toothpaste design requires careful evaluation of criteria and constraints.

3 **EVALUATE** Think about some criteria that are important when developing a product such as toothpaste. What tradeoffs would you consider making to ensure that your most important criteria are met in your final design solution?

_____

_____

_____

_____

_____

Tradeoffs may be made because of social, financial, or environmental constraints. For example, engineers may find that the dye in the blue stripe is harmful to aquatic organisms. Engineers may decide to replace the blue dye with one that is more expensive but is not harmful to aquatic organisms. Using the alternative dye might raise the price of making the toothpaste.

4 **Evidence Notebook** If tradeoffs are necessary, it can be helpful for engineers to rank the design criteria so they can decide which tradeoffs to make. What are the design criteria for your unit project? How important is each criterion relative to the others?

 ETS1.A Defining and Delimiting Engineering Problems

Have students work in small groups to research an environmental problem and identify a way chemical engineering has offered a solution to the problem. Have each group produce a short presentation in which they describe the criteria, constraints, and tradeoffs used in the design process to solve the problem.

Nature of Science

Have students work in small groups to explore the benefits of brainstorming. Tell them to imagine that they have constructed a doghouse, but the roof leaks. Have students brainstorm ways to optimize the design of the doghouse to correct the problem. Allow class time for each group to describe its design to the class.

Environmental Science Connection

Point out to students that costs and benefits often are distributed differently across different species, locations, groups of people, and time. Engineers or policymakers must consider whether a technology that has a short-term benefit for humans might be harmful over the longer term. DDT is an example of a technology that was abandoned after its environmental and long-term consequences became apparent. Have students do research to learn more about DDT or another abandoned technology and share their findings with the class.

3 Students may discuss the tradeoffs mentioned in the text before the question, such as trading the amount of foam in favor of the mint flavor. They might also consider a tradeoff such as decreasing the concentration of flavorings if it will make the toothpaste more abrasive and thus more effective.

 **Evidence Notebook**

4 This Evidence Notebook question refers to the Unit Project. Students should list and rank criteria for their project. Their lists should include any criteria implied or given in the unit project introduction and any that students have previously generated.

Math Connection

Point out that scale models used in design optimization have all dimensions reduced by the same ratio when compared with the real object. Have students calculate the dimensions of a box with a scale ratio of 20 to 1 if the real object is 100 centimeters wide, 60 centimeters long, and 45 centimeters tall. The scale model of the box will be approximately 5 centimeters wide, 3 centimeters long, and 2.25 centimeters tall. **(MP.2)**

Differentiate Instruction

ELL Support Be sure students understand that to *optimize* a solution means to make it work as well as possible. Emphasize that the *optimizing the solution* part of the engineering design process occurs after a solution has already been proposed.

SEP **Asking Questions and Defining Problems**

Have students write a short paragraph describing the **everyday phenomenon** of an object that is made to a smaller scale. Examples include a trophy, a dollhouse, and a model plane.

1 Accept all reasonable answers. **Sample answer:** Qualitative ways information could be reported include the user's opinion about the taste of the toothpaste or the visual appeal of the blue color. Quantitative information could include measuring the whiteness of the user's teeth with an optical instrument after use. Quantitative data might be preferred if a product such as a remedy for acid reflux could cause side effects in the user. Qualitative data would be acceptable for a new formula of shampoo or mouthwash that probably would not harm the user.

2 Answers will vary. Student models should show a logical flow of decision making that includes defining the problem, identifying criteria and constraints, and planning the weekend. Students should not copy the engineering design process flowchart in the book.

3 Answers will vary. Students should point out how their model incorporates steps from the engineering design process.

Optimizing Solutions

Optimization is the process of further evaluating a solution or design in order to improve or refine it. Scale models, prototypes, and computer simulations are often used in this step. Chemical engineers often optimize processes rather than products. Based on the test results, engineers may decide to implement a solution or return to an earlier step. Their goal may be minimizing cost, maximizing efficiency, or both. One way to optimize and test a design is through user testing. Suppose a chemical engineer develops a prototype for the toothpaste with a blue minty stripe. User tests can provide engineers with information about the flavor, the amount of foaming, and the effectiveness of the toothpaste.

1 **Collaborate** With a partner, discuss qualitative and quantitative ways of reporting user testing results for a toothpaste. Discuss other products for which each would be more useful.

Small-scale prototypes may be developed as a way to test a solution without the expense of large-scale manufacturing. Chemical engineers may develop models, conduct lab experiments, or run computer simulations to test solutions. For example, they may do lab experiments to test how fast a blue dye breaks down in different temperatures of water. They may even test two prototypes to determine how well each one meets the criteria and constraints of the design. If neither prototype fully satisfies the criteria and constraints, engineers may refine the problem definition or brainstorm new solutions.

Chemical engineers use the results of their testing to optimize their solutions. Even a finished design can be made better as new opportunities or unanticipated problems arise.

2 **MODEL** Suppose you have a lot of homework that has to be done this weekend, and an important event on Saturday. Devise a plan for how to meet all of your obligations. Make a flowchart or other model that describes the key steps of your plan.

3 **EXPLAIN** How does your model relate to the engineering design process?

Engineering

Process Design

Chemical engineers often work in process design, where they are tasked with designing or refining systems involved in large-scale production of chemicals for industrial use. Because it is not feasible to build and test multiple prototype chemical processing plants, chemical process engineers rely heavily on models such as diagrams and computer simulations. Such models enable engineers to identify unnecessary steps or other inefficiencies in a process, or to track how much product and waste is produced. Diagrams may be simple block flow diagrams, showing only a basic overview of how a starting material is converted into a final product, or they may be more complex diagrams that indicate energy flows or piping and instrumentation.

FIGURE 5: This chemical engineer is reviewing a process flow diagram.

 EVALUATE Which problem would a process engineer be likely to work on?

○ **a.** developing new uses for a material in the marketplace

○ **b.** optimizing a method to increase the yield of a material

○ **c.** studying how a material behaves under different conditions

○ **d.** studying how to synthesize a material from different components

The production of methanol from syngas is an example of a chemical process. Syngas is produced by treating a starter material to yield a mixture of carbon dioxide, carbon monoxide, and hydrogen. It is often used to make methanol, an additive in fuel. Chemical engineers might use a process flow diagram to increase the yield from a given quantity of starter material such as coal, natural gas, or biomass. The process can be diagrammed with arrows showing the steps from starter material to finished product. This helps engineers analyze the process and refine it to achieve a maximum yield of methanol from a minimum amount of syngas, at the lowest cost. Constraints such as worker safety and environmental regulations may also need to be addressed.

Heat is important in syngas production, and there are many ways to produce and maintain high temperatures with minimum fuel use. Engineers use process flow diagrams along with models, computers, and sometimes prototype plants to determine whether a plant design meets temperature and fuel needs. After full-scale manufacturing begins, temperature, pressure, and input-output data are collected. Analysis of the data may reveal that changes in settings or materials could improve efficiency.

 Language Arts Connection Use several sources to research process flow diagrams. Synthesize your research in a presentation that shows an example diagram, describes the system it is used for, and explains the symbols used.

 Evidence Notebook Think about how the engineering design process could be used to develop an edible utensil. In your Evidence Notebook, explain how a chemical engineer might go about defining and delimiting the problem.

Lesson 2 Chemistry and the Engineering Design Process **33**

© Houghton Mifflin Harcourt Publishing Company • Image Credits: ©AP Stringer/AFP/Getty Images

---

 CCC Influence of Science, Engineering, and Technology on Society and the Natural World

Engineering Design Connection In the 2010s, researchers optimized the design of syngas production so that the syngas mixture had a greater concentration of hydrogen and less carbon monoxide. Carbon monoxide is an atmospheric pollutant that indirectly increases atmospheric warming. Have students research this design change and write several sentences describing how the researchers were able to accomplish it. They used copper to enrich a gold catalyst used in the production process.

 Language Arts Connection
RST.11-12.7 Integrate and evaluate multiple sources of information presented in diverse formats and media in order to address a question or solve a problem.
Remind students that they can find tips for conducting research, citing sources, and making presentations in the online **English Language Arts Handbook.**

4 b

5 Answers should include a sample diagram, clear explanations of each symbol used, and the process the diagram is used for. All sources should be cited properly.

 Evidence Notebook

6 Students may suggest criteria such as tasting good and constraints such as being made of biodegradable materials and being safe to eat.

FORMATIVE ASSESSMENT

3-2-1 Have students make a list of three things they learned about the engineering design process in this Exploration, two things they found interesting, and one question they still have about any part of the engineering design process. After each student has completed the list, ask volunteers to share what they wrote with the class. Encourage others in the class to comment on the items and discuss ideas about answers to the questions.

Lesson 2 Chemistry and the Engineering Design Process 33

EXPLORATION 3 Systems and Models

3D Learning Objective

Students use models to *simulate systems and interactions.* They explore the use of physical models based on evidence to *develop possible solutions* and to *predict the interactions between systems.*

DCI ETS1.B Developing Possible Solutions

Point out to students that the emergence of computers in scientific research had a significant influence on scientists' ability to produce and use models of systems found in **everyday phenomena.** Have students work in small groups to research how a three-dimensional model can be used for a large industrial system, such as an assembly line for making T-shirts. Students should give a short presentation to the class demonstrating an example of the model and explaining how it is used.

Nature of Science

Use the Evaluate prompt to point out to students that engineers often have to sift through lots of information and discard any that is irrelevant or superfluous. Ask students to think of a common engineering problem, such as building a new school. Ask what information would be relevant and what would not be relevant.

1 Students should notice that not all the information given is important. **Sample answer:** The information about obstructions, dimensions, number of people, and locations of entrances and exits would be useful because these all affect the amount of space people have to walk in and the paths they might take. The temperature and color are unlikely to affect foot-traffic patterns.

Systems and Models

You have been tasked with optimizing the flow of foot traffic in a public place such as a grocery store or your school. You decide to make a scale model to test different traffic patterns and layouts. Your client gives you an information sheet that includes the dimensions of the space, the number of people who use it each day, the locations of entrances and exits, the average temperature in the area, the floor color, and the positions of obstructions such as shelves or benches.

1 **EVALUATE** Which of the factors listed on the information sheet would be useful to you in modeling the problem and testing potential solutions? Which would not? Explain.

_____

_____

_____

_____

Systems Define Scientific Problems

In choosing which features are relevant to the foot-traffic problem and which are not, you did what scientists and engineers do frequently: you defined the problem by isolating it as a system. A **system** is a set of interacting, interrelated, or interdependent parts that are treated as a whole for the purpose of study. Scientists or engineers define the boundaries of a system according to the question or problem they are studying.

FIGURE 6: A syngas methanol plant is a complex system. Its chemical processes use natural gas or coal as inputs to produce methanol, one of the system's outputs.

Interactions within and between Systems

A system's *inputs* are the matter, energy, or information that flow into the system. *Outputs* are the matter, energy, or information that flow out of the system.

Methanol production at the plant shown in Figure 6 involves a series of chemical reactions in which reactants, usually natural gas or coal, enter as inputs, and methanol leaves as a product, or desired output. There are many intermediate steps in this process, carried out by multiple components. Each component of the overall methanol production system can be viewed as its own system. For example, a reactor in the plant, such as the one illustrated in Figure 7, can be studied as a subsystem interacting with other subsystems inside the plant.

The components of the syngas system include controls to keep the system working properly by monitoring and managing the inputs and outputs. An important control is feedback, information from one step of a cycle that changes the behavior of a previous step. So, feedback is an output that becomes an input.

Categorizing Systems

We can use the idea of a system to study the flow of matter or energy. Energy is the capacity to change matter. Both energy and matter are conserved—that is, neither one can be created or destroyed. A system can be categorized according to whether matter or energy can move across its boundaries. In an open system, such as your body, energy and matter flow between the system and its surroundings. The boundary between the Earth system and the surrounding outer-space environment is open to energy but closed to matter. Some systems are closed to both matter and energy.

Everything inside a system's boundary is part of that system, and everything outside of the boundary is part of the surrounding environment. In a system closed to matter, or to matter and energy, the boundary often corresponds to a physical boundary, such as the glass walls of a beaker. The boundaries of an open system may or may not have a corresponding physical structure.

2 ANALYZE If we define the boundary of the hot air balloon system in Figure 8 as the balloon, cables, and basket, what happens to matter and energy as they flow through the system?

○ **a.** Both matter and energy move in and out of the system.

○ **b.** Energy crosses the system boundaries, but matter does not.

○ **c.** Neither matter nor energy can cross the system boundaries.

3 MODEL Draw a sketch of a hot air balloon and of a helium balloon. Define the systems by identifying the system boundaries. Show inputs and outputs of matter and energy in each.

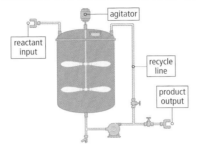

FIGURE 7: A syngas methanol plant is made of smaller subsystems, each of which can be isolated. A reactor is an example of a smaller system inside a larger system.

FIGURE 8: A hot air balloon burns fuel to heat air in the balloon, causing the balloon to float.

Collaborate

Think-Pair-Share Have each student work with a partner to identify the type of system the hot air balloon in **Figure 8** represents and explain why. Have them identify the boundaries, inputs, and outputs of the system. Ask student pairs to describe any smaller systems inside the larger system. Have them share their ideas with the class.

CCC Systems and System Models

Have students consider a thermos. Ask them if the system is closed to matter or to energy when the top is off. Then ask them the same question about the system when the top is on. Have them give their reasoning in each case. The thermos with the top off represents a system open to both energy and matter. The thermos with the top on represents a system closed to the flow of matter but not to the flow of energy.

CCC Energy and Matter

Different fields of science may define closed systems differently. A closed system is sometimes defined as one whose boundaries are open to the transfer of energy but not matter. At other times a closed system is defined as having boundaries that are closed to both energy and matter. Students should understand that it is important to establish what is meant by the term "closed system," but that the laws of conservation of matter and energy hold true in all cases.

2 a

3 Boundaries should be shown and will probably follow the physical boundary of the balloon. The hot air balloon system may or may not include the basket and torch. Students should show that air can enter and leave the hot air balloon system and also that energy can leave the system anywhere along the boundary, whereas only energy can enter or leave the helium balloon system.

SEP **Using Mathematics and Computational Thinking**

Have students imagine that they are engineers who have been asked to make their school cafeteria food-preparation system more efficient. Ask students to consider changes in both matter and energy that they might make in the system and to develop a mathematical model for the improved system. Students can draw diagrams of their systems or describe their changes in a class presentation.

1 **Sample answer:** A three-dimensional physical model could be used to show atoms in a substance. For example, a model using balls connected by wires could show how atoms fit together in a substance. A two-dimensional sketch could also be used to model atoms in a substance. The sketch could show what atoms make up a substance and how they are connected to one another.

 Evidence Notebook

2 **Sample answer:** The spoon itself could be a system, or the spoon and a bowl of food (and the user's hand and mouth) could be a system. Looking at the spoon as a system could help define criteria and constraints for the materials that make up the spoon. Looking at the spoon and a bowl of food (and the user's hand and mouth) as a system could help define criteria and constraints for the size and shape of the spoon and for how the material of the spoon interacts with the food in the bowl.

FORMATIVE ASSESSMENT

One-Sentence Summary Have students look back through the Exploration and read each head and look at the images again. Then, ask them to write a sentence answering this question: *Why is it important to define systems in chemistry?*

Modeling Systems

Engineers often use models to study systems and the interactions within and among them. Think back to the hot air balloon system you sketched. You identified the system's boundaries, inputs, and outputs. This sketch is a type of model. Models can also be equations, simulations, or physical models, such as the one shown in Figure 9.

FIGURE 9: These engineers are using a physical model to study pollution.

Another way to study a system is to use a mathematical model that describes how the flow of energy or matter is affected by changes in one or more components. For example, a mathematical model might enable an engineer to figure out how hot the air inside the balloon needs to be for it to rise at a certain rate. A different mathematical model might enable the engineer to determine how much weight a balloon of a certain size can carry.

A mathematical model may include chemical or mathematical equations that represent relationships among the components of a system. Such models can be used to generate computer simulations of the system's behavior under different conditions and over different periods of time.

FIGURE 10: This computer model was generated to study how a network of tin atoms responds to changes in temperature.

 APPLY An atom can be described as a subsystem that makes up part of a substance. The computer model in Figure 10 shows one way atoms can be modeled. Describe two other ways you could model atoms in a substance.

_____
_____
_____
_____
_____
_____
_____
_____

2 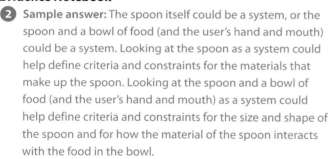 **Evidence Notebook** What are some different ways you could define systems involving an edible spoon? List at least two, and describe how each one could help you define the criteria and constraints of the design problem.

EXPLORATION 4   Case Study: Biosphere 2

EXPLORATION 4

Case Study: Biosphere 2

Imagine you are tasked with designing a miniature version of Earth that could be used to colonize faraway planets or moons. That idea was the basis of Biosphere 2, a domed structure made of glass and concrete in Oracle, Arizona. The facility is now a tourist destination and research site, but it was originally built as a research prototype for self-sustaining space-colonization technology—a system that would contain everything needed to support human life in the hostile conditions outside the Earth system.

3 **Collaborate** With a partner, discuss the features a system would need to have in order to support human life in space. What are some criteria and constraints of the design?

Engineering an Earth-System Prototype

Biosphere 2, shown in Figure 11, contained seven biomes, including a farm area to produce food for humans living inside. The human habitat served as living quarters, and an underground technosphere housed heating, cooling, electrical, and plumbing systems. Two "lungs," connected to the structure by tunnels, regulated air pressure.

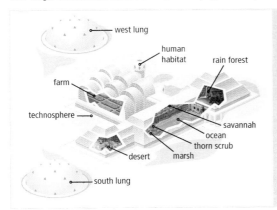

FIGURE 11: Biosphere 2 was designed to support humans and other organisms using only the sun's energy as an input from outside its boundaries.

4 ANALYZE The boundaries of Biosphere 2 were closed to matter but not to energy. How do you think this feature of the design helped to address its criteria and constraints?

3D Learning Objective

Students explore how **engineering problems are defined and delimited.** They evaluate Biosphere 2 as a potential **solution to a complex real-world problem** and explain the project's failure in terms of the **flow of matter and energy within the system.**

Astronomy Connection

Have students give a class presentation in which they suggest reasons that humans might want to establish a base on Mars. Students might consider exploring the availability of minerals, the sense of adventure, or the ability to use Mars for studying faraway planets in our solar system. Encourage students to use their imaginations.

SEP **Constructing Explanations and Designing Solutions**

Have students make a list of factors that are required to sustain life. Then have them explain how each factor within Biosphere 2 contributed to a system that would sustain life on Mars.

Collaborate

Discussion Have student groups brainstorm examples of **everyday phenomena** that are similar to Biosphere 2. Ask them to compare and contrast ways that the two systems are similar and different. Although greenhouses may come to mind, they are not closed systems because they can be opened to the environment.

3 **Sample answer:** Criteria would be that it should provide or be capable of producing everything humans need to survive. Constraints would include that it has to be survivable and cannot rely on resources from outside the structure.

4 **Sample answer:** Energy from the sun was important to keep the plants inside the biosphere growing. Without it, the scientists would have had a much harder time producing their own food.

Lesson 2 Chemistry and the Engineering Design Process   37

CCC Energy and Matter

Have students research the inputs and outputs of the process of photosynthesis. Then, have each student make a labeled drawing suitable for a middle-school student that explains photosynthesis and why animals need plants to live.

Claims, Evidence, and Reasoning

Have students study the layout of Biosphere 2 in **Figure 11**. Ask them to choose one component of the system and make a claim explaining what it contributes to the system. Then have students give evidence for their claim and their reasoning. For example, the rain forest with its thick plant growth provides oxygen for the scientists to breathe. Evidence and reasoning include the chemical nature of photosynthesis, which converts carbon dioxide and releases oxygen.

Math Connection

Have students examine the graph in **Figure 12**. *Ask: What is the normal concentration of oxygen in Earth's atmosphere?* 21% *At what point in the experiment did the oxygen level drop fastest?* after approximately day 470 *What could explain this drop?* Answer will vary. The soil microbes might have had growth spurts, or plant growth might have slowed for some reason. **(MP.2)**

Differentiate Instruction

Extension Have students research one of the cycles found in nature, such as the carbon cycle, carbon dioxide-oxygen cycle, water cycle, or nitrogen cycle. Have students give a class presentation or make a pamphlet in which they describe the events of this cycle in the **everyday phenomena** that occur inside Biosphere 2. Students can use **Figure 12** as a basis for their work.

1 **Sample answer:** Because no matter was being exchanged with the outside surroundings, and matter cannot be created or destroyed, the oxygen must have gone somewhere else in the structure, it was just not in the atmosphere.

Energy and Matter

Oxygen Loss in Biosphere 2

The first Biosphere 2 mission began in 1991, when eight scientists went into the structure and stayed for nearly two years. The scientists grew their own food, maintained the facility, and gathered data about the ecological interactions and environment inside the biosphere system over time.

The cycling of carbon and oxygen through photosynthesis and cellular respiration was crucial to the design. Plants inside provided oxygen and food for the scientists and other organisms. Cellular respiration by these organisms, in turn, provided carbon dioxide, which is necessary for photosynthesis. On Earth, these processes help keep the atmospheric oxygen concentration at about 21%. Inside Biosphere 2, however, oxygen levels began to drop soon after the experiment began, as shown in Figure 12.

Atmospheric Oxygen Concentrations in Biosphere 2

FIGURE 12: Oxygen concentrations decreased steadily over the first 500 days of the first Biosphere 2 mission.

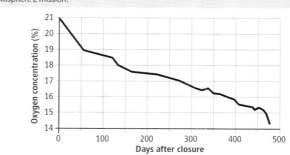

Credit: Adapted from "Oxygen Loss in Biosphere 2" by Jeff Severinghaus, et al., from *Eos, Transactions*, 75(3) 33-37. DOI: 10.1029/94EO000285. Copyright © 1994 by American Geophysical Union. Adapted and reproduced by permission of American Geophysical Union.

1 **PREDICT** Biosphere 2 was closed to the transfer of matter across its boundaries. What does that tell you about the oxygen inside Biosphere 2?

_____

_____

_____

Eventually, oxygen levels decreased so much that it was not safe for the scientists to continue the experiment. Outside oxygen was pumped into the facility. The experiment to build a self-sustaining, closed system had failed, but now the researchers could continue their research safely.

Analyzing the Results

The cause of the oxygen loss in Biosphere 2 was not immediately clear, but later analysis revealed that the problem was due in part to the highly enriched farm soil. Organic matter added to the soil allowed important microbes to flourish, but the microbes' rate of respiration was faster than the plants' rate of photosynthesis.

2 **ANALYZE** Given the decrease in oxygen inside Biosphere 2, would you expect the carbon dioxide levels to have increased, decreased, or remained stable? Explain.

_____

_____

_____

_____

FIGURE 13: Despite its lush appearance and high farm productivity, the Biosphere 2 system did not provide enough atmospheric oxygen for the organisms living inside.

Carbon dioxide levels in Biosphere 2 did not increase, which pointed to a cause other than excessive respiration. That turned out to be the structure itself. Rather than being taken up by plants for photosynthesis, some of the carbon dioxide released during respiration reacted with chemicals in the concrete walls to form calcium carbonate, also known as limestone. Thus, carbon dioxide was no longer available in the atmosphere and water for photosynthetic plants and algae.

3 **Collaborate** What constraints were not met in the first Biosphere 2 experiment? Do you think engineers would respond to this result by redefining the design constraints and criteria or by modifying the design? Discuss with a partner.

4 **Evidence Notebook** Think back to the idea of an edible spoon that will not fill up landfills. What are some potential negative impacts of designing or implementing this solution?

© Houghton Mifflin Harcourt Publishing Company • Image Credits: ©Lindasj22/Shutterstock

---

DCI **ETS1.B Developing Possible Solutions**

Ask: *Why was Biosphere 2 considered a scientific failure?* Because oxygen was pumped into the system, the facility was no longer a closed system. Adding oxygen would not be possible on Mars. Ask students if they can think of another solution that could have been used to increase the amount of oxygen in the facility.

History of Science

Encourage students to research the history of this mini-Earth modeling project, including both the physical constraints and psychological challenges that were encountered. The International Space Station (ISS) is a similar ecological and psychological experiment that can also be researched, though it is different from Biosphere 2 in a number of respects. For example, external shipments of matter resources are regularly sent to the station; the ISS was not designed to be independent of the matter resources of Earth.

2 Accept all reasonable answers. **Sample answer:** The carbon dioxide levels should increase because the plants are not using it to make oxygen.

3 Students should realize that the survivability of the design is a constraint and cannot be redefined, so engineers might modify the design to ensure that the structure did not sequester oxygen. This might include defining new criteria or constraints related to oxygen in the atmosphere.

Evidence Notebook

4 Answers will vary. **Sample answer:** If the spoons get damp or wet during the manufacturing process, bacteria and molds may begin to grow on them. This could be a health hazard to users of the spoons.

FORMATIVE ASSESSMENT

Quick Write Allow students about 10 minutes to write a paragraph answering the following question: *If you were in charge of Biosphere 2, what might you have done to keep the project from failing due to dangerously low levels of oxygen?*

TAKE IT FURTHER Engineering

Collaborate

You may choose to assign this activity or direct students to the Interactive Online Student Edition, where they can choose from all available paths. These activities can be assigned individually, to pairs, or to small groups.

Differentiate Instruction

ELL Support Before students read the page, explain that the word *multiscale* is derived from the root *multi-*, meaning "many," and *scale*, in this context meaning the size of something.

Extension Students may wish to explore how scientists manipulate the carbon-carbon bonds in nanotubes to change the physical and chemical properties.

Explore Online ▶

Encourage students to go online to interact with a 3D model of cylindrical graphene. Students can zoom in and out and swivel the model to see the cylindrical graphene from all sides.

 The molecular model shows how the atoms in the molecule are arranged. The model of the CNT yarn might show how a material made from molecules with this type of arrangement can be made into a fiber material and what that material looks like at a larger scale. The combination could help researchers understand how molecular structure is related to the properties of a material.

TAKE IT FURTHER

Engineering

Multiscale Modeling

Engineers often use models to understand problems and develop solutions. If a system problem is complex, they may use more than one model. A model is designed to represent a system at a certain scale. For example, a process flow diagram for a chemical plant shows the flow of energy and matter through the system, but it does not indicate the molecular structures of the reactants or products. The scale used for a model depends on what the engineer needs to study about the system.

Engineers who want to understand systems at different scales can use multiple-scale, or multiscale, modeling. This approach can increase the effectiveness of each model. Information obtained from a model of a system at a very small scale can be used to alter the design of a larger-scale model. Similarly, information from a larger model can reveal areas of a system that might need to be studied on a smaller scale.

FIGURE 14: Graphene is shown at two different scales.   Explore Online ▶

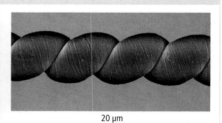

a This 3D model shows the molecular structure of cylindrical graphene, also known as a carbon nanotube.

b This yarn is made up of carbon nanotubes woven together. Engineers want to use the yarn to convert mechanical energy to electrical energy.

Figure 14a is a model of a carbon nanotube (CNT) at the particle level, and Figure 14b shows a prototype for a CNT yarn that can be used to convert mechanical energy to electrical energy. CNTs are very strong, have unique electrical properties, and are good conductors of heat. Graphene molecules can be arranged in a single layer to make single-walled nanotubes, or they can be layered to form multi-walled nanotubes. The properties of CNTs vary with their structure. Because the function of a CNT is related to its molecular structure, multiscale models can be helpful to engineers and scientists studying them.

1 **ANALYZE** What unique information does each model in Figure 14 provide?

_____

_____

_____

_____

When designing a product to have a specific property, a scientist might use a physical model, such as the CNT prototype in Figure 14b, to study its physical properties. They may also use a molecular model, such as the one in Figure 14a, to understand the chemical properties of the CNT.

To better understand or solve complex problems involving many variables, scientists and engineers also often use computer simulations. Computer simulations are based on mathematical models of systems. These models enable scientists to test the effects of changing one or more variables, and to understand how a system behaves over yet another scale—time.

Use a Model Research ways that computer simulations can be used in multiscale modeling. Next, find a simulation that depicts a specific property of matter on a particle level. Ask your teacher for suggestions if you are not sure where to find a simulation.

2 EVALUATE What property of matter will you choose to study? How does the simulation you found model this property?

_____

_____

_____

_____

Develop a Model Now, design your own model that depicts the same property of matter as the computer simulation, but on a different scale. You may design a computer simulation, a prototype, a 3D model, or an image. Be sure to have your plan approved by your teacher before you begin development.

3 EXPLAIN Think about the systems that your two models work within. What are the boundaries, inputs, and outputs of each system? How does each model show the interaction of matter within and between systems at different scales?

_____

_____

_____

_____

 Language Arts Connection Present your research, the computer simulation you studied, the model you designed, and the systems involved in each of your models to your class. In your presentation, explain how modeling a property of matter at two different scales helped you learn more about that property.

 © Houghton Mifflin Harcourt Publishing Company

| CORRELATION VS. CAUSATION | FOOD TECHNOLOGIST | MODELING A SYSTEM | Go online to choose one of these other paths. |

 Language Arts Connection
WHST.9-12.9 Draw evidence from informational texts.
Students should describe the simulation they identified that represents the properties and behavior of matter on a particle level as well as the model they designed about the behavior of matter on a macroscopic level. They should also describe what they learned from their research about the benefits and methods of multiscale modeling.

2 Answers should state the property of matter students intend to study and how the simulation models that property. Professional societies and universities offer many free simulations that students can find online. They may also refer to the simulations available through the University of Colorado, Boulder or the Concord Consortium.

3 Answers will vary. Boundaries, inputs, and outputs of the two systems will vary with student models.

Explore Online

Correlation vs. Causation

Students conduct guided research to explore the difference between correlation and causation in the cause-and-effect relationship between two variables.

Food Technologist

Students learn how food technologists develop new food products, analyze or improve existing products, and make sure food-processing facilities are safe and efficient.

Modeling a System

Students use the engineering design process to identify a problem in a familiar system of their choosing, make a model of the system, and use their model to develop and test improvements in the system.

Lesson 2 Chemistry and the Engineering Design Process　41

EVALUATE Lesson Self-Check

Can You Solve the Problem?

Claims, Evidence, and Reasoning

Have students clearly state their claim—their explanation for the phenomenon they have been investigating throughout this lesson. They should present their reasoning for making this claim, along with evidence such as facts, examples, and statistics that support their claim. You may want to have students present their arguments orally, in writing, or as a debate.

Cultivating Student Questions

Assessing Student Growth Review the list of questions students generated at the beginning of the lesson. Have volunteers select any unanswered questions and suggest how they could be investigated. After approving student plans, have small groups conduct the investigations and report back to the class.

As the year progresses, the number of volunteers for this task will likely increase. The sophistication of the means of investigation also may increase. Both outcomes are measures of positive growth that are essential to the scientific mindset and demonstrate that students are beginning to understand that the correct answer is less important than the means used to investigate the question. You will find that students are more engaged and more willing to take the risk of being "wrong," which indicates positive growth in scientific thinking.

  Evidence Notebook

1 An edible spoon should have a shape useful for lifting food (criterion), must be strong and not fall apart when used (constraints), be made of substances that are safe to eat (constraint), do not react with most foods (constraint or criterion), and have a pleasant taste (criterion). Evidence includes properties of typical spoons, a description of the design problem (spoon must be functional and safe to eat), the observation that some substances in a mixture can separate when combined with water, knowledge of how a spoon is used, and the fact that criteria and constraints are the wants and needs of a design solution.

EVALUATE

Lesson Self-Check

CAN YOU SOLVE THE PROBLEM?

FIGURE 15: Edible spoons may be a viable alternative to plastic, because they do not accumulate in landfills.

Now that you have learned about criteria and constraints in the engineering design process, you can apply them to the problem of developing an edible spoon. Like any solution, the edible spoon design should fulfill certain wants and must address certain needs. These criteria and constraints apply not just to the spoon itself but to the process by which it is manufactured. The evidence you have collected during your study of the engineering design process can be used to understand some of the criteria and constraints that might develop during the process of designing an edible spoon.

  Evidence Notebook Refer to your notes in your Evidence Notebook to make a claim about the criteria of an edible spoon design. Your explanation should include a discussion of the following points:

Claims What properties should an edible spoon have—that is, what are the design criteria? What are the design constraints?

Evidence What information or evidence supports your list of criteria and constraints?

Reasoning How does the evidence you provided support your claim about the criteria and constraints for an edible spoon design?

© Houghton Mifflin Harcourt Publishing Company • Image Credits: ©HMH

 Formal Assessment Go online for student self-checks and other assessments.

Name _____ Date _____

CHECKPOINTS

Check Your Understanding

1. Why is it important to identify and rank criteria before designing a solution to an engineering problem?
   - a. to establish a budget for the solution
   - b. to identify challenges to the solution
   - c. to avoid pursuing solutions that do not meet key goals or needs
   - d. to determine the economic impact

2. Which step would scientists and engineers be least likely to use a model for?
   - a. simulating interactions within or between systems
   - b. defining and delimiting a problem
   - c. studying systems at different scales
   - d. demonstrating the flow of matter or energy through a system

3. An engineer is testing a new recipe for canned vegetable soup. She finds that the squash in the soup gets mushy when the soup is heat-treated to make it safe to eat. She rejects this recipe and tests a new one without squash. What does that indicate about the constraints of the soup design?
   - a. The soup must be safe to eat.
   - b. The soup must cost less than a certain amount to produce.
   - c. The soup's texture is not a constraint.
   - d. The engineer changed her mind about the constraints.

4. Complete the statement about Biosphere 2.

   The Biosphere 2 system was designed to be

   open | closed to the transfer of matter across

   its boundaries. The unexpected drop in oxygen

   in the Biosphere 2 atmosphere resulted from a

   combination of factors including soil composition

   and building materials. This indicates that the

   system boundaries | interactions were not

   correctly identified.

5. A chemical engineer is developing a manufacturing process for a new kind of fertilizer. Which factor would be unlikely to appear in a diagram of the process?
   - a. amount of reactant input
   - b. amount of product output
   - c. boundaries between the system and the environment
   - d. tradeoffs among different criteria

6. Which statements are true of an open system? Select all correct answers.
   - a. Matter enters and leaves the system but energy does not.
   - b. Both matter and energy leave the system.
   - c. Energy enters and leaves the system but matter does not.
   - d. Its boundaries are defined by the person studying the system.

7. You have been hired by a state government to help decide whether to retrofit a coal plant to reduce its emissions or to build a new power plant that does not rely on coal. Place these steps in the order in which you would proceed.

   _____ a. Collect and evaluate data about each model.

   _____ b. Design models of potential solutions to test whether they meet the criteria and constraints.

   _____ c. Use the results of testing to choose a solution to use or optimize.

   _____ d. Identify and define the goals of the project and any limitations such as budget, time, and community concerns.

© Houghton Mifflin Harcourt Publishing Company

Lesson 2 Chemistry and the Engineering Design Process   43

Answers

8. Sample answer: Modeling a system at smaller than full size enables scientists and engineers to study it and make changes at a smaller scale, which could be easier and less expensive than modeling it at full size. Disadvantages include that the model, because it is simplified, may not fully reflect the behavior of the system in the real world.

9. Sample answer: Thinking about how a solution might affect the environment or a community is important because it can help engineers define the constraints of the problem they are trying to solve. For example, a chemical engineer designing a new plant would need to think about how noise, light, or emissions from the plant would affect people living nearby in order to avoid having to redesign it later in the process.

10. Sample answer: Iteration is the repeating of steps in the engineering design process. It may occur after testing, if results of the testing show that a design needs revisions. It may also occur when solutions are proposed and evaluated, if the problem is not well defined. It may also occur long after a design has been implemented, as new technologies or unanticipated problems arise. Iteration is important because it enables designers to improve their designs and develop the best possible solution. For example, in the toothpaste example, iteration would allow the testing of different blue dyes and revising the constraints if test results revealed an unanticipated problem.

Make Your Own Study Guide

Have students create a study guide that helps them organize and visualize the important information from this lesson. Their study guide should focus on the main ideas from this lesson and tie multiple ideas together. Students can make an outline, a concept map, a graphic organizer, or another representation.

EVALUATE

CHECKPOINTS (continued)

8. What are some advantages to modeling a system? What are some limitations?

_____

_____

_____

_____

9. Why is it important to take into account potential environmental or social impacts when evaluating possible solutions to a problem? Give an example to support your explanation.

_____

_____

_____

_____

10. How and when does iteration occur in the engineering design process? Why is it such an important aspect of designing solutions? Use an example to explain.

_____

_____

_____

_____

_____

MAKE YOUR OWN STUDY GUIDE

 In your Evidence Notebook, design a study guide that supports the main ideas from this lesson:
Scientists and engineers define systems in order to isolate and study interactions within and between components of systems.

Chemical engineers use chemistry to define and solve problems. They use the engineering design process to find optimal solutions to these problems, and to refine solutions as new data or technologies become available.

Remember to include the following information in your study guide:
• Use examples that model main ideas.
• Record explanations for the phenomena you investigated.
• Use evidence to support your explanations. Your support can include drawings, data, graphs, laboratory conclusions, and other evidence recorded throughout the lesson.

Consider how chemical engineers use the engineering design process to find solutions to unanticipated impacts of new technologies.

UNIT 1 Connections

Earth Science Connection

Building Stone Used for centuries to construct some of the world's most enduring structures, building stone such as granite, limestone, slate, and marble is known for its sustainability and durability. When choosing stone for countertops, roofing, or flooring, architects must consider the unique properties of each material. For example, slate can easily be split into thin sheets, making it ideal as a roofing material. Granite and marble make good countertops, because both stay cool near a hot stove.

> Using a range of sources, develop a brochure on two different types of building stone and their applications. The brochure should emphasize the properties of each material that make it a good choice for a specific use. It should also include other considerations, such as price and environmental impact, which affect the decision to use one over another.

FIGURE 1: This roof is made of slate.

Music Connection

Designing Musical Instruments If you knock on metal and then knock on wood, you might hear that different materials make different types of sounds. The materials used to make a musical instrument are as important as the shape of the instrument for producing its unique sound. Sounds move through materials in different ways, and these differences affect the tone and quality of the sound the instrument produces.

> Select an instrument or a family of instruments and research how the material it is made from affects the sound. Synthesize your findings into a presentation. If possible, have audio examples of sound differences or demonstrate using your own "homemade" instruments.

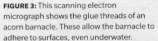

FIGURE 2: Some instruments are made of wood, while others are made of metal.

Technology Connection

Barnacle Glue Barnacles attach to docks, boats, and anything they come across. Their glue sets in salt water and stays set, as anyone who has cleaned the bottom of a boat can tell you. Engineers are developing ways to make similar glues that work underwater. They are also investigating using barnacle glue as a medical adhesive.

> Research the properties of barnacle glue, what makes it so strong, and its ability to work underwater. How does the ability to work underwater make it useful as biomedical glue? Summarize two scientific papers or articles on the uses of barnacle glue. Do the authors come to the same conclusion? Cite specific evidence to support your analysis.

FIGURE 3: This scanning electron micrograph shows the glue threads of an acorn barnacle. These allow the barnacle to adhere to surfaces, even underwater.

Support for Unit Connections

Earth Science Connection

Brochures should discuss the positives and negatives of each material. For example, limestone's texture allows it to be easily shaped to fit any architectural design, and its homogeneous appearance means that any later additions would look similar and not be out of place. However, limestone is not as durable as granite or marble, and many people do not find it as aesthetically pleasing. Marble and granite are aesthetically pleasing, durable, and common, but they can stain and scratch if not properly maintained. Slate is durable and stain resistant, but mining it must be done very carefully to avoid waste. Brochures should highlight the properties of each material so that the developer can make an informed decision. Students should resolve conflicting information from different sources into a cohesive final product.

Music Connection

The material used to make an instrument can have noticeable effects on its sound. Each type of instrument is generally made of a certain type of material, such as wood or metal, and the type of wood or metal can have significant influence on its sound. The material can influence factors such as stiffness and density, and these factors determine how well sound waves are transmitted through the material. Students' presentations should describe several possible materials used to make an instrument and explain differences in sound produced by each material—for example, an acoustic guitar made of wood as opposed to a steel guitar.

Technology Connection

Students' summaries should explain that barnacles first place a drop of oil on the surface, which pushes away the water. Then the barnacles are able to apply the adhesive directly to the surface. Barnacle adhesive contains many proteins that, when synthesized in a lab, have been shown to greatly increase the adhesive properties of glues. Students may find summaries of scientific papers on scientific news websites. They may also use scientific journals at the school or local library.

THING EXPLAINER BY RANDALL MUNROE

A BOOK EXPLAINING COMPLEX IDEAS USING ONLY THE 1,000 MOST COMMON WORDS

HOW TO COUNT THINGS

A counting system to help people agree with each other

You've learned that scientists all over the world have agreed on a single measurement system called SI. Here's a look at how we use SI to measure the length, velocity, temperature, and mass of things in our world.

THING EXPLAINER
COMPLICATED STUFF IN SIMPLE WORDS

RANDALL MUNROE
author of *What If?* and creator of *xkcd*

RANDALL MUNROE
XKCD.COM

THE STORY OF COUNTING HOW LONG, WARM, FAST, AND HEAVY

TO COUNT HOW HEAVY THINGS ARE, WE PICK A WEIGHT TO CALL "ONE." THEN, IF YOU SAY A WEIGHT IS "TEN," PEOPLE UNDERSTAND IT'S AS HEAVY AS TEN "ONES."

I THINK I LOST THREE ONES.

DO YOU FEEL THINNER?

WE DO THE SAME FOR COUNTING OTHER THINGS, LIKE HOW FAST OR HOT THINGS ARE.

I'M 37. YOU?

YOU DON'T WANT TO KNOW . . .

PEOPLE DON'T ALWAYS AGREE ON HOW MUCH "ONE" IS, WHICH CAN CAUSE A LOT OF PROBLEMS. A SPACE BOAT ONCE MISSED A WORLD BECAUSE PEOPLE GOT CONFUSED ABOUT WHICH "ONE" THEY SHOULD BE USING FOR WEIGHT.

SPACE OFFICE

I THINK IT'S TOO CLOSE!

MOST COUNTRIES HAVE AGREED TO MAKE "ONE" THE SAME THING EVERYWHERE. HERE'S WHAT NUMBERS FROM ONE TO TEN HUNDRED MEAN IN THAT COUNTING SYSTEM.

I WANT ONE!

ME TOO!

HOW LONG THINGS ARE

In this system, "one" is about half as tall as a tall person.

TEN HUNDRED — A very tall road
(like the Gold Gate Tall Road)

ALMOST TEN HUNDRED — The world's tallest building

EIGHT HUNDRED — All the law makers in my country, if they all stood on one another's shoulders.

SEVEN HUNDRED

SIX HUNDRED — A very long train

FIVE HUNDRED — The farthest a person has thrown anything (a plastic ring)

FOUR HUNDRED

THREE HUNDRED

TWO HUNDRED — The farthest a person has hit a ball in a stick-ball game

ONE HUNDRED — About how long a normal spoken word is, from start to finish, as it flies through the air

ALMOST ONE HUNDRED — One of these, rolled out on the floor all the way

EIGHT TENS — All the leaders my country has had, if they all stood on each other's shoulders.

SEVEN TENS

SIX TENS — A big sky boat's wings

FIVE TENS — The old building well known for not standing up straight

FOUR TENS — A very tall tree

THIRTY — The biggest wave anyone has ever slid down the front of while standing on a board

Each of these is as long as one of these.

TWENTY

TEN — The Thing Explainer book, if it were on one long page instead of a lot of normal ones

ONE MORE THAN EIGHT — The farthest a person can jump

EIGHT — The longest one of these

SEVEN — The food hallways in your body

SIX — A very long person-eating fish

FIVE — A car

FOUR — How high a person can jump if they run and then push a bendy stick into the ground

THREE

TWO — The distance up to a circle that tall people jump up and drop a ball through

ONE — A tall person

NONE — A tall person's pants

Teacher Notes

Teacher Notes

_____

_____

_____

_____

_____

_____

_____

_____

_____

_____

_____

_____

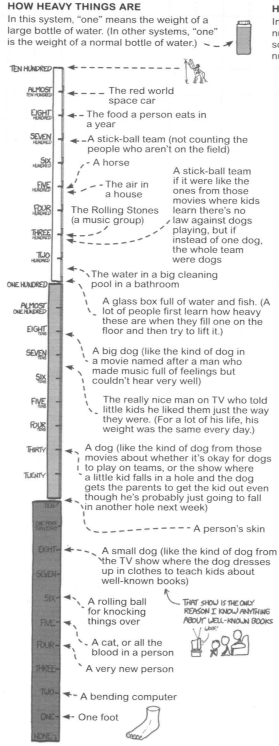
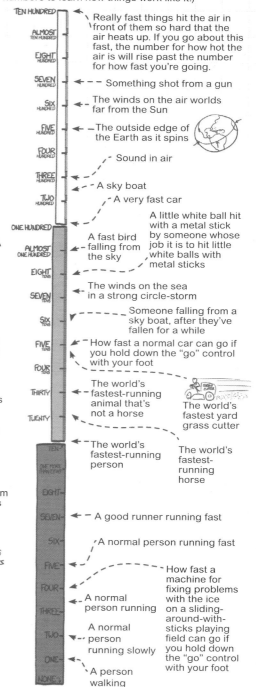

HOW WARM THINGS ARE

In this system, "none" means how cold water has to be to turn to ice, and "one hundred" means how hot it has to be to turn to air.

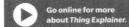

Go online for more about *Thing Explainer.*

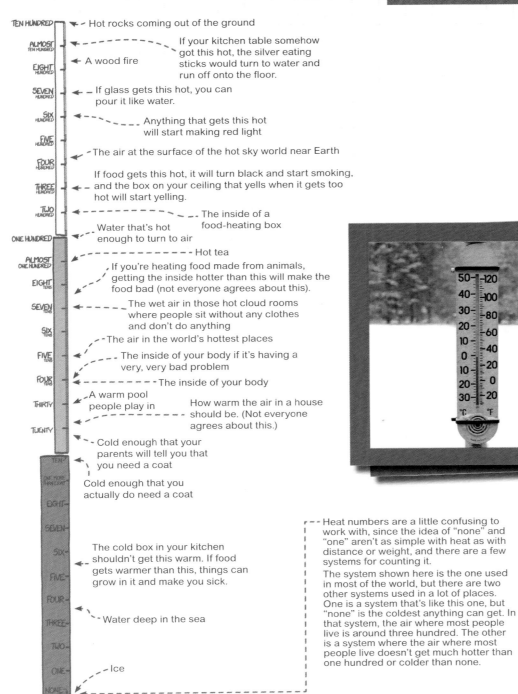

TEN HUNDRED — Hot rocks coming out of the ground

ALMOST TEN HUNDRED — If your kitchen table somehow got this hot, the silver eating sticks would turn to water and run off onto the floor.

EIGHT HUNDRED — A wood fire

SEVEN HUNDRED — If glass gets this hot, you can pour it like water.

SIX HUNDRED — Anything that gets this hot will start making red light

FIVE HUNDRED

FOUR HUNDRED — The air at the surface of the hot sky world near Earth

THREE HUNDRED — If food gets this hot, it will turn black and start smoking, and the box on your ceiling that yells when it gets too hot will start yelling.

TWO HUNDRED — The inside of a food-heating box

ONE HUNDRED — Water that's hot enough to turn to air

ALMOST ONE HUNDRED — Hot tea

EIGHT TENS — If you're heating food made from animals, getting the inside hotter than this will make the food bad (not everyone agrees about this).

SEVEN TENS — The wet air in those hot cloud rooms where people sit without any clothes and don't do anything

SIX TENS — The air in the world's hottest places

FIVE TENS — The inside of your body if it's having a very, very bad problem

FOUR TENS — The inside of your body

THIRTY — A warm pool people play in

How warm the air in a house should be. (Not everyone agrees about this.)

TWENTY — Cold enough that your parents will tell you that you need a coat

TEN — Cold enough that you actually do need a coat

ONE MORE THAN NONE

EIGHT

SEVEN

SIX — The cold box in your kitchen shouldn't get this warm. If food gets warmer than this, things can grow in it and make you sick.

FIVE

FOUR

THREE — Water deep in the sea

TWO

ONE — Ice

NONE

Heat numbers are a little confusing to work with, since the idea of "none" and "one" aren't as simple with heat as with distance or weight, and there are a few systems for counting it.

The system shown here is the one used in most of the world, but there are two other systems used in a lot of places. One is a system that's like this one, but "none" is the coldest anything can get. In that system, the air where most people live is around three hundred. The other is a system where the air where most people live doesn't get much hotter than one hundred or colder than none.

Teacher Notes

_____

_____

_____

_____

_____

_____

_____

_____

_____

_____

_____

_____

_____

_____

_____

_____

_____

_____

👥 Small Groups 🕐 Three 45-minute class periods

Investigating the Viscosity of Oil

SEP **Analyzing and Interpreting Data**

Students compare the viscosities of different types of oil.

Answers

1. Students might consider which properties to expect from a high-viscosity or a low-viscosity oil, how the viscosities can be compared, and how temperature affects viscosity.

2. Suggest that students focus on how oils are used in cars and why oils with different viscosities might be chosen. Students should collect the information they need in order to carry out the investigation.

3. Students should develop a procedure to determine the identity of the oils based on their viscosities at different temperatures. Instruct students to have a plan of their investigation approved by you before starting.

4. Suggest that students produce graphs of their data to enable them to display their results and make the analysis easier.

5. Provide an opportunity for each group to present their data to the class and explain the results of their investigation. Presentations should explain how data collected from the investigation support their findings.

Performance Task Scoring Rubric

Points	Criteria
	Guiding questions are answered in the final presentation.
	Explanation describes SAE ratings, properties of different oils, and conditions under which different oils are developed to be used.
	Set of graphs is developed based on analysis of data.
	Conclusions identify the type of oil in each can.

Hands-On Lab: *Student lab worksheet and teacher support available online.*

Investigating the Viscosity of Oil

You have been contacted by an automotive service shop that received a shipment of bulk containers of motor oil. Conditions during the transport, however, caused the labels to peel off the cans. Before the shop uses this oil in cars, the service technicians must match the cans with the types of oil that were listed on the shipping invoice based on the viscosity and the Society of Automotive Engineers (SAE) rating of each oil. Viscosity is a measurement of a liquid's resistance to flow. A fluid with high viscosity flows more slowly than a fluid with low viscosity does. SAE ratings give relative viscosity values for the oils. A low SAE rating means the fluid flows more readily, so it has lower viscosity.

FIGURE 4: This mechanic tests the viscosity of an oil sample. If the viscosity of the oil is too high or too low, it could cause damage to the engine.

1. ASK QUESTIONS

Develop a set of questions you have about viscosity, SAE ratings, and how you could assign these ratings to a set of oil samples. Identify all the factors you will research to answer these questions.

2. CONDUCT RESEARCH

Oils of different viscosities are used under different conditions. Low-viscosity oils are meant to be used in cold climates because they flow more easily at low temperatures. High-viscosity oils are better used when the engine may experience high temperatures because the excessive heat thins the oil. Oils of different viscosities must be tested to ensure that the oil chosen will work properly under the conditions the engine must run in. Research the different SAE oil ratings and examples of oils for each rating. Then, use the information you gathered to answer the question set you developed.

3. CARRY OUT AN INVESTIGATION

With your team, investigate the viscosities of the oil samples in the cans.

Explore Online ▶

🧪 **Hands-On Lab**

Viscosity of Liquids Build a viscometer to test the viscosity of a set of oil samples. Rank them in order of their SAE ratings using data from your investigation.

4. ANALYZE DATA

Using data you collected in the investigation, assign an SAE rating to each oil sample. Then, graph the relationships between SAE rating and flow time, density, and viscosity, as well as between viscosity and density.

5. COMMUNICATE

Present the results of your investigation to the automotive service shop. Explain how the SAE rating relates to recommendations for which oil to use at a given temperature. Your presentation should include evidence from your investigation and your analysis of this evidence.

 CHECK YOUR WORK

A complete presentation should include the following information:

- a set of guiding questions that are answered in the final presentation
- an explanation of SAE ratings, the properties of different oils, and the conditions under which different oils are meant to be used
- a set of graphs based on an analysis of your data
- your conclusions of the identity of the type of oil in each can

UNIT 1 Practice and Review

Name _____   Date _____

SYNTHESIZE THE UNIT

In your Evidence Notebook, make a concept map, other graphic organizer, or outline using the Study Guides you made for each lesson in this unit. Be sure to use evidence to support your claims.

When synthesizing individual information, remember to follow these general steps:
- Find the central idea of each piece of information.
- Think about the relationships among the central ideas.
- Combine the ideas to come up with a new understanding.

DRIVING QUESTIONS

Look back to the Driving Questions from the opening section of this unit. In your Evidence Notebook, review and revise your previous answers to those questions. Use the evidence you gathered and other observations you made throughout the unit to support your claims.

PRACTICE AND REVIEW

1. Which of the following are chemical changes? Select all correct answers.
   - ☐ **a.** table salt dissolving in water
   - ☐ **b.** a liquid evaporating to form a gas
   - ☐ **c.** a force causing a sheet of metal to bend
   - ☐ **d.** wooden logs burning to form ash
   - ☐ **e.** hydrogen and oxygen forming water

2. Select the correct terms to complete the statement.

   An example of a pure substance is carbon dioxide | salt water | wood. A mixture is heterogeneous | homogeneous if it has a uniform composition. A mixture is heterogeneous | homogeneous if its composition is not uniform. A mixture | pure substance can often be separated by techniques such as evaporation or filtration.

3. A group of scientists and engineers are developing a medication to treat a disease. Which statement describes a possible constraint for the medication?
   - ○ **a.** The effectiveness of the medication will be tested during production.
   - ○ **b.** The cost of producing the medication will be kept as low as possible.
   - ○ **c.** A process for manufacturing the medication will have to be designed.
   - ○ **d.** Compounds used in the medication should be easy to obtain or produce.

4. Select the correct terms to complete the statement.

   The density of a liquid substance in a container is an intensive | extensive physical property of the substance, so it can be used to help identify the substance. The volume of the substance is an intensive | extensive property, so it cannot be used in identification because it changes | does not change with the amount of the substance present.

5. A chemical engineer is modifying the formula for a window cleaner. Order the steps of the engineering design process she might follow to accomplish this.
   - _____ **a.** do research to identify potential solutions
   - _____ **b.** test a new formula to see if it meets the desired criteria and constraints
   - _____ **c.** identify the ways she will try to improve the formula
   - _____ **d.** test a revised formula and consider any tradeoffs
   - _____ **e.** revise the formula based on test results

Synthesize the Unit

Suggest that students begin by writing the titles of the lessons and the explorations in each unit as well as any associated vocabulary. Encourage students to recognize relationships between concepts introduced in different lessons.

Driving Questions

Students may wish to write a brief explanation of how their understanding of each question has changed since the start of the unit.

Practice and Review

SUMMATIVE ASSESSMENT

Answers

1. DOK 2 d, e
2. DOK 1 carbon dioxide, homogeneous, heterogeneous, mixture
3. DOK 2 b
4. DOK 2 intensive, extensive, changes
5. DOK 2 c, a, b, e, d

3D Item Analysis	1	2	3	4	5
SEP Planning and Carrying Out Investigations					•
SEP Constructing Explanations and Designing Solutions	•			•	
SEP Scientific Knowledge is Based on Empirical Evidence					•
DCI PS1.A Structure and Properties of Matter			•		
DCI PS1.B Chemical Reactions	•				
DCI Defining and Delimiting Engineering Problems					•
DCI Developing Possible Solutions		•			
CCC Patterns		•			
CCC Science is a Human Endeavor				•	

Answers

6. **DOK 3** Drawings should show the bottle with a solution inside, the balloon on top being inflated, and the flow of matter (the gas) from the water bottle into the balloon. Students should identify this as a system closed to matter. Matter cannot flow into and out of the system, but energy can.

7. **DOK 2 Sample answer:** The engineer would first define the problem. In this example, the problem is adjusting the formula for the mold so that it sets in less than two minutes. The chemical engineer would then develop several possible new formulas that could result in a quicker-setting mold and test the most promising ones. If no formulas result in a quicker-setting mold, the engineer may have to try to develop new formulas.

8. **DOK 3** Students may reply that the slightly greater cost to manufacture the first formula is an acceptable tradeoff to get the improved product onto the market quickly and not lose any profits. The increased cost could be passed on to the customer. Others might argue that the initial costs and time required to equip the factory would be an acceptable tradeoff, because actual production will be much more cost effective and there would be no need to increase the cost to the customer.

3D Item Analysis	6	7	8
SEP Asking Questions and Defining Problems		•	•
SEP Constructing Explanations and Designing Solutions	•	•	•
DCI PS1.A Structure and Properties of Matter	•		
DCI ETS1.A Defining and Delimiting Engineering Problems		•	•
DCI Developing Possible Solutions		•	•
CCC Systems and System Models	•		
CCC Energy and Matter	•		

6. During a laboratory experiment, a student mixes baking soda with vinegar in a water bottle. The student quickly places a balloon on top of the water bottle. As the experiment proceeds, the balloon expands. Diagram this experiment, identifying the system boundaries and components, the type of system, and the flows of matter and energy.

7. A chemical engineer is asked to modify the formula for quick-setting mold casts used in forensics so the material sets in under two minutes. How can the engineer use the engineering design process to solve this problem?

8. Two formulas for the quick-setting mold casts described in the previous question are proposed. One formula will cost slightly more to manufacture, but can be manufactured immediately. The other will cost much less to manufacture, but will require upfront costs and time to equip the factory to produce it properly. How might the engineering teams analyze tradeoffs as they decide which formula is the best solution?

UNIT PROJECT

Return to your unit project. Prepare a presentation using your research and materials, and share it with the class. In your final presentation, evaluate the strength of your claim, evidence, and conclusions.

Remember these tips while evaluating:

- Was your claim supported by your evidence?
- What are some criteria and constraints of your toothpaste design?

- Look at the evidence gathered from your experiment. Does your evidence support your claim and reasoning regarding which ingredients make a better toothpaste?

- How could you revise your setup and procedure to further test your prediction, model, or the evidence you collected?

Integrating the NGSS* Three Dimensions of Learning

Building to the Performance Expectations

The learning experiences in this unit prepare students for mastery of

Matter and Its Interactions

HS-PS1-1 Use the periodic table as a model to predict the relative properties of elements based on the patterns of electrons in the outermost energy level of atoms.

HS-PS1-8 Develop models to illustrate the changes in the composition of the nucleus of the atom and the energy released during the processes of fission, fusion, and radioactive decay.

Engineering Design

HS-ETS1-1 Analyze a major global challenge to specify qualitative and quantitative criteria and constraints for solutions that account for societal needs and wants.

HS-ETS1-3 Evaluate a solution to a complex real-world problem based on prioritized criteria and trade-offs that account for a range of constraints, including cost, safety, reliability, and aesthetics, as well as possible social, cultural, and environmental impacts.

Assessing Student Progress

Students practice aspects of the Performance Expectations by completing the **Unit Project: Designing an Atomic Model.** After completing the lessons, students practice or can be assessed on aspects of the Performance Expectations by completing the **Unit Performance Task: Identifying Elements Using Patterns.**

Unit Storyline Students model the charged substructures of atoms and use patterns in the periodic table to predict the behavior of elements. They analyze forces that determine the stability of nuclei and model nuclear reactions. Students explore impacts of using nuclear fission as an energy source.

Lesson 1
Modeling Atomic Structure

In Lesson 1, students use models to investigate atomic structure (SEP Developing and Using Models). They explore the structure of atoms and explain how the elements are identified based on the number of protons in the atomic nucleus (SEP Constructing Explanations and Designing Solutions, DCI PS1.A, CCC Scale, Proportion, and Quantity). Students use patterns and evidence from investigations to model the outer electron states of atoms of different elements (SEP Scientific Knowledge is Open to Revision in Light of New Evidence, DCI PS1.A, CCC Patterns).

Lesson 2
Investigating Patterns in the Periodic Table

In Lesson 2, students use patterns in the periodic table to predict properties of elements (SEP Scientific Knowledge is Based on Empirical Evidence, DCI PS1.A, CCC Patterns). Students explain various patterns in the periodic table, including atomic size, ionization energy, and electronegativity (SEP Developing and Using Models, DCI PS1.A, CCC Patterns).

Lesson 3
Analyzing Nuclear Reactions

In Lesson 3, students use models to explore nuclear forces between neutrons and protons and explain how these forces can make some nuclei stable and others unstable (CCC Energy and Matter). They develop models to explore radioactive decay and consider how the atomic structure changes during nuclear processes (SEP Developing and Using Models, DCI.PS1.C, CCC Energy and Matter). Students use nuclear equations to model changes that take place in the atomic nucleus during fission and fusion (SEP Developing and Using Models, DCI PS1.C). They explore the impacts on society and the environment as a result of using nuclear fission as an energy source and evaluate this energy source based on a range of criteria and constraints (SEP Constructing Explanations and Designing Solutions, DCI ETS1.A, DCI ETS1.B, CCC Influence of Engineering, Technology, and Science on Society and the Natural World).

*Next Generation Science Standards and logo are registered trademarks of Achieve. Neither Achieve nor the lead states and partners that developed the Next Generation Science Standards were involved in the production of, and do not endorse, these products.

Integrating the NGSS, continued

NGSS across This Unit

Next Generation Science Standards	Unit Project	Lesson 1	Lesson 2	Lesson 3	Unit Performance Task
SEP Developing and Using Models	•	•	•	•	•
SEP Constructing Explanations and Designing Solutions		•		•	
SEP Scientific Knowledge is Based on Empirical Evidence		•	•		
DCI **HS-PS1.A** Structure and Properties of Matter	•	•	•		•
DCI **HS-PS1.C** Nuclear Processes	•			•	
DCI **HS-PS2.B** Types of Interactions	•	•			
DCI **HS-ETS1.B** Developing Possible Solutions			•	•	
CCC Patterns	•	•	•		•
CCC Energy and Matter	•			•	
CCC Scientific Knowledge Assumes an Order and Consistency in Natural Systems		•		•	

NGSS across the Grades

Middle School

MS-PS1-1 Develop models to describe the atomic composition of simple molecules and extended structures.

MS-ETS1-1 Define the criteria and constraints of a design problem with sufficient precision to ensure a successful solution, taking into account relevant scientific principles and potential impacts on people and the natural environment that may limit possible solutions.

MS-ETS1-3 Analyze data from tests to determine the similarities and differences among several design solutions to identify the best characteristics of each that can be combined into a new solution to better meet the criteria for success.

Grades 9–12

HS-PS1-1

HS-PS1-8

HS-ETS1-1

HS-ETS1-3

 Trace Tool to the NGSS Go online to view the complete coverage of standards across lessons and units.

Differentiate Instruction

Differentiate with Technology

3D Periodic Trends

Have students spend time exploring one of the online three-dimensional periodic tables that show the element blocks with relative heights indicating differences in electronegativity, ionization energy, atomic radius, or electron affinity. Students will be able to observe how the properties change across a period or down a group. Suggest that students use the interactive periodic table to look for exceptions in the trends, and discuss how atomic structure might provide an explanation. You might also have students compare trends in two different properties.

Atomic Structure Podcasts

Set up a webpage where students, working in small groups, can upload short podcasts in which they describe a specific type of nuclear reaction. Encourage groups to carefully discuss the podcast content.

Nuclear Reaction Animation

Students should work in small groups and use presentation software or another computer program to construct an animation in which the user drags onscreen images of nuclei and other particles into place, causing fission, fusion, or radioactive decay.

Key Word Support

Key Words

element *Lesson 1*

atom *Lesson 1*

electron *Lesson 1*

nucleus *Lesson 1*

proton *Lesson 1*

neutron *Lesson 1*

atomic number *Lesson 1*

isotope *Lesson 1*

valence electron *Lesson 1*

atomic radius *Lesson 2*

ionization energy *Lesson 2*

electronegativity *Lesson 2*

nucleon *Lesson 3*

nuclide *Lesson 3*

radioactive decay *Lesson 3*

nuclear radiation *Lesson 3*

half-life *Lesson 3*

nuclear fission *Lesson 3*

nuclear fusion *Lesson 3*

Reinforcing Key Words

After students complete a lesson, have them write each key term on an index card with its definition on the back of the card. Then have students work in pairs and take turns quizzing each other by holding up either the word or its definition.

Academic Vocabulary

Challenge students to skim through the lessons and identify at least five words they think are important to understand when describing chemistry concepts—but which are not highlighted key words. Provide the example of the word *particle,* and explain how knowing its meaning can help students understand some of the key words. After students identify their words, create a class list on the board, and invite volunteers to define a word and explain its importance in chemistry.

English Language Learners

Help students learn the concepts in each lesson by pausing after each page or after each section of a lesson to summarize its concept. Write key words from the section on the board. Help students pronounce each term and define it. Then have students say or write several sentences to explain the important concepts in the section.

ELL

ELL teaching strategies in this unit include

Lesson 1 pp. 59, 66

Lesson 2 pp. 93, 99

Lesson 3 pp. 105, 109, 116

MTSS/RTI

Strategies for students who need extra support in this unit include

Lesson 1 pp. 61, 67, 73, 75, 78

Lesson 2 pp. 85, 95

Lesson 3 pp. 107, 118

Extension

Strategies for students who have mastered core content in this unit include

Lesson 1 pp. 63, 67, 74, 78

Lesson 2 pp. 90, 97

Lesson 3 pp. 107, 110, 118

Making Connections

Connections to Community

Use these opportunities for informal science learning to provide local context and to extend and enhance unit concepts.

At Home

PATTERNS Students may be surprised to realize the number of patterns they can identify around them. Have them look around their home and community for patterns in objects and things people do. For example, they may notice traffic patterns or patterns in floor tiles used in their home. Have them discuss the answer to this question with a partner: What are some ways patterns you identified around you are useful, similar to the way patterns in the periodic table are useful? *Use with Lessons 1 and 2.*

ORGANIZING OBJECTS Like Mendeleev, students organize various objects in their lives. Have them look around their home at the organization systems they use and identify the various methods of organization. For example, they may use color to organize their clothing and alphabetization to organize their books. Have them try to apply the organization system from one item to another. *Use with Lesson 2.*

In the Community

COMMUNITY IMPACT Many businesses rely on the worldwide trade in chemical elements. Trade in elements such as iron, gold, carbon, and silver has led to the exploration and exploitation of land areas and has affected entire cultures. Encourage students to examine how or why different elements are utilized for commerce in their community. For example, aluminum is collected because of its cost of production, corrosion resistance, durability, and ability to be reused almost indefinitely. Promote student discussions based on their findings. *Use with Lessons 1, 2, and 3.*

Culture

HOW MINING SHAPES CULTURES Have students examine the impact of mining and refining various materials on cultures around the world. Student pairs can choose a metal and follow it backward from its point of use to its refining to its mining. For example, many rare Earth elements are mined in China, much of the world's titanium is refined in Russia, and most aluminum is mined in African countries. Have students examine how the mining and refining of these elements can shape the culture in the surrounding areas. If students in your class have lived in areas where mining is prevalent, invite them to share their experiences. *Use with Lessons 1 and 3.*

Home Letters Use these letters to engage family members with unit concepts.

Collaborate

Opportunities for students to work collaboratively in this unit:

Accessing Prior Knowledge pp. 58, 96

Discussion pp. 65, 70, 84, 86

Say Something pp. 94, 123

Think-Pair-Share, Draw-Pair-Share pp. 66, 76, 92, 108

Which Is False? pp. 75, 97

Connections to Other Disciplines

Opportunities to connect to other content areas in this unit:

Engineering Connection pp. 63, 117

Industry Connection p. 98

Language Arts Connection p. 67, 79, 91, 98, 99, 117, 124

Math Connection, Statistics Connection pp. 68, 97, 109, 113

Physics Connection pp. 62, 88

3D Unit Planning

Lesson 1 Modeling Atomic Structure pp. 57–82

Overview

Objective Students investigate and model atomic structure, describe atoms using various numbers, and use the periodic table to predict the properties and behavior of an element.

SEP Developing and Using Models
SEP Constructing Explanations and Designing Solutions
SEP Scientific Knowledge is Open to Revision in Light of New Evidence
DCI **PS1.A** Structure and Properties of Matter
DCI **PS2.B** Types of Interactions
CCC Patterns
CCC Scale, Proportion, and Quantity
CCC Scientific Knowledge Assumes an Order and Consistency in Natural Systems

Math and **English Language Arts** standards and features are detailed on lesson planning pages.

Print and **Online** Student Editions	**Explore Online**
ENGAGE	**Investigative Phenomenon** p. 57 **Can You Explain the Phenomenon?** How do you think matter in the atmosphere can cause a phenomenon such as the northern lights?	**ELA Handbook**
EXPLORE/ EXPLAIN	**Comparing Elements Based on Their Properties** p. 58 Exploring Reactivity **Investigating Atomic Structure** p. 62 **Using Numbers to Describe Atoms** p. 66 **Math Connection** Explaining Average Atomic Mass Identifying Elements Using a Flame Test p. 69 **Modeling Electron Configurations** p. 73	**Hands-On Lab Worksheets** **Hands-On Lab Teacher Support** **Lab Safety Handbook** **Video** Charged Particles **Video** Cathode Ray Tube **Animation** Gold Foil Experiment **Math Handbook**
ELABORATE	**Take It Further** p. 78 Mass Spectrometry	**Take It Further** Practice with Electron Configurations Evidence for the Atomic Model Cryo-Electron Microscopy
EVALUATE	**Lesson Self-Check** p. 80	**Lesson Quiz**

 Hands-On Lab Planning

Exploring Reactivity

⏱ 45 minutes
👥 Pairs

Objective Students carry out an investigation to compare the reactivity of aluminum, magnesium, and zinc.

Materials
- aluminum, small sample
- hydrochloric acid solution, 1 M
- magnesium, small sample
- test tube rack
- test tubes (3)
- zinc, small sample

Advance Preparation Arrange access to a fume hood, or have students conduct the investigation in a well-ventilated room.

Identifying Elements Using a Flame Test

⏱ 90 minutes
👥 Small Groups

Objective Students design an experiment to compare differences in the color of light emitted when metals in solution are heated in a flame. Students then apply their results to identify the metal present in an unknown solution based on the color of its flame when heated.

Materials
- beaker, 250 mL
- Bunsen burner
- crucible tongs
- distilled water
- flame test wire, 5 cm
- glass test plate or well plate
- hydrochloric acid solution, 1 M
- Test Solutions, 0.05 M: calcium chloride, lithium sulfate, potassium sulfate, sodium sulfate, strontium chloride, unknown solution

Advance Preparation Prepare the 1.0 M HCl solution, the test solutions, and the unknown solution. Prepare lithium sulfate as the unknown solution, or prepare various unknown solutions.

3D Unit Planning, continued

Lesson 2 Investigating Patterns in the Periodic Table pp. 83–102

Overview

Objective Students explore patterns in the periodic table and use them to make predictions about the behavior of elements.

SEP Developing and Using Models
SEP Scientific Investigations Use a Variety of Methods
SEP Scientific Knowledge is Based on Empirical Evidence
SEP Scientific Knowledge is Open to Revision in Light of New Evidence
DCI **PS1.A** Structure and Properties of Matter
DCI **ETS1.B** Developing Possible Solutions
CCC Science is a Human Endeavor
CCC Patterns

Math and **English Language Arts** standards and features are detailed on lesson planning pages.

Print and Online Student Editions

Explore Online ▶

ENGAGE

Investigative Phenomenon p. 83
Can You Explain the Phenomenon? How do you think scientists can use properties of existing elements to predict the existence of synthetic elements?

ELA Handbook

EXPLORE/ EXPLAIN

 Modeling Periodic Trends p. 84
Predicting the Properties of Elements p. 86
🔬 The Noble Gases
Patterns in Atomic Size p. 90
Patterns in Ionization Energy p. 92
Patterns in Electronegativity p. 95
🔬 Developing Halogen Bulbs

ELA Handbook
Hands-On Lab Worksheets
Hands-On Lab Teacher
    Support
Lab Safety Handbook
Math Handbook

ELABORATE

Take It Further p. 99
    Careers in Science Analytical Chemist

Take It Further
Periodic Trends in History
Discovering New Elements
🔬 The Mendeleev Lab
    of 1869
Hands-On Lab Worksheet
Hands-On Lab Teacher
    Support
Lab Safety Handbook

EVALUATE

Lesson Self-Check p. 100

Lesson Quiz

Hands-On Lab Planning

Modeling Periodic Trends

⏱ 45 minutes
👥 Small Groups

Objective Students make a model of a periodic table based on colors of paint chips rather than on reactivity of elements. They construct explanations about the patterns of properties in the periodic table.

Materials
• set of paint chip cards

Advance Preparation Place paint chips of similar colors in a bag for each group. Leave gaps in the colors for students to discover, as Mendeleev did when arranging elements.

Additional Downloadable Lab Option

The Mendeleev Lab of 1869

⏱ 45 minutes
👥 Small Groups

Objective Student use their knowledge of the periodic table to determine the identity of each of the nine unknown elements in this activity.

Lesson 3 Analyzing Nuclear Reactions pp. 103–128

Overview

Objective Students analyze the forces operating at the nuclear scale and how those forces affect matter.

SEP Asking Questions and Defining Problems
SEP Developing and Using Models
SEP Planning and Carrying Out Investigations
SEP Constructing Explanations and Designing Solutions
DCI **PS1.C** Nuclear Processes
DCI **ETS1.A** Defining and Delimiting Engineering Problems
DCI **ETS1.B** Developing Possible Solutions
CCC Energy and Matter
CCC Scientific Knowledge Assumes an Order and Consistency in Natural Systems
CCC Influence of Engineering, Technology, and Science on Society and the Natural World

Math and **English Language Arts** standards and features are detailed on lesson planning pages.

Print and Online Student Editions

Explore Online ▶

ENGAGE	**Investigative Phenomenon** p. 103 **ELA Handbook** **Can You Explain the Phenomenon?** Why do you think atoms in the body usually do not emit radiation?
EXPLORE/ EXPLAIN	**Explaining Nuclear Stability** p. 104 **Investigating Radioactive Decay** p. 108 Modeling Radioactive Half-Lives **Analyzing Nuclear Fission and Fusion** p. 116 **Case Study: Exploring Nuclear Energy** p. 119
ELABORATE	**Take It Further** p. 125 **Careers in Engineering** Environmental Engineer
EVALUATE	**Lesson Self-Check** pp. 126

ENGAGE

EXPLORE/ EXPLAIN
Modeling Fusion
Hands-On Lab Worksheets
Hands-On Lab Teacher Support
Lab Safety Handbook
Math Handbook

ELABORATE
Take It Further
Nuclear Disasters
Half-Life and Radiometric Dating
Nuclear Medicine

EVALUATE
Lesson Quiz

 Hands-On Lab Planning

Modeling Radioactive Half-Lives

⏱ 45 minutes
👥 Small Groups

Objective Students use a model to explore probability patterns related to nuclear decay.

Materials
- beans, color 1 (100)
- beans, color 2 (100)
- box or self-sealing bag

Additional Downloadable Lab Option
Modeling Fusion

⏱ 90 minutes
👥 Small Groups

Objective Students develop models to describe a series of fusion reactions that forms helium from hydrogen in stars.

3D Unit Planning, continued

Assessment Planning

Preassessment

Assessment Guide, Unit Pretest

Formative Assessment

Interactive Worktext: Explorations, Lesson Self-Check

Summative Assessment

Assessment Guide, Lesson Quiz

Interactive Worktext: Unit Performance Task, p. 138

Interactive Worktext: Unit Practice and Review, p. 139

Assessment Guide, Unit Test and Modified Unit Test

HMH Field Trips
powered by

 Google Expeditions

Go to **HMH Google Expeditions** in the Resources tab on **Ed: Your Friend in Learning** for 3D, 360-degree experiences to share with your students and a Teacher Guide for you.

Teacher Notes

Unit Project

Overview and Planning

Designing an Atomic Model

3D Learning Objective

Students develop and use models to explore the structure of an atom.

Students develop and use models to describe an atom and its substructure, a nucleus surrounded by electrons. They use their models to illustrate how the periodic table can predict the properties of elements based on their atomic structure. Students also use their models to illustrate the conservation of mass and energy during a nuclear reaction. Students incorporate peer feedback to compare, evaluate, and improve their models.

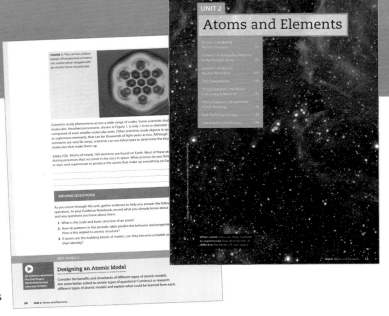

NGSS Focus

This project supports building student mastery of Performance Expectations **HS-PS1-1** and **HS-PS1-8**. Students use their models to show how the periodic table arranges elements according to their properties. They also develop models to illustrate changes in the nucleus of the atom and the energy released during a nuclear reaction.

Science and Engineering Practices
- Developing and Using Models

Disciplinary Core Ideas
- **PS1.A** Structure and Properties of Matter
- **PS1.C** Nuclear Processes

Crosscutting Concepts
- Patterns
- Energy and Matter

Classroom Management

👥 Individuals or Small Groups

🕐 Three 45-minute class periods

Suggested Materials
- balloons
- beads
- cardboard
- colored paper
- duct tape or masking tape
- foam balls, various sizes
- foil, sheets
- glue
- marbles
- markers
- meter stick or metric rulers
- scissors
- string
- toothpicks
- wire, heavy gauge

Safety
- Check to see if any students have allergies to the adhesives used in the duct tape. Limit the contact these students have with the tape, or pair them with students who are not allergic.

Suggested Resources

- **RSC:** The Royal Society of Chemists has put together videos describing all elements, their properties, and how they are isolated.

- **Nobel Prizes:** Discover how the modern understanding of the atom developed along with the important discoveries that helped the model evolve.

▶ Go Online

Go online to download the teacher version of the student worksheet for this unit project, which includes additional questions, sample answers, and additional scaffolding to help students use evidence and reasoning to support their claims.

Unit Project, continued

Getting Started

Introducing the Project

Prepare students for their investigation by asking the following questions:

- **Will your models be to scale?**
- **How will your models differ for the three parts of the project?**
- **How will your models represent how energy is released during nuclear reactions?**
- **How will your models show how the composition of atomic nuclei change during nuclear reactions?**

Student Deliverables

A **student worksheet** is available to help students in planning and completing the project. Students can turn in their worksheets, or they can be assessed on a final lab report, their model, and/or final presentation explaining their project. Evidence Notebook prompts throughout the unit refer to the Unit Project to help keep its connection to the investigative phenomenon present in students' minds.

In addition to the worksheet, students will produce and design an atomic model. A report should accompany the model, explaining the rationale behind why the model was designed as it was. Finally, students will provide an evaluation of the model from their classmates.

Scoring Rubric for Unit Project	
	Predictions of changes in atomic structure during a nuclear reaction are correct and supported with adequate evidence and reasoning, such as an explanation of the reaction and the particles formed.
	The model focuses on the change in atomic structure. The representation of components of each type of atom is correct and creative.
	The student's choices concerning materials and method of modeling a reaction reflect critical thinking about the model's purpose.
	The evaluation of each model includes adequate consideration of peer feedback. If the Extend portion of the project is completed, student identifies at least one way to improve the model(s).
	The concluding scientific argument presents a clear claim that is supported by compelling evidence and adequate reasoning.

Guiding Students on Project Planning

Once students understand the project goals and their deliverables, the next step is for them to conduct research and develop their atomic models.

- **What type of models will you develop?**
  Students can look online to get ideas of the types of models they might choose to make. You may wish to display images or 3D models to spur their thinking, but encourage individuality in their choices.

- **What type of model do you think will effectively show the components of an atomic nucleus and how the nuclei change during a nuclear reaction?**
  Students could suggest a 3D model or a computer simulation that identifies the components of the nuclei and the energy released during a reaction.

- **How could you gather data about your model?**
  Students might suggest looking at government and educational webpages or the webpages of companies that perform research on their selected model.

Be sure to review and approve project plans before students begin. The Unit Project Worksheet can be used for formal approval.

Differentiate Instruction

MTSS/RTI For students who are having trouble visualizing what their models should look like, suggest that they work in pairs to do online research to find helpful images of atoms. Encourage students to write in a journal or their Evidence Notebook about why their efforts in some aspects of the Unit Project succeeded or failed and what they might do differently another time.

Extension Have students research the structure of the atom in the quantum model. Students can examine and model our current understanding of the atom. Have them investigate how and why this knowledge is changing technology.

UNIT 2

Atoms and Elements

@Houghton Mifflin Harcourt Publishing Company • Image Credits: @NASA Goddard Space Flight Center

When some stars die, they explode as supernovas that send atoms of different elements off into space.

The learning experiences in this unit prepare students for mastery of

Performance Expectations

HS-PS1-1 Use the periodic table as a model to predict the relative properties of elements based on the patterns of electrons in the outermost energy level of atoms.

HS-PS1-8 Develop models to illustrate the changes in the composition of the nucleus of the atom and the energy released during the processes of fission, fusion, and radioactive decay.

ETS1-1 Analyze a major global challenge to specify qualitative and quantitative criteria and constraints for solutions that account for societal needs and wants.

HS-ETS1-3 Evaluate a solution to a complex real-world problem based on prioritized criteria and trade-offs that account for a range of constraints, including cost, safety, reliability, and aesthetics, as well as possible social, cultural, and environmental impacts.

Explore Online

In addition to the print resources, the following resources are available online to support this unit.

Lesson 1 Modeling Atomic Structure
- Online Student Edition
- Lesson Quiz

Lesson 2 Investigating Patterns in the Periodic Table
- Online Student Edition
- Lesson Quiz

Lesson 3 Analyzing Nuclear Reactions
- Online Student Edition
- Lesson Quiz

Unit Performance Task

Unit Test

Unit Prerequisite Knowledge

Students should understand these concepts before starting the unit:

- All matter is made of atoms. An element is made of one type of atom.
- The periodic table organizes elements based on patterns of behavior.
- Elements combine in predictable ratios to form molecules.
- Matter cannot be created or destroyed.

Collaborate

Driving Questions You may wish to have partners discuss their initial thoughts about the Driving Questions for this unit before you discuss the questions as a class. Encourage students to record the questions and their initial responses in their Evidence Notebook, where they can revise and add to their answers as they work through the unit.

Anchoring Phenomenon

Designing an Atomic Model

SEP Developing and Using Models

An anchoring phenomenon connects student learning across the lessons in a unit. The Unit Project serves as an anchoring phenomenon as students develop models and use them to explain what they discover about atomic structure and patterns in the periodic table in Lessons 1 and 2 and about forces within atoms in Lesson 3.

Tips on Cultivating Questions Arrange students in a circle. Have them toss a beach ball to one another. After a random number of tosses, say "Stop!" The person with the ball has to ask a question. Have the last person who asked questions record them on the board.

1 Students may know that nuclear reactions occur within stars. This is what gives stars their shine. These nuclear reactions form atoms of various elements, and when a star explodes as a supernova, these atoms are sent off into space.

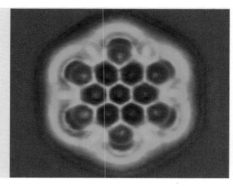

FIGURE 1: The carbon-carbon bonds of hexabenzocoronene are visible when imaged with an atomic force microscope.

Scientists study phenomena across a wide range of scales. Some scientists study tiny molecules. Hexabenzocoronene, shown in Figure 1, is only 1.4 nm in diameter and composed of even smaller molecular units. Other scientists study objects in space, such as supernova remnants, that can be thousands of light-years across. Although supernova remnants are very far away, scientists can use telescopes to determine the tiny atoms and molecules that make them up.

 ANALYZE Atoms of nearly 100 elements are found on Earth. Most of these atoms formed during processes that occurred in the stars in space. What process do you think occurred in stars and supernovae to produce the atoms that make up everything on Earth?

_____

_____

_____

DRIVING QUESTIONS

As you move through the unit, gather evidence to help you answer the following questions. In your Evidence Notebook, record what you already know about these topics and any questions you have about them.

1. What is the scale and basic structure of an atom?
2. How do patterns in the periodic table predict the behavior and properties of elements? How is this related to atomic structure?
3. If atoms are the building blocks of matter, can they become unstable or change their identity?

UNIT PROJECT

Go online to download the Unit Project Worksheet to help plan your project.

Designing an Atomic Model

Consider the benefits and drawbacks of different types of atomic models. Are some better suited to certain types of questions? Construct or research different types of atomic models and explain what could be learned from each.

©Houghton Mifflin Harcourt Publishing Company • Image Credits: ©IBM Research/Science Source

Language Development

Use the lessons in this unit to complete the chart and expand your understanding of the science concepts.

TERM: nucleus

Definition	Example

Similar Term	Phrase

TERM: atomic number

Definition	Example

Similar Term	Phrase

TERM: valence electron

Definition	Example

Similar Term	Phrase

TERM: ionization energy

Definition	Example

Similar Term	Phrase

Language Development

The summary chart graphic organizer allows students to practice using unit vocabulary to convey meaning and to communicate clearly. The chart shown, which is continued on the next page, may not include every unit vocabulary term.

Using the Chart As you encounter a highlighted vocabulary term, direct students to fill in the corresponding boxes in the summary chart. Students should always fill in the Definition box, but they need not fill in all others. Students can write a cognate from their home language in the Similar Term box. Students whose home language is English can fill in a synonym or word with the same root (such as *atomic* for the word *atom*). Accept all reasonable answers.

If desired, hand out to students a blank summary chart. Provide the starting words or have students select their own from the list of unit vocabulary. Work with students to complete the charts for each word. You may also ask students to work in pairs and then share and compare their work with that of their classmates.

Students can explore all vocabulary terms in the Online Glossary. A multilingual glossary is also available online.

SAMPLE ANSWERS

nucleus: an atom's central region, which is made up of protons and neutrons; a helium-4 nucleus has two protons and two neutrons; núcleo; An atomic nucleus is composed of protons and neutrons.

atomic number: the number of protons in the nucleus of an atom; the atomic number for carbon is 6; número atómico; Oxygen isotopes all have the same atomic number.

valence electron: an electron that is found in the outermost shell of an atom; all Group 1 metals have one valence electron; electrón de valencia; In an ionic bond, valence electrons are transferred from the metal's valence shell to the nonmetal's valence shell.

ionization energy: the energy required to remove an electron from an atom or ion; alkali metals have a low ionization energy; energía de ionización; Halogens have very high ionization energies, making it hard for them to donate electrons.

SAMPLE ANSWERS

electronegativity: a measure of the ability of an atom in a chemical compound to attract electrons; fluorine has the highest electronegativity of any element; electronegatividad; Metals have a low affinity for electrons as compared with nonmetals because non-metals have much higher electronegativities than metals do.

radioactive decay: the disintegration of an unstable atomic nucleus into one or more different types of atoms or isotopes, accompanied by the emission of radiation, the nuclear capture or ejection of electrons, or fission; alpha decay, beta decay, and gamma decay; desintegración radiactiva; The radioactive decay of carbon-14 produces nitrogen-14 with the release of a beta particle.

nuclear fission: the process by which a nucleus splits into two or more fragments and releases neutrons and energy; the fission of uranium-235 when a neutron strikes it; fisión nuclear; Plutonium-239 undergoes nuclear fission to produce tellurium-137 and molybdenum-100.

nuclear fusion: the process by which nuclei of small atoms combine to form a new, more massive nucleus; the process releases energy; hydrogen isotopes in the sun undergo fusion to produce helium; fusión nuclear; The nuclear fusion of helium-3 and helium-4 produces beryllium-4.

TERM: electronegativity

Definition	Example

Similar Term	Phrase

TERM: radioactive decay

Definition	Example

Similar Term	Phrase

TERM: nuclear fission

Definition	Example

Similar Term	Phrase

TERM: nuclear fusion

Definition	Example

Similar Term	Phrase

Modeling Atomic Structure

Building to the Performance Expectations

The learning experiences in this lesson prepare students for mastery of
HS-PS1-1 Use the periodic table as a model to predict the relative properties of elements based on the patterns of electrons in the outermost energy level of atoms.

 Trace Tool to the NGSS
Go online to view the complete coverage of standards across lessons, units, and grade levels.

 SEP Science & Engineering Practices

Developing and Using Models
Use a model to predict the relationships between systems or between components of a system.

Constructing Explanations and Designing Solutions
Construct and revise an explanation based on valid and reliable evidence obtained from a variety of sources (including students' own investigations, models, theories, simulations, peer review) and the assumption that theories and laws that describe the natural world operate today as they did in the past and will continue to do so in the future.

Scientific Knowledge is Based on Empirical Evidence
Science includes the process of coordinating patterns of evidence with current theory.

 **DCI** Disciplinary Core Ideas

PS1.A Structure and Properties of Matter
Each atom has a charged substructure consisting of a nucleus, which is made of protons and neutrons, surrounded by electrons. (HS-PS1-1)

PS1.A Structure and Properties of Matter
The periodic table orders elements horizontally by the number of protons in the atom's nucleus and places those with similar chemical properties in columns. The repeating patterns of this table reflect patterns of outer electron states. (HS-PS1-1)

PS2.B Types of Interactions
Attraction and repulsion between electric charges at the atomic scale explain the structure, properties, and transformations of matter, as well as the contact forces between material objects. (HS-PS1-1)

 **CCC** Crosscutting Concepts

Patterns
Different patterns may be observed at each of the scales at which a system is studied and can provide evidence for causality in explanations of phenomena.

Scale, Proportion, and Quantity
Using the concept of orders of magnitude allows one to understand how a model at one scale relates to a model at another scale.

Scientific Knowledge Assumes an Order and Consistency in Natural Systems
Science assumes the universe is a vast single system in which basic laws are consistent.

MATH STANDARDS

MP.2 Reason abstractly and quantitatively.

ELA STANDARDS

RST.9-10.7 Translate quantitative or technical information expressed in words in a text into visual form (e.g., a table or chart) and translate information expressed visually or mathematically (e.g., in an equation) into words.

WHST.9-12.5 Develop and strengthen writing as needed by planning, revising, editing, rewriting, or trying a new approach, focusing on addressing what is most significant for a specific purpose and audience.

Supporting All Students, All Standards

Integrating the Three Dimensions

In this lesson, students explore the development of models (**SEP Developing and Using Models**) that represent the structure of atoms at different scales (**CCC Scale, Proportion, and Quantity**). They learn that an atom has a central nucleus, composed of positively charged protons and neutral neutrons, around which negatively charged electrons move (**DCI PS1.A**). Students learn that elements have repeating patterns (**CCC Patterns**) in their outer electrons that account for their placement on the periodic table (**DCI PS1.A**). Electrostatic attractions and repulsions between like and unlike charges help influence the stability of an atom (**DCI PS2.B**). Students evaluate evidence and reasoning to construct and revise an explanation based on valid and reliable evidence behind currently accepted explanations (**SEP Constructing Explanations and Designing Solutions**) of observable phenomena related to atomic structure. This assumes the universe is a vast, single system in which basic laws are consistent (**CCC Scientific Knowledge Assumes an Order and Consistency in Natural Systems**).

Preassessment

Have students complete the unit pretest or see the Assessment Guide.

Build on Prior Knowledge

Have students list what they know about atomic structure. After they have made a comprehensive list, ask them to share their list with a partner and discuss any differences. Create a classroom list that can be added to over the course of this lesson.

You may want to review the following concepts:
- An atom is the basic particle that makes up an element.
- The atoms of an element are unique to that element.
- The basic components of an atom are positively charged protons and neutral neutrons in the nucleus as well as negatively charged electrons surrounding the nucleus.

Professional Development Go online to view **Professional Development videos** with strategies to integrate CCCs and SEPs, including the ones used in this lesson.

Content Background

The basic structure of an atom is a nucleus composed of protons and neutrons with electrons moving in the area surrounding the nucleus. Electrostatic attraction between the positively charged protons and negatively charged electrons holds the electrons near the nucleus. Within the nucleus, however, protons have an electrostatic repulsion for one another. This force is overcome by the strong nuclear force that acts between protons and neutrons and holds the nucleus together.

A series of important discoveries over time led to changes in the scientific model of the atom. In the early 1800s, English chemist John Dalton argued for the existence of atoms based on the fact that elements in chemical compounds are always present in whole-number ratios (the law of multiple proportions). But Dalton saw atoms as resembling tiny billiard balls. In the late 1800s, English physicist J. J. Thomson discovered electrons in experiments with cathode-ray tubes. He also concluded that electrons must be present in atoms. The structure of atoms, therefore, was more complex than previously thought.

The first important clue to atomic structure came with Ernest Rutherford's gold foil experiment, which showed that most of the mass in atoms must be concentrated in a very small space, the nucleus. The nucleus contains all positive charge in an atom. Electrons are now understood as occupying probabilistic regions of space rather than specific locations.

Differentiate Instruction

KEY WORDS

- element
- atom
- electron
- nucleus
- proton
- neutron
- atomic number
- isotope
- valence electron

ELL SUPPORT

Have students copy the list of key terms and write definitions in their own words as they encounter each term in the lesson. Have students work in pairs to write a sentence correctly using each term after agreeing on its definition.

ENGAGE: Investigative Phenomenon

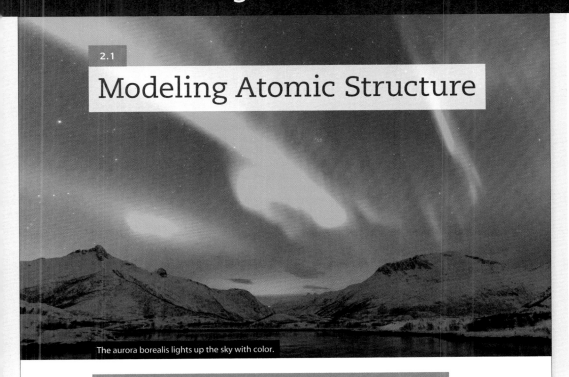

2.1
Modeling Atomic Structure

The aurora borealis lights up the sky with color.

© Houghton Mifflin Harcourt Publishing Company • Image Credits: ©Sjoerd van der Wal/iStock/Getty Images Plus

CAN YOU EXPLAIN THE PHENOMENON?

At certain times of year, a phenomenon called the aurora polaris lights up the sky in areas near the northern and southern poles. When it occurs, different colored lights can be seen moving around in the sky. Sometimes only one color is seen, but at other times several colors appear. The lights are usually pink, green, yellow, blue, violet, red, and, less often, orange and white. They may appear as a steady glow or as constantly changing sources of light. In the northern latitudes, this phenomenon is known as the aurora borealis or northern lights. In southern latitudes, they are called aurora australis or southern lights.

1 APPLY How do you think matter in the atmosphere can cause a phenomenon such as the northern lights?

_____

_____

_____

_____

_____

2 **Evidence Notebook** As you explore the lesson, gather evidence to explain how atomic structure is related to the different colors displayed as part of the aurora polaris phenomenon.

Lesson 1 Modeling Atomic Structure **57**

Lesson Objective

Students investigate and model atomic structure, describe atoms using various numbers, and use the periodic table to predict the properties and behavior of an element.

Cultivating Student Questions

Have students look at the photo of the aurora polaris. Prompt them to ask all questions that come to mind about how the aurora polaris can shine brightly in the night sky. Record the questions on chart paper, and then sort the questions based on their focus. With students, narrow the questions down to ones that directly relate to the learning objective. Have students reflect on this list throughout the lesson and check off questions as they are answered.

Can You Explain the Phenomenon?

The Investigative Phenomenon is the focus of the lesson. Students are asked to record their initial thoughts about what causes the aurora polaris. These lights are not like rainbows, which are caused by sunlight passing through raindrops, because they are visible when the sun is not shining. Students will collect evidence related to this phenomenon throughout the lesson. They will revisit the question at the end of the lesson and use what they have learned to explain how atomic structure is related to the aurora polaris.

1 **Sample answer:** Something in the air might react with another substance, and particles in the air might change in some way that produces the light.

Evidence Notebook

2 The topic of the aurora polaris will be revisited throughout this lesson. Students should record evidence that can be used to support a claim for how atomic structure is related to this phenomenon. Students will learn that electrons give off energy in the form of light when they move from a higher energy level to a lower energy level. The color of the light is related to the amount of energy given off.

EXPLORATION 1 Comparing Elements Based on Their Properties

3D Learning Objective

Students identify **patterns** in the properties of elements and **construct explanations** for why these patterns occur. They begin exploring the idea that **properties of matter** are related to the structure of atoms.

Everyday phenomena discussed throughout the Explorations of the lesson can often be used to connect the science content to students' personal experiences.

 Patterns

As students read about the properties of metals, nonmetals, and metalloids, emphasize that the properties are generalities. Metals, for example, are often described as highly reactive, but in fact they have a range of reactivities. Metals are also generally described as malleable, but there are a few exceptions. Metalloids have found wide use in the electronics industry because their conductivity can be controlled by means of "doping" with other elements or by exposure to heat and electric fields.

 Collaborate

Accessing Prior Knowledge Divide the class into small groups, and have students discuss what *reactivity* means in an **everyday phenomenon.** Have them look at **Figure 1**, but tell them they should not yet read the text that accompanies it. After a few minutes, have a representative from each group explain to the class the group's ideas about reactivity.

1 **Sample answer:** Magnesium appears to react most strongly with the acid because it is giving off a lot of bubbles. Zinc gives off some bubbles, and copper does not appear to give off any. These elements might differ in properties related to reactivity.

2 **Sample answer:** The silverware in the cafeteria is made of metal because it is shiny and can be easily bent. Plates must be made of nonmetals because they are brittle and dull. The lead in my pencil is also dull and brittle, so it must be a nonmetal.

Comparing Elements Based on Their Properties

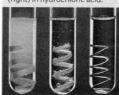

FIGURE 1: Magnesium (left), zinc (center), and copper (right) in hydrochloric acid.

The gases in Earth's atmosphere are an example of matter in the Earth system. Matter can be classified as either a pure substance or a mixture. The metals shown in Figure 1 are all pure substances.

1 **Collaborate** Discuss the following with a partner: In Figure 1, three different metals are combined with an acid. What differences do you notice in the way these metals react? What do you think causes these differences in reactivity?

The metals shown in Figure 1 are all elements, or pure substances that cannot be broken down into simpler substances. The particles that make up these elements are called atoms. Each element contains only one type of atom.

Classifying Elements

Certain groups of elements have similar properties and can be classified together. The most general way to classify elements is as metals, nonmetals, or metalloids. *Metals* are shiny, and they are generally good conductors of electricity and heat. They can be bent or hammered into sheets easily, and almost all metals are solid at room temperature.

In contrast, *nonmetals* are generally very poor conductors of electricity and heat. Many nonmetals, such as nitrogen, oxygen, fluorine, and chlorine, are gases at room temperature. The nonmetals that are solids at room temperature, such as carbon, phosphorus, sulfur, selenium, and iodine, tend to be brittle and dull rather than shiny.

FIGURE 2: Elements are categorized into broad categories based on similar properties.

a Metals   **b** Nonmetals   **c** Metalloids

Metalloids have characteristics of metals and nonmetals. Metalloids are solids at room temperature. They are not as brittle as nonmetals. Metalloids do conduct electric current but not as well as metals. The "semiconducting" properties of metalloids, such as boron and silicon, make them useful in computer chips.

2 **APPLY** Describe some examples of metals and nonmetals from your daily life. How can you tell which type of elements are metals and which are not?

_____

_____

_____

Hands-On Lab

Exploring Reactivity

Observing the behavior of an element allows chemists to draw conclusions about the properties of the atoms that form that element. Reactivity is a measure of how readily an element undergoes a chemical reaction. In this lab, you will react three metal elements with an acid and draw conclusions about the relative reactivities of the metals.

The metals you will test in this lab are aluminum, magnesium, and zinc. When these metals react with an acid, such as hydrochloric acid, hydrogen gas is given off as a product. The rate of hydrogen production can therefore be used to draw conclusions about the relative reactivities of the metals.

RESEARCH QUESTION What can observing properties such as reactivity tell us about the atoms that make up an element?

3 MAKE A CLAIM

Which metal do you think will react most vigorously when placed in hydrochloric acid? Explain your thinking.

_____

_____

_____

_____

_____

_____

MATERIALS

- indirectly vented chemical splash goggles, nonlatex apron, nitrile gloves
- aluminum, small sample
- hydrochloric acid solution, 1 M
- magnesium, small sample
- test tube rack
- test tubes (3)
- zinc, small sample

SAFETY INFORMATION

- Wear indirectly vented chemical splash goggles, a nonlatex apron, and nitrile gloves during the setup, hands-on, and takedown segments of the activity.
- The reaction between a metal and hydrochloric acid gives off hydrogen gas. Hydrogen gas and fumes from hydrochloric acid should not be inhaled, so these reactions should be completed inside a fume hood or in a well-ventilated room.
- Use caution when working with glassware, which can shatter and cut skin.
- Hydrochloric acid (HCl) is a strong acid that is highly corrosive to skin and other tissues. During a reaction with metals, inhalation of the fumes can cause irritation of the respiratory tract and shortness of breath, and the hydrogen released should be kept away from open flames.
- Tell your teacher immediately if you spill chemicals on yourself, the table, or floor.
- Follow your teacher's instructions for disposing of all waste materials.
- Wash your hands with soap and water immediately after completing this activity.

indirectly vented chemical splash goggles

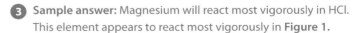

Differentiate Instruction

ELL Support Rotate among groups as they make observations during the lab. Ask questions that provide them with an opportunity to give their ideas orally about what is happening to the metals.

Hands-On Lab 👥 Pairs ⏱ 45 minutes

Exploring Reactivity

SEP Constructing Explanations and Designing Solutions

Students carry out an investigation to compare the reactivity of aluminum, magnesium, and zinc.

Advance Preparation Prepare 1 M HCl, and divide it into small containers for groups to use. Arrange for all groups to have access to a fume hood, or have students conduct the investigation in a well-ventilated room. If possible, lightly sand the metals to remove the oxides that naturally form on and adhere to their surfaces.

Safety Information / Materials Alert Hydrochloric acid is a strong acid that is highly corrosive to skin and other tissues. During a reaction with metals, inhalation of the fumes can cause irritation of the respiratory tract and shortness of breath. The hydrogen released should be kept away from open flames.

Demonstration Perform a splint test as a demonstration to show that hydrogen is produced in this reaction. Burn a wooden splint in a flame for a few seconds, and then blow out the flame so that the splint is glowing. Place the splint over a test tube as the reaction occurs. There should be a popping sound, indicating that a flammable gas is given off. In this case, that gas is hydrogen.

CCC Patterns

Before students start the investigation, discuss the types of observations they might make about the reactivity of the three metals. Have students discuss what they would observe if a metal is highly reactive, mildly reactive, or nonreactive.

3 Sample answer: Magnesium will react most vigorously in HCl. This element appears to react most vigorously in **Figure 1.**

DCI PS1.A Structure and Properties of Matter

Point out to students that the metal in each test tube is a solid and the hydrochloric acid is a liquid. Ask them what they think the bubbles are composed of. Some students may incorrectly assume the bubbles are air, but remind them that air is a mixture of substances. Point out that the bubbles must come from the metal and the hydrochloric acid. Students may then conclude that the bubbles must be hydrogen. Commonly, an acid reacts with a reactive metal to produce hydrogen gas and a salt.

Claims, Evidence, and Reasoning

If students have difficulty thinking about what claims they can make and what evidence they have to support the claim, encourage them to consider the observations they made and what they can infer from the observations. For example, students observed the production of hydrogen, which indicates that a new product is being made. Therefore, the greater the hydrogen production, the more reactive the metal is.

1 Students' answers will reflect their thinking about how the properties of matter are related to atomic structure. Students may explain that atoms of different elements have a different structure or different numbers of subatomic particles.

2 **Sample answer:** Magnesium has the highest relative reactivity when combined with hydrochloric acid, and aluminum has the lowest. When the metals were combined with the acid, the rate of bubbling was the greatest for magnesium and lowest for aluminum. Bubbles are a sign that hydrogen is being produced, which means that a chemical reaction is occurring. Therefore, the rate of bubbling can be used to infer relative reactivity.

PLAN THE INVESTIGATION

1. In your Evidence Notebook, write a procedure and safety plan for this investigation. For each reaction, you should combine a small piece of metal with a few drops of hydrochloric acid in a test tube. As part of your procedure, explain what variables should be kept constant and how you will ensure that this happens.

2. Draw a data table in your Evidence Notebook to record the relative reactivities of each metal element. Because hydrogen is a product of these reactions, you can use the rate of hydrogen production and the volume of hydrogen bubbles produced to infer relative reactivity. Develop a rating system to use when quantifying the relative reactivity of each metal based on hydrogen production.

3. Have your teacher approve your procedure, safety plan, and data table before you carry out your investigation.

---

1 ANALYZE

How do you think the atoms that make up the most reactive metal you tested differ from the atoms of the least reactive metal?

_____

_____

_____

_____

---

2 DRAW CONCLUSIONS

Write a conclusion that addresses each of the points below.

Claim Which of the metal elements that you tested has the highest relative reactivity when combined with hydrochloric acid? Which has the lowest?

Evidence Give specific evidence from your data and other observations you have made to support your claim.

Reasoning Explain how the evidence you gave supports your claim. Describe, in detail, the connections between the evidence you cited and the argument you are making.

_____

_____

_____

_____

_____

_____

_____

_____

_____

_____

_____

Understanding Atoms

People's understanding of the atom has changed over time. The idea that matter is made up of smaller, individual units was proposed many centuries ago. Empirical evidence to support the existence of atoms did not come until much later. By the mid 1800s, most scientists agreed that each element was made up of a unique type of atom. However, they saw atoms as tiny, indivisible balls, differing only in mass.

 MODEL Draw a diagram to show how a scientist in the 1800s might have modeled atoms. Include different types of atoms in your diagram and indicate how they differ in this model.

The theory that atoms were indivisible units differing only in mass did not fully explain the patterns that scientists observed in the properties of elements. For example, the metals you tested in the lab react with hydrochloric acid, but not with water. But some metals, such as sodium and potassium, are so reactive that they ignite when they are combined with water. Then there are elements, such as the gases shown in Figure 3, that almost never react with other substances. These gases are part of a group of elements known as the noble gases.

Because the noble gases appeared not to have any chemical properties that could be used to compare them, early chemists struggled to organize them into a classification scheme. Even passing an electric current through these gases did not cause a reaction. It did, however, cause the gases to produce light of different colors.

FIGURE 3: Each sign spells out the element symbol of the gas with which it is filled: helium, neon, and argon.

 Collaborate Discuss these questions with a partner: Why do you think the elements in Figure 3 give off different colors of light when an electric current passes through them? How might the colors given off be related to the type of atom that makes up each element?

Over time, scientists concluded that something other than mass alone must be causing the patterns they observed in the properties of elements. Further experimentation would allow scientists to determine what made one type of atom different from others.

 Evidence Notebook How might the properties of different elements, such as the noble gases and the metals you tested, be related to the phenomenon of the aurora polaris?

Differentiate Instruction

MTSS/RTI Have students work in pairs to read each paragraph under the heading "Understanding Atoms." Partners should then collaborate to write a one-sentence summary of the main idea of each paragraph. Ask pairs to share and discuss their summaries.

Use this activity to provide an opportunity for students to develop and practice communication, social, and assertiveness skills. Try to balance pairs so that natural leaders can inspire the partners they are working with.

SEP Asking Questions and Defining Problems

After students read the text on this page, have them write several questions they have about different properties scientists use to classify elements. Then, provide an opportunity for students to read aloud one or more of their questions. Discuss the questions as a class.

3 Students' diagrams may have circles of different sizes to represent indivisible atoms with different masses.

4 **Sample answer:** The elements might give off light when electricity is applied to them because they absorb energy and then give off energy. The colors of light might be related to the structure of each type of atom.

Evidence Notebook

5 **Sample answer:** The atmosphere is made up of different gases, which contain different elements. Because each element has unique properties, these elements might react differently when the aurora polaris occurs. As seen with the noble gases, some of these interactions may produce different colors of light depending on the elements involved.

FORMATIVE ASSESSMENT
One-Sentence Summary Ask students to look back through the Exploration. Have them read each heading and look at the photographs. Then, have them write a one-sentence summary for the text under each heading.

EXPLORATION 2 Investigating Atomic Structure

3D Learning Objective

Students learn that **scientific knowledge is based on empirical evidence** by exploring different experiments scientists conducted to learn about the structure of the atom. They synthesize information to explain that **an atom has a charged substructure** consisting of a nucleus, which is made of protons and neutrons, surrounded by electrons. Students consider how **scale, proportion, and quantity** are related to atomic models.

Explore Online ▶

Balloon Attracting Water Students can go online and watch a video of a negatively charged balloon attracting a stream of water.

Physics Connection

When different substances are rubbed against each other, electrons may transfer from one substance (in which they are more loosely held) to the other (in which they are more strongly attracted). As far back as the experiments performed by Benjamin Franklin, scientists empirically developed Electrostatic or Triboelectic Tables that ranked materials by whether they tended to become electropositive or electronegative when rubbed against each other. The terms *positively charged* and *negatively charged* were used more than 100 years before scientists had compelling evidence for subatomic particles. Ask students to identify other **everyday phenomena** that produce charges, such as static electricity of clothing or a shock when touching metal.

Explore Online ▶

Cathode-Ray Tube Encourage students to go online and watch a video showing how a magnet can deflect the electron beam in a cathode-ray tube.

1 **Sample answer:** Maybe the water has a charge, and the charge on the balloon attracts the charge on the water.

2 Opposite, negatively

Investigating Atomic Structure

Explore Online ▶

FIGURE 4: A negatively charged balloon attracts a stream of water.

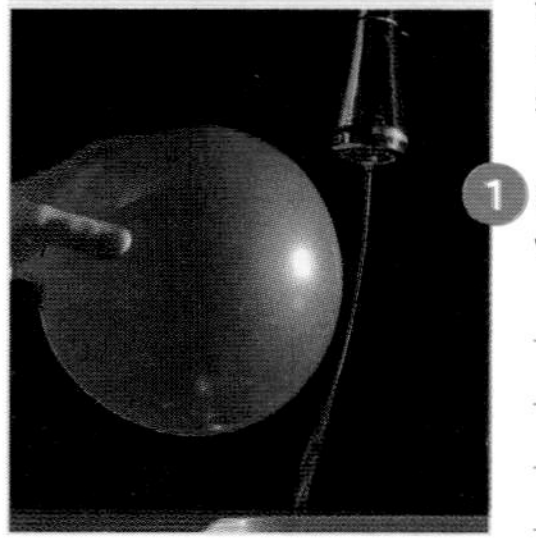

You may have experienced a shock when touching a door knob after walking across a carpeted floor. When you walk across carpet, a charge can build up on the surface of your body. When you touch a metal object, the charge is transferred with a shock. In a similar way, a balloon rubbed with a cloth builds up a negative charge. When the balloon is placed near a thin stream of water, as shown in Figure 4, the water is attracted to the balloon.

1 **PREDICT** In Figure 4, a negatively charged balloon attracts a thin stream of water. Why do you think this happens?

_____

_____

_____

Identifying Electrons

Like charges repel, and opposite charges attract. Thus, the attraction between a negatively charged balloon and a stream of water is evidence that opposite charges are present. If atoms were simply tiny indivisible spheres, as scientists once theorized, how could these opposite charges form? In the late 1800s, experiments with cathode rays led to the discovery of a charged particle called the electron.

A cathode-ray tube, as shown in Figure 5, is a glass tube containing a gas at very low pressure. At one end, it has a cathode, a metal disk connected to the negative terminal of the energy source. At the other end, it has an anode, a metal disk connected to a positive terminal. When an electric current is passed through the tube, a glowing stream of particles called a cathode ray can be observed. In 1897, a scientist named J.J. Thomson noted that a magnetic or electric field could cause the cathode ray to bend. The ray bent toward a positive charge and away from a negative charge.

FIGURE 5: A cathode ray bends away from a magnet.   Explore Online ▶

2 **EXPLAIN** Select the correct terms to complete the statement.

Opposite | like charges attract one another. So, if an electric current causes a cathode ray to bend toward a positive charge, the ray must be positively | negatively charged.

Further experimentation with cathode rays allowed J.J. Thomson to calculate the charge-to-mass-ratio of the particles that made them up. He noticed that this ratio remained constant even when different gases or metals were used in the cathode ray tube. The very small, negatively charged particles Thomson identified later became known as electrons. It was determined that electrons had a mass of 9.109×10^{-31} kg, or 1/1836 the mass of a hydrogen atom. Because electrons are so much smaller than an atom, and atoms have no overall charge, it was clear that atoms could not be made up solely of electrons.

3 **INFER** What could be inferred about atomic structure after the discovery of the electron? Select all correct answers.

☐ **a.** Atoms are made up of smaller "subatomic" particles.

☐ **b.** Atoms of different elements contain the same number of electrons.

☐ **c.** The electrons in an atom are attracted to each other due to their negative charge.

☐ **d.** Atoms must also contain a positively charged component.

FIGURE 6: A plum pudding

The discovery of the electron led scientists to develop a new atomic model. In this model, called the "plum pudding model," negatively charged electrons are evenly distributed within a mass of positively charged material. Thus, the electrons are like raisins in a cake, as shown in Figure 6. The cake itself represents the area of positive charge that surrounds the electrons.

Identifying the Nucleus

In the early 1900s, a physicist and former student of Thomson's named Ernest Rutherford devised an experiment to learn more about atomic structure. In this experiment, called the gold foil experiment, positively charged particles called alpha (α) particles were focused into a narrow beam and shot at a very thin piece of gold. Rutherford hypothesized that if the plum pudding model was correct, the area of positive charge in the gold atoms would be too spread out to repel the positively charged alpha particles. So, most of the particles should pass straight through the foil undeflected.

FIGURE 7: Gold foil experiment

Explore Online ▶

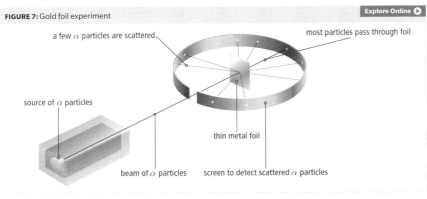

a few α particles are scattered

most particles pass through foil

source of α particles

thin metal foil

beam of α particles   screen to detect scattered α particles

4 **Collaborate** With a partner, analyze the diagram of the gold foil experiment shown in Figure 7 and answer these questions: What happened when the alpha particles encountered the gold foil? What do you think these results indicate about atomic structure?

© Houghton Mifflin Harcourt Publishing Company • Image Credits: ©magnetix/Shutterstock

History of Science

Ernest Rutherford and two of his graduate students devised the gold foil experiment. Help students understand that this is an example of the importance of the relationships among students, their mentors, and future mentees. Advancements in science often result from such teamwork.

SEP **Scientific Knowledge is Based on Empirical Evidence**

Explain that the model of the atom is based on empirical evidence, which is information obtained through observation or experimentation. For example, observations from cathode-ray tube experiments led scientists to conclude that atoms contained both negative and positive particles. Evidence from the gold foil experiment then helped scientists further develop the model of the atom by showing that the positive charge in an atom is located in a small, dense area at the center of the atom rather than being spread throughout the atom.

Differentiate Instruction

Extension To demonstrate the general idea of the gold foil experiment, students can place an object under a box that has had sections of its sides removed and roll marbles at the object. The results can be used to infer the size and shape of the object.

Engineering Connection

Draw students' attention to **Figure 7.** *Ask:* Why was a thin foil used? Why was it important for the foil to be made of gold, a heavy element? Why was it useful for the screen to be circular?

Explore Online ▶

Gold Foil Experiment Students can go online to watch a simulation of how a beam of alpha particles can be deflected by gold foil.

3 a, d

4 **Sample answer:** Most of the particles passed through the foil, but some were scattered. This might indicate that something inside the atoms repelled or collided with the particles.

DCI **PS2.B Types of Interactions**

Point out to students that the particle beam used in the gold foil experiment was composed of alpha particles, which are positively charged. **Ask:** *Why was this important, and how would the results have been different if the scientists had used a beam of neutral particles?* Neutral particles would not have been deflected by the nucleus. Particles of the same electrical charge repel each other, so the positively charged beam was deflected when it interacted with the protons in the nuclei of the gold atoms.

Exploring Visuals

Results of the Gold Foil Experiment Ask questions about **Figure 8** to help students understand the results of the gold foil experiment.

Ask: *What could the scientists infer about atomic structure from the fact that some alpha particles were deflected at large angles?* Its center is positively charged because it repels positively charged alpha particles.

Ask: *What could the scientists infer about atomic structure from the fact that most alpha particles passed straight through undeflected?* The nucleus takes up a very small space within an atom.

CCC **Scale, Proportion, and Quantity**

Emphasize that the diagram in **Figure 8** does not show correct relative sizes. The nucleus is much smaller relative to the size of the atom. A common analogy is that the nucleus in an atom is similar to the size of a penny in the middle of a football stadium.

Evidence Notebook

1 Atoms have a very small, dense core—some alpha particles were repelled at large angles. The core of an atom has a positive charge—alpha particles are positively charged, and they were repelled by the core. Atoms are made up of mostly empty space—most of the alpha particles went straight through the gold foil. Students should explain how these ideas relate to their unit project.

2 The number of protons must be equal to the number of electrons in order for the atom to be neutral overall.

In the gold foil experiment, most of the alpha particles passed straight through the gold foil as expected. However, some alpha particles were deflected at large angles, as shown in Figure 8. A few alpha particles were even deflected backwards from the foil. Rutherford was very surprised by the results, later saying that it was almost as incredible as if you fired a cannonball at a piece of tissue paper and it came back to hit you.

FIGURE 8: The results of the gold foil experiment led to a new model of the atom.

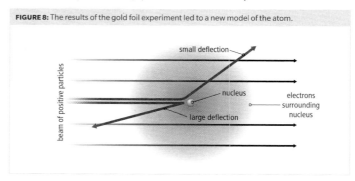

The model that Rutherford developed to explain his results depicted atoms as being made up of mostly empty space. In the center of the atom is a small, dense, positively-charged core, or **nucleus**, that makes up most of an atom's mass. The much lighter electrons surround the nucleus in a relatively large electron cloud.

 Evidence Notebook Explain how evidence from the gold foil experiment supports each of these claims. How can you apply these ideas to the atomic model in your unit project?
• atoms have a very small, dense core
• the core of an atom has a positive charge
• atoms are made up of mostly empty space

Describing Atomic Structure

Properties of Subatomic Particles		
Particles	Electric charge	Actual mass (kg)
Electron	−1	9.109×10^{-31}
Proton	+1	1.673×10^{-27}
Neutron	0	1.675×10^{-27}

The gold foil experiment showed that the nucleus of an atom contains a small, dense nucleus with a positive charge. Further studies of the nucleus showed that it is composed of protons, which are positively charged particles, and neutrons, which have no charge. Protons and neutrons are much larger than electrons, with a proton having about 1836 times the mass of an electron. The much smaller, negatively-charged electrons surround the nucleus.

2 **INFER** If atoms are neutral (have no overall charge), what can you infer about the number of protons and electrons in an atom? How should these numbers compare? Explain your thinking.

Scale, Proportion, and Quantity

Scale and Atomic Models

Atoms are too small to observe directly. So, to help scientists understand the structure of atoms, they develop models. Atomic models are useful because they allow scientists to visualize the structure of atoms. However, it can be difficult to develop a model of the atom that is to scale.

The models of atoms shown in textbooks are not to scale because it would be impossible to represent the proportions of the atom in a two-dimensional diagram. In a scale model, the electron cloud would be 100 000 times the diameter of the nucleus. To visualize this, imagine the nucleus were the size of a grain of sand. An atom with a nucleus this size would be as large around as a baseball stadium, such as the one shown in Figure 9.

FIGURE 9: An atom with a nucleus the size of a grain of sand would be the size of a baseball stadium.

In addition, atoms are three-dimensional objects, so any drawing does not show its true shape. Scientists acknowledge that their atomic models are not drawn to scale and that the distances between the nucleus and electrons are not accurate.

 PREDICT What types of information do you think scientists can gain from a computational, physical, or two-dimensional atomic model that is not to scale?

_____

_____

_____

_____

Some models can be useful even when they are not to scale. For example, models of very large objects, such as the solar system, are not to scale. This is because the interplanetary distances involved are so great that it would be hard to make an accurate scale model. Consider this: If a model of the solar system were on a football field, the sun would be about the size of a dime. The planet Neptune would be 60 yards (55 m) away and about the diameter of the lead on a mechanical pencil.

Some models, however, must be made to scale. For example, blueprints for a building are a type of model. It is important that they be made to scale to make sure the rooms, plumbing, and electrical wiring are all properly constructed and fit in the required space.

 Collaborate Work with a partner to develop criteria for situations that require a scale model or do not require a scale model.

 Evidence Notebook Summarize what you have learned about the structure of the atom. How do you think atomic structure might be related to the aurora polaris phenomenon?

Collaborate

Discussion As a class, discuss how the dimensions of textbooks are not able to depict the to-scale diameter of the nucleus and orbiting electrons, much less the relatively immense distance between them. Across the periodic table, atomic radii vary by a factor of 10 and are in the picometer (10^{-12} meter) range. But nuclear radii are measured in femtometers (10^{-15} meter), or about 10 000 times smaller than atomic radii. Therefore, if the nucleus were a 10 cm diameter softball, a barely visible electron would be over a kilometer away, with a vacuum in between. The submicroscopic world of the atom is far stranger than we can easily visualize. It is critical for students to understand that textbook visuals "have to lie" and grossly misrepresent the almost unbelievable scale of the atom in ways that are analogous to the textbook visuals of our solar system. The crosscutting concept of scale is critical to have students develop an appreciation for sizes of objects in phenomena as small as atoms or as large as the universe.

3 Students may say that atomic models can provide information about the numbers, charges, and locations of subatomic particles.

4 **Sample answer:** Scale models are needed when it is important to measure actual distances, such as for a map or a diagram of nuts and bolts. Not-to-scale models are adequate when the features being examined are not dependent on relative size or distance.

Evidence Notebook

5 **Sample answer:** Atoms contain protons, neutrons, and electrons. Protons are positively charged and located in the atom's nucleus. Neutrons are neutral and are also found in the nucleus. Electrons are negatively charged and surround the nucleus. Different gases in the atmosphere might produce different colors because different types of atoms in the gases are made up of different combinations of protons, neutrons, and electrons.

FORMATIVE ASSESSMENT

3-2-1 Have students write three things they found out in this Exploration about atomic structure, two things they found interesting, and one question they still have about the concepts presented in the Exploration.

EXPLORATION 3 Using Numbers to Describe Atoms

3D Learning Objective

Students apply the idea that scientific knowledge assumes an order and consistency in natural systems to describe the charged substructure of atoms. They use numbers such as atomic number and mass number to describe the substructure of atoms. Students construct explanations for how average atomic mass is calculated.

DCI PS1.A Structure and Properties of Matter

Have students read the first paragraph under the heading "Atomic Number and Mass Number." Then, ask them to think about how the atomic number and mass number are related. Have students predict which parts of an atom contribute the most to the mass of the atom.

Differentiate Instruction

ELL Support Have students create a vocabulary list of key terms as they work through this exploration. Encourage them to write definitions in their own words for the key terms as they encounter them in the text.

Collaborate

Think-Pair-Share Have students work in pairs to complete the Infer activity. Have each student in the pair complete the statements and then share their answers with their partner. Students should explain how they arrived at their answers.

1 Students may say that the number of protons, neutrons, or electrons is related to the different properties of these elements. Encourage students to think about which particle is likely to be involved in chemical reactions based on its location in the atom.

2 13, 14, 13

Evidence Notebook

3 Students should record information related to atomic number and mass number, explaining how they are related to the number of protons, neutrons, and electrons in an atom. Students should explain how this applies to the atom they will model in their unit project.

EXPLORATION 3

Using Numbers to Describe Atoms

You have learned that elements are made up of individual units called atoms, and that atoms are made up of smaller particles called protons, neutrons, and electrons. The differences in reactivity that you observed in the hands-on lab are related to the number of subatomic particles in the atoms of each element.

1 **PREDICT** Think back to the metals you studied in the hands-on lab. Which subatomic particles do you think most influenced reactivity? How might the numbers of subatomic particles in each type of atom explain your observations?

_____

_____

_____

Atomic Number and Mass Number

One way that scientists identify atoms is by the number of protons in the nucleus. The number of protons in an atom's nucleus is called the atomic number. Each element has a certain number of protons, so this means the atomic number of an atom corresponds to a specific element. If the atomic number changes, the element has a different identity. For example, the elements you combined with acid in the hands-on lab—magnesium, aluminum, and zinc—have atomic numbers of 12, 13, and 30 respectively.

FIGURE 10: This helium nucleus has 2 protons and 2 neutrons, so it has an atomic number of 2 and a mass number of 4.

The atomic number is a handy number because it is also tells you the number of electrons in a neutral atom. Because atoms do not have a charge, the positive charges from the protons and the negative charges from the electrons must be the same. Thus, if you know the atomic number of an atom, you not only know the number of protons but also the number of electrons. So magnesium, aluminum, and zinc have 12, 13, and 30 electrons respectively.

Another way scientists describe atoms is with the mass number. The mass number is equal to the total number of protons and neutrons in an atom's nucleus. Therefore, you can find the number of neutrons in an atom by subtracting the atomic number from the mass number for that atom.

2 **INFER** Select the correct terms to complete the statement.

The element aluminum has an atomic number of 13 and a mass number of 27. The number of protons in the nucleus of an aluminum atom is 27 | 13 | 40 | 14. The number of neutrons in the nucleus is 27 | 13 | 40 | 14. The number of electrons in the atom is 27 | 13 | 40 | 14.

3 **Evidence Notebook** Summarize what you have learned about how numbers can be used to describe subatomic particles in atoms. Then write an explanation of how this information will apply to the atomic model you are developing for your unit project.

Isotopes

The mass number and atomic number are different in an important way. If two atoms have different atomic numbers, and therefore different numbers of protons, they are from different elements. But two atoms can have different numbers of neutrons and still be the same element as long as they have the same number of protons. Atoms of the same element with different numbers of neutrons are called isotopes. Different isotopes of the same element have the same number of protons and electrons, but each isotope has a different number of neutrons.

Scientists refer to isotopes of elements in different ways. An isotope may be identified by writing the mass number as a superscript and the atomic number as a subscript to the left of the chemical symbol, such as $^{14}_{7}N$ and $^{15}_{7}N$ for two isotopes of nitrogen. Scientists might also write the mass number after the name of the element such as uranium-235 and uranium-238 for the isotopes. In this type of notation, the atomic number is omitted because it can be assumed from the identity of the element.

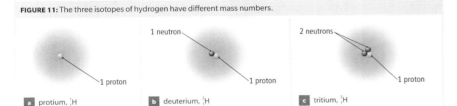

FIGURE 11: The three isotopes of hydrogen have different mass numbers.

1 neutron

2 neutrons

1 proton

1 proton

1 proton

a protium, $^{1}_{1}H$ **b** deuterium, $^{2}_{1}H$ **c** tritium, $^{3}_{1}H$

4 **SOLVE** Write the mass number for each of the isotopes of hydrogen.

protium _____   deuterium _____   tritium _____

Atomic Mass

Today, scientists measure the mass of atoms in unified atomic mass units (u). Originally, scientists defined the atomic mass unit as being the mass of a proton or neutron. So, the mass number was considered equal to the atomic mass of an element. As scientists learned more about the mass of atoms and could begin measuring the masses of atoms with more accuracy, they developed a more precise unit of measure. An atomic mass unit is defined as 1/12 of the mass of a carbon-12 isotope, or $1.660\,539\,040 \times 10^{-24}$ g.

The atomic mass unit is not the same as the mass of a proton or neutron because the mass of the carbon atom also includes the very small but necessary mass of the electrons. Carbon was chosen as the standard because a carbon atom with 6 protons, 6 neutrons, and 6 electrons was the easiest atomic mass to determine. The other common isotope of carbon, carbon-13, is relatively rare compared to carbon-12.

5 **Language Arts Connection** Conduct research to learn more about how the atomic mass unit has changed over time. Then use your findings to make a flow chart to show how and why the measurement of atomic mass has changed. Last, write an explanation for how the unit is currently quantified. Include a list of references with your final product.

Differentiate Instruction

MTSS/RTI Help students internalize the content. Place them in pairs, and have them collaborate to complete these sentences: *The atomic number is _____. The mass number is _____. The average atomic mass is _____.* Follow up by having pairs share their completed sentences, discuss differences they find, and make revisions, if needed.

Extension You may wish to have advanced students relate the number of electrons in an atom to the placement of the element on the periodic table.

CCC Patterns

Students may note that as atomic number increases, atoms seem to have increasing numbers of neutrons relative to the number of protons. Because positively charged protons "should" repel each other, students might be led to hypothesize that neutrons provide some kind of nuclear "glue" that prevents nuclei from being pushed apart by the protons. Minimally, students might question how protons can be "crammed" so close together in such relatively small nuclei.

Language Arts Connection
RST.9-10.7 Translate quantitative or technical information expressed in words in a text into visual form and translate information expressed visually or mathematically into words.

Remind students that they can find information about conducting research, presenting information in graphical form, and citing resources in the online **English Language Arts Handbook.**

4 1, 2, 3

5 Students should develop a flow chart that accurately reflects their findings. This will require researching both historical and more current investigations. Students' charts should show how the atomic mass unit has changed over time.

Exploring Visuals

Have students look at **Figure 12.** *Ask: What does the number 6 represent?* the atomic number *What does the capital C represent?* the symbol for the chemical element *What does 12.01 represent?* the average atomic mass for carbon

Math Connection
MP.2 Reason abstractly and quantitatively.

Help students understand that the atomic mass of one atom is measured in whole units because the mass of a proton or neutron is 1 unit. Because atoms may have only whole protons and neutrons, the mass of an atom is measured in whole numbers. However, the average atomic mass for an element takes into account the weighted average of all the isotopes and usually is not a whole number.

1 14.008 163 u

2 Students' explanations should describe the difference between average atomic mass and mass number. Mass number reflects the number of protons and neutrons in the nucleus of one atom of an element. Average atomic mass is an average that takes into account all of the isotopes of that element and their abundances. When using the periodic table to determine mass number of the most common isotope of an element, you should round the average atomic mass.

Evidence Notebook
3 **Sample answer:** The atomic number gives the number of protons in the atoms of a given element. The atomic number also equals the number of electrons in a neutral atom of a given element. Because no two elements have the same atomic number, no two elements will have neutral atoms with the same number of electrons. The difference in the number of electrons could cause the different colors of the aurora borealis.

FORMATIVE ASSESSMENT
Quick Write Have students select an element from the periodic table at the back of this book and use the information from the table to find the number of protons, neutrons, and electrons for that element.

Average Atomic Mass

FIGURE 12: The periodic table tile for carbon shows its average atomic mass, 12.01.

6
C
Carbon
12.01

Because different isotopes of an element may be present in naturally-occurring samples, we cannot use a single atomic mass to describe a sample of an element. The atomic mass shown on the periodic table for an element is an average atomic mass that accounts for all of the isotopes of that element.

When calculating the atomic mass of a typical sample of an element, the relative abundance of each isotope must be taken into account. For example, carbon has two naturally occurring isotopes—carbon-12 and carbon-13. Carbon-12 has an atomic mass of exactly 12 u and a relative abundance of 98.89%. This means that a naturally occurring sample of carbon will be made up of 98.89% carbon-12. Carbon-13 has an atomic mass of 13.003 35 u and a relative abundance of 1.11%.

To calculate the average atomic mass of an element, the exact atomic mass for each isotope is multiplied by the isotope's relative abundance (in decimal form), and the products are summed. This gives an average atomic mass, which is a more accurate measure of the mass of a typical, real-world sample of an element. The following equation can be used to calculate the average atomic mass of carbon.

Average atomic mass of C $= (12 \text{ u} \times 0.9889) + (13.003\,35 \text{ u} \times 0.0111) = 12.0111 \text{ u}$

 SOLVE Calculate the average atomic mass of nitrogen.

Nitrogen-14 has an atomic mass of 14.003 074 u and a relative abundance of 99.64%. Nitrogen-15 has an atomic mass of 15.000 109 u and a relative abundance of 0.37%.

_____.

 Math Connection

Explaining Average Atomic Mass

When using the periodic table to determine the atomic mass of an element, it is common for people to confuse average atomic mass and mass number. Imagine you wanted to determine the number of neutrons in a carbon atom. If you referenced the periodic table, you would see that the average atomic mass of carbon is 12.01 u.

You can calculate the number of neutrons in the nucleus by subtracting the atomic number from the mass number for an element. However, it would be incorrect to use the value 12.01 when performing this calculation, which would give an answer of 6.01 neutrons. Instead, you should round the average atomic mass to 12. This will give you the mass number of the most abundant isotope; in this case, carbon-12.

 Collaborate With a partner, write a brief explanation that another student could reference when using the periodic table to calculate the number of neutrons in atoms of a certain element. Explain how average atomic mass differs from mass number and how this difference should be considered when using the periodic table as a reference tool.

 Evidence Notebook How might the fact that each element has a unique atomic number help explain the different colors in the aurora polaris? Think about what information the atomic number provides about the subatomic particles in an atom.

Hands-On Lab

Identifying Elements Using a Flame Test

The work of Rutherford and other scientists helped establish a model that depicted the atom as having a small, dense nucleus surrounded by electrons. But this model could not fully explain all the properties of elements. For example, a tube of hydrogen gas emits a pinkish glow when an electric current is passed through it, as shown in Figure 13a. Passing this light through a prism or a tool called a spectroscope separates the light into its different wavelengths. Figure 13b shows the results of this test for hydrogen, known as an emission-line spectrum.

FIGURE 13: The pinkish light emitted by hydrogen can be separated by a spectroscope.

a Hydrogen emission tube

b Hydrogen's emission-line spectrum

When an electric current is passed through hydrogen gas, the hydrogen atoms absorb energy. When an atom absorbs energy, the electrons are raised to higher energy levels referred to as "excited" states. When an electron falls from a higher energy level to a lower energy level, energy in the form of light is released. This light has a specific amount of energy and so will appear as a certain color with a certain wavelength.

 Collaborate With a partner, write an analogy you could use to explain what causes hydrogen gas to glow when an electric current is passed through it.

When studying hydrogen, scientists expected to observe the emission of a continuous range of frequencies, not the distinct lines shown in Figure 13b. In 1913, Danish physicist Niels Bohr developed a new model of the atom that accounted for the emission-line spectrum of hydrogen.

In Bohr's model, the electron can circle the nucleus only in allowed paths, or *orbits*, called atomic energy levels. When the electron is in one of these orbits, the atom has a definite, fixed energy. The electron is in its lowest energy state, or ground state, when it is in the orbit closest to the nucleus. The energy of the electron is higher when the electron is in orbits that are successively farther from the nucleus. Bohr used the different wavelengths of the hydrogen emission-line spectrum to calculate the allowed energy levels for the hydrogen atom. He then related the possible energy-level changes to the lines in the hydrogen emission-line spectrum.

In this lab, you will observe the colors given off by several metal salts by performing a flame test to determine the identity of an unknown substance. In a flame test, a wire or splint is coated in a solution containing a metal salt. The coated end of the wire is then placed in a flame.

FIGURE 14: Colors of light emitted when the electron in hydrogen loses energy and drops back down to its original energy level

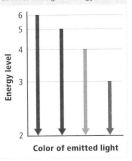

Energy level / Color of emitted light

© Houghton Mifflin Harcourt Publishing Company • Image Credits: ©Chip Clark/Fundamental Photographs

3D Learning Objective

Students carry out a flame test and **construct an explanation** for how the colors of light they observed are related to the charged substructure of atoms. They learn that electrons follow predictable patterns as they move from one energy level to another.

Hands-On Lab 👥 Small groups ⏱ 90 minutes

Identifying Elements Using a Flame Test

SEP **Constructing Explanations and Designing Solutions**

Students design an experiment to compare differences in the color of light emitted when metals in solution are heated in a flame. Students then apply their results to identify an unknown solution based on the color of its flame when heated.

Advance Preparation / Materials Alert Prepare the 1.0 M HCl solution, each of the test solutions, and the unknown solution. Prepare potassium sulfate as the unknown solution. If spectroscopes are available, students can use them to view the line spectrum of the flame, which will give more precise data to work with.

Anything that contacts the solutions should be rinsed with distilled water, and the water used in preparing the solutions should be sodium free. Any little bit of sodium—even from perspiration when touching glassware—may completely mask other colors of flame.

Arrange for all groups to have access to a fume hood, or have students conduct the investigation in a well-ventilated room. Hydrochloric acid is highly corrosive to skin and other tissues.

Safety Information Remind all students that safety goggles, a nonlatex apron, and nonlatex gloves are to be worn during the setup, hands-on, and takedown segments of the activity.

 Sample answer: Energy levels are like the rungs of a ladder. When an electron gains energy from the flame, it jumps up to a higher rung of the ladder. When it falls down to a lower rung, it gives off energy in the form of light.

Student Lab Worksheet and complete Teacher Support are available online.

DCI **PS1.A Structure and Properties of Matter**

As students are considering the reason different metals produce different colors of flames, encourage them to think about what they already know about the structure of an atom. Remind them that protons and neutrons are tightly bound in the nucleus of an atom, but electrons are in motion around the nucleus. It is therefore the electrons that absorb energy and then release the energy as colors of light.

SEP   **Analyzing and Interpreting Data**

Students may have difficulty distinguishing similar flame colors well enough to identify the unknown solution. Have them repeat the test for the two solutions that gave similar colors and compare them with the unknown solution's flame color again.

Collaborate

Discussion Point out to students that the flame test gives qualitative information about the metal in the sample. How would they obtain quantitative data about the proportion of elements in the sample? Help them understand that quantitative data can be obtained by the related methods of flame photometry and flame emission spectroscopy. Have interested students do research into these techniques and report back to the class.

1 **Sample answer:** A flame test can be used to identify an unknown metal by matching the color of a flame of a solution containing that metal to the colors of flames of solutions of known metals. This will reveal what the unknown metal is.

RESEARCH QUESTION How can scientists use the properties of elements to identify unknown substances?

1 **MAKE A CLAIM**

How do you think you can use the results of a flame test to identify an unknown metal?

_____

_____

_____

_____

_____

MATERIALS

- indirectly vented chemical splash goggles, nonlatex apron, nitrile gloves
- beaker, 250 mL
- Bunsen burner
- crucible tongs
- distilled water
- flame-test wire, 5 cm
- glass test plate, or microchemistry plate with wells
- hydrochloric acid, HCl, solution, 1.0 M

Test Solutions

- calcium chloride solution, $CaCl_2$, 0.05 M
- lithium sulfate solution, Li_2SO_4, 0.05 M
- potassium sulfate solution, K_2SO_4, 0.05 M
- sodium sulfate solution, Na_2SO_4, 0.05 M
- strontium chloride solution, $SrCl_2$, 0.05 M
- unknown solution

SAFETY INFORMATION

- Wear indirectly vented chemical splash goggles, a nonlatex apron, and nitrile gloves during the setup, hands-on, and takedown segments of the activity.
- Do not touch any of the chemicals used in this experiment. Only touch them with the flame-test wire.
- Tell your teacher immediately if you spill chemicals on yourself, the work surface, or floor.
- If you get a chemical in your eye, use an eyewash station immediately.
- Secure loose clothing, wear closed-toe shoes, and tie back long hair.
- Do not stare directly into the flames for extended periods of time. Look at the flame for the shortest amount of time needed to determine the color. Run multiple trials to avoid looking at the flame for too long.

indirectly vented chemical splash goggles

PLAN THE INVESTIGATION

In your Evidence Notebook, develop a procedure and safety plan for your investigation. Carefully consider the controls of your experiment, what the variables are, and that you are only testing one solution at a time. Decide how much solution you will need for each test and how many trials you will need to accurately determine the color of the flame. Have your teacher approve your procedure and safety plan before proceeding.

70   **Unit 2** Atoms and Elements

COLLECT DATA

In your Evidence Notebook, develop a data collection strategy. The metal ions in the salt solutions are responsible for producing the light you will observe. Consider how you will record the colors produced in each trial of the flame test. Make sure your data are clear and ordered so you can easily compare the results of the known solutions to the results of the unknown solution.

2 CARRY OUT THE INVESTIGATION

Before you begin testing your compounds, it is important that you clean your flame-test wire. Clean the test wire by dipping it in 1.0 M HCl solution and then holding it in the flame of the Bunsen burner. Repeat this procedure until the flame is not colored by the wire. Make sure to clean the wire between each test solution to avoid contamination.

ANALYZE

1. The images show solutions containing copper, strontium, and sodium compounds burning in Petri dishes. The colors, from left to right, are: orange, red, and green. Write a caption for each image that identifies the metal ion in each solution and briefly explains your reasoning.

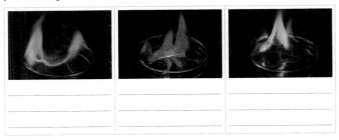

2. Did you notice any differences in the individual trials for the flame tests of each metal solution? Why do you think these differences occurred?

3. How could the level of accuracy of your results for the flame test be improved?

CCC   Patterns

Different metals will produce different colors due to differences in the change in energy level. Sometimes multiple electrons are involved in producing different colors. As a result, different metals will have different patterns of colors and a slightly different flame color. The patterns have dominant colors, but other colors may make the flame appear to be a different color. For example, strontium and lithium both produce a red flame, while potassium produces a lilac flame, and calcium produces an orange-red flame. The flame on a gas stove is blue because the natural gas burns cleanly. An **everyday phenomenon** that can change the gas flame color is when food boils over and is burned. *Ask: Sodium chloride, table salt, is commonly used in cooking. How would table salt affect the color of the flame?*

2 The colors students should observe when completing their flame tests are as follows: calcium—orange-red, lithium—red, potassium—lilac (pink), sodium—orange, strontium—red.

Analyze

1. **Sample answer:** The orange flame shows sodium being burned. This is the same color that sodium sulfate burned in the experiment. The red flame show strontium being burned. This is the same color that strontium chloride burned in the experiment. The green flame must be copper. None of the known test solutions burned with a green flame so this must be copper.

2. **Sample answer:** Yes, I noticed that often the first trial produced a flame color that differed from later trials, while the later trials all tended to give the same flame color. Possibly we did not completely clean out the flame-test wire in these cases. If the wire was contaminated with small amounts of solution from a previous test, the colors may have combined, giving the inconsistent results we observed during the first trial.

3. **Sample answer:** Having a better way to analyze the colors would produce more accurate results. Spectroscopes could be used to determine the actual wavelengths of the light emitted during a flame test, which is more accurate than observing colors visually alone.

Lesson 1 Modeling Atomic Structure   71

Astronomy Connection

The Auroras Explain to students that the colors of the aurora polaris are produced by the same effect demonstrated in this lab. In the lab, students provide energy to the electrons by heat. In the auroras, collisions between charged particles in solar wind and electrons in atmospheric atoms provide energy to excite the electrons.

1 The electrons in the atoms of each element gave off a unique amount of energy, so the amount of energy associated with each energy level must differ from one element to another.

2 Check the accuracy of students' claims and evidence concerning the identity of their unknown metal. Students should state that the evidence came from matching the color of the unknown solution flame test to the color from one of the known solutions.

3 Students should include information about the colors of the firework and the metal salt(s) required to produce each color. Common examples: red—strontium, orange—calcium, yellow—sodium, green—barium, white—magnesium and aluminum.

Evidence Notebook

4 In the flame test, different colors were produced by different elements as electrons moved from a higher energy level to a lower energy level. The color of light given off was related to the amount of energy given off. Similarly, the different colors in the aurora polaris could be produced by different elements in Earth's atmosphere. Electrons in atoms that make up the gases in the atmosphere might be excited by some type of energy source and then fall back to a lower energy level, giving off light in the process.

FORMATIVE ASSESSMENT

3-Minute Pause Have students pause to think of their results of this investigation. Have them respond to the following prompts.

I became more aware of . . .

I didn't realize that . . .

I still don't understand . . .

Have volunteers share their responses with the class.

1 CONSTRUCT AN EXPLANATION
Each metallic element you tested gave off a unique color when burned. What does this tell you about the energy levels in the atoms of these metallic elements? Explain your answer.

2 DRAW CONCLUSIONS
Write a conclusion that addresses each of the points below.

Claim Based on the data you gathered from the flame tests, what metal is present in the unknown solution?

Evidence Give specific examples from your data to support your claim.

Reasoning Explain how the evidence you gave supports your claim. Describe, in detail, the connections between the evidence you cited and the argument you are making.

3 EXTEND
Research the use of metal salts in fireworks. Make a visual guide explaining which metal ions are responsible for producing which colors of fireworks. Then write a brief explanation for how energy levels in atoms are related to the colors observed.

4 Evidence Notebook How might the different colors you observed in the flame test be related to the different colors produced in the aurora polaris?

Modeling Electron Configurations

In the Bohr model of the atom, electrons circle the nucleus only in allowed paths. The development of a new model of the atom, called the quantum mechanical model, would show that electrons are actually located in three-dimensional areas around the nucleus. The quantum mechanical model is a mathematical model that describes the areas where electrons are most likely to be found.

Electron Shells and Orbitals

Electrons, like light, have properties that describe them as both particles and waves. Because of these properties, their exact location cannot be determined. Instead, we can only consider electrons as having a high probability of being somewhere within a certain region. This region, called an energy shell, is a three-dimensional region around the atom. The lowest energy shells, closest to the nucleus, correspond to the lowest energy levels. Energy shells fill up in a specific order and are numbered 1–7.

5 **PREDICT** Hydrogen has one electron, which is located in the first energy shell. Helium has two electrons in the first energy shell. Lithium has three electrons—two in the first energy shell and one in the second. How might this pattern be related to the fact that hydrogen and lithium are both reactive, but helium is nonreactive?

_____

_____

_____

Regions within each energy shell where electrons have a high probability of being found are called subshells. Each subshell contains orbitals of different shapes. An orbital can hold up to two electrons. The first subshell, called 1s, has the lowest energy and contains one orbital that is spherical in shape. This is shown in Figure 15a.

FIGURE 15: These models show the shape of orbitals in the s and p subshells.

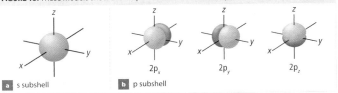

a s subshell **b** p subshell

The second energy shell has two subshells, labeled s and p. The p subshell has three orbitals, as shown in Figure 15b. Each of these orbitals can hold two electrons. So, the second energy shell can hold a total of 8 electrons, with 2 in the s subshell and 6 in the p subshell. The third energy shell has three subshells, s, p, and d. The d subshell has five orbitals and can therefore hold 10 electrons. The fourth energy shell has four subshells, s, p, d, and f. The f subshell has seven orbitals and can therefore hold 14 electrons.

3D Learning Objective

Students use **patterns** in the periodic table to **model** the **patterns of outer electron states** of atoms of different elements.

CCC **Structure and Function**

As students begin to learn about the importance of electrons in the properties and functioning of an atom, the focus at first will be the total number of electrons the atom has. The focus will change to valence electrons when students learn to draw the electron-dot notation for each element.

Preconception Alert

Students may have learned about the electron cloud and pictured it as electrons randomly arranged within an area around the atomic nucleus. In this Exploration, students learn that within the electron cloud, electrons are arranged in a distinct structure.

Differentiate Instruction

MTSS/RTI Have students work in pairs and look at the models in **Figure 15**. Guide students' understanding according to their abilities, such as asking students questions about the orbitals and their shapes that students can respond to with _yes_ or _no_. Alternatively, ask questions about the orbitals and their shapes, and have students discuss the answers with a partner. Pair more-proficient students with partners, and have them discuss the orbitals and their shapes and how they connect to the total number of electrons in an atom.

5 **Sample answer:** Maybe having one electron in the outermost energy shell makes an element reactive.

SEP **Developing and Using Models**

Figure 16 is a model of the electron subshells for the first thirteen elements. Point out to students that this model shows how the subshells are filled. *Ask: What is the maximum number of electrons in an s subshell?* 2 *What is the maximum number of electrons in a p subshell?* 6 *What must happen before electrons can be added to a new subshell?* The previous subshell must be full.

Exploring Visuals

Direct students' attention to **Figure 16.** Point out that valence electrons are the electrons in the outermost energy shell. So, for the elements lithium through neon, the valence electrons are those in the second energy shell. This includes electrons in both the 2s and 2p subshells. It may help students to circle the cells of the table that contain the valence electrons for each element. For example, when analyzing the element boron, students would circle the cells of the table showing the number of electrons in the 2s and 2p subshells. Students would then add together these two numbers to determine the total number of valence electrons.

Differentiate Instruction

Extension Encourage advanced students to conduct research about patterns in the way energy shells, subshells, and orbitals are filled. Then have students make visual guides that explain what they learned. Give students an opportunity to describe how their guides illustrate the filling of electron subshells and orbitals.

1 Silicon: 2, 2, 6, 2, 2, 4; Phosphorus: 2, 2, 6, 2, 3, 5; Sulfur: 2, 2, 6, 2, 4, 6; Chlorine: 2, 2, 6, 2, 5, 7; Argon: 2, 2, 6, 2, 6, 8

Figure 16 shows the subshells that electrons occupy for the elements hydrogen through helium. The 1s subshell holds 2 electrons, and is filled first. The 2s subshell is filled next, followed by 2p. Each energy shell must be full before electrons begin filling the next energy shell. For example, the second energy shell must be full, with 2 electrons in the 2s subshell and 6 electrons in 2p subshell, before electrons begin filling the third energy shell. The electrons occupying the outermost energy shell are called valence electrons. For example, oxygen has 2 electrons in the 2s subshell and 4 electrons in the 2p subshell, so it has 6 valence electrons, or 6 total electrons in the outermost energy shell.

FIGURE 16: This chart shows how the subshells of the first 13 elements are filled.

| Name | Symbol | Atomic number | Number of electrons in each subshell | | | | | Total number of valence electrons |
			1s	2s	2p	3s	3p	
Hydrogen	H	1	1					1
Helium	He	2	2					2
Lithium	Li	3	2	1				1
Beryllium	Be	4	2	2				2
Boron	B	5	2	2	1			3
Carbon	C	6	2	2	2			4
Nitrogen	N	7	2	2	3			5
Oxygen	O	8	2	2	4			6
Fluorine	F	9	2	2	5			7
Neon	Ne	10	2	2	6			8
Sodium	Na	11	2	2	6	1		1
Magnesium	Mg	12	2	2	6	2		2
Aluminum	Al	13	2	2	6	2	1	3

1 **APPLY** Fill out this table for the next five elements after aluminum. Indicate the number of electrons present in each subshell. If a subshell is empty, leave the cell blank. Remember that valence electrons are those in the outermost energy shell.

| Name | Symbol | Atomic number | Number of electrons in each subshell | | | | | Total number of valence electrons |
			1s	2s	2p	3s	3p	
Silicon	Si	14						
Phosphorus	P	15						
Sulfur	S	16						
Chlorine	Cl	17						
Argon	Ar	18						

Valence electrons may take part in forming bonds in chemical reactions. So, the number of valence electrons in an atom determines the chemical properties of that element and the types of chemical reactions atoms of that element may take part in. If the outer energy shell of electrons is full, that element will typically not undergo chemical reactions. Elements that are one electron "short" from having a full outer energy shell and elements that have only one electron in the outer energy shell are typically very reactive.

2 **EXPLAIN** Revise your earlier explanation for this question based on what you now know about valence electrons, chemical reactions, and full outer shells of electrons: Hydrogen has one electron, helium has two electrons, and lithium has three electrons. Hydrogen and lithium are both reactive, but helium is nonreactive. How can electrons be used to explain this pattern of behavior?

_____

_____

_____

_____

_____

Modeling Electron Configuration

The electron configuration for an element can be written using a notation that expresses numbers of electrons as superscripts following the names of the subshells they occupy. For example, the electron configuration for sulfur, which has 16 electrons, is written as: $1s^2 2s^2 2p^6 3s^2 3p^4$. Figure 17 shows another way scientists model electron configuration by logically following how electrons fill their orbitals. This method gives each element a unique configuration of electrons. Because the energy shells and subshells are typically filled in the same way, it is easy to model the electron configuration for each element.

FIGURE 17: The electron configuration for sulfur has four electrons in the 3p subshell.

Using this model, each circle represents an orbital with two electrons. Each electron is represented by a line drawn through the circle. Each subshell must be completely filled before electrons can be placed in the next subshell. Therefore, the 1s subshell must be filled before electrons can be placed in the 2s subshell. This is represented by two lines through the circle. For the p subshell, one electron is placed in each circle before a second electron is placed in any of the circles. The p subshell must be filled before electrons can go in the next s subshell.

3 **MODEL** Using the method shown in Figure 17, draw the electron configuration of argon. Remember to fill the subshells in order.

1s 2s 2p 3s 3p

© Houghton Mifflin Harcourt Publishing Company

Collaborate

Which Is False? Have each student write two true statements and one false statement regarding the arrangement of electrons within the atoms of elements 1 to 20 on the periodic table. Then, with their books closed, students can present their statements to the class or to members of a group who try to figure out which statement is false.

SEP **Developing and Using Models**

Emphasize the importance of the order of filling the orbitals as shown in **Figure 17**. Make sure students realize that when filling a p orbital, each circle should receive one line before starting to draw a second line in any of the orbitals. The total number of lines in all the orbitals is the total number of electrons an uncharged atom of the element has.

Differentiate Instruction

MTSS/RTI Use a model based on an analogy to help students learn the rules for how electrons fill orbitals. For example, subshells can be compared to different floors in a building. The 1s floor is closest to the ground, 2s is above it, and so on. The floors are filled in the order of lowest energy to highest energy because more energy is required to walk up the stairs to higher floors. Orbitals are like individual rooms on each floor of the building. Each room can hold a maximum of two occupants. Have students draw this model on a piece of paper. Provide manipulatives such as paper clips for students to use when modeling the filling of orbitals for atoms of different elements.

2 Helium has a full outermost energy shell with 2 electrons, so it is not reactive. Hydrogen and lithium do not have full outer energy shells, so they are more reactive.

3 Argon has 18 electrons. It is a noble gas and fills all of the orbitals up through 3p. The diagram should show two diagonal lines in each circle.

DCI PS1.A Structure and Properties of Matter

Students should begin using patterns in the periodic table to model the outer electron states of different elements. Have students use the periodic table in **Figure 18** to determine how many valence electrons should be shown in each electron-dot structure. Emphasize that electron-dot structures allow scientists to quickly view the number of valence electrons for atoms of a given element. Using a notation that only shows valence electrons is useful because these electrons are involved in the formation of chemical bonds.

Exploring Visuals

Electron-Dot Notation Emphasize that the dots around each element symbol are only the valence electrons of the atoms, not the total number of electrons. As students draw the dot structures of heavier elements, you may want them to first draw the s and p orbital distribution of the element.

Collaborate

Draw-Pair-Share Have students work in pairs to complete the Model activity. For each pair of students, designate a "Partner 1" and "Partner 2." To draw the first electron-dot notation, have Partner 1 use the periodic table in **Figure 18** to determine the number of valence electrons that should be placed around the element symbol. Then, have Partner 2 draw the electron-dot notation. Last, have Partner 1 check Partner 2's work. Students should trade roles each time they start a new electron-dot notation.

1 The electron-dot notations should be the same as those for lithium through neon but with the correct element symbol: Na—one dot, Mg—two dots, Al—three dots, Si—four dots, P—five dots, S—six dots, Cl—seven dots, Ar—eight dots.

Modeling Atoms with Electron-Dot Notation

Valence electrons will most often interact with the electrons of other atoms in chemical reactions. So, when trying to predict the chemical properties of an element, it is useful to have a model for showing only valence electrons. One way to easily visualize valence electrons is by using electron-dot notation. Electron-dot notation only shows the valence electrons of a particular element. Valence electrons are indicated by dots placed around the element's symbol.

To write an element's electron-dot notation, first determine the number of valence electrons in an atom of that element. Because the periodic table, as shown in Figure 18, is organized by proton number, it also reflects patterns in numbers of valence electrons. For example, hydrogen and lithium are in the first column, or Group 1, and have 1 valence electron. Beryllium is in Group 2 and has 2 valence electrons. Boron is Group 13 and has 3 valence electrons. Carbon is in Group 14 and has 4 valence electrons, and so on. Except for helium, elements in Group 18 have 8 valence electrons, or an *octet*.

Element	Number of valence electrons	Electron-dot notation	Element	Number of valence electrons	Electron-dot notation
Hydrogen	1	H·	Carbon	4	·C̈·
Helium	2	He:	Nitrogen	5	·N̈:
Lithium	1	Li·	Oxygen	6	·Ö:
Beryllium	2	Be·	Fluorine	7	:F̈:
Boron	3	·B̈·	Neon	8	:N̈e:

To draw the correct electron-dot notation for an element, place the corresponding number of valence electrons (as dots) around the element's symbol. Each side of the element symbol gets one dot until all four sides have a dot. Dots are then added around the four sides again until all four sides have pairs of two.

1 MODEL Use the information above and the periodic table in Figure 18 to complete the electron-dot notations for the next eight elements after neon (sodium through argon).

| Na | Mg | Al | Si |
| P | S | Cl | Ar |

Patterns

Analyzing the Periodic Table

The periodic table shows all the elements arranged by their atomic number. Because atomic number is equal to the number of protons and electrons in atoms of an element, the periodic table can be used to predict chemical properties of different elements.

Consider the elements in Group 1. They have 1 valence electron and are very reactive. For example, hydrogen is an explosive gas, and lithium, sodium, and potassium metal all react vigorously with water. Elements in Group 17, have 7 valence electrons (one short of an octet) and are also highly reactive. The elements in Group 18, on the other hand, have a full outer energy shell with 8 electrons, and are generally nonreactive.

FIGURE 18: The periodic table lists all the elements by their atomic number in rows and columns.

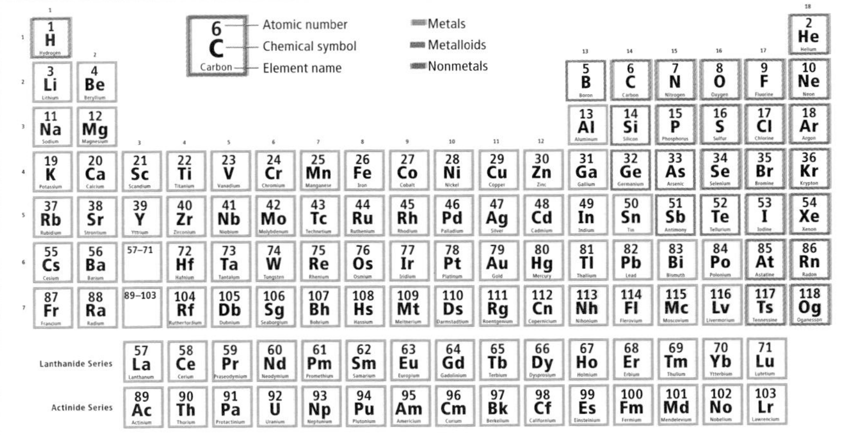

							Atomic number			Metals								
						6				Metalloids								
						C	Chemical symbol			Nonmetals								
						Carbon	Element name											

1 H																		2 He
3 Li	4 Be											5 B	6 C	7 N	8 O	9 F	10 Ne
11 Na	12 Mg											13 Al	14 Si	15 P	16 S	17 Cl	18 Ar
19 K	20 Ca	21 Sc	22 Ti	23 V	24 Cr	25 Mn	26 Fe	27 Co	28 Ni	29 Cu	30 Zn	31 Ga	32 Ge	33 As	34 Se	35 Br	36 Kr
37 Rb	38 Sr	39 Y	40 Zr	41 Nb	42 Mo	43 Tc	44 Ru	45 Rh	46 Pd	47 Ag	48 Cd	49 In	50 Sn	51 Sb	52 Te	53 I	54 Xe
55 Cs	56 Ba	57–71	72 Hf	73 Ta	74 W	75 Re	76 Os	77 Ir	78 Pt	79 Au	80 Hg	81 Tl	82 Pb	83 Bi	84 Po	85 At	86 Rn
87 Fr	88 Ra	89–103	104 Rf	105 Db	106 Sg	107 Bh	108 Hs	109 Mt	110 Ds	111 Rg	112 Cn	113 Nh	114 Fl	115 Mc	116 Lv	117 Ts	118 Og

| Lanthanide Series | 57 La | 58 Ce | 59 Pr | 60 Nd | 61 Pm | 62 Sm | 63 Eu | 64 Gd | 65 Tb | 66 Dy | 67 Ho | 68 Er | 69 Tm | 70 Yb | 71 Lu |
| Actinide Series | 89 Ac | 90 Th | 91 Pa | 92 U | 93 Np | 94 Pu | 95 Am | 96 Cm | 97 Bk | 98 Cf | 99 Es | 100 Fm | 101 Md | 102 No | 103 Lr |

2 **INFER** Based on their location on the periodic table, what can you infer about the chemical properties of elements in Group 2 of the periodic table? Would you expect these elements to readily react with other substances as compared to other groups? Explain your answer.

_____

_____

_____

_____

© Houghton Mifflin Harcourt Publishing Company

3 **Evidence Notebook** Two elements that make up gases in Earth's atmosphere are nitrogen and oxygen. Use the periodic table to explain how many valence electrons these elements have. How might differences in the electron distribution of these elements relate to the aurora polaris?

CCC **Patterns**

Emphasize to students the importance of patterns in helping scientists understand nature and explain **everyday phenomena.** While observing properties of a single element can be useful, observing and comparing properties of many elements is even more useful because it allows scientists to observe patterns that help them relate structure to function.

Exploring Visuals

Patterns in Elements Have students label Groups 1, 2, and 13–18 of the periodic table in **Figure 18** with the number of valence electrons that elements in that group have. Then, have them read the text on this page and use it to label the most reactive and least reactive groups of elements. Help students see that patterns in the number of valence electrons can be used to make predictions about properties such as reactivity.

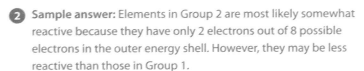

2 Sample answer: Elements in Group 2 are most likely somewhat reactive because they have only 2 electrons out of 8 possible electrons in the outer energy shell. However, they may be less reactive than those in Group 1.

Evidence Notebook

3 Nitrogen has 5 valence electrons, and oxygen has 6 valence electrons. The energy levels in the electron clouds of these elements most likely differ, and this might be why the elements give off different colors.

FORMATIVE ASSESSMENT
3-Minute Pause Have students pause to think of the concepts presented in this Exploration and in the lesson as a whole. Have them respond to the following prompts.

I became more aware of . . .

I didn't realize that . . .

I still don't understand . . .

Have volunteers share their responses with the class

TAKE IT FURTHER Language Arts

Collaborate

You may choose to assign this activity or direct students to the Interactive Online Student Edition, where they can choose from all available paths. These activities can be assigned individually, to pairs, or to small groups.

Differentiate Instruction

MTSS/RTI Use the image in **Figure 19** to help students summarize the content of the article. Ask questions such as, *What is the purpose of the accelerator plate?* Guide students toward the correct answers. Provide authentic feedback, and ask open-ended questions that invite students to engage in deeper reflection about the content of the article and their own interests related to it.

Extension Encourage students to present their blog posts to the class. Have students practice presentation skills such as speaking audibly, engaging with the audience, and answering questions.

1 Sample answer: The model would consist of metal balls of different masses. You would roll the metal balls past a strong magnet and measure the angle of deflection.

TAKE IT FURTHER

Language Arts

Mass Spectrometry

Imagine you needed to identify an unknown substance. How might you determine its identity? Scientists use a method called mass spectrometry to estimate the purity of samples, monitor complex chemical and biochemical reactions, and identify the composition of samples. Mass spectrometry can also be used to identify new compounds and organic structures quickly and easily.

In a mass spectrometer, shown in Figure 19, atoms in a sample pass through a high-energy beam of electrons. This beam knocks off one or more of the atoms' electrons, giving the atoms a positive charge. These positively charged particles are called ions. When these ions are projected through a strong magnetic field, their paths change.

The change in path, or deflection, of each particle in the sample depends on its mass. The heavier particles have the most inertia and so their path is deflected the least. The paths of the lighter particles are deflected the most. This separates the particles by mass. Finally, positions where the particles hit a detector plate are used to calculate their relative masses. Scientists can then identify the elements found in a sample by knowing their masses.

1 EXPLAIN Imagine you wanted to construct a physical model to demonstrate how a spectrometer works. What would your model consist of?

_____

_____

_____

_____

An important use of mass spectrometry is in the study of individual elements. For example, scientists can use mass spectrometry to determine the average atomic mass of an element. It can also be used to determine the mass of individual isotopes of an element.

Carbon has two stable isotopes, carbon-12 and carbon-13. Data from mass spectrometry shows that the ratio of the masses of carbon-12 and carbon-13 is

$$\frac{\text{mass}^{13}\text{C}}{\text{mass}^{12}\text{C}} = 1.0836$$

Because the atomic mass of carbon-12 is exactly 12 u by definition, this ratio can be used to calculate the mass of carbon-13.

$$\text{mass}^{13}\text{C} = 1.0836 \times 12\ \text{u} = 13.0034\ \text{u}$$

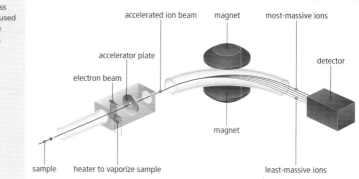

FIGURE 19: A mass spectrometer is used to determine the mass of an atom.

accelerated ion beam   magnet   most-massive ions

accelerator plate

electron beam

detector

sample   heater to vaporize sample   magnet   least-massive ions

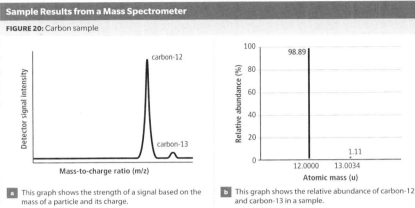

Sample Results from a Mass Spectrometer

FIGURE 20: Carbon sample

a This graph shows the strength of a signal based on the mass of a particle and its charge.

b This graph shows the relative abundance of carbon-12 and carbon-13 in a sample.

Mass spectrometry can be used to determine the percentage composition of a sample of particles of known masses. Scientists also use mass spectrometry to identify the chemical composition of a compound based on the mass-to-charge ratio of the particles.

For example, the graph in Figure 20a shows how signal intensity can be used to determine the mass-to-charge ratio of carbon-12 and carbon-13. The graph in Figure 20b shows how a mass spectrometer can be used to determine the relative abundance of these two isotopes in a sample.

Practical applications of mass spectrometry include medical applications, such as the study of different proteins. Mass spectrometry has also been used in space to identify the composition of various planets and moons.

Mass spectrometry even helps us learn about our own environment. It can be used to analyze air, soil, and water for pollutants. This technique may also be used to determine how quickly pesticides break down in the environment and identify what they break down into.

2 PREDICT Describe an environmental problem that could be studied using mass spectrometry. Explain how this method would help scientists learn more about the problem.

_____

_____

_____

_____

_____

3 **Language Arts Connection** Conduct research to find an example of how mass spectrometry has helped scientists learn something about the natural world. Then, write a short blog post describing your findings. After writing the first draft, make your blog post more effective by strengthening your writing through revising, editing, and rewriting. Make sure your blog post focuses on what is most significant about the use of spectrometry by the scientists. In addition, implement revisions that make your blog post easy to read, informative, and concise.

| PRACTICE WITH ELECTRON CONFIGURATIONS | EVIDENCE FOR THE ATOMIC MODEL | CRYO-ELECTRON MICROSCOPY | Go online to choose one of these other paths. |

Language Arts Connection
WHST.9-12.5 Develop and strengthen writing as needed by planning, revising, editing, rewriting, or trying a new approach, focusing on addressing what is most significant for a specific purpose and audience.

Before writing their blog post, have students make an outline describing the main points they want to discuss. Remind students to focus on the most important information and think about how they will convey the information in an engaging and understandable way. Next, have students write their first draft and then trade drafts with a partner. Each student in a pair should review their partner's draft and suggest revisions to it. Students should then use the feedback they received from their partner to edit their first draft and continue editing it until it is in its final form.

2 Sample answer: Scientists could use mass spectrometry to determine what compounds are causing pollution-related problems in a lake. The spectrometer would tell scientists the mass of the substances, and they could use this knowledge to determine the identity of the substances.

3 Check students' blog posts for accuracy and clarity. They should be written in a clear and concise manner. You may need to help students as they revise, edit, and rewrite their blog posts to use the best language to clearly present their topic.

Explore Online ▶

Practice with Electron Configurations

Students explore the different orbital shapes and learn how to use Hund's rule, the Aufbau principle, and the Pauli exclusion principle to determine further details about electron configuration.

Evidence for the Atomic Model

Students conduct research and develop a report to explain how the atomic model was refined over many years.

Cryo-Electron Microscopy

Students research and prepare a presentation about the development of cryo-electron microscopy.

EVALUATE Lesson Self-Check

Can You Explain the Phenomenon?

Claims, Evidence, and Reasoning

Have students clearly state their claim—their explanation for the phenomenon they have been investigating throughout this lesson. They should present their reasoning for making this claim, along with evidence such as facts, examples, and statistics that support their claim. You may want to have students present their arguments orally, in writing, or as a debate.

Cultivating Student Questions

Assessing Student Growth Review the list of questions students generated at the beginning of the lesson. Have volunteers select any unanswered questions and suggest how they could be investigated. After approving student plans, have small groups conduct the investigations and report back to the class. As the year progresses, the number of volunteers for this task will likely increase. The sophistication of the means of investigation also may increase. Both outcomes are measures of positive growth that are essential to the scientific mindset and demonstrate that students are beginning to understand that the correct answer is much less important than the means used to investigate the question.

 Evidence Notebook

 Sample answer: Electrons in the atoms that make up atmospheric gases most likely absorb energy from an energy source and move to a higher energy state. When those electrons lose energy and return to their original energy levels, energy is released in the form of light. The color of light given off depends on the specific arrangement of energy levels for that element. This same phenomenon was observed while carrying out flame tests with solutions containing different metal ions. The colors observed during the flame tests were caused by electrons in the metal ions emitting energy when they moved from higher energy levels to lower energy levels. Electrons in the atoms of atmospheric gases are likely to exhibit a similar pattern of behavior.

EVALUATE

Lesson Self-Check

CAN YOU EXPLAIN THE PHENOMENON?

FIGURE 21: The northern lights is a phenomenon that lights up the sky with different colors.

The aurora polaris are multicolored lights seen in the night sky near the northern and southern poles. These lights are usually pink, green, yellow, blue, violet, red, and sometimes orange and white, and are often seen as a glow moving across the sky. These lights are not visible every night—they only occur when conditions are just right. Sometimes the colors are very faint and barely visible while other times they can provide dazzling displays. The aurora polaris may also be observed from the space station. Scientists have even observed the same phenomenon at the poles of other planets in our solar system.

Evidence Notebook Refer to your notes in your Evidence Notebook to make a claim about how atomic structure is related to the different colors seen in the aurora polaris. Your explanation should include a discussion of the following points:

Claim How is atomic structure related to the different colors displayed as part of the aurora polaris phenomenon?

Evidence Give specific evidence to support your claim.

Reasoning Explain, in detail, how the evidence you cited supports your claim.

 Formal Assessment Go online for student self-checks and other assessments.

CHECKPOINTS

Check Your Understanding

1. Chlorine has a total of 17 electrons and 7 valence electrons. Why are these two numbers different?
   - ○ **a.** Valence electrons are the electrons in the innermost orbital.
   - ○ **b.** Valence electrons are the electrons in the outermost energy shell.
   - ○ **c.** Some electrons are located in the nucleus of the atom.
   - ○ **d.** Some electrons are located outside the atom.

2. Why does the mass number for an element differ from the average atomic mass for that element?
   - ○ **a.** The mass number only accounts for the number of protons, while the average atomic mass only accounts for the average number of neutrons.
   - ○ **b.** The mass number accounts for the number of protons and neutrons, while the average atomic mass only accounts for the average number of protons.
   - ○ **c.** The mass number accounts for the mass of each isotope. The average atomic mass is a weighted average of the number of neutrons.
   - ○ **d.** The mass number only accounts for the mass of protons and neutrons, while the average atomic mass is a weighted average of the masses of the isotopes.

3. Select the correct terms to complete the statement.

   Electron-dot notation shows only the electrons in the innermost | outermost energy shell of an atom. These electrons are called valence | orbital electrons and are | are not involved in chemical reactions. Elements with a full outer energy shell are typically very reactive | unreactive.

4. Select from the number values below to complete the statement. A value may be used more than once or not at all.

   38   50   88

   Strontium has an atomic number of 38 and an atomic mass number of 88. Therefore, it has

   _____ protons, _____ neutrons, and

   _____ electrons.

5. A scientist picks up a sample of an element. She thinks it might be a metal. Which of the following properties would support her conclusion? Select all correct answers.
   - ☐ **a.** The element is shiny.
   - ☐ **b.** The element is dull.
   - ☐ **c.** The element partially conducts electricity.
   - ☐ **d.** The element is a good conductor of electricity.
   - ☐ **e.** The element is very brittle.

6. Which of these claims are supported by the results of a flame test? Select all correct answers.
   - ☐ **a.** Different metallic elements give off different colors when they are burned in a flame.
   - ☐ **b.** Electrons absorb energy when they move from one atom to another.
   - ☐ **c.** Protons absorb light when exposed to electricity.
   - ☐ **d.** Neutrons give off energy in the form of light when they absorb energy from a source such as a flame.
   - ☐ **e.** Electrons emit energy when they move from a higher energy level to a lower energy level.

Answers

1. b
2. d
3. outermost, valence, are, unreactive
4. 38, 50, 38
5. a, d
6. a, e

© Houghton Mifflin Harcourt Publishing Company

Answers

7. Valence electrons are the outer electrons in an atom, and they participate in forming bonds during chemicals reactions. So, they determine how the atom chemically reacts.

8. Oxygen has an atomic number of 8, so the model should show 8 total electrons. There should be 2 electrons in the 1s orbital and 2 electrons in the 2s orbital. The first of the 2p orbitals should have 2 electrons, and the second and third of the 2p orbitals should have 1 electron each. The 3s and 3p orbitals should be empty.

9. Student answers should show an understanding of the gold foil experiment and what it implied. Students should know that alpha particles have a positive charge and are repelled by the positively charged nucleus. Answers should cite the experimental evidence that led to the discovery of the nucleus. **Sample answer:** More particles would pass through the aluminum foil than through the gold foil because the nuclei of aluminum atoms have only 13 protons, and the nuclei of gold atoms have 79 protons. Fewer alpha particles would bounce back or be deflected because the positive nuclei are smaller and would be harder to hit.

Make Your Own Study Guide

Have students create a study guide that helps them organize and visualize the important information from this lesson. Their study guide should focus on the main ideas from this lesson and tie multiple ideas together. Students can make an outline, a concept map, a graphic organizer, or another representation.

EVALUATE

CHECKPOINTS (continued)

7. What are valence electrons, and why are they important to consider when predicting the properties of elements?

_____

_____

_____

_____

8. Complete the electron configuration for oxygen using the model below.

◯   ◯   ◯◯◯   ◯   ◯◯◯
1s   2s   2p   3s   3p

9. A chemist repeats the gold foil experiment, but she uses foil made of aluminum (atomic number 13) instead of gold (atomic number 79). How would you expect her results to compare with the experiment that used gold foil?

_____

_____

_____

_____

_____

_____

MAKE YOUR OWN STUDY GUIDE

In your Evidence Notebook, design a study guide that supports the main ideas from this lesson:
Chemical elements are described by their atomic mass and mass number.

Valence electrons determine the chemical properties of elements, such as how they react with other substances.

Remember to include the following information in your study guide:
- Use examples that model main ideas.
- Record explanations for the phenomena you investigated.
- Use evidence to support your explanations. Your support can include drawings, data, graphs, laboratory conclusions, and other evidence recorded throughout the lesson.

Consider how patterns observed at different scales can explain the behavior of elements.

Investigating Patterns in the Periodic Table

Building to the Performance Expectations

The learning experiences in this lesson prepare students for mastery of

HS-PS1-1 Use the periodic table as a model to predict the relative properties of elements based on the patterns of electrons in the outermost energy level of atoms.

 **Trace Tool to the NGSS**

Go online to view the complete coverage of standards across lessons, units, and grade levels.

 **Science & Engineering Practices**

Developing and Using Models
Use a model to predict the relationships between systems or between components of a system.

Scientific Knowledge is Open to Revision in Light of New Evidence
Most scientific knowledge is quite durable but is, in principle, subject to change based on new evidence and/or reinterpretation of existing evidence.

Scientific Knowledge is Based on Empirical Evidence
Science includes the process of coordinating patterns of evidence with current theory.

Scientific Investigations Use a Variety of Methods
Science investigations use diverse methods and do not always use the same set of procedures to obtain data.

Scientific Investigations Use a Variety of Methods
Scientific inquiry is characterized by a common set of values that include: logical thinking, precision, open-mindedness, objectivity, skepticism, replicability of results, and honest and ethical reporting of findings.

 Disciplinary Core Ideas

PS1.A Structure and Properties of Matter
Each atom has a charged substructure consisting of a nucleus, which is made of protons and neutrons, surrounded by electrons. (HS-PS1-1)

PS1.A Structure and Properties of Matter
The periodic table orders elements horizontally by the number of protons in the atom's nucleus and places those with similar chemical properties in columns. The repeating patterns of this table reflect patterns of outer electron states. (HS-PS1-1)

ETS1.B Developing Possible Solutions
When evaluating solutions, it is important to take into account a range of constraints including cost, safety, reliability and aesthetics and to consider social, cultural and environmental impacts. (HS-ETS1-3)

CCC Crosscutting Concepts

Patterns
Different patterns may be observed at each of the scales at which a system is studied and can provide evidence for causality in explanations of phenomena.

Science is a Human Endeavor
Scientific knowledge is a result of human endeavor, imagination, and creativity.

ELA STANDARDS

RST.9-10.7 Translate quantitative or technical information expressed in words into visual form and translate information expressed visually or mathematically into words.

WHST.9-12.7 Conduct short as well as more sustained research projects to answer a question.

WHST.9-12.9 Draw evidence from informational texts to support analysis, reflection and research.

Supporting All Students, All Standards

Integrating the Three Dimensions

In this lesson, students investigate patterns in the periodic table (CCC Patterns) and use them to make predictions about the properties of elements (DCI PS1.A). Students explore early attempts to categorize the elements and how the periodic table has changed over time (SEP Scientific Knowledge is Open to Revision in Light of New Evidence, DCI PS1.A). They model Mendeleev's process for the development of the periodic table by arranging paint chip cards based on different patterns and using these patterns to find missing cards (CCC Patterns). Students examine the periodic table to learn how patterns in ionization energies, atomic radii, electronegativities, and number of outer electrons relate to an element's position on the periodic table (SEP Developing and Using Models, DCI PS1.A, CCC Patterns). They construct explanations about how atomic structure influences these trends (SEP Developing and Using Models, DCI PS1.A).

Preassessment

Have students complete the unit pretest or see the Assessment Guide.

Build on Prior Knowledge

Students may need a review of the following concepts:

- the structure of the atom, including subatomic particles
- determining atomic number and mass number for an element
- electron configurations

Ask students to list what they know about the structure of atoms. Have them draw a diagram of a carbon atom (atomic number 6, mass number 12). Drawings should show that the nucleus has six protons and six neutrons, with a total +6 charge. There should be six electrons, two paired and four unpaired, with a total –6 charge.

Have students share their list and drawing with a partner and discuss any differences. Compile a classroom list that can be added to over the course of this lesson.

Professional Development Go online to view **Professional Development videos** with strategies to integrate CCCs and SEPs, including the ones used in this lesson.

Content Background

The periodic table had no single developer. From the early 19th century, chemists had been proposing ways to organize the known elements according to their physical and chemical properties, how they combined to form compounds (i.e., their valance), and their average atomic masses. As the list of elements became larger and the determinations of atomic masses became more accurate, classification schemes became more complex.

Most attribute the first true periodic table to Dmitri Mendeleev, who published his table in 1869. What distinguished Mendeleev's table from earlier organizational schemes was that it contained the implicit idea that relationships between recognized trends in element properties and atomic masses could be used to both refine the values for atomic masses and predict the existence of new elements. Mendeleev famously predicted the existence of the elements scandium, gallium, and germanium based on "holes" he identified in his table to preserve the trends he observed.

Mendeleev knew nothing about the existence of protons or atomic number, the basis for organization in the modern periodic table. But Mendeleev's work demonstrates how identifying patterns in the natural world can be a powerful aid for uncovering causal relationships and making predictions.

Differentiate Instruction

KEY WORDS

- atomic radius
- ionization energy
- electronegativity

ELL SUPPORT

Have students write the key terms in their notebooks. Help them notice that each word is made up of one or more word parts that offer a clue as to the word's meaning. For example, you can suggest that ionization has something to do with ions, particles with net electric charges due to the loss or gain of one or more electrons. Students should then surmise that ionization energy might be the energy required to form ions.

ENGAGE: Investigative Phenomenon

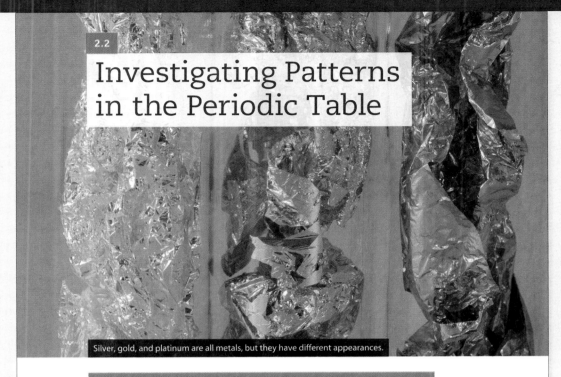

2.2

Investigating Patterns in the Periodic Table

Silver, gold, and platinum are all metals, but they have different appearances.

CAN YOU EXPLAIN THE PHENOMENON?

For centuries, chemists have identified and studied the elements that are naturally found on Earth. Some elements, such as silver, gold, and platinum, have similar physical and chemical properties. For example, these elements do not react violently with water or oxygen. Other metals, such as potassium, do. Only about 90 elements are known to exist naturally. Other, synthetic elements can be made in a lab. Using the periodic table, scientists are able to predict some of the properties these elements should have.

1 **PREDICT** How do you think scientists can use properties of existing elements to predict the existence of synthetic elements?

_____

_____

_____

_____

2 📓 **Evidence Notebook** As you explore the lesson, gather evidence to explain how the periodic table can be used to predict the behavior of new elements.

© Houghton Mifflin Harcourt Publishing Company · Image Credits: ©Statu nascend/iStock / Getty Images Plus/Getty Images

Lesson 2 Investigating Patterns in the Periodic Table **83**

Build on Prior Lessons

In Lesson 1, students learned about atomic structure. Lesson 2 builds on those concepts as students explore how the periodic table can be used to predict the structure and behavior of an element's atoms.

Lesson Objective

Students explore patterns in the periodic table and use them to make predictions about the behavior of elements.

Cultivating Student Questions

Have students look at the photo of silver, gold, and platinum. Prompt them to ask all questions that come to mind about the metals, such as how they are isolated from nature and how they are used. Record the questions on chart paper, and then sort the questions based on their focus. Have students reflect on this list throughout the lesson and check off questions as they are answered.

Can You Explain the Phenomenon?

The Investigative Phenomenon is the focus of the lesson. Students are asked to record their initial thoughts about how scientists can use properties of existing elements to predict the existence of synthetic ones.

Students will collect evidence related to this phenomenon throughout the lesson and revisit the question at the end of the lesson to use what they have learned to explain the different patterns of behavior in different groups of elements.

1 **Sample answer:** Scientists can predict the existence of synthetic elements by looking at gaps in the periodic table. Identifying patterns in the properties of elements above, below, or adjacent to the gap in the periodic table helps scientists predict the existence and behavior of these synthetic elements.

📓 **Evidence Notebook**

2 The topic of using the periodic table to predict the behavior of new elements will be revisited throughout this lesson.

Lesson 2 Investigating Patterns in the Periodic Table 83

EXPLORATION 1 Modeling Periodic Trends

3D Learning Objective

Students **develop and use a model** similar to the periodic table to explore how the periodic table shows **patterns** in the **structure and properties** of elements.

Everyday phenomena discussed throughout the Explorations of the lesson can often be used to connect the science content to students' personal experiences.

Hands-On Lab 👥 Small Groups 🕐 45 minutes
Modeling Periodic Trends

SEP Developing and Using Models

Students make a model of a periodic table based on colors of paint chip cards rather than on reactivity of elements. They construct explanations about the patterns of properties in the periodic table.

Advance Preparation Place paint chip cards of similar colors in a bag for each group. Leave gaps in the colors for students to discover.

Collaborate

Discussion As student groups plan their procedure, have them discuss how Mendeleev arranged elements according to properties, why he left gaps if there was no known element with predicted properties for that spot, and how this relates to the card arrangement.

DCI PS1.A Structure and Properties of Matter

Remind students that they previously investigated patterns of chemical reactivity of different metals with hydrochloric acid. What did they learn in that lab that they could apply in this lab?

❶ If the color change from card to card is not continuous, a card is probably missing. When choosing an arrangement most beneficial for customers, consider which pattern leaves the fewest gaps, is least confusing for customers, and is aesthetically pleasing.

Hands-On Lab
Modeling Periodic Trends

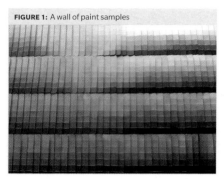

FIGURE 1: A wall of paint samples

When trying to decide what color to paint a wall, you might view paint samples to compare your choices. Samples on a palette, such as those shown in Figure 1, might have a similar color but vary by shade or intensity. For instance, samples on a palette containing different shades of red might be arranged from pink to maroon. Another palette may arrange shades of blue in a similar way. Figure 1 shows just a small selection of paint palettes a store may carry. You can also obtain paint chip cards, which are individual cards that have just one paint color on them, from stores.

Imagine that you work in a paint store and you receive a shipment of paint chip cards from your supplier. You have a box full of paint chip cards of different colors and hues, but the supplier failed to inform you how many cards there should be. You first need to determine if any cards are missing. Then, you need to find the best way to display the paint cards so your customers can easily find the colors and hues they're looking for.

RESEARCH QUESTION Recognizing patterns is an extremely important skill for scientists. How might a chemist use patterns to understand phenomena?

❶ **MAKE A CLAIM**

What patterns will help you determine if any paint chip cards are missing from the set? What should you consider when determining which arrangement of paint chip cards is most beneficial to customers?

_____

_____

_____

_____

_____

MATERIALS
• set of paint chip cards

PLAN THE INVESTIGATION

Obtain a set of paint chip cards from your teacher. Lay out all the cards so you can see the colors. Make a list of all the potential ways you can arrange your cards. For each arrangement, take notes on how the arrangement will help you find any missing cards. Also note how easily customers would be able to find the paint sample they want using each arrangement.

 Student Lab Worksheet and complete Teacher Support are available online.

CARRY OUT THE INVESTIGATION

Choose the three arrangements you think will work best, and set your paint chip cards according to each plan. Develop a data table to record any missing cards. Take a picture or make a sketch of each arrangement before you set up the next one.

2 ANALYZE

Were any paint chip cards missing from your set? How did you determine they were or were not missing? How would you describe the missing cards to someone?

_____

_____

_____

_____

3 DRAW CONCLUSIONS

Write a conclusion that addresses each of the points below.

Claim What patterns helped you determine whether paint chip cards were missing? What should you consider when determining which arrangement of paint chip cards is most beneficial for customers?

Evidence Give specific examples from your data to support your claim.

Reasoning Explain how the evidence you gave supports your claim. Describe, in detail, the connections between the evidence you cited and the argument you are making.

_____

_____

_____

_____

_____

_____

_____

_____

_____

_____

_____

_____

4 **Evidence Notebook** Based on your observations in this investigation, how might observing patterns in the properties of the elements have helped scientists identify missing elements?

© Houghton Mifflin Harcourt Publishing Company

Differentiate Instruction

MTSS/RTI Ensure that students understand the relationship between arranging paint chips for the lab and arranging elements on the periodic table. Emphasize that arranging the paint chips and arranging the elements according to how they are similar makes the patterns in them easier to understand.

CCC **Patterns**

Have students conclude their investigation by summarizing how the pattern of color of the paint chip cards models the periodic table. What property shows a periodic trend? What other ways could they model the periodic table by connecting to **everyday phenomena**?

2 **Sample answer:** A shade of blue was missing because there were shades of red and green that were similar in brightness that no shade of blue matched. The missing blue card would be similar in brightness to the corresponding red and green color chips.

3 **Sample answer:** To determine if paint chips were missing, we organized the cards so that hues of similar brightness were arranged in columns. That way there will be a gap if a color does not have a hue represented that matches the others in brightness. When we arranged the cards, there was a gap where no blue card matched the brightness of the red and green. This pattern is useful for customers because they can easily find a particular color hue and compare it with the others.

Evidence Notebook

4 Students should understand that scientists can organize elements by their properties and look for gaps in patterns to identify the properties of elements that may not be known. This is how scientists knew that many of the synthetic elements should exist and how the most recently discovered elements were predicted to exist.

FORMATIVE ASSESSMENT

Quick Write Have students write a short evaluation of whether this lab was an accurate model for making a periodic table.

EXPLORATION 2 Predicting the Properties of Elements

3D Learning Objective

Students explore how the periodic table orders elements and predict the relationships between the patterns in the table and properties of the elements.

Collaborate

Discussion Display a periodic table. Start a discussion about it by asking students to share what they have learned about it previously.

Explore Online

Hands-On Lab Small Groups 45 minutes

The Mendeleev Lab of 1869

SEP Developing and Using Models

Students use their knowledge of periodic trends to determine the identity of nine unknown elements on Mendeleev's periodic table. *Student lab worksheet and teacher support available online.*

Exploring Visuals

Ask students to compare Mendeleev's periodic table in **Figure 2** with the modern periodic table. In Mendeleev's table, periods are vertical and groups are horizontal. ***Ask:*** *How is this pattern different from the modern periodic table?* It is the opposite of the modern periodic table, which has horizontal periods and vertical groups.

CCC Patterns

Give an example of how elements in the same group of the modern periodic table have similar properties. For example, Group 1 elements are all metals that are very reactive in water. Have students look for to see if there are similar patterns of properties across a period.

1. Mendeleev was organizing the elements by both their atomic mass and by patterns in their properties. He had to leave gaps in order to fit the known elements into this pattern. He predicted that each gap represented an undiscovered element.

EXPLORATION 2

Predicting the Properties of Elements

In the last activity, you likely observed and used a gradually changing pattern when arranging the paint chips. In the 1800s, scientists used a similar approach when trying to organize the known elements. They began by noting patterns in the properties of elements and how these properties changed with increasing and decreasing atomic mass.

Organizing the Periodic Table

Explore Online

Hands-On Lab

The Mendeleev Lab of 1869 Use your knowledge of the periodic table to determine the identity of nine unknown elements.

Russian chemist and teacher Dmitri Mendeleev published the first periodic table in 1869 as an attempt to include all elements in one classification scheme. To do this, he began by writing element names and their characteristics on separate note cards and arranging them in various ways. This helped him compare atomic mass and other chemical and physical properties of each element. When arranging the elements by increasing atomic mass, he saw that chemical properties occurred in a repeating pattern.

FIGURE 2: Mendeleev's original periodic table

			Ti=50	Zr=90	?=180.
			V=51	Nb=94	Ta=182.
			Cr=52	Mo=96	W=186.
			Mn=55	Rh=104,4	Pt=197,4
			Fe=56	Ru=104,4	Ir=198.
			Ni=Co=59	Pl=106,6,	Os=199.
H=1			Cu=63,4	Ag=108	Hg=200.
	Be=9,4	Mg=24	Zn=65,2	Cd=112	
	B=11	Al=27,4	?=68	Ur=116	Au=197?
	C=12	Si=28	?=70	Su=118	
	N=14	P=31	As=75	Sb=122	Bi=210
	O=16	S=32	Se=79,4	Te=128?	
	F=19	Cl=35,5	Br=80	I=127	
Li=7	Na=23	K=39	Rb=85,4	Cs=133	Tl=204
		Ca=40	Sr=87,6	Ba=137	Pb=207.
		?=45	Ce=92		
		?Er=56	La=94		
		?Yt=60	Di=95		
		?In=75,6	Th=118?		

1. **PREDICT** Why do you think Mendeleev left gaps in the periodic table shown in Figure 2?

Mendeleev arranged the elements so the atomic mass increased going down a column. He arranged the columns so elements in the same row shared similar properties. Sometimes, however, he found that he needed to reverse the order of atomic masses in order to make elements with similar properties fall in the same row. Notice that iodine, I, is listed after tellurium, Te, even though iodine has a smaller atomic mass. This arrangement allowed iodine to be placed in a group of elements with which it shares similar properties.

Recognizing Periodic Patterns

Mendeleev's table of elements revealed a repeating pattern, or *periodicity*, of properties, hence the name *periodic table*. Mendeleev's ability to explain known patterns and predict unknown elements led to the acceptance of the table and the idea of periodic patterns. Scientists continue to study elements to better understand their properties.

In 1913, British chemist Henry Moseley discovered a new periodic pattern based on nuclear charge, or the number of the protons in the nucleus. Organizing the periodic table based on atomic number better fit the patterns of chemical and physical properties Mendeleev had observed. Moseley's work led to our current understanding of atomic number and the order of elements on the modern periodic table, shown in Figure 3.

FIGURE 3: The periodic table shows which elements are classified as metals, metalloids, or nonmetals.

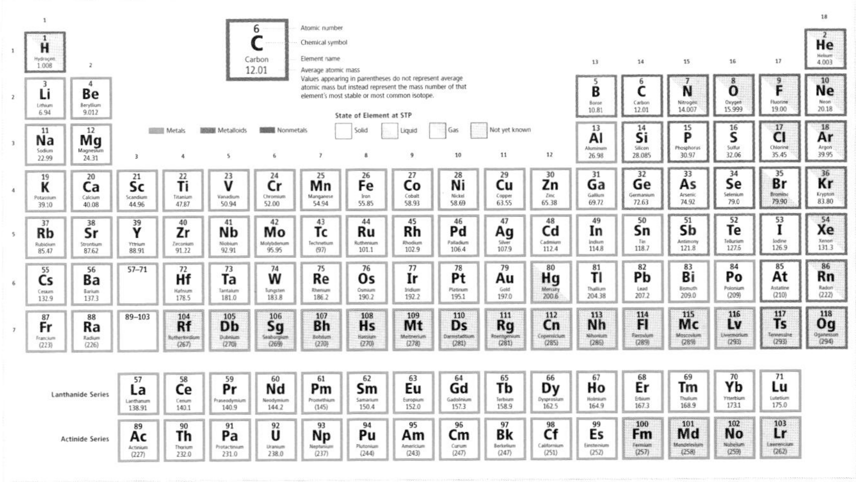

2 **ANALYZE** What patterns do you notice in the table in terms of protons, electrons, and valence electrons? How might these relate to an element being a metal or a nonmetal?

_____

_____

_____

_____

As scientists continued to study the properties of elements, they identified additional patterns that supported what would be known as the periodic law. The periodic law states that the chemical and physical properties of elements are periodic functions of the elements' atomic number. A row across the periodic table is called a *period*. A column down the periodic table is called a *group* or *family*. Adjacent elements in a period may have similar or different properties, but elements in the same group have similar properties. For example, chlorine, Cl, and argon, Ar, are adjacent in Period 3 but are in different groups, and they have very different properties. Chlorine is very reactive and easily forms compounds. Argon is nonreactive and does not readily form compounds.

History of Science

Remind students that scientists constantly look for order in the universe. Explain that early chemists searched for ways to organize the elements before the establishment of the periodic table, but no one was able to discern the relationships among the elements. German chemist Julius Lothar Meyer arranged the elements by atomic mass and produced findings similar to those of Mendeleev. Meyer published his findings in 1870, one year after Mendeleev published his. Meyer was among the first chemists to discover trends in the properties of the elements, and many historians consider him to be the cofounder of the periodic table. After describing these events, have small groups of students spend a few minutes discussing the importance of scientists looking for order in the elements. Then have each group share their ideas with the class.

DCI PS1.A Structure and Properties of Matter

To emphasize that the modern periodic table arranges elements according to increasing atomic numbers rather than atomic masses, have students examine the atomic numbers on the periodic table to see if they can spot a pattern. Then have them do the same with atomic masses. Students will find that Ar and K, Co and Ni, and Te and I are reversed in terms of atomic mass, but all elements are in order in terms of atomic number. Explain that Mendeleev reordered elements in his table to preserve the periodic relationship in properties. How did this predict atomic number?

2 Encourage students to use the table's keys and coloring of the boxes to identify patterns. They might notice that protons and electrons both increase by one when the atomic number increases by one. Groups contain elements with the same number of valence electrons. Metals have few valence electrons and are on the left side of the periodic table. Nonmetals have more valence electrons and are on the right side.

Claims, Evidence, and Reasoning

Have student groups assign letters or numbers to all or some of the elements. They should then write the chemical and physical characteristics of each element on index cards. Students should make a claim describing a property that can be used to arrange the elements into a periodic table. Have students formulate their own periodic table according to their claim. They should organize the "unknown" elements according to this property, providing evidence for why the arrangement is valid. Students may organize their elements in a manner similar to the modern periodic table, or they may develop less orthodox styles. They should provide reasoning for using that property and arrangement to create their periodic table.

DCI **PS1.A Structure and Properties of Matter**

As students study **Figure 5,** emphasize that the lanthanides and actinides are not "extra" elements. They have similar properties to the other elements in their respective period. These elements simply do not fit in the periodic table as it is currently arranged.

Physics Connection

Explain to students that superconductors are materials that conduct electricity with no resistance. This means they can carry an electric current indefinitely without losing energy due to friction. Superconductors are used to make powerful electromagnets, which have applications in many **everyday phenomena,** such as maglev trains, MRI medical imaging machines, fusion reactors, and particle accelerators. Have students research one of these applications of superconductors or another everyday phenomenon and present their findings to the class.

1 Students may mistakenly think the lanthanides and actinides are in their own groups, but they are printed below the main table simply because it is easier to fit all the elements on a single page. Adding these series to the main body of the periodic table would also have made the table confusing to look at and analyze.

2 Potassium and sodium are in the same group, so they have similar chemical properties. Both of these alkali metals would react with the same nonmetals to produce similar compounds.

Grouping Elements Using Properties

FIGURE 4: Metals and nonmetals

Elements are categorized as metals, metalloids, or nonmetals. Some examples are pictured in Figure 4. The metals are divided into several categories, which can be seen in Figure 5, based on their specific properties. Group 1 contains the alkali metals, which have low melting points and are very reactive. The alkaline-earth metals located in Group 2 are stronger, denser, and have higher melting points than alkali metals. Groups 3 through 12 are transition metals. These metals are less reactive and some exist as free elements in nature. Post-transition metals are usually more brittle and poor conductors. The lanthanides are shiny, reactive, and soft. Actinides are radioactive, and most are synthetic elements.

1 **ANALYZE** The lanthanides and actinides belong to Periods 6 and 7, respectively. Why do you think they are grouped below the other elements?

Most nonmetals are gases at normal temperatures but as solids they tend to be dull, brittle, and poor conductors of heat and electric current. The nonmetals are also divided into several groups. For example, Group 17 contains the halogens, which are extremely reactive, toxic, and many are colorful. Metalloids have properties of both metals and nonmetals, being either shiny and malleable or dull and brittle. They are semiconductors, meaning they conduct electric current better than nonmetals but not as well as metals.

FIGURE 5: This periodic table highlights different categories of elements.

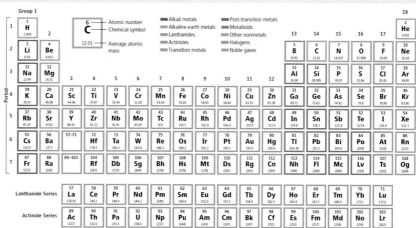

2 **Evidence Notebook** Identify which period and group the elements you are modeling in your unit project belong to. Based on their location on the periodic table, what properties should these elements have?

© Houghton Mifflin Harcourt Publishing Company • Image Credits: (tl) ©Richard Megna/Fundamental Photographs

Patterns in Chemical Properties

Recall that valence electrons are those in the outermost electron shell of an atom. They are the ones most easily gained or lost when atoms interact. Valence electrons play an important role in determining the properties of an element. As a result, an element's location on the periodic table indicates the number of valence electrons it has.

3 PREDICT What pattern do you think exists between the number of valence electrons an element has and its placement on the periodic table?

_____

_____

 Engineering

The Noble Gases

The Group 18 elements are called the noble gases because these elements are all gases that are generally not reactive. The Group 18 elements are rarely found combined with other elements in compounds, so they were seen as being similar to nobility—not mixing with the "common" elements. Noble gases have extremely low reactivity because of their valence shell electron configuration.

4 EXPLAIN Which properties do the valence shells of every noble gas have in common? Select all correct answers.

☐ **a.** All electrons are paired.　　☐ **c.** All electrons are unpaired.

☐ **b.** They are filled with electrons.　　☐ **d.** They have exactly two electrons.

The unreactive nature of noble gases makes them useful in many ways. Helium is used in toy and weather balloons because it floats in air and is not flammable. Argon is used during welding to shield hot metals from reacting with oxygen and other gases in air. Argon is also used in fluorescent lighting and other gas discharge tubes.

Helium has two valence electrons, and the other noble gases have eight valence electrons. Other main-group elements can become more stable by gaining, losing, or sharing electrons so they also have full valence shells like the noble gases. The millions of unique natural and synthetic chemical compounds are due to the chemical reactivity of most of the naturally occurring elements.

5 APPLY Complete the statement by selecting the correct terms.

Sodium, Na, a Group 1 element, has one | two | seven | eight valence electron(s). It can easily react with chlorine, Cl, a Group 17 element, with one | two | seven | eight valence electron(s). During bonding, each sodium atom gains one | gains seven | loses one | loses seven electron(s) to become stable, and each chlorine atom gains one | gains seven | loses one | loses seven electron(s) to become stable.

6 **Evidence Notebook** How could modern scientists use the periodic table to predict the properties of newly synthesized elements? Assume the synthesized elements are stable enough for their properties to be observed.

Collaborate

Have students work with a partner to write a paragraph explaining what it means if an element has extremely low reactivity and how this applies to its placement on the periodic table. Students should explain that elements of low reactivity undergo fewer chemical changes. The noble gases are highly unreactive and are in Group 18.

ccc Cause and Effect

Industrial applications of lanthanides, elements 57 through 71, include metallurgy, glass, ceramics, catalysts, and phosphors. Have students research mining methods, including surface and subsurface mining. They should also research the environmental impact of such mining methods.

3 Sample answer: Elements in a group have the same number of valence electrons, but the number of valence electrons increases from left to right across a period.

4 a, b

5 one, seven, loses one, gains one

Evidence Notebook

6 Sample answer: Scientists could use it to determine how many protons and valence electrons a new element will have and to determine whether that element should have properties of a metal, nonmetal, or metalloid.

FORMATIVE ASSESSMENT

Card Responses Have students write *metal, nonmetal,* and *metalloid* on three notecards. Then call out the names of elements in the periodic table, and have students raise the appropriate card to show their understanding of each of the elements. This activity can be made more specific by having students write more specific categories on their cards, such as *noble gas, lanthanide, actinide,* and *alkali metal.*

EXPLORATION 3 Patterns in Atomic Size

3D Learning Objective

Students **develop and use models** to explain how atoms have **charged substructures** that determine the chemical properties of elements. Students use an understanding of how the periodic table orders elements to understand **patterns** in atomic size.

History of Science

In 1905, Albert Einstein used **everyday phenomena** to calculate the size of molecules. Based on observations of sugar dissolved in water, he calculated the diameter of the sugar molecules. Later scientists determined the sizes of atoms by observing how crystals scattered x-rays. Have students research and make a timeline of other atomic size discoveries and ways everyday phenomena were used.

Differentiate Instruction

Extension Have students compare the atomic radii of sodium and cesium in **Figure 7.** They should see that cesium has a larger atomic radius, so it has a greater effective nuclear charge. This should negate the larger size caused by more energy levels, but a cesium atom is larger. Ask students to explain, based on electron shielding.

SEP **Developing and Using Models**

Collaborate Have students debate whether atomic radius can be accurately measured if atoms are bonded rather than simply next to each other. They should recognize that bonds draw atoms closer. The distance between nuclei is smaller than if the atoms were unbonded.

1 The exact locations of electrons in an atom cannot be pinpointed. The boundary of the electron cloud is not well defined, so it cannot be used to determine atomic radius.

2 Within a period, elements with lower atomic numbers tend to have larger atomic radii, so Al has a larger atomic radius than P because it has a lower atomic number. In a group, a higher atomic number tends to have a larger atomic radius. Na has a smaller atomic number than K, so Na has a smaller atomic radius than K.

EXPLORATION 3

Patterns in Atomic Size

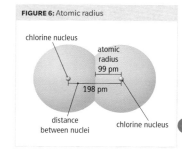

FIGURE 6: Atomic radius

chlorine nucleus

atomic radius 99 pm

198 pm

distance between nuclei

chlorine nucleus

The exact size of an atom is difficult to define. Ideally, the size of an atom is defined by the edge of its outermost shell, but that is not easy to measure. One way to express an atom's radius is to measure the distance between the nuclei of two identical atoms that are chemically bonded, and then divide this distance by two. Therefore, the **atomic radius** is often expressed as half the distance between the nuclei of identical atoms that are bonded together. Figure 6 shows the atomic radius of chlorine is about 99 picometers (pm). A picometer is 1×10^{-12} meters.

1 **Collaborate** With a partner, discuss why it is challenging for scientists to measure the atomic radius of an atom.

Analyzing Trends in Atomic Radii

The atomic radius can be measured using techniques such as x-ray imaging and spectroscopy. The data from these measurements can be graphed against atomic number. Figure 7 shows the relationship between atomic radius and atomic number for elements in the same period.

Atomic Radius

FIGURE 7: A graph of atomic radius versus atomic number reveals a pattern in the data.

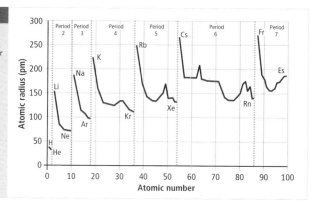

2 **ANALYZE** How does atomic radius change with atomic number? Use the elements sodium, Na; aluminum, Al; phosphorus, P; and potassium, K, to support your claim.

Explaining Trends in Atomic Radii

When the data from Figure 7 are placed on the periodic table, the patterns are even more apparent. The periodic table below shows the relative atomic radii (in picometers) of the elements. Darker colors correspond to larger atomic radii. Gray indicates atomic radii that have not been measured.

3 **MODEL** Model the pattern of atomic radii as you move across a period or down a group by drawing arrows on the periodic table.

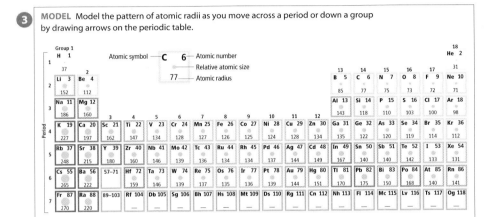

4 **APPLY** Select the correct terms to complete the statement.

Moving across a period, as electrons are added to a higher | a lower | the same energy shell, they are pulled closer to the nucleus. This increased pull results in a(n) increase | decrease in atomic radius. The atomic radius increases | decreases as you move down a group because electrons occupy successively lower | higher energy shells farther from the nucleus. The farther away from the nucleus the electrons are, the more | less tightly they are held.

Trends in atomic radius data can be used to predict the reactivity of an element. For metals, as atomic radius increases, reactivity increases because the outer electrons are not held as strongly. The sodium metal in Figure 8 is highly reactive in the presence of oxygen. Nonmetals show the opposite trend—as atomic radius increases, reactivity decreases because the outer electrons are held more strongly.

FIGURE 8: Sodium metal corrodes when exposed to air.

5 **EXPLAIN** Why is fluorine, F, more reactive than bromine, Br?

_____

_____

_____

6 **Evidence Notebook** Explain how chemists could use trends in atomic radii to predict the size of a new element that has not yet been discovered.

© Houghton Mifflin Harcourt Publishing Company • Image Credits: (b) ©Richard Megna/Fundamental Photographs

---

DCI **PS1.A Structure and Properties of Matter**

Exploring Visuals Ask students if they observe anything unusual about the trend in atomic radii across each period in the periodic table. They should observe that the atomic radii in Periods 4, 5, and 6 first decrease and then increase slightly before decreasing again. Explain that this results from how sublevels of transition elements fill.

Language Arts Connection

Have students research and write an explanatory paragraph relating different ways to measure atomic radius. (**WHST.9-12.2**)

Information Literacy Skills Have students consider these questions when obtaining information: *What is the best search engine or database for my research? How can I distinguish scholarly and popular publications?* Remind students to skim resources to determine what they should read in depth. Use responses to assess students' information literacy skills.

3 Students should draw arrows showing that atomic radius increases from right to left and increases down a group.

4 the same, decrease, increase, higher, less

5 Fluorine has a smaller atomic radius than bromine. Therefore, fluorine's nucleus has a stronger attraction to the electrons in other elements, making fluorine more reactive than bromine.

Evidence Notebook

6 **Sample answer:** Chemists could first determine the location of the new element on the periodic table. The atomic radius would likely be slightly smaller than the element to its left and slightly larger than the element just above it.

FORMATIVE ASSESSMENT

Quick Write Allow students additional time to consider the Evidence Notebook question more fully. Have them write a paragraph to answer the question. If time allows, students can draw a diagram to illustrate their response.

EXPLORATION 4 Patterns in Ionization Energy

3D Learning Objective

Students **use a model** to explore how **patterns** in ionization energies of elements reflect **patterns of outer electron states.**

DCI **PS1.A Structure and Properties of Matter**

Preconception Alert Make sure students understand that ionization energy concerns only the loss of electrons. Explain that electron loss can be represented by A + energy → A⁺ + e⁻. They may find this equation confusing because the electron is added to the right side of the equation and because ions can have positive and negative charges. Students may mistakenly think atoms should become more negative (as on a number line) as they lose electrons. List the number of protons and electrons for some atoms and their ions. Show how the charges add to give a neutral (atom) or charged particle (ion).

SEP **Developing and Using Models**

Exploring Visuals Have students discuss why the large blue arrow in **Figure 9** has darker blue on the left and lighter blue on the right. Students should recognize that the inner electrons are attracted to the positive nucleus more strongly than the outer electrons are.

Collaborate

Draw-Pair-Share Have student pairs draw a two-column table and title it "Trends in the Periodic Table." Have them label the left column "Period Trends" and the right column "Group Trends." As students work through this lesson, they should fill in the rows about the various periodic trends. After completing the lesson, ask partners to exchange tables with another pair and discuss any changes that are needed.

1. Phosphorus and sulfur, the same as, magnesium and aluminum, smaller

2. Elements with high ionization energy do not lose a valence electron as easily as elements with low ionization energy. Thus, a higher ionization energy means an element is less reactive.

EXPLORATION 4

Patterns in Ionization Energy

Neutral atoms have an equal number of protons and electrons. These oppositely charged particles are electrically attracted to each other. The energy required to remove an electron from a neutral atom is known as ionization energy. This is the energy required to overcome the attraction, remove an electron, and produce a charged atom, called an *ion*.

Analyzing Ionization Energy

As Figure 9 shows, the force needed to remove an inner electron is greater than it is to remove an outer electron. Electrons closer to the nucleus partially shield the outer electrons from the attraction of the positive charge. Also, a repulsive force exists between the inner and outer electrons, pushing outer electrons outwards. Thus, valence electrons are held more loosely than inner electrons and require less energy to remove. Ionization energy depends on the net force that keeps a valence electron in an atom.

FIGURE 9: Inner electrons partially shield outer electrons from the attraction of protons in the nucleus. They also repel the outer electrons, further weakening the nucleus's hold on them.

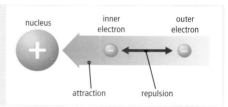

1 **APPLY** Complete the statement explaining which elements have an ionization energy greater than that of silicon, Si.

Magnesium and aluminum |Phosphorus and sulfur have a greater ionization energy because their atoms have more protons than silicon has. The additional electrons do not increase shielding because their valence shells are the same as |different from those of the outer electrons of silicon. Magnesium and aluminum |Phosphorus and sulfur have a smaller ionization energy because their atoms have fewer protons than silicon. Germanium has a smaller |larger ionization energy because the shielding effect on its outermost electron is greater than that of silicon.

Nuclei with a greater number of protons more strongly attract electrons in all energy levels. Therefore, as atomic number increases across a period, so does ionization energy. Atoms whose outermost electrons occupy higher energy shells, however, are farther from the nucleus. The increased distance and shielding from inner electrons weakens the attraction of the electrons to the nucleus causing ionization energy to decrease.

2 **INFER** How can ionization energy be used as a measure of chemical reactivity?

_____

_____

Patterns

Patterns in Ionization Energies

To avoid the influence of nearby atoms, measurements of ionization energies are made on isolated atoms in the gas phase. In this phase, atoms are at a much greater distance from each other than they are in the liquid or solid phase. A sample of the element is heated to produce a gas. A beam of light or a stream of electrons is used to eject an electron from the atom.

Ionization Energy

FIGURE 10: Ionization energy can be graphed as a function of an element's atomic number.

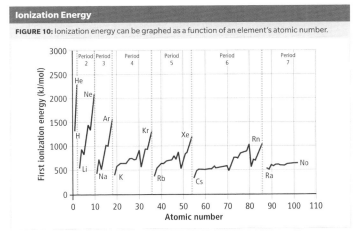

Figure 10 shows the ionization energy required to remove a single electron from a neutral atom of an element as a function of the atomic number of the element, shown on the horizontal axis. The dotted lines note the beginning of a period.

3 ANALYZE How does ionization energy change with atomic number? Use evidence from the graph to support your claim.

_____

_____

_____

_____

4 EXPLAIN How does ionization energy change across a period and down a group on the periodic table? Use evidence from the graph to support your claim.

_____

_____

_____

_____

Differentiate Instruction

ELL Support Draw students' attention to the definition in the text of the term *ionization energy* and the sentence after it that explains the relationship to an ion. Write *ionization* on the board. Draw a circle around the suffix *-ization*, and explain that it means "to make." Use a drawing or model of an atom to demonstrate making an ion by removing an electron from the atom.

Exploring Visuals

Remind students that each segment between the dotted lines on the *x*-axis on the graph in **Figure 10** corresponds to a different period from the periodic table. Suggest that they use paper to cover portions of the graph and examine one period at a time. They should readily see that ionization energies generally increase across periods, with the noble gas in that period having the highest ionization energy.

3 As atomic number increases, ionization energy generally increases. It then decreases abruptly and then generally increases again. The graph shows that the abrupt decreases occur after the atomic numbers corresponding to the elements helium, neon, argon, krypton, xenon, and radon (that is, for He and then the Group 18 noble gases). Also, the overall pattern is for lower ionization energies with increasing atomic number.

4 Ionization energy generally increases from left to right across a period and decreases from top to bottom in a group.

CCC Patterns

Have students summarize the patterns in ionization energy on the periodic table. Then ask questions to be sure they understand the reasons for these patterns. For example, ask students to explain why the noble gases have the highest ionization energy, why Group 1 elements have the lowest ionization energies, and why helium follows the ionization energy pattern of the Group 18 elements.

Collaborate

Say Something Pair students with different reading abilities. Have them take notes about the Exploration as they work through it. Afterward, have students turn to their partner and "say something" about how a particular trend relates to **everyday phenomena.** Rotate among the pairs to monitor and support students as needed.

1 Arrows should indicate that ionization energy increases from left to right across a period and decreases down a group.

2 b, c

3 Noble gases have high ionization energies because they have filled valence shells and do not lose electrons easily. An extremely large amount of energy would be required to remove an electron from a noble gas atom. Therefore, noble gases tend to be chemically nonreactive and react only under extreme conditions.

Evidence Notebook

4 Scientists can use trends in ionization energy to predict how reactive an element will be. If they know the ionization energy of an element near the element of interest, they can predict whether the element they are studying will be more or less reactive.

FORMATIVE ASSESSMENT

One-Sentence Summary Ask students to look back through the Exploration. Have them read each heading and look at the graphs and tables. Then have them write a one-sentence summary of the text under each heading.

Explaining Trends in Ionization Energy

The graphical representation of ionization energies of the elements reveals some clear patterns. These same data are mapped onto the periodic table below, and the patterns are even more apparent. Darker colors correspond to higher ionization energies. Gray indicates ionization energies that have not been measured.

1 **MODEL** Model the pattern of ionization energy as you move across a period or down a group by drawing arrows on the periodic table.

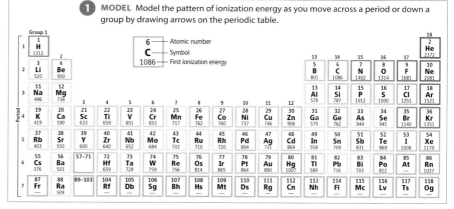

Moving from left to right across a period, one proton and one electron are added to the atoms of each element. These electrons are added to the same energy shell, so they are the same distance from the nucleus. It requires more energy to remove a single electron as more electrons are added across a period, so the ionization energy increases.

2 **ANALYZE** What describes an effect on ionization energy when moving down a group? Select all correct answers.

☐ **a**. the ionization energy increases down a group

☐ **b**. the ionization energy decreases down a group

☐ **c**. the valence electrons are in energy levels farther from the nucleus

☐ **d**. the shielding effect is less

Within each period and within some groups the individual ionization values do go up and down. In Period 2, for example, nitrogen has a higher ionization energy than oxygen. In Group 14, the ionization of lead is higher than that of tin, which is just above it. Inconsistencies in the trends remind us that all scientific models are limited approximations of nature's ultimate reality.

3 **INFER** Why do noble gases have high ionization energies? What does this pattern suggest about their chemical stability?

_____

_____

4 **Evidence Notebook** How can scientists use patterns in ionization energy to learn more about elements that have not been discovered yet?

EXPLORATION 5 Patterns in Electronegativity

Patterns in Electronegativity

When atoms combine to form compounds, electrons may be lost, gained, or shared between the atoms. When two identical atoms bond, electrons are shared equally. When different types of atoms bond, one atom in a compound usually attracts electrons more strongly than the other atom. You can imagine this as a sort of "tug of war" for the electrons being shared or transferred in a compound.

5 **APPLY** Write your own analogy for the sharing of electrons in a compound. With a partner, discuss how the dogs playing tug of war in Figure 11 is a good analogy for this phenomenon.

FIGURE 11: In a game of tug of war, one player may exert a stronger pull on the rope.

_____

_____

_____

Analyzing Electronegativity

In Figure 11, think of the knot in the center of the rope as an electron. If the dog on the right "tugs" more strongly than the dog on the left, the dog on the right will be slightly more negative than the one on the left. This uneven concentration of charge strongly affects the physical and chemical properties of a compound. Electronegativity measures the relative attraction an atom has for the electrons it shares in a molecule.

Atoms with more protons tend to have a greater attraction for shared electrons because of their greater positive nuclear charge. Atoms with a large atomic radius tend to have a weaker attraction for shared electrons because the distance between the nucleus and the shared electrons is larger. So, electronegativity is greater for smaller atoms with a larger number of protons. It is smaller for larger atoms with a smaller number of protons.

6 **EXPLAIN** Using this information, explain how the electronegativities of the following elements compare to that of phosphorus.

                    higher   lower

Sulfur is to the right of phosphorus on the periodic table. It has _____ electronegativity than phosphorus because a sulfur atom has more protons. Silicon is to the left of phosphorus on the periodic table. It has _____ electronegativity because its atoms have fewer protons than phosphorus.

Nitrogen is above phosphorus on the periodic table. It has _____ electronegativity than phosphorus because its atomic radius is smaller. Arsenic is below phosphorus on the periodic table. It has _____ electronegativity because it has a larger atomic radius than phosphorus.

3D Learning Objective

Students **use models** and an understanding of how **the periodic table orders elements** to explain the **patterns** in the electronegativities of elements and how atoms attract one another.

Differentiate Instruction

MTSS/RTI Give students this scenario for the tug-of-war analogy: _A large truck and a motorcycle are tied to the two ends of a rope and start to move in opposite directions._ Ask students what will happen to each vehicle. Ask what would happen to the valence electrons if the truck and the motorcycle were atoms of different elements. Have students work collaboratively to share ideas about other **everyday phenomena** that are analogies for the attractions different atoms have for valence electrons.

History of Science

Linus Pauling, an American chemist, biochemist, and peace activist, won a Nobel Prize in chemistry for his work on the nature of the chemical bond and electronegativity. Pauling won a Nobel Peace Prize for his work against atmospheric nuclear testing and the buildup of nuclear arsenals. Have students research Pauling's life and prepare a report for the class. Reports should emphasize Pauling's work related to the effect of electronegativity on the chemical bond.

DCI **PS1.A Structure and Properties of Matter**

Point out to students that electronegativity is a property of bonded atoms and thus differs from ionization energy, which is a property of isolated atoms.

5 **Sample answer:** Sharing of electrons is similar to two children who reach for a toy at the same time. Both pull on the toy, and neither is willing to give it up.

6 higher, lower, higher, lower

Collaborate

Accessing Prior Knowledge Point out to students that metals generally have lower electronegativities than nonmetals. Ask students to predict what type of ion they think each forms. Metals form cations by losing electrons, and nonmetals form anions by gaining electrons. You may wish to have students discuss their predictions as a whole-class activity. In this way, you can get a good sense of the level of prior knowledge that students have about the formation of ions.

CCC Patterns

Have students compare **Figure 12** and the periodic table showing patterns in electronegativity with **Figure 10** and the periodic table showing patterns in ionization energy. What general trends do they observe? Electronegativity follows the same periodic trend as ionization energy: values generally decrease or remain about the same down a group and, with some exceptions, increase across a period.

1 Students should describe the repeating pattern of electronegativity increasing, suddenly dropping, and then increasing again with increasing atomic number. On the periodic table, electronegativity generally increases across a period and decreases down a period. Electronegativities are relatively constant for transition metals.

2 **Sample answer:** The trend in electronegativity is opposite that of atomic radius. The larger the atomic radius, the greater the distance is between the nucleus and the shared electrons. This increased distance results in a weaker attraction between the nucleus and the shared electrons and, thus, a lower electronegativity.

3 **Sample answer:** The trend in electronegativity is the same as that of ionization energy. As the pull of the nucleus on the electrons increases, both the amount of energy needed to remove an electron from an atom (ionization energy) and the attraction of the nucleus for other electrons (electronegativity) increase. The opposite is true when the pull of the nucleus on the electrons decreases.

 Patterns

Patterns in Electronegativity

Electronegativity cannot be measured directly. It is calculated using the average energy required to remove an electron from an atom and the energy given off when an electron is added to an atom. Both methods express electronegativity as a quantity without units on a relative scale. The most electronegative element, fluorine, is arbitrarily assigned an electronegativity of 4.0. Other values are calculated in relation to this value. The results of the calculations are shown in Figure 12 as a function of atomic number.

Electronegativity

FIGURE 12: Electronegativity can be described as a function of an element's atomic number.

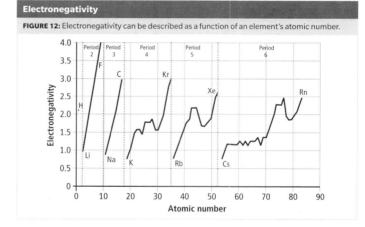

1 **ANALYZE** How would the pattern of electronegativities shown in Figure 12 appear across a period and down a group on the periodic table?

_____

_____

2 **EXPLAIN** How does the trend in electronegativity in the periodic table compare with the trend in atomic radii? Explain why this relationship makes sense.

_____

_____

3 **EXPLAIN** How does the trend in electronegativity in the periodic table compare with the trend in ionization energy? Explain why this relationship makes sense.

_____

_____

_____

Explaining Trends in Electronegativity

Figure 12 shows a pattern between an element's atomic number and electronegativity. The pattern is more apparent when the data are mapped onto the periodic table below, which shows the electronegativities of the elements. Darker colors correspond to greater electronegativities. Gray indicates an undetermined electronegativity.

4 **MODEL** Model the pattern of electronegativity as you move across a period or down a group by drawing arrows on the periodic table. Circle the region of the periodic table where the most electronegative elements are located.

Group 1																	18
1 **H** 2.1	2		6 — Atomic number / **C** — Symbol / 2.5 — Electronegativity									13	14	15	16	17	2 **He** —
3 **Li** 1.0	4 **Be** 1.5											5 **B** 2.0	6 **C** 2.5	7 **N** 3.0	8 **O** 3.5	9 **F** 4.0	10 **Ne** —
11 **Na** 0.9	12 **Mg** 1.2	3	4	5	6	7	8	9	10	11	12	13 **Al** 1.5	14 **Si** 1.8	15 **P** 2.1	16 **S** 2.5	17 **Cl** 3.0	18 **Ar** —
19 **K** 0.8	20 **Ca** 1.0	21 **Sc** 1.3	22 **Ti** 1.5	23 **V** 1.6	24 **Cr** 1.6	25 **Mn** 1.5	26 **Fe** 1.8	27 **Co** 1.8	28 **Ni** 1.8	29 **Cu** 1.9	30 **Zn** 1.6	31 **Ga** 1.8	32 **Ge** 1.8	33 **As** 2.0	34 **Se** 2.4	35 **Br** 2.8	36 **Kr** 3.0
37 **Rb** 0.8	38 **Sr** 1.0	39 **Y** 1.2	40 **Zr** 1.4	41 **Nb** 1.6	42 **Mo** 1.8	43 **Tc** 1.9	44 **Ru** 2.2	45 **Rh** 2.2	46 **Pd** 2.2	47 **Ag** 1.9	48 **Cd** 1.7	49 **In** 1.7	50 **Sn** 1.8	51 **Sb** 1.9	52 **Te** 2.1	53 **I** 2.5	54 **Xe** 2.6
55 **Cs** 0.7	56 **Ba** 0.9	57–71	72 **Hf** 1.3	73 **Ta** 1.5	74 **W** 1.7	75 **Re** 1.9	76 **Os** 2.2	77 **Ir** 2.2	78 **Pt** 2.2	79 **Au** 2.4	80 **Hg** 1.9	81 **Tl** 1.8	82 **Pb** 1.8	83 **Bi** 1.9	84 **Po** 2.0	85 **At** 2.2	86 **Rn** 2.4
87 **Fr** 0.7	88 **Ra** 0.9	89–103	104 **Rf** —	105 **Db** —	106 **Sg** —	107 **Bh** —	108 **Hs** —	109 **Mt** —	110 **Ds** —	111 **Rg** —	112 **Cn** —	113 **Nh** —	114 **Fl** —	115 **Mc** —	116 **Lv** —	117 **Ts** —	118 **Og** —

5 **APPLY** Select the correct terms to complete the statement.

Moving from left to right across a period, electronegativity usually increases | decreases. Because Group 1 metals have only one valence electron, they are the most | least electronegative elements. Group 17 elements are the least | most electronegative elements because they need one | seven electron(s) to fill their valence shells.

Trends in electronegativity can be used to predict reactions between elements. When elements have a large difference in electronegativity, the element with greater electronegativity has a much stronger attraction for shared electrons. These elements bond by one atom donating one or more electrons to the other atom. Elements that have similar electronegativities are more likely to share valence electrons because their attraction for the electrons is similar.

6 **INFER** Some nonstick pans, such as the pan in Figure 13, are coated with PFTE which is made of many fluorine and carbon atoms that form very strong bonds. Why do you think the bond between carbon and fluorine is so strong? How do you think this bond is related to the nonstick properties of PFTE?

FIGURE 13: PFTE is a chemical that gives some nonstick pans their properties.

Differentiate Instruction

Extension Ask students who already may know the distinction between ionic and covalent bonds to argue, for or against, if they think certain chemical bonds might not be completely ionic or covalent. Tell them to consider electronegativity values and how these might influence the strength of a chemical bond.

SEP **Developing and Using Models**

Have students make models of the shielding effect of electrons. One model can represent a calcium atom; a second can represent a barium atom. The atoms have the same number of valence electrons but different total electrons and therefore different atomic radii.

Math Connection

Have students work in small groups to make vertical bar graphs using values given in the periodic table showing the pattern of electronegativities. Each graph should represent values in a single period or a single column. Have groups compare their results. **(MP.4)**

Collaborate

Which Is False? Point out to students that they have now learned about different periodic trends in reactivity, ionization energy, atomic radii, and electronegativity. Divide the class into small teams. Have each student write two true statements and one false statement about periodic trends. Then have them take turns sharing their statements as teammates try to identify the false statement.

4 Students should draw arrows that show electronegativity increasing from left to right across a period and decreasing down a group. The area circled should be the upper right corner of the periodic table, excluding the noble gases.

5 increases, least, most, one

6 Fluorine is very electronegative because a fluorine atom is small and needs only one electron to fill its valence shell. Carbon needs four electrons to fill its valence shell, so it is less electronegative. The fluorine-carbon bonds in the material are so strong that fluorine resists attraction to other substances.

Lesson 2 Investigating Patterns in the Periodic Table   97

Industry Connection

Help students understand that halogen light bulbs have many uses in spite of their drawbacks. They are used in automobile and watercraft headlights and in many outdoor floodlights. Because of the heat they generate, halogen bulbs are used as the heating elements in halogen ovens. The light fixtures and spotlights in most theater, art, and television studios contain halogen bulbs. Because of their bright light, they are also used in movie and slide projectors. Students may wish to learn more about one of these uses and report to the class.

Language Arts Connection
RST.9-10.7 Translate quantitative or technical information expressed in words in a text into visual form and translate information expressed visually or mathematically into words.

Encourage students to think about the process an engineer might use when deciding which type of bulb to use. Students might make a flow chart or a table that shows this thought process.

1 An engineer might consider the brightness needed, lifespan, cost of materials and manufacturing, efficiency, and aesthetics.

 Evidence Notebook

2 **Sample answer:** The electronegativity would most likely be very close to 0.7 because an element with atomic number 119 would be a Group 1, Period 8 element below francium. Elements with the lowest electronegativities are located in this part of the periodic table.

FORMATIVE ASSESSMENT

3-Minute Pause Have students pause to think of the concepts about electronegativity presented in this exploration. Have them respond to the following prompts:

I became more aware of . . .

I didn't realize that . . .

I still don't understand . . .

Have volunteers share their responses with the class.

Engineering
Developing Halogen Bulbs

FIGURE 14: Halogen bulb

A halogen bulb consists of a tungsten filament surrounded by halogen gas inside a clear bulb. Typical incandescent light bulbs also have a tungsten filament but they are surrounded by argon, a noble gas, that prevents oxygen in the air from corroding the metal filament and shortening the life of the bulb. In contrast, the gas in a halogen lamp is a highly reactive Group 17 element, such as bromine or iodine. As electricity begins to flow through the bulb, the tungsten filament becomes extremely hot and begins to vaporize. The halogen gas readily reacts with the tungsten vapor. A cyclic process occurs in which tungsten is redeposited onto the filament, extending the lifetime of the bulb.

The earliest halogen bulbs had a carbon filament surrounded by chlorine gas. Tungsten soon replaced carbon because it could operate at a higher temperature, emitting more light. Chlorine was replaced by iodine to avoid the blackening of the bulb that occurred with previous designs. Later, bromine was used instead of iodine to improve efficiency.

Halogen bulbs are often used in workplaces, overhead lighting, car lights, and spotlights because of their brightness. They also have a longer lifespan than other types of incandescent bulbs. A drawback, however, is that halogen bulbs are extremely hot, and the glass bulb must be kept clean to avoid breakage when the bulb reaches high temperatures.

1 **DEFINE** Engineers are designing a new car and need to decide if the headlight should use halogen bulbs or LED bulbs. What criteria might they consider?

_____

_____

_____

_____

Both standard incandescent and halogen bulbs are inefficient. They convert more electricity into energy in the form of heat than light. They are increasingly being replaced by LED bulbs that use much less energy to produce the same amount of light. An LED is a light-emitting diode, a solid state electronic device similar to the devices used in computers and calculators. When electric current passes through the LED, it emits light.

> **Language Arts Connection** Research the benefits and drawbacks of a halogen bulb and a LED bulb that contain the same light output (measured in lumens). For a given amount of light produced, how do the halogen bulb's cost of production, lifespan, and cost of electricity needed to operate compare with those of the LED bulb? Develop a visual guide that an engineer could use to decide which type of bulb is most appropriate for a given situation.

2 **Evidence Notebook** Suppose chemists attempt to produce an element with atomic number 119. Based on its likely position on the periodic table, what would you expect its electronegativity to be? Explain how you can make this prediction.

TAKE IT FURTHER Careers in Science

TAKE IT FURTHER

Careers in Science

Analytical Chemist

Have you ever read a mystery novel or watched a detective show where a scientist solved a case by analyzing a sample? These movie scientists often use techniques developed by analytical chemists. The work of analytical chemists often requires "detective" work, careful analysis of samples, and the use of precise equipment. Important skills of these chemists include the ability to ask questions and identify patterns.

This drive to solve mysteries about why a product or a process is not working the way it should is part of the reason Barbara Belmont became an analytical chemist. She uses many different types of analytical methods, such as gas chromatography-mass spectrometry and gas chromatography-flame ionization, to determine if a client's products meet regulation standards. Part of this work is asking questions about what portion of the materials could be causing the product to not meet the standards, and then giving recommendations based on evidence for how to fix the problem.

Barbara Belmont identifies as a member of the LGBTQ+ community and takes on an active role increasing the visibility and inclusion of LGBTQ+ peoples in science, technology, engineering, and mathematics (STEM) programs. She performs this work through memberships in the American Chemical Society, the American Association for Advancement of Science, and the National Organization of Gay and Lesbian Scientists and Technical Professionals (NOGLSTP).

Among Barbara Belmont's most important work is her teaching career where she brings her real-life experience to the classroom. She mentors student-driven research projects and has created a safe space on campus for students to discuss LGBTQ+ issues.

She is also focusing on ways to re-design her course to be more environmentally friendly and cost-effective. This is an important task that all scientists, including analytical chemists, must consider on any project.

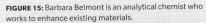

FIGURE 15: Barbara Belmont is an analytical chemist who works to enhance existing materials.

Chemistry in Your Community Research an analytical chemist, company, or government agency that performed a chemical analysis on a project in your community. For example, you may research a company that analyzed building materials for a construction project or a municipal water sanitation department. Consider the following to guide your research:

• What materials were tested by the analytical chemist, and what equipment was used to run the tests?
• What kinds of questions do you think the chemist asked before analyzing the materials?
• Did the chemist run any tests to determine the effect the materials might have on the environment or human health?

Write a magazine article or blog about the findings and contributions of the chemist. You may wish to conduct an interview with the chemist or with a group of chemists to gather this information.

| PERIODIC TRENDS IN HISTORY | THE MENDELEEV LAB OF 1869 | DISCOVERING NEW ELEMENTS | Go online to choose one of these other paths. |

© Houghton Mifflin Harcourt Publishing Company • Image Credits: ©Barbara Belmont

Collaborate

You may choose to assign this activity or direct students to the Interactive Online Student Edition, where they can choose from all available paths. These activities can be assigned individually, to pairs, or to small groups.

People in Science Barbara Belmont works in both university and private sectors. She performs and directs lab work, trains personnel, and ensures safety in the lab. Ms. Belmont is also a member of and an activist for the LGBTQ+ community.

Differentiate Instruction

ELL Support Discuss with students what the word *analytical* means. Point out that it has the same base word as *analyze,* which means "to carefully examine." An analytical chemist carefully examines substances to determine their properties.

Language Arts Connection

Conducting online interviews with analytical chemists may be easiest. Ensure that students have a clear and concise set of questions prepared before the interview. (WHST.9-10.7)

Explore Online ▶

Periodic Trends in History

Students learn how periodic trends influence human history.

The Mendeleev Lab of 1869

Students determine the identity of nine unknown elements.

Discovering New Elements

Students research the discovery of a new element.

EVALUATE   Lesson Self-Check

Can You Explain the Phenomenon?

Claims, Evidence, and Reasoning

Have students clearly state their claim—their explanation for the phenomenon they have been investigating throughout this lesson. They should present their reasoning for making this claim, along with evidence such as facts, examples, and statistics that support their claim. You may want to have students present their arguments orally, in writing, or as a debate. Refer students to the **English Language Arts Handbook** for more information on evaluating claims and presenting arguments.

Cultivating Student Questions

Assessing Student Growth   Review the list of questions students generated at the beginning of the lesson. Have volunteers select any unanswered questions and suggest how they could be investigated. After approving student plans, have small groups conduct the investigations and report back to the class.

As the year progresses, the number of volunteers for this task will likely increase. The sophistication of the means of investigation also may increase. Both outcomes are measures of positive growth that are essential to the scientific mindset and demonstrate that students are beginning to understand that the correct answer is much less important than the means used to investigate the question.

Evidence Notebook

1. Scientists can use information from existing elements to infer the behavior of an element they want to develop. Patterns of atomic number, ionization energy, reactivity, and atomic size help scientists learn about the behavior of the element they want to produce. Scientists have used information about how atoms interact, how elements decay, and what happens when atoms collide to develop a procedure for producing the new elements. Several new elements have been discovered in this way.

100   Unit 2 Atoms and Elements

EVALUATE

Lesson Self-Check

CAN YOU EXPLAIN THE PHENOMENON?

FIGURE 16: Certain elements, such as silver, gold, and platinum, look somewhat different but they still share some similar properties. These elements occur in nature while others are made synthetically in a lab.

The periodic table lists 118 elements. The vast majority of these are naturally occurring elements, and the rest have been produced in laboratories. With some exceptions, the arrangement of the elements on the periodic table reveals patterns in the properties of the elements. Scientists can use these patterns when searching for new elements. The newest elements on the periodic table require advanced technology to produce and they have high atomic numbers. These elements are so unstable that only tiny amounts are produced, and they may last only a few microseconds. Most of these elements have no practical or commercial use outside of research labs. Nevertheless, scientists continue the effort to develop elements with even higher atomic numbers to gain a better theoretical understanding of the nature of atoms.

1. **Evidence Notebook**   Refer to the notes in your Evidence Notebook to make a claim about how scientists are able to use the periodic table to predict the behavior of new elements. Make sure you include a discussion of periodic trends. Your explanation should include a discussion of the following points:

   Claim   How can scientists use the periodic table to predict the behavior of new elements?

   Evidence   Give specific evidence to support your claim.

   Reasoning   Describe, in detail, the connections between the evidence you cited and the claim you are making.

 Formal Assessment   Go online for student self-checks and other assessments.

Answers

1. more, lower, electrons, electronegativity
2. c
3. d
4. a, d
5. b
6. c, a, e, d, b
7. d
8. less, more, Group 17, Group 1

Name _____ Date _____

CHECKPOINTS

Check Your Understanding

1. In 1937, a limited supply of helium resulted in the airship Hindenburg being filled with hydrogen instead. On one trip, the Hindenburg burst into flames and was destroyed in less than one minute. Complete the statement about the Hindenburg.

   Hydrogen burns easily and is more | less

   reactive than helium because it has a higher |

   lower ionization energy. Helium is unreactive

   because it does not lose electrons | protons

   easily and therefore does not have an assigned

   atomic radius | electronegativity .

2. Which element would you expect to have the highest electronegativity?
   - a. calcium because it has one valence electron
   - b. cesium because it has a large atomic mass
   - c. fluorine because it needs one electron to fill its valence shell
   - d. phosphorus because it is a nonmetal

3. A scientist determines that an element has a high reactivity and a large atomic radius. What other properties does the element most likely have?
   - a. high electronegativity and high ionization energy
   - b. high electronegativity and low ionization energy
   - c. low electronegativity and high ionization energy
   - d. low electronegativity and low ionization energy

4. According to periodic trends, at which position on the periodic table would an element most likely have an electronegativity higher than that of calcium? Select all correct answers.
   - a. just above calcium
   - b. just below calcium
   - c. just to the left of calcium
   - d. just to the right of calcium

5. What statement best explains why fluorine has a smaller atomic radius than oxygen?
   - a. Fluorine has fewer electrons than oxygen.
   - b. Fluorine has one more proton than oxygen.
   - c. Fluorine has low electronegativity.
   - d. Fluorine forms bonds readily with oxygen.

6. Put these elements in order of decreasing electronegativity, with the highest electronegative element as being first.

   _____ a. tin (Sn, Group 14, Period 5)

   _____ b. rubidium (Rb, Group 1, Period 5)

   _____ c. bromine (Br, Group 17, Period 4)

   _____ d. lithium (Li, Group 1, Period 2)

   _____ e. cadmium (Cd, Group 12, Period 5)

7. Photoelectric cells produce an electric current when electromagnetic radiation shines on them. This happens only when the radiation shining on the material contains a certain amount of energy. Why is cesium often used in photoelectric cells?
   - a. Cesium has one of the largest atomic radii, so its electrons are tightly held.
   - b. Cesium has one of the highest ionization energies, so its electrons are tightly held.
   - c. Cesium has a high electronegativity, so its electrons are easily ejected.
   - d. Cesium has one of the lowest ionization energies, so its electrons are easily ejected.

8. A sample of potassium (K, found in Group 1) and a sample of iodine (I, found in Group 17) react, forming potassium iodide, KI, which is used to treat thyroid conditions. Complete the statement to describe this reaction.

   The reaction that creates potassium iodide

   happens because electrons are pulled away

   from the more | less electronegative element,

   potassium, by the more | less electronegative

   element, iodine. The more electronegative

   element is found in Group 1 | Group 17 . The less

   electronegative element is in Group 1 | Group 17 .

Answers

9. Answers should include a description of trends in ionization energy and atomic radii. **Sample answer:** Ionization energy increases across a period because the number of protons increases, but the additional electrons are added to the same energy level and are pulled closer to the nucleus. Atomic radius, however, decreases across a period because the electrons experience a greater attraction from the nucleus with no increase in energy level.

10. Answers may vary but should include a description of the periodic trends of ionization energy and electronegativity, as well as a description of the valency of Group 1 elements. **Sample answer:** Because potassium is a Group 1 element, you know it has a low ionization energy, so it will be highly reactive. Electronegativity increases from left to right across a period. You also know that Group 1 elements have one valence electron, so you can expect potassium to form a strong bond with Group 17 elements.

11. Answers should include an explanation of the properties of noble gases due to their atomic structure. **Sample answer:** The noble gases have filled valence shells. They have high ionization energy because removing an electron from a filled shell requires a lot of energy. They have small atomic radii because they are farthest right in each period. As the number of protons increases across a period, the additional electrons added to the same shell experience a greater attraction from the nucleus, which decreases the atomic size.

Make Your Own Study Guide

Have students create a study guide that helps them organize and visualize the important information from this lesson. Their study guide should focus on the main ideas from this lesson and tie multiple ideas together. Students can make an outline, a concept map, a graphic organizer, or another representation.

EVALUATE

CHECKPOINTS (continued)

9. Explain how the pattern in ionization energy across a period of the periodic table compares to the pattern in atomic radius size across a period.

10. Suppose you have a sample of potassium. Describe several ways you could use periodic trends and a knowledge of valence electrons to predict the element's reactivity and how the element will behave in a chemical bond.

11. Describe generally how the trends in ionization energy and atomic radius apply to the noble gases, and explain the reason for these trends.

MAKE YOUR OWN STUDY GUIDE

In your Evidence Notebook, design a study guide that supports the main idea from this lesson:

Patterns in ionization energy, atomic size, and electronegativity can be used to make predictions about the properties and interactions of elements on the periodic table.

Remember to include the following information in your study guide:
- Use examples that model main ideas.
- Record explanations for the phenomena you investigated.
- Use evidence to support your explanations. Your support can include drawings, data, graphs, laboratory conclusions, and other evidence recorded throughout the lesson.

Consider the organization of elements on the periodic table and how patterns in properties such as ionization energy and electronegativity can be used to predict the way elements bond and react in nature and in everyday applications of the elements.

Analyzing Nuclear Reactions

Building to the Performance Expectations

The learning experiences in this lesson prepare students for mastery of

HS-PS1-8 Develop models to illustrate the changes in the composition of the nucleus of the atom and the energy released during the processes of fission, fusion, and radioactive decay.

HS-ETS1-3 Evaluate a solution to a complex real-world problem based on prioritized criteria and trade-offs that account for a range of constraints, including cost, safety, reliability, and aesthetics, as well as possible social, cultural, and environmental impacts.

 Trace Tool to the NGSS

Go online to view the complete coverage of standards across lessons, units, and grade levels.

 **SEP Science and Engineering Practices**

Developing and Using Models
Develop a model based on evidence to illustrate the relationships between systems or components of systems.

▶ **VIDEO** Developing and Using Models

Constructing Explanations and Designing Solutions
Evaluate a solution to a complex real-world problem, based on scientific knowledge, student-generated sources of evidence, prioritized criteria, and tradeoff considerations.

▶ **VIDEO** Constructing Scientific Explanations

Asking Questions and Defining Problems
Analyze complex real-world problems by specifying criteria and constraints for successful solutions.

 **DCI Disciplinary Core Ideas**

PS1.C Nuclear Processes
Nuclear processes, including fusion, fission, and radioactive decays of unstable nuclei, involve release or absorption of energy. The total number of neutrons plus protons does not change in any nuclear process. (HS-PS1-8)

ETS1.A Defining and Delimiting Engineering Problems
Criteria and constraints also include satisfying any requirements set by society, such as taking issues of risk mitigation into account, and they should be quantified to the extent possible and stated in such a way that one can tell if a given design meets them. (HS-ETS1-1)

ETS1.A Defining and Delimiting Engineering Problems
Criteria and constraints also include satisfying any requirements set by society, such as taking issues of risk mitigation into account, and they should be quantified to the extent possible and stated in such a way that one can tell if a given design meets them. (HS-ETS1-1)

ETS1.B Developing Possible Solutions
When evaluating solutions, it is important to take into account a range of constraints including cost, safety, reliability and aesthetics, and to consider social, cultural, and environmental impacts. (HS-ETS1-3)

▶ **VIDEO** Engineering: Chemistry

CCC Crosscutting Concepts

Energy and Matter
In nuclear processes, atoms are not conserved, but the total number of protons plus neutrons is conserved.

Influence of Engineering, Technology, and Science on Society and the Natural World
New technologies can have deep impacts on society and the environment, including some that were not anticipated. Analysis of costs and benefits is a critical aspect of decisions about technology.

Scientific Knowledge Assumes an Order and Consistency in Natural Systems
Scientific knowledge is based on the assumption that natural laws operate today as they did in the past and they will continue to do so in the future.

MATH STANDARDS

MP.2 Reason abstractly and quantitatively.

MP.4 Model with mathematics.

HSN-Q.A.1 Use units as a way to understand problems and to guide the solution of multi-step problems.

HSN-Q.A.2 Define appropriate quantities for the purpose of descriptive modeling.

ELA STANDARDS

RST.11-12.9 Synthesize information from a range of sources into a coherent understanding of a process, phenomenon, or concept.

Supporting All Students, All Standards

Integrating the Three Dimensions

In this lesson, students apply evidence using models of atomic nuclei to explore forces inside the nucleus **(SEP Developing and Using Models, DCI PS1.C, CCC Energy and Matter).** Students explain changes that occur in atomic nuclei during nuclear reactions using the framework of conservation of mass-energy **(SEP Constructing Explanations, DCI PS1.C, CCC Energy and Matter).** Students explore naturally occurring and human-directed nuclear processes and the benefits and tradeoffs regarding their uses **(SEP Constructing Explanations and Designing Solutions, SEP Asking Questions and Defining Problems, DCI ETS1.A, DCI ETS1.B, CCC Influence of Engineering, Technology, and Science on Society and the Natural World).**

Preassessment

Have students complete the unit pretest or see the Assessment Guide.

Build on Prior Knowledge

Have students list what they know about nuclear energy—examples of it, how powerful it is, how it is used, and so on. After they have made a comprehensive list, ask them to share their list with a partner and discuss any differences. Then make a classroom list that can be added to over the course of this lesson.

You may want to review the following concepts:
- An atomic nucleus contains protons and neutrons. Protons are positively charged; neutrons have no charge.
- Energy changes form but is not created or destroyed. If energy is released, it must come from somewhere.
- The definition of an isotope of an element relates to the meaning of atomic number and atomic mass.
- Gravitational and electromagnetic forces are non-contact forces and can be calculated using formulas.

Professional Development   Go online to view **Professional Development videos** with strategies to integrate CCCs and SEPs, including the ones used in this lesson.

Content Background

The most amazing thing about atoms is that they stay together at all. The electrostatic force between the positively charged protons in the nucleus implies that they should repel one another. However, at distances in the nucleus, there is another force—the strong nuclear force—holding protons and neutrons together. The electrostatic force does not disappear, and when the composition of the nucleus becomes such that the strong force cannot overcome the electrostatic repulsion, nuclei become unstable. This is when radioactive decay occurs.

During radioactive decay, the nucleus emits particles and radiation to achieve stability again. What sets nuclear reactions apart from chemical reactions is that mass and energy are interrelated. In other words, when protons and neutrons, collectively known as nucleons, come together to form a nucleus, mass converts into energy. The relationship between mass and energy is given by the equation $E = mc^2$, where c is the speed of light. Students should understand that this does not mean that there is no conservation of mass. It instead implies that the concept of conservation of mass must be expanded to include the conversion of mass and energy in nuclear processes.

Differentiate Instruction

KEY WORDS
- nucleon
- nuclide
- radioactive decay
- nuclear radiation
- half-life
- nuclear fission
- nuclear fusion

ELL SUPPORT

The words *fusion* and *fission* are sometimes confused. Use examples of fusion and fission in a context outside nuclear physics. *Fusion* refers to combining two or more things into a single entity. The term might be used to describe a combination of ideas from different fields or a new practice that melds elements of two or more other practices. A synonym is *joining*. *Fission* refers to breaking things apart. A group might fission into subgroups over disagreements. A synonym is *rupture*.

ENGAGE: Investigative Phenomenon

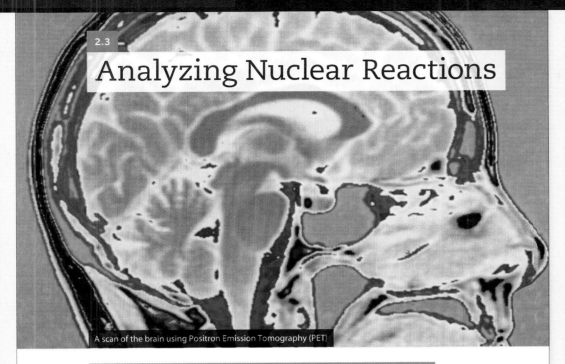

2.3

Analyzing Nuclear Reactions

A scan of the brain using Positron Emission Tomography (PET)

CAN YOU EXPLAIN THE PHENOMENON?

Various forms of imaging can be used to diagnose and treat medical disorders. One of the most powerful imaging tools available in medicine today is Positron Emission Tomography (PET), which uses specific isotopes of certain elements, called radioisotopes. Unlike most atoms, these atoms emit radiation, which consists of high-energy subatomic particles that can penetrate tissue. When small amounts of radioisotopes are introduced into the body, they accumulate in specific areas. Devices that detect the radiation produce images of tissue and biochemical processes in the body.

1 EXPLAIN   Before medical images are taken, radioisotopes are often injected into a vein in a patient's arm, or the patient drinks a solution containing the radioisotopes. Why do you think atoms in the body usually do not emit radiation?

_____

_____

_____

_____

2 **Evidence Notebook** As you explore the lesson, gather evidence to explain what types of nuclear reactions cause atoms to give off radiation that can be detected in a medical image, and how forces within the nuclei cause these reactions.

Lesson 3 Analyzing Nuclear Reactions   **103**

Build on Prior Lessons

In Lesson 1, students learned about subatomic particles, including properties of the protons and neutrons that make up the nucleus. Lesson 2 described how electrons influence chemical properties. Lesson 3 builds on these concepts as students learn about forces that act on the nucleons and ways nuclei change during nuclear reactions.

Lesson Objective

Students analyze the forces operating at the nuclear scale and how they affect matter.

Cultivating Student Questions

Have students look at the photo of a scanned brain. Prompt them to ask all questions that come to mind about how nuclear reactions and radiation relate to medical imaging. Record the questions on chart paper, and then sort the questions based on their focus. With students, narrow the questions down to the ones that directly relate to the learning objective. Have students reflect on this list throughout the lesson and check off questions as they are answered.

Can You Explain the Phenomenon?

The Investigative Phenomenon is the focus of the lesson. Students are asked to record their initial thoughts about how some atoms give off radiation that can be detected in a medical image. Students will collect evidence related to this phenomenon throughout the lesson and revisit the question at the end of the lesson to use what they have learned to explain nuclear reactions.

1 Students should attempt to explain how radioactive atoms differ from nonradioactive atoms. Radioactive atoms emit radiation because they are unstable.

Evidence Notebook

2 The topic of radiation will be revisited throughout this lesson.

EXPLORATION 1 Explaining Nuclear Stability

3D Learning Objective

Students **use models** to explore nuclear forces between **neutrons and protons** to determine how the forces make some nuclei stable and others unstable and to understand the relationship of matter and energy in nuclear processes.

Everyday phenomena discussed throughout the Explorations of the lesson can often be used to connect the science content to students' personal experiences.

CCC **Scale, Proportion, and Quantity**

Nucleons are extremely dense, about 10^{14} g/cm³. Have students compare this density with water at 1 g/cm³ and osmium, the densest element, at 22.59 g/cm³. Explain that if Earth had the density of an average nucleus, Earth's mass would fit within a sphere with a radius of 0.2 km. Ask students to determine roughly how large this is, using the school grounds as a comparison.

DCI **PS1.C Nuclear Processes**

Make sure students realize that although the helium-4 nucleus shown has the same number of neutrons as protons, that is not usually the case with atoms. Some isotopes have fewer neutrons than protons, and some have many more neutrons than protons. Explain to students that they will learn later in the lesson how protons can change to neutrons and neutrons can change to protons in some nuclear processes.

Claims, Evidence, and Reasoning

Collaborate The nucleus cannot be directly observed in the same way that larger-scale structures can, with an optical or electron microscope. Instead, researchers observe how particles interact with nuclei. Have students discuss with a partner how to support their claims about the size and structure of atoms with evidence and reasoning.

 c

Explaining Nuclear Stability

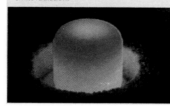

FIGURE 1: A pellet of plutonium gives off energy in the form of heat and light as it emits radiation.

The element plutonium, shown in Figure 1, has an orange glow due to the enormous amount of energy it releases in the form of heat and light. Unlike other fuels that "burn up" quickly, plutonium releases its energy over a long period of time. This makes it an ideal fuel source for applications such as spacecraft used for interplanetary exploration because they cannot stop to refuel.

Plutonium's position on the periodic table explains why it glows. The atomic number of plutonium is 94. All elements with an atomic number greater than that of lead, 82, have nuclei that are unstable and emit radiation in the form of either particles or high-energy electromagnetic waves. As they do so, they produce other nuclei that are more stable.

Electrostatic Force and the Nucleus

To explain trends in the periodic table, you saw that the varying strengths of the attraction between the negatively charged electrons and the positively charged protons in the nucleus play an important role. Oppositely charged particles attract one another as a result of the *electrostatic force*. The electrostatic force explains why electrons closer to the nucleus in the electron cloud partially shield outer electrons from the positive charge of the nucleus. Like charges repel one another, so inner electrons repel outer electrons, partially negating the pull the nucleus has upon them. You likely have seen the electrostatic force in action when two pieces of clothing either stick to or repel one another. The cling or repulsion occurs because rubbing of the fabric surfaces together causes an imbalance in charge between them.

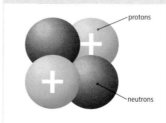

FIGURE 2: A helium-4 nucleus consists of two neutrons and two protons.

protons

neutrons

The strength of the electrostatic force between two charges depends upon both the magnitude of the charges and the distance between them. As charge increases, so does the electrostatic force. However, the force becomes weaker as the distance between charges increases.

Now, consider a helium-4 nucleus such as the one shown in Figure 2. The nucleus stays intact despite the two positively charged protons being so close together. All stable atomic nuclei contain protons and neutrons, and the electrostatic force exists between all charges. Many even larger nuclei are quite stable despite having many protons.

1 **INFER** What is the most probable explanation for how two positively charged protons could be held together within the incredibly small and dense nucleus?

○ **a.** The charge on the protons is so small that the repulsion is very weak.

○ **b.** Neutrons provide enough distance between protons to make the repulsion weak.

○ **c.** There is another force at work in the nucleus holding protons and neutrons together.

○ **d.** Electrons surrounding the nucleus keep it from breaking apart.

Nuclear Forces

If only the electrostatic force existed, atomic nuclei would not remain intact. But the elements and compounds surrounding us are evidence that nuclei are, in general, stable. Scientists concluded, therefore, that there must be another force at work in the nucleus. This force had to be opposite to the electrostatic force and sufficiently strong enough to counteract it. Scientists called this force the *strong nuclear force*, and found that it acted between all particles in the nucleus. Figure 3 shows how the strong nuclear force and electrostatic force increase as two protons come together.

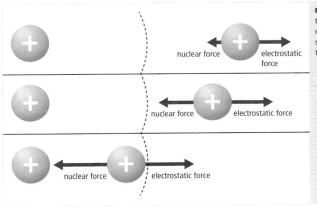

FIGURE 3: As two protons move toward each other, electrostatic repulsion increases, but the strong nuclear force attracting them increases even more.

2 EXPLAIN Using the diagram in Figure 3, describe how the relative influences of the electrostatic force and the strong nuclear force compare as two protons approach one another. How does the nuclear strong force keep nuclei together?

_____

_____

_____

_____

As two protons move closer together, the electrostatic force increases. When the protons get sufficiently close, however, the strong nuclear force takes hold to keep protons together. Notice that the attraction of the strong nuclear force becomes stronger than the repulsion of the electrostatic force, but the electrostatic force does not stop acting on the nucleus. A stable nucleus, therefore, is influenced by both the electrostatic force and the strong nuclear force.

3 ANALYZE Select the correct terms to complete the statement about stable nuclei.

Stable nuclei are stable because the repulsion of the electrostatic | strong nuclear force is overcome by the attraction of the electrostatic | strong nuclear force at very short distances. Because the electrostatic force is always present, a nucleus might be unstable if protons and neutrons are too far apart from | close to each other. This would most likely affect larger | smaller nuclei.

Differentiate Instruction

ELL Support Nuclides contain nuclei made of nucleons. Students may find these words easy to confuse. As a mnemonic, connect the *i* in *nuclides* to the *i* in *isotopes*. The two terms are not synonyms, but they have overlapping meanings. Connect the *-on* suffix in *nucleon* to *proton* and *neutron*. **Ask:** *What other physics terms end in* -on? Have students work in pairs or small groups to brainstorm. Answers may include the particles electron and photon from this course and many other particles (muons, baryons, gluons, etc.) from particle physics.

CCC **Influence of Engineering, Technology, and Science on Society and the Natural World**

Elements (within compounds) tend to concentrate in different parts of an ecosystem or living organism. Have students research the use of radioactive tracers in the study of ecosystems.

Exploring Visuals

Ask: *In* **Figure 3,** *in what direction is the net force on the right proton in each image?* right, right, left

Ask: *Why doesn't the right proton move away from the left one?* The proton's motion is determined by a combination of its initial motion and the acceleration due to the net force on the proton. If the initial speed is fast enough, the repulsion is not enough to divert it away.

SEP **Developing and Using Models**

Have students use balls labeled with + signs to model the effects of the strong nuclear force and the electrostatic force between nucleons. Make sure students show how the nuclear force acts only at small distances but the electrostatic force acts at larger distances.

2 As the protons get closer together, the repulsive electrostatic force between them increases. If they get very close, however, the attractive strong nuclear force is stronger than the electrostatic force and can hold the protons together.

3 electrostatic, strong nuclear, far apart from, larger

ccc **Matter and Energy**

Tell students that while experiencing **everyday phenomena,** they have observed examples of potential energy, such as the gravitational potential energy as a result of height. **Ask:** *What is an everyday phenomenon that might explain potential energy in a nucleus due to the strong force?* **Sample answer:** water whose level in a vessel doesn't matter until it overflows

Exploring Visuals

Band of Stability Guide students in analyzing the graph in **Figure 4.**

Ask: *What is the meaning of the band of stability?*

It is a band of stable nuclei with an N/Z ratio between approximately 1:1 and 1.5:1.

Ask: *What does each horizontal line on the graph show?*

Each horizontal line corresponds to a different element. Within that row are isotopes that have the same number of protons but different numbers of neutrons.

Ask: *How can a nucleus move from one place on the graph to another?*

When a nucleus not on the band of stability undergoes radioactive decay, the number of protons or neutrons can change. Its location changes on the graph, possibly moving it onto the band of stability.

1 Stable: 1:1, 1:1, 1:1.5; Unstable: 1:1.3, 1:1.3, 1:1.4

2 For small nuclei, all of the protons are relatively close together. Nuclides with 1 to 20 protons are most stable when the numbers of protons and neutrons are in a ratio of 1:1. Large nuclei must have a larger number of neutrons because of the strong electrostatic force from so many protons. For larger nuclides, the ratio of protons to neutrons is closer to 1:1.5. This is consistent with what the band of stability predicts.

Nuclear Stability

Nuclear forces affect both protons and neutrons. It is convenient, therefore, to speak of these particles collectively. A nucleon is either a proton or a neutron. A nuclide is a nucleus with a specific number of protons and neutrons. Unlike isotopes, nuclides can be compared without reference to which elements are involved. These terms help scientists emphasize nuclear composition rather than the chemical identity of the element.

Scientists found that when the number of protons (Z) in a nuclide is plotted against the number of neutrons (N), stable nuclides cluster in a limited area. This area is referred to as the band of stability, shown in Figure 4. Unstable nuclides are found outside this region.

Band of Stability

FIGURE 4: The area where stable nuclides cluster is known as the band of stability.

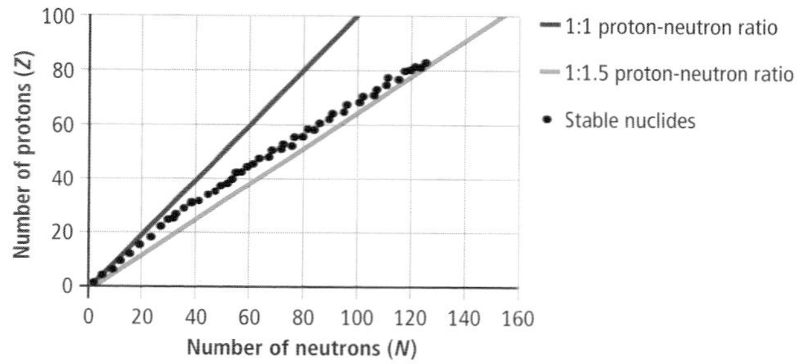

Credit: Adapted from "Band of Nuclear Stability". Copyright © 2018 by the Commonwealth of Australia as represented by the Australian Radiation Protection and Nuclear Safety Agency (ARPANSA). Adapted and reprinted by permission.

1 **SOLVE** Calculate the ratio of protons to neutrons in stable and unstable nuclides. Round values to the nearest tenth place.

Stable Nuclides		Unstable Nuclides	
$^{12}_{6}C$		$^{14}_{6}C$	
$^{40}_{20}Ca$		$^{45}_{20}Ca$	
$^{192}_{76}Os$		$^{182}_{76}Os$	

2 **EXPLAIN** Using Figure 4 and the ratios you calculated, explain why the ratio of stable nuclides is different for nuclides with 1 to 20 protons compared to larger nuclides.

_____

_____

_____

_____

When the number of nucleons is high enough that the nucleus is too large for the strong nuclear force to hold it together, the electrostatic force pushes the protons apart. This is why elements that are heavier than lead, atomic number 82, are always unstable.

© Houghton Mifflin Harcourt Publishing Company

Energy and Matter

Mass Defect

To understand how atomic nuclei can be stable, observe what occurs when nucleons form a nucleus. A proton has a mass of 1.007 276 u. A neutron's mass is 1.008 665 u. Logically, the mass of a nucleus should equal the sum of the masses of its nucleons.

3 **ANALYZE** For each nuclide, use the masses of the proton and neutron to calculate the expected mass, and the difference between the measured and expected masses.

Nuclide	Expected	Measured	Difference
$^2_1$H		2.014 102 u	
$^3_1$H		3.016 049 u	
$^4_2$He		4.002 603 u	
$^7_3$Li		7.016 004 u	

FIGURE 5: A helium-4 nucleus and one neutron (right) has less mass than a hydrogen-2 nucleus and a hydrogen-3 nucleus (left), even though the total number of nucleons is the same in both cases.

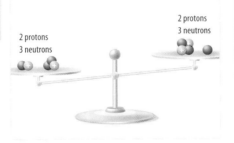

2 protons
3 neutrons

2 protons
3 neutrons

A nucleus actually has less mass than the sum of the nucleons that compose it. The difference between the mass of a nucleus and the sum of the masses of its nucleons is known as the *mass defect*. Where did the mass go? You may have heard of Albert Einstein's famous equation $E = mc^2$. With this equation, Einstein proposed that mass and energy are related. Energy is equal to mass, measured in kilograms, times the speed of light (3.00×10^8 m/s) squared. In other words, mass can be converted to energy and energy can be converted to mass.

4 **INFER** Describe how mass defect relates to what you know about the conservation of matter and energy. Can the law of conservation of matter still be true?

_____

_____

_____

Mass defect corresponds to the amount of energy released when nucleons come together. This is also known as *nuclear binding energy*. The larger the nucleus, the larger the binding energy, but also the larger the number of nucleons this energy needs to hold together. Thus, nuclides with low and intermediate numbers of nucleons are most stable.

As you can calculate with the equation $E = mc^2$, the amount of energy released when one helium-4 nucleus forms is only about 4.5×10^{-12} J. This is a very small amount, but it adds up quickly when you consider how unimaginably tiny atoms are.

5 **Evidence Notebook** Do you think the nuclei of the atoms used in medical imaging are stable or unstable? Use evidence to support your claim.

© Houghton Mifflin Harcourt Publishing Company

Differentiate Instruction

MTSS/RTI Emphasize that binding energy is the amount of energy required to break the nucleus into its nucleons. Have students work as a group to use objects in a gravitational field as an example. Demonstrate that when a tennis ball moves from a desk to the floor, its potential energy decreases. Energy must be put in to move it back to the desktop. In a similar way, when particles come together in a small nucleus, their potential energy decreases. Energy must be put in to separate them again.

Extension The relationship between the binding energy and missing mass is found using the equation $E = mc^2$. **Ask:** *What is the mass associated with 1.0 J of energy?* 1.1×10^{-17} kg

3 H-2 Expected: 2.015 941 u; Difference: 0.001 839 u
H-3 Expected: 3.024 606 u; Difference: 0.008 557
He-4 Expected: 4.031 882 u; Difference: 0.029 279 u
Li-7 Expected: 7.056 488 u; Difference: 0.040 484 u

4 The laws of conservation of matter and energy are still true because when matter is turned into energy, or energy is turned into matter, it is neither destroyed nor created. Instead, it changes form. Without Einstein's equation, the laws of conservation of mass and energy would be violated by nuclear reactions.

Evidence Notebook

5 Students should suggest that the nuclei are unstable and that they change their numbers of protons and neutrons when they emit radiation.

FORMATIVE ASSESSMENT

Card Responses Have students write *stable* on one side of a note card and *unstable* on the other. Using a list of isotopes, quickly give students a series of examples of isotopes, including the atomic number and atomic mass for elements with $Z < 20$. They should hold up their cards to indicate that those with a 1:1 ratio of protons to neutrons are stable and other nuclides of the isotopes are unstable. Then, turn to the upper end of the scale, and compare two isotopes of a heavy element. Ask students to indicate which isotope is more stable.

EXPLORATION 2 Investigating Radioactive Decay

3D Learning Objective

Students **develop a model based on evidence** to explore decays of unstable nuclei and show that matter and energy are conserved in the total number of protons plus neutrons in nuclear processes.

SEP Developing and Using Models

Explain to students that atomic structure was first explored by streaming alpha particles at thin metal foil. Have them arrange desks in the classroom to model nuclei spaced close together. Then, have them model nuclei that are far apart. Have a stream of students flow toward the desks in both models. Ask which model allows them to easily pass through and from which model do most students "bounce back" because they encounter a barrier. As a class, discuss which model represents a small nucleus surrounded by much open space.

DCI PS1.C Nuclear Processes

Display a chart of the binding energy per nucleon, and explain to students that nuclei become more stable as the binding energy per nucleon increases, with the region of greatest stability around iron. *Ask: Where is helium-4 on the chart? What does this position indicate about its stability?* Helium-4 is at a local maximum and is therefore more stable than the nuclides to either side of it.

Collaborate

Think-Pair-Share Have students work in pairs to identify the isotopes and give the number of protons and neutrons in each. Then, have volunteers share and explain their answers with the class.

1 146 neutrons and 92 protons, 6 protons and 8 neutrons, 19 protons and 21 neutrons, 18 protons and 12 neutrons

2 Overall, the number of nucleons is conserved during alpha decay. There are 92 protons in uranium-238 and 90 protons in thorium-234. The additional two protons are present in the alpha particle. There are 146 neutrons in uranium-238 and 144 in thorium-234. The additional two neutrons are present in the alpha particle.

Investigating Radioactive Decay

Nuclei are unstable when the forces among their nucleons are unbalanced because of an excess of either protons or neutrons. Unstable nuclei will spontaneously break apart. This spontaneous transformation of an unstable nucleus into a more stable form is called radioactive decay. When a nucleus undergoes radioactive decay, it releases nuclear radiation in the form of energy, subatomic particles, and, in many cases, one or more new nuclei. The original nuclide is called the parent nuclide, and the resulting nuclide is called the daughter nuclide. If a daughter nuclide is unstable, it will also decay.

1 **Collaborate** With a partner, identify the following nuclides and give the number of protons and neutrons in each: $^{238}_{92}U$, $^{14}_{6}C$, $^{40}_{19}K$, and $^{30}_{18}Ar$.

Alpha Decay

Alpha decay occurs when an atomic nucleus emits an alpha (α) particle, which is a high-energy helium nucleus consisting of two neutrons and two protons bound together. Alpha decay usually occurs in very heavy nuclei of elements with atomic numbers of 83 or higher, such as polonium, uranium, and radium. Alpha decay reduces both the number of protons and the overall number of nucleons, so the daughter nuclide is more stable than the parent nuclide. Alpha particles are not very penetrating—they can be stopped by a piece of paper—but are dangerous if ingested or inhaled. An example is the alpha decay of uranium-238, shown in Figure 6.

FIGURE 6: Uranium-238 is a large, unstable nuclide that decays into thorium-234.

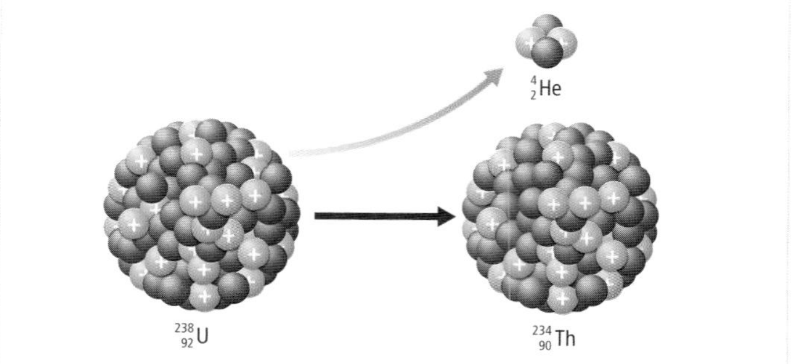

$^{4}_{2}He$

$^{238}_{92}U$ $^{234}_{90}Th$

2 **EXPLAIN** Using uranium-238 as an example, explain whether alpha decay conserves the number and type of atoms and nucleons during the process.

_____

_____

_____

_____

Writing nuclear equations is one way to model radioactive decay. The parent nuclide is shown on the left of a reaction arrow, and the daughter nuclide and the emitted particles are on the right. The nuclear equation for the decay of uranium-238 is $^{238}_{92}\text{U} \rightarrow ^{234}_{90}\text{Th} + ^{4}_{2}\text{He}$.

3 **MODEL** Model the alpha decay of americium-241, a radioisotope used in smoke detectors. Then write a nuclear equation that models the alpha decay of americium-241.

Beta Decay

In beta (β) decay, an unstable nuclide produces a more-stable daughter nuclide by transforming a neutron into a proton, or vice versa. Because the number of protons changes, the daughter nuclide is of a different element than the parent nuclide. Beta decay is observed as a natural process in the heavier isotopes of some elements, which have too many neutrons to be stable. In this type of decay, a neutron changes into a proton by emitting a high-energy electron ($^{0}_{-1}\text{e}$).

4 **APPLY** Fill in the missing text to complete the model of the beta decay of carbon-14.

Because the subscripts in nuclear symbols represent protons, which have a positive charge, it makes sense to think of the subscripts as representing charge. In beta decay, the total charge and number of nucleons remain the same—are conserved—but the ratio of protons to neutrons changes.

5 **EVALUATE** Consider the decay of carbon-14. Between the parent and the daughter nuclide, what changes, and what remains the same? Which nuclide is more stable?

_____

_____

Alternately in isotopes of an element that have too few neutrons to be stable, a proton can decay into a neutron by emitting a *positron* ($^{0}_{+1}\text{e}$), a particle with the same mass as the electron but the opposite charge. An example is the decay of carbon-11, represented by the equation $^{11}_{6}\text{C} \rightarrow ^{11}_{5}\text{B} + ^{0}_{+1}\text{e}$. In Positron Emission Tomography (PET) scans, the radioactive substance injected into a patient's body might be a lighter isotope of carbon, oxygen, nitrogen, or fluorine. Beta radiation can be damaging to tissues. Therefore, doctors and patients must consider the tradeoffs involved in repeated use of PET scans and other medical imaging procedures that use radiation.

Houghton Mifflin Harcourt Publishing Company

© Houghton Mifflin Harcourt Publishing Company

Explain to students that radioactive materials pose dangers to people because of the energy carried by the particles. Have students research ways people might be exposed to alpha particles and beta particles in **everyday phenomena,** the dangers this poses, and countermeasures used to protect the health of people and the environment.

Math Connection

In the equations used to model radioactive decay, the number of nucleons is conserved—that is, the number of nucleons on the left should match the number on the right. Similarly, the net charge on the left should match the net charge on the right. Give students examples of alpha and beta decay equations, and ask them to confirm this rule. **(MP.4)**

Differentiate Instruction

ELL Support Write the symbols for alpha (α), beta (β), and gamma (γ) on the board. Explain that these are Greek symbols used to represent different types of radiation emitted during radioactive decay. Help students pronounce the names and draw the symbols.

3 Americium-241 decays into neptunium-237 and an alpha particle. Students' models should represent an americium-241 nucleus emitting a particle with two protons and two neutrons, resulting in a daughter nuclide with two fewer protons and two fewer neutrons.
$^{241}_{95}\text{Am} \rightarrow ^{237}_{93}\text{Np} + ^{4}_{2}\text{He}$

4 The nuclear equation for carbon-14 decay is $^{14}_{6}\text{C} \rightarrow ^{14}_{7}\text{N} + ^{0}_{-1}\text{e}$.

5 The total number of nucleons is the same, reflected in the superscript 14 for both. The type of atom has changed. A neutron has changed into a proton, and energy has been released, so the daughter nuclide will have a lower binding energy. The daughter nuclide is more stable, as its ratio of protons to neutrons is closer to the band of stability.

Differentiate Instruction

Extension Atomic nuclei have energy levels determined by the arrangement of nucleons, analogous to the energy levels of the atom as determined by the arrangement of electrons. The differences in energy levels in the nucleus are a thousand to a million times greater than the differences due to electron arrangements, and the photons that carry away the energy are much more energetic and potentially damaging. ***Ask:*** *How do the frequencies of photons in the gamma radiation range compare with those in visible light?* Visible light is on the order of 10^{14} Hz, while gamma radiation is on the order of 10^{22} Hz.

Nature of Science

Scientific Knowledge Assumes an Order and Consistency in Natural Systems Gamma rays are detected by their effects on the matter they pass through, ionizing gases or altering semiconductors as the photons transfer energy to the surrounding matter. Unlike alpha and beta particles, which have charge, gamma rays are not affected by magnetic fields. Show the class images of cloud chamber tracks. Discuss what the tracks might show about the particles—such as charge and mass, based on how they respond to a magnetic field.

1 Drawings should show a gamma ray emitted from technetium-99, resulting in parent and daughter nuclides, both with 43 protons and 56 neutrons before and after decay, and gamma radiation.

2 The technetium-99 nucleus becomes more stable by emitting excess energy. The energy released is equal to the energy of the gamma ray and the difference in energy between the high-energy and ground states. The masses of the nuclides would be the same.

3 Alpha particle: decreases by 2, Electron: increases by 1, Positron: decreases by 1, Gamma ray: unchanged

Evidence Notebook

4 Sample answer: A three-dimensional model can show alpha particles, electrons, and positrons by representing protons and neutrons. Representing gamma rays is more difficult, but they could be represented by a computer model.

Gamma Decay

Gamma (γ) rays are high-energy photons, a form of electromagnetic radiation, emitted from a nucleus. Gamma decay usually occurs immediately following other types of decay. A high-energy nucleus releases excess energy by emitting gamma rays and returning to its ground energy state. An example is the gamma decay of technetium-99: $^{240}_{94}\text{Tc} \rightarrow {}^{240}_{94}\text{Tc} + \gamma$.

1 MODEL Draw the gamma decay of technetium-99. Make sure your model includes the numbers of nucleons in the parent and daughter nuclide.

2 EXPLAIN How does the nucleus change in your model of technetium-99 decay? Does it become more or less stable? Is energy taken in or released? How would the masses of the parent and daughter nuclides compare?

Gamma rays, which have more energy than x-rays, are the most penetrating type of radiation and thus they have many medical applications. They easily pass through the body, allowing images to be taken. However, as they are the most potentially damaging form of radiation, care must be taken by patients and medical professionals to minimize repeated exposure. Gamma rays can be stopped by a heavy lead shield, such as a lead apron.

3 SOLVE Complete the table of types of radioactive decay by selecting the correct term for each row.

increases by 1   decreases by 1   decreases by 2   unchanged

Type	Symbol	Charge	Neutron/proton ratio	Atomic number of the nucleus
Alpha particle	$^{4}_{2}\text{He}$	2+	decreases	
Electron	$^{0}_{-1}\beta$	1−	decreases	
Positron	$^{0}_{+1}\beta$	1+	increases	
Gamma ray	$^{99}_{43}\gamma$	0	unchanged	

4 **Evidence Notebook** Is the atomic model from your unit project able to model the release of radiation, either in the form of particles or gamma rays? Explain.

Analyzing Rates of Decay

Each radioactive nuclide has a specific rate at which it decays, defined by its half-life. One half-life is the time it takes for half of the radioactive nuclei in a sample to decay. After one half-life, half of the original nuclei will remain in the sample and half will have decayed into other nuclides. After two half-lives, one-fourth of the original nuclei will remain and three-fourths will have decayed to other nuclides, and the process continues.

Rate of Decay by Half-Life

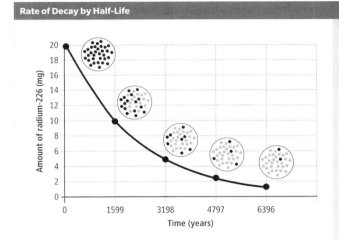

FIGURE 7: The half-life of radium-226 is 1599 years. Half of the remaining radium-226 decays by the end of each additional half-life.

The half-lives of radioactive nuclides vary widely. Some nuclides found in nature have half-lives of billions of years, while others have half-lives of only seconds. The heaviest synthetic nuclides are very unstable, having half-lives of just a fraction of a second. Such a short existence can only be detected with special equipment. Regardless of its duration, the half-life of each nuclide is constant over time.

Some Radioactive Nuclides and Their Half-Lives

Nuclide	Half-life	Nuclide	Half-life
$^{3}_{1}H$	12.32 years	$^{214}_{84}Po$	1.64×10^{-4} seconds
$^{14}_{6}C$	5700 years	$^{218}_{84}Po$	3.1 minutes
$^{32}_{15}P$	14.268 days	$^{218}_{85}At$	1.5 seconds
$^{40}_{19}K$	1.248×10^{9} years	$^{238}_{92}U$	4.469×10^{9} years

 Collaborate Radioactive nuclides have many uses in industry and medicine. With a partner, discuss how the half-life of a radioactive nuclide might influence the way it is used. What could be the advantage of using radioactive nuclides with shorter or longer half-lives?

DCI PS1.C Nuclear Processes

Ask students how the graph in **Figure 7** would change if it showed the rate of decay by half-life of a nuclide other than radium-226. Students should realize that although the name of the element and the length of the half-life on the axes would change, the curve would be the same and the representations in the circles showing half of the original isotope decaying during each half-life would be the same.

Exploring Visuals

Half-Life Guide students in analyzing the graph in **Figure 7.**

Ask: How does the amount of radium-226 change over time? How does the amount of its daughter nuclides present change over time?

The amount of radium-226 decreases by half every 1599 years. The amount of its daughter nuclides increases over time.

Ask: Does the mass of radium-226 decrease by the same amount each half-life? Explain.

No, the mass of radium-226 decreases by the same percentage (50%) each half-life.

Ask: According to the graph, how long will it take before all of the radium-226 is gone?

It will never go away completely. It will continue to decrease by 50% each half-life.

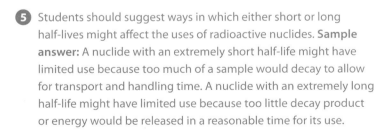 Students should suggest ways in which either short or long half-lives might affect the uses of radioactive nuclides. **Sample answer:** A nuclide with an extremely short half-life might have limited use because too much of a sample would decay to allow for transport and handling time. A nuclide with an extremely long half-life might have limited use because too little decay product or energy would be released in a reasonable time for its use.

Lesson 3 Analyzing Nuclear Reactions 111

Hands-On Lab 👥 Small Groups ⏱ 45 minutes
Modeling Radioactive Half-Lives

SEP **Developing and Using Models**

Students use a model to explore probability patterns related to nuclear decay.

Safety Information Because students will use so many beans or other small objects in their model, avoid using round objects that could easily roll onto the floor. Immediately pick up any items dropped on the floor so they do not become a slip/fall hazard. Have students wash their hands with soap and water immediately after completing this activity. Remind all students that indirectly vented chemical splash goggles are to be worn during the setup, hands-on, and takedown segments of the activity.

1 Students' claims should provide a reasonable way that radioactive decay could be modeled using the beans falling on a target. **Sample answer:** I think that about half the beans will fall close to the center of the target, and half will land farther away. I could use the grid and this fall pattern to model the radioactive decay of an isotope.

Hands-On Lab
Modeling Radioactive Half-Lives

The decay of any single radioactive nucleus is a random event. You cannot predict when it will occur. However, as the number of nuclei in a sample increases, so does our ability to predict the time required for a certain percentage (half) of the nuclei to decay. Experimentation is involved. Over and over, scientists observe the time needed for half of a large sample of a particular radioactive isotope to decay in a laboratory. The time required for half the nuclei to decay will be fairly consistent when the sample sizes are very large. Once scientists have determined this average time, they define it as the half-life of that radioactive isotope. Importantly, the half-life is a prediction. If the half-life of a certain isotope is 10 years, it is likely that half the original sample will have decayed in 10 years. But just because something is likely to occur, that does not mean that it will happen. In any one sample, the actual number of nuclei that decay in 10 years will deviate from 50%. Some samples will have more than half decayed, and some samples will have less.

To explore probability further, consider how easy it is to predict whether a coin will land face-side up ("heads") or face-side down ("tails"). You have a 50% chance of predicting the result of each flip correctly. This chance does not mean that 10 flips will produce five heads and five tails. You are just as likely to flip two heads and eight tails. However, if you flip 1000 coins, you are not likely to get 200 heads and 800 tails. The 50/50 prediction will be more likely the bigger your sample size is.

Using coin flips is one way to model patterns related to half-life. In this lab, you will use a different model. You will use the probability of objects falling onto a target to model the probability of nuclear decay. If you drop a bean from a certain height onto the center of a grid, the way it will strike the ground, bounce, and come to rest is an unpredictable event. Most beans will land and remain near the center, but many will spread in a 360° circle around the center in a predictable pattern.

RESEARCH QUESTION How do scientists use the known half-life of a radioactive nuclide to determine how long ago a sample of it formed?

- -

1 MAKE A CLAIM

How do you think dropping beans on a target could be used to model radioactive decay?

_____

_____

_____

_____

_____

- -

MATERIALS

- indirectly vented chemical splash goggles
- beans, color 1 (100)
- beans, color 2 (100)
- box or self-sealing bag

 Student Lab Worksheet and complete Teacher Support are available online.

SAFETY INFORMATION

- Wear indirectly vented chemical splash goggles during the setup, hands-on, and takedown segments of the activity.
- Immed̶~~...~~ ~~...~~ dropped on the floor so they do not become a slip/fall b~~...~~

indirectly vented
chemical splash
goggles

PLAN THE INVESTIGATION

In your Evidence Notebook, describe a procedure to safely model radioactive decay. Include the data you plan to collect in your description. As you plan, consider the following questions:

- Assume all beans are radioactive nuclei of a substance. What would each drop represent? What would show successive decrease in radioactive nuclei in the bean-and-grid model?

- How does the use of a grid as a target provide you with an opportunity to collect quantitative data related to the research question?

- How will half-life relate to what data you will collect?

Make a table and graph in your Evidence Notebook to record your data. Your data table and graph should reflect your investigational choices. For example, if you used each bean type to represent a different isotope, include columns in your table to record numbers for each isotope.

Have your teacher approve your procedure and safety plan before you begin. Your safety plan should also include steps you will take to keep all beans in a contained area.

COLLECT DATA

Follow your procedure, and record your data in the table that you constructed. Then use your data to construct a graph to help you identify the pattern in your results. Label the x-axis "Trials," and label the y-axis "Parent Isotopes Remaining." If you gathered data on two isotopes, remember to plot data for each isotope type.

ANALYZE

1. What happens to the starting number of beans after each trial?

_____

_____

_____

2. What variable in this lab represents one half-life? Is this a valid representation? Explain your answer.

_____

_____

_____

_____

Math Connection

Decay Fraction Make sure students focus on half-life as a fraction (or percentage) of the original number of parent isotopes instead of an absolute number. ***Ask:*** *How would the data you collect in the lab be different if you used 200 beans instead of 100?* The amount would still decrease by half during each half-life, but the number of parent isotopes that decay at each step would be greater. **(HSN-Q.A.2)**

DCI PS1.C Nuclear Processes

Point out to students that it is unnecessary to identify which nuclide is involved in the decay modeled by this lab because the half-life decay process is the same regardless of the length of the half-life. For any type of radioactive isotope, half the number of parent isotopes decay during each half-life.

Analyze

1. After each trial, the starting number of beans decreases.

2. **Sample answer:** The variable that represents one half-life is a trial. It is a valid representation because a half-life is a measure of time, and each trial can be thought of as the passage of a certain amount of time during which approximately half the atomic nuclei decay.

DCI **PS1.C Nuclear Processes**

Point out to students that the concept of half-life applies to all types of radioactive decay, although the length of each half-life depends on the parent nuclide and the type of decay it experiences. In some cases, such as the beta decay of carbon-14, the parent decays to form a different element. The half-life can then be used to describe the fraction of the substance that has transformed to the new element. In some types of gamma emission, however, the parent decays to form an isotope of the same element.

Statistics Connection

Law of Large Numbers A theorem in statistics states that predicting trends for a large sample size is more reliable than predicting trends for a small number of items. Radioactive decay half-life is highly reliable in predicting the number of decayed isotopes because even in a small amount of a substance, the number of isotopes is extremely high.

Analyze (continued)

3.   **Sample answer:** One predictable event was that the beans would fall to the ground due to gravity. Unpredictable events included how the beans would bounce and which square they would land on in the grid.

4.   **Sample answer:** Scientists use defined numbers (constants) to describe predictable events. For example, the acceleration due to gravity on Earth is 9.8 m/s^2 for all objects. Unpredictable events are described using probabilities, such as ratios or percentages. For example, there is a 1 in 2 chance (50% chance) that a flipped coin will land heads up.

5.   **Sample answer:** Yes, the graph shows an exponential trend in the way the beans landed on the target. Radioactive decay displays an exponential trend.

Construct an Explanation

1.   The graph should show a decreasing exponential curve that is based on half of the nuclei decaying every 50 000 years.

3. What individual events were predictable when you dropped the beans? What individual events were unpredictable?

_____

_____

_____

_____

4. How do scientists use numbers to describe predictable events? How do scientists use numbers to describe unpredictable events?

_____

_____

_____

_____

_____

_____

5. **Interpret Data** While individual events may be unpredictable, trends may emerge when sample sizes are large. Does your graph reveal any trends related to unpredictable events? Explain your answer.

_____

_____

_____

_____

_____

_____

CONSTRUCT AN EXPLANATION

1. **Use Mathematics** Suppose that a radioactive sample included 200 nuclei. How would you graph the change in the number of undecayed nuclei over time if the half-life of the isotope is 50 000 years? Sketch a graph of the decay of the isotope on the grid provided. Label each axis with a descriptive title.

2. Argue from Evidence Suppose you only used 10 beans in your model. Would your model still accurately represent nuclear decay? Why or why not? Use evidence from your investigation to justify your claims and explain your reasoning.

_____

_____

_____

_____

1 DRAW CONCLUSIONS

Write a conclusion that addresses each of the points below.

Claim How did your experiment model half-life in the process of radioactive decay?

Evidence What evidence from your investigation supports your claim?

Reasoning Explain how the evidence you gave supports your claim. Describe in detail the connections between the evidence you cited and the argument you are making.

_____

_____

_____

_____

_____

_____

_____

2 EXTEND

Suppose you have 500 grams of a radioactive substance with a half-life of 15 000 years. How many grams of the undecayed sample would remain after 45 000 years? Do you think you would have exactly that mass of parent nuclide? Why or why not?

_____

_____

_____

_____

_____

3 **Evidence Notebook** How does half-life relate to radioactive decay? Why might radioactive nuclides with short half-lives be used in medical imaging?

© Houghton Mifflin Harcourt Publishing Company

Construct an Explanation (continued)

2. Yes, the model would still accurately represent decay, but it may not show the half-life pattern very well. The model would accurately show that the decay of any one nucleus is a random event. The 10 dropped beans may not follow the half-life probability because 10 beans is a very small sample size. In the investigation, there were several trials in which the number of beans did not decrease by exactly one half. The smaller the number of beans that were dropped, the more the number decayed deviated from the half-life pattern.

1 Students should explain how their model revealed the half-life pattern of nuclear decay. They should include whether they accurately predicted a way for beans dropping on a target to model probability patterns related to nuclear decay and provide evidence for their answer.

2 Students should explain that 45 000 years would include three half-lives. After three half-lives, 12.5% of the original mass would remain because (100% / 2 = 50%), (50% / 2 = 25%), and (25% / 2 = 12.5%). 12.5% of 500 g = 62.5 g. Students should explain that it is not likely that exactly 62.5 g will remain after 45 000 years because decay is a random process. The half-life represents a probability, not a definite outcome.

Evidence Notebook

3 Half-life is the time it takes for half of a radioactive nuclide in a sample to decay to its daughter nuclide. Radioactive nuclides with short half-lives might be used in medical imaging so that they will decay quickly and minimize the amount of radiation a patient is exposed to.

FORMATIVE ASSESSMENT

Which Is False? Ask students to look back through the Exploration and write three statements: two true statements and one false. Have students share their statements with the class and see if they can determine which statement is false.

EXPLORATION 3 Analyzing Nuclear Fission and Fusion

3D Learning Objective

Students use nuclear equations to **illustrate relationships between components of a system** and show that the total number of protons plus neutrons is conserved in **nuclear processes, including fission and fusion.**

Differentiate Instruction

ELL Support Help English language learners differentiate between fission and fusion by having them identify the cognate in their native language for both terms. For example, the Spanish cognate for *fission* is *fisión*, and the Spanish cognate for *fusion* is *fusión*. Explain that fission is the process of nuclei breaking apart to form smaller nuclei, and fusion is the process of smaller nuclei joining to form a larger nucleus. To distinguish the terms, help them identify analogies in **everyday phenomena.** For example, fission is like breaking an orange into slices, and fusion is like groups of students going into the same room to form a class.

SEP Developing and Using Models

Draw students' attention to the nuclear equation for the fission of uranium-235. Have them count the superscripts and count the subscripts on either side of the arrow to confirm that the number of nucleons is conserved. Be sure they multiply the superscript 1 by the coefficient 3 for the neutrons on the right side of the arrow.

1 a

2 Because a small amount of mass is converted into energy, the total mass of the products would be less than that of the starting material. By the equivalence of mass and energy, the release of energy is proportional to the mass defect in the products.

EXPLORATION 3

Analyzing Nuclear Fission and Fusion

Nuclear reactions can change atomic nuclei in different ways, and various particles can be emitted. Radioactive decay can emit alpha particles, beta particles, or gamma rays. Large nuclei can also break apart into smaller nuclei, and small nuclei can join to produce a larger nucleus. Energy is emitted in a variety of forms during each of these reactions.

Nuclear Fission

In nuclear fission, a large nucleus splits into two smaller, more stable fragments, releasing energy. When a nucleus undergoes fission, it may also undergo decay.

1 **INFER** Which type of radioactive decay is also a type of fission?

○ **a**. alpha decay   ○ **b**. beta decay   ○ **c**. gamma decay

Fission can be induced by bombarding certain large, unstable nuclei with neutrons, which are not repelled by the electrostatic force of the protons in the nucleus. The nucleus briefly captures the neutron ($^1_0$n) and becomes more unstable. Then, this nucleus splits into two smaller nuclei. In Figure 8, a uranium-235 nucleus is struck with a neutron and splits into barium-141 and krypton-92 nuclei, releasing three more neutrons in the process:

$$^1_0n + \,^{235}_{92}U \rightarrow \,^{141}_{56}Ba + \,^{92}_{36}Kr + 3\,^1_0n$$

FIGURE 8: A neutron is briefly captured by a uranium-235 nucleus, initiating fission.

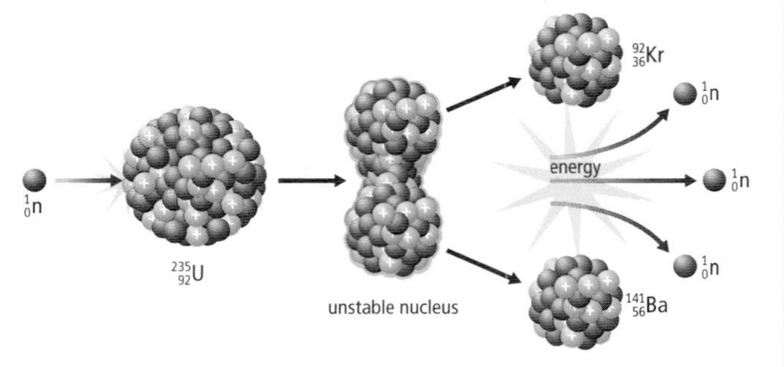

2 **ANALYZE** Consider the decay of uranium-235 shown in Figure 8. How do the masses of the particles in the ending materials compare to the mass of the starting material? How does this relate to the energy released?

_____

_____

_____

_____

The fission of uranium-235 produces neutrons that can induce the fission of other uranium-235 nuclei. If, on average, one of the three released neutrons causes another fission reaction, a chain reaction can occur. A chain reaction is a self-sustaining reaction in which the material that starts the reaction is also one of the products and so can start other reactions. In the chain reaction shown in Figure 9, the uranium-235 will continue to undergo fission until the uranium-235 is used up.

 3 **Collaborate** With a partner, come up with an analogy that describes nuclear fission. What aspects of fission does the analogy capture? What aspects are not captured by the analogy?

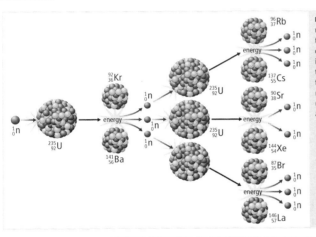

FIGURE 9: A slow-moving neutron is briefly bound to a uranium-235 nucleus, destabilizing it and causing it to undergo fission into two smaller nuclei and three free neutrons. Each free neutron collides with another uranium-235 nucleus, starting a chain reaction.

4 MODEL Draw the next step in the chain reaction in Figure 9.

The minimum amount of a radioactive substance needed to sustain a chain reaction is called the *critical mass*. If the starting mass of uranium-235 is lower than this critical mass, many neutrons will escape the sample rather than bind to other uranium-235 nuclei. As a result, the chain reaction is subcritical, and the rate will decrease. If the starting mass is greater than this critical mass, more than one neutron from each fission event causes another event. The chain reaction is supercritical, and the rate will increase uncontrollably.

 Language Arts Connection One of the first nuclear bombs was developed by using a supercritical chain reaction to trigger fission in plutonium-239. Research this reaction and the energy it releases relative to explosives based on chemical reactions. Prepare a report that synthesizes your research and includes images.

Engineering Connection

Collaborate Have students work in pairs to research the makeup of uranium in nature and to write a short report on how it must be enriched for use in reactors. Most of a natural sample is uranium-238. Less than 1% of the sample is the unstable uranium-235 needed for a reactor. A natural sample may be enriched to 3–5% for a light-water reactor or 20% for a research reactor.

History of Science

Tell students that while many scientists were exploring nuclear fission in the 1930s, it was World War II and the effort to produce a nuclear bomb that sparked extensive research in the field. A major step forward was in 1942 with the production of a chain reaction in uranium-235. Have interested students do research to find out more.

Language Arts Connection
RST.11-12.9 Synthesize information.
Students should research and write a report about the use of a supercritical chain reaction to trigger fission in plutonium-239. Have them include a comparison of the energy released with this reaction and the energy released by explosive chemical reactions.

Information Literary Skills Have students ask themselves the following questions when obtaining information: *Do I know how to organize information using keywords and metadata? Which technology tools do I use for specific purposes? Do I use ethical and legal behavior when I'm sharing information?* Use written or verbal responses as needed to assess students' information literacy skills.

3 Analogies may focus on the initial reaction or the description of the chain reaction. **Sample answer:** The first reaction in fission is like the first turn in a game of pool. The cue ball is the free neutron, and the balls grouped in a triangle shape are neutrons in the nucleus. When the cue ball hits the other balls, the balls that leave the triangle are like neutrons. This analogy does not capture the change in identity of the nuclei or the fact that there are different types of nucleons in the nucleus.

4 Models should show radioactive decay of a daughter nuclide, such as beta decay of cesium-137 to barium-137.

Lesson 3 Analyzing Nuclear Reactions 117

Differentiate Instruction

Extension Emphasize that the stability of a nucleus is related to the binding energy *per nucleon*, not the entire nucleus. This value reflects how tightly each nucleon is held within the nucleus. Heavy nuclei have a binding energy per nucleon of about 7.6 MeV (mega electron volts), and midrange nuclei have binding energies of about 8.5 MeV. **Ask:** *What is the approximate binding energy of uranium-235? Of krypton-93?* 235 × 7.6 MeV/nucleon = 1786 MeV; 93 × 8.5 MeV/nucleon = 791 MeV *If uranium's binding energy is greater, why is krypton more stable?* The binding energy per nucleon is greater for krypton.

Explore Online ▶

Hands-On Lab 👥 Small Groups 🕑 90 minutes

Modeling Fusion

SEP Developing and Using Models

Students make a model to show the fusion of hydrogen and helium nuclei. *Student lab worksheet and teacher support available online.*

1 The hydrogen nuclei combine to form a helium-4 nucleus and two positrons. The energy released is equivalent to the mass deficit of the helium-4 nucleus.

Evidence Notebook

2 Nuclear fission splits a large nucleus into smaller nuclei, and nuclear fusion combines small nuclei to form a larger nucleus. Both reactions release large amounts of energy and can produce other particles, such as alpha particles, beta particles, and neutrons. They differ from decay in that they are not spontaneous.

FORMATIVE ASSESSMENT

One-Sentence Summary Ask students to look back through the Exploration. Have them read each heading and look at the illustrations. Then have them write a one-sentence summary of each nuclear process.

Nuclear Fusion

In nuclear fusion, small nuclei combine to form larger nuclei. To overcome electrostatic repulsion, the nuclei must be moving at high speed or subject to high temperature or high pressure, such as within an artificial fusion reactor or a star, which is a natural fusion reactor. Large amounts of energy are released in the fusion of light nuclei such as hydrogen. An example of nuclear fusion that is constantly occurring in the sun is the reaction $^1_1H + {}^1_1H \rightarrow {}^2_1H + {}^0_{+1}e$, in which two protons fuse to form deuterium and a positron. Another reaction that also occurs in the sun is $^2_1H + {}^3_1H \rightarrow {}^4_2He + {}^1_0n$, in which deuterium and tritium form a helium nucleus, emitting a high-energy neutron.

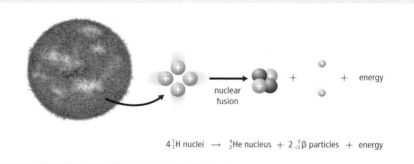

FIGURE 10: Fusion of hydrogen nuclei into more-stable helium nuclei provides the energy of our sun and other stars.

$$4\,{}^1_1H\ \text{nuclei} \longrightarrow {}^4_2He\ \text{nucleus} + 2\,{}^0_{-1}\beta\ \text{particles} + \text{energy}$$

Explore Online ▶

Hands-On Lab 🔬

Modeling Fusion
Model the fusion of hydrogen and helium nuclei.

1 **ANALYZE** Consider the fusion reaction shown in Figure 10. Describe how the nuclei change. Is energy taken in or released? What is this energy equal to?

_____

_____

_____

The binding energy per nucleon in a nucleus varies with the atomic mass, with a maximum at a mass of around 56, the atomic mass of iron. Energy is released by the fusion of elements lighter than iron and by the fission of elements heavier than iron.

When two light nuclei combine and the new mass is lighter than the mass of iron, the nucleons will be more tightly bound than they were in the lighter nuclei. This tighter bond corresponds to a decrease in mass, and this decrease in mass corresponds to a release of energy.

When a heavy nuclide breaks apart, its daughter nuclides are closer to the mass of iron. The daughter nuclides are more tightly bound together than the large parent nuclide, and these tighter bonds are reflected in a decrease in mass and release of energy.

2 **Evidence Notebook** What changes occur in atomic nuclei, and what particles are emitted during nuclear fission and nuclear fusion? How do these processes compare to radioactive decay?

© Houghton Mifflin Harcourt Publishing Company

EXPLORATION 4 Case Study: Exploring Nuclear Energy

EXPLORATION 4

EXPLORATION 4

Case Study: Exploring Nuclear Energy

The binding energy of the nucleus is orders of magnitude greater than the energy in chemical bonds that is released in chemical reactions. Energy released in nuclear reactions is therefore orders of magnitude greater than that released in chemical reactions, such as combustion. Ever since scientists discovered that huge amounts of energy are released in nuclear fission, they have tried to develop methods to harness this energy in useful ways, especially in generating electricity. Some have thought that nuclear power held the promise of meeting all of the world's growing energy needs as an alternative to fossil fuels such as coal, which are in limited supply and produce air pollution. But evaluating nuclear power as an energy solution requires carefully weighing its costs and benefits.

Nuclear Fuel

One way in which energy from fission and radioactive decay can be harnessed is in thermoelectric batteries such as those used in space probes. This engineering design harnesses the thermoelectric effect, in which a change in temperature generates electricity. One benefit of nuclear power for thermoelectric batteries is a long lifetime. Radiation from the decay of plutonium used in thermoelectric batteries, such as in the Mars rover Curiosity shown in Figure 11, generates continuous heat at a reliable level for many years. Such nuclear-powered batteries also have the advantage over solar power in that they can be used in areas with little sunlight. Another benefit of thermoelectric batteries is that they use no moving parts, which wear down over time and require maintenance and replacement.

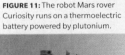

FIGURE 11: The robot Mars rover Curiosity runs on a thermoelectric battery powered by plutonium.

3 **EVALUATE** Why would nuclear fuel be appropriate for thermoelectric batteries in space probes but less appropriate for thermoelectric batteries on Earth?

_____

_____

_____

_____

In nuclear power plants that generate electricity, a uranium fuel pellet such as the one shown in Figure 12 can produce the same amount of thermal energy as the combustion of about 900 kg of coal. Unlike combustion of fossil fuels, nuclear fission produces no air pollutants or greenhouse gases such as carbon dioxide. If these are the only facts taken into account, then nuclear power would seem to be an ideal replacement for fossil fuels as an energy source. However, a fair comparison of sources of energy requires taking into account their fuel life cycles—the entire process of harvesting the fuel and using it. When the cost in energy of a fuel life cycle is subtracted from that produced by the actual generation of electricity, it yields the _net energy_—the balance of energy that the fuel source provides.

FIGURE 12: A fuel pellet of uranium dioxide, the source of energy for a common type of fission reactor

© Houghton Mifflin Harcourt Publishing Company • Image Credits: (cr) ©JPL-Caltech/MSSS/NASA Jet Propulsion Laboratory; (br) ©Patrick Landmann/Science Source

3D Learning Objective

Students explore the impacts on society and the environment of using nuclear fission and fusion as energy sources and **evaluate a solution to a complex real-world problem** based on a range of constraints.

DCI PS1.C Nuclear Processes

Explain to students that an isotope used as nuclear fuel must be _fissile,_ meaning that when the nucleus fissions, it releases multiple neutrons that can in turn induce fission in neighboring nuclei of the isotope. In this way, a chain reaction can be maintained as an energy source. The two most common fissile isotopes used as nuclear power plants are uranium-235 and plutonium-239.

Exploring Visuals

Fuel Pellets Have students observe the uranium fuel pellet shown in **Figure 12.** Explain that the nuclear fuel to be used in a nuclear reactor is packaged in these ceramic pellets. Each pellet is about 3/8-inch diameter and 5/8-inch long. The pellets are packed into metal tubes that are then assembled into an array for use in the reactor. Ask students to consider why the uranium is packaged in pellets rather than a single mass of uranium. Explain that processing the uranium into pellets ensures the homogeneous density and purity of the fuel required to maintain a chain reaction.

3 Students should suggest that the radiation emitted by nuclear fuel such as plutonium would be hazardous around people and other organisms.

Collaborate

Jigsaw Divide students into four groups. Assign each group one of the following topics: how uranium ore is mined, how uranium is extracted from uranium ore, how the uranium ore is refined to increase the percentage of uranium-235, how the uranium is further processed to make it suitable for use in a power plant. Have each group make a presentation to the class, and involve the entire class in a question-and-answer session.

SEP **Developing and Using Models**

Emphasize to students the importance of enriching the uranium to achieve a higher percentage of the fissile isotope uranium-235. Have students research the enrichment process and then produce a flow chart with images to explain the purification methods.

Exploring Visuals

Gas Centrifugation Column Explain to students that a centrifuge is a rapidly spinning device that uses centripetal force to separate a mixture based on the difference in masses of its parts. **Figure 14** shows tubes filled with gaseous uranium. The tubes are connected so that the more purified gas of one tube is passed to the next tube for further purification.

1 Students should suggest that the net energy of uranium as nuclear fuel is significantly affected by the processes of mining and purifying uranium, which require a lot of energy and use of fossil fuels.

Extraction and Enrichment of Uranium

FIGURE 13: Workers at uranium mines have to take special precautions to limit their exposure to radiation.

The fuel cycle of uranium is a process with several stages, most of which involve significant use of fossil fuels. The first step is extraction of ore at mines such as the one shown in Figure 13. Uranium ore is found naturally in Earth's crust and can therefore be mined in areas where a relatively high concentration is present. Uranium is radioactive, as is the noble gas radon, a natural decay product of uranium that is always present where uranium is found. Therefore, uranium mining poses unique hazards. The entire process of mining the ore and separating of uranium oxide (UO_2) from it is heavily dependent on fossil fuels.

The isotope of uranium that undergoes fission is uranium-235, but more than 99% of natural uranium consists of the isotope uranium-238. To be used for nuclear fuel, uranium must be enriched to increase the concentration of uranium-235. After uranium is converted to gaseous form, chains of centrifuges such as those shown in Figure 14 use the slight difference in mass between the two isotopes to increase the concentration of uranium-235. Each centrifuge spins at an extremely high speed. The centrifugal force draws heavier isotopes of uranium toward the walls of the cylinder, while uranium-235 becomes more concentrated near the center. The process is repeated through a number of columns, leaving more and more of the heavier isotopes behind until the concentration of uranium-235 is 3–5%. This enriched uranium is made into fuel pellets.

FIGURE 14: Gas centrifugation columns used in isotopic enrichment of uranium

1 **ANALYZE** What aspects of the total process required to produce uranium fuel pellets do you think have significant impact on the net energy of nuclear power?

_____

_____

_____

Nuclear Fission Power Plants

Nuclear power plants are a type of thermoelectric power plant, which uses a heat source to turn water into steam. The expansion of the steam spins a turbine, which generates electricity by the spin of a magnet near a wire coil. For nuclear power plants, the source of the heat is the energy produced by the fission of nuclear fuel in a nuclear reactor. A nuclear reactor is a device that can initiate and control a sustained fission chain reaction. Nuclear reactors are used for research; to produce radioactive isotopes, such as those used in nuclear medicine; to propel some ships and submarines; and, most commonly, in nuclear power plants.

The fuel pellets are arranged into fuel rods. Between the fuel rods are movable control rods containing a neutron-absorbing substance such as boron. When the control rods are lowered between the fuel rods, the control rods absorb neutrons, and thus prevent an uncontrolled, runaway nuclear reaction that could cause a reactor meltdown. Fully inserting the control rods will shut down the fission reaction. The nuclear reactor is housed inside a containment structure of concrete and steel designed to prevent the escape of radioactive material if a meltdown occurs.

Water continuously circulates, both acting as a coolant and transferring heat to another water system, which is heated into steam. A third water system takes in cool water from a nearby source, such as a lake or ocean, and condenses the steam back into water. Heated water is returned to the water source or is released as steam from cooling towers.

2 ANNOTATE On the diagram, trace the path of the energy released as heat from its source through the nuclear power plant.

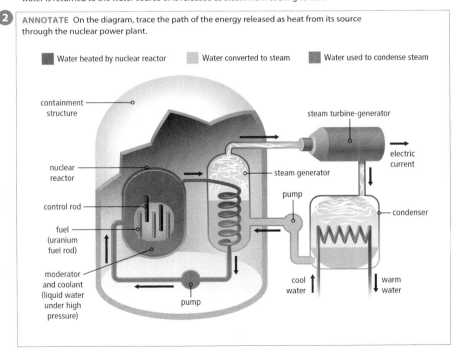

- Water heated by nuclear reactor
- Water converted to steam
- Water used to condense steam

containment structure

steam turbine-generator

nuclear reactor

steam generator

electric current

control rod

pump

condenser

fuel (uranium fuel rod)

moderator and coolant (liquid water under high pressure)

pump

cool water

warm water

Exploring Visuals

Direct students' attention to the diagram of a nuclear reactor. Note that the cycle in thermoelectric power plants can be the same for other sources of heat, such as a geothermal vent or burning coal. ***Ask:*** *Where is energy input into the system shown? Where is it output? In each case, what does the energy do?* Input from the thermal energy source expands water into steam. Output into rotational energy of the turbine generates electricity.

SEP **Developing and Using Models**

Model the chain reaction that keeps a fission reactor generating electricity. Give each student two lightweight balls, such as pompoms or table-tennis balls. Take one yourself. With students widely separated, toss your ball lightly at a student, who when hit will toss the two original balls in the air. Students hit by a ball will toss their balls in the air. With students far apart, expect the chain reaction to end quickly. Move students in an array about 3 feet apart, and toss the ball at one student. The reaction should last longer. With students closer, in an array 1 foot apart, the reaction should continue until the class has no more balls. As students moved closer, the reaction became easier to sustain. This is analogous to either more purified uranium (fissionable U-235 nuclei are closer together) or to moving pieces of uranium closer together.

DCI **PS3.B Conservation of Energy and Energy Transfer**

As a class, examine the cycle in the reactor in the diagram. ***Ask:*** *Where are motion or changes in motion involved in the cycle?* the motion of the fluid, expansion and condensation of the fluid, the spinning of the turbines *How does this compare with the thermoelectric batteries described at the end of this section?* The batteries have no moving parts to wear out. While heat is generated, there is no waste heat from the friction of parts moving against each other.

2 The path should lead from the reactor to the steam generator to the turbine to the condenser. From the condenser, the energy exits in the warm water.

DCI ETS1.B Developing Possible Solutions

Collaborate Have students work in small groups to identify and analyze tradeoffs in nuclear power. First have them read through this page and the next to list benefits and drawbacks. Then have them discuss other ideas they have and add them to the lists. Afterward, have groups compare their lists and debate whether the benefits outweigh the drawbacks.

Preconception Alert

Cooling Towers Students may think that cooling towers emit smoke, like a fossil-fuel burning plant would, or that the steam released from cooling towers contains radioactive material. Have students look back at the nuclear reactor diagram and analyze the part of the system that contains the cooling water. Point out the spiral tubes through which the high-pressure water from the reactor flows. Students should notice that the reactor water is kept separate from the coolant water. Explain that only coolant water is released to the cooling tower, so it contains no radioactive material. Students may also think that cooling towers are found only at nuclear power plants. Explain that some coal-fired power plants also use cooling towers to cool water that can be reused to spin the turbine.

1 a, c, d

Analyzing Tradeoffs in Nuclear Power

The concept of the total fuel cycle and its energy demands provides a model that can be used to evaluate the net energy of an energy resource. Likewise, the use of any energy resource has an effect on social, cultural, and environmental systems that must be critically evaluated when considering tradeoffs.

Because of the enormous amount of energy that is released by nuclear fission, nuclear energy is very reliable and has a very high power output compared to other sources of energy. Because of the dangers of radioactivity that go along with its high energy output, however, the power of nuclear fission also poses unique safety challenges. This tradeoff is the single largest issue that must be considered in regard to nuclear power. Uranium is a radioactive element, and it remains radioactive throughout its fuel cycle. This makes it far more hazardous to obtain, process, and use than other energy sources. Nuclear power plants are also more expensive to build than other types of power plants, in part because safety constraints require a number of systems to be put in place to prevent disasters.

Thermal Pollution

A large amount of energy is given off by a nuclear reactor, but not all of it is converted into electricity. Any machine converts some energy into heat that is not used. Large amounts of water are required to absorb heat in a nuclear power plant, which is why most nuclear power plants are built near bodies of water such as lakes or oceans.

Some of the water becomes steam that is released into the atmosphere by cooling towers, as shown in Figure 15. The steam does not have a significant impact on the environment. As with other kinds of thermoelectric power plants, some of the heated water is normally released back into the water source. The water is not radioactive, but it can increase the water temperature enough to be harmful to temperature-sensitive organisms. This is considered to be thermal pollution, which is a negative environmental impact.

FIGURE 15: The cooling towers of a nuclear power plant release steam into the air.

1 **IDENTIFY CONSTRAINTS** What are some of the constraints for building a nuclear power plant? Select all correct answers.

☐ **a.** The radioactivity of the fuel rods needs to be contained.

☐ **b.** It needs to be able to handle a large amount of nuclear fuel at a time.

☐ **c.** The cost of building the plant requires a significant amount of funding.

☐ **d.** It needs to be built where it can have access to a large amount of water.

☐ **e.** It needs to be prevented from releasing pollutants into the atmosphere.

Radioactive Waste

One of the biggest concerns about nuclear power is the production of nuclear waste in the form of spent fuel rods, which still contain radioactive products. In many cases, the first step in processing the rods is to submerge them in large water tanks, such as the one shown in Figure 16, to be cooled. Then, they must be permanently stored in special containment facilities because radioactive products in spent fuel rods have half-lives of many thousands of years. This constraint has a large social impact because communities generally do not want radioactive waste to be stored near them. More than 60 000 tons of spent nuclear fuel is currently stored at facilities near U.S. nuclear power plants.

FIGURE 16: A water cooling tank for spent nuclear fuel rods

2 ANALYZE Suppose you are voting on a decision on whether to build a nuclear power plant near your town. Describe two pairs of tradeoffs you would consider that would inform your vote.

_____

_____

_____

_____

Energy Production and Energy Demands

The potential of producing plentiful energy for electricity is perhaps the main factor that has made nuclear power an attractive energy solution. For this to be an important benefit assumes that energy demands will remain high or keep increasing. But many new ways have been developed to reduce energy use in society. For example, LED light bulbs use 75% less energy than traditional incandescent bulbs.

When the goal of energy conservation is taken into account, nuclear power's energy benefits may be evaluated as less worth its costs than if energy demands are considered to be a factor that society cannot change. With energy conservation measures put into practice, other forms of energy production that produce less power but involve less cost and environmental impact, such as wind and solar energy, become more attractive.

SEP **Asking Questions and Defining Problems**

Ask students to imagine that a radioactive waste storage facility is going to be built near their town. Engage the class in a discussion of concerns they would have and ways those concerns might be addressed. Describe the concept of NIMBY (not in my backyard) and how some people have insisted that storage facilities should be built in remote, unpopulated areas. Ask students to comment on whether they think this is an acceptable option.

Collaborate

Say Something Have students take turns leading discussions in small cooperative groups. First, have students discuss **everyday phenomena** that demonstrate why producing energy for electricity is important. Then, have them discuss various ways of meeting this need. Next, have them discuss ways of reducing energy use in everyday life to decrease the amount of energy that is required. Finally, have them consider whether nuclear power is the best way to meet this need. For each topic, ask a different student to lead the discussion. Student groups should make a claim and support it with evidence and reasoning.

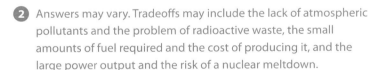

2 Answers may vary. Tradeoffs may include the lack of atmospheric pollutants and the problem of radioactive waste, the small amounts of fuel required and the cost of producing it, and the large power output and the risk of a nuclear meltdown.

EXPLORATION 4   Case Study: Exploring Nuclear Energy, continued

 CCC **Influence of Engineering, Technology, and Science on Society and the Natural World**

Have students work in small groups to investigate the types of events that can lead to nuclear disasters and how engineers have designed reactors to avoid these events. Have groups share what they have learned with the class. Then have the class debate this question: *Should the use of nuclear power plants continue, even though disasters are a possibility?*

 Language Arts Connection
RST.11-12.9 Synthesize information from a range of sources.

Encourage students to read through various accounts of the disaster they research and then describe the major events in their own words. Students may benefit from discussing the events with another person before writing about them.

Remind students that they can find tips on synthesizing information in the online **English Language Arts Handbook.**

Evidence Notebook

1 Students may observe that the use of radioactive nuclides in nuclear power provides the societal benefit of large amounts of energy but also the societal risk of large-scale radiation concerns, while their use in medical imaging poses less risk but also a societal benefit that is more limited to those who need such methods for medical diagnosis.

FORMATIVE ASSESSMENT

One-Sentence Summary Have students work with a partner to look back through the Exploration. Have them skim the text and look at the images. Then have them discuss the content and together write a one-sentence summary for the text under each heading.

The Possibility of Nuclear Disasters

Most of all, the possibility of an accident that releases radiation into the environment is always a significant concern wherever there are nuclear power plants. Such accidents can be caused by human error or by natural disasters. For example, the Fukushima Daiichi nuclear disaster in 2011 was caused by a tsunami from a powerful offshore earthquake. The reactors automatically shut down when the earthquake struck, but water from the tsunami that followed knocked out the backup generators that kept the coolant water circulating in the reactor. As a result, the uncontrolled heat of the reactors caused meltdowns, explosions, and the release of radioactive material into the environment.

FIGURE 17: An aerial view shows the aftermath of the reactor explosions at the Fukushima Daiichi power plant.

The Fukushima accident was the most significant nuclear disaster since the 1986 reactor meltdown in Chernobyl, Ukraine (then part of the Soviet Union). There, a flawed reactor design coupled with poor safety practices led to a meltdown that caused a steam explosion. A significant amount of radioactive material was released and spread over a large area. Over a period of weeks, many people died from acute radiation exposure, and many more suffered ill health effects from the radioactive material spread over the area.

 Language Arts Connection Research a nuclear disaster and determine what caused the accident, as well as its social and environmental impacts. Write a report in which you critically analyze the accident to illustrate how nuclear power plants had impacts that were not anticipated.

Nuclear accidents such as the one in Chernobyl may be considered to have been avoidable. But it is impossible to completely prevent the possibility of human error, which raises the concern about what could be done to ensure that such accidents never happen again. Such concerns still loom large in the public view, and although the possibility of such accidents is very slight, the fact that they have happened has had a major impact on society. The huge social and environmental impacts of nuclear accidents when they do happen highlight the risks that nuclear power always carries with it.

 1 **Evidence Notebook** Compare the benefits and risks involved in the use of radioactive nuclides in nuclear power with those involved in their use in medical imaging.

TAKE IT FURTHER Careers in Engineering

Careers in Engineering

Environmental Engineer

Environmental engineers research efficient and cost-effective ways to clean up toxic material in the environment. Some environmental engineers research ways to remove radioactive waste from the environment.

In Figure 18, toxic waste is poured into a biomagnetic separator. The waste contains uranyl ions, a type of waste produced at sites where uranium ore was mined. A chemical is mixed into the separator and bacteria are added. The bacteria carry out chemical reactions that cause the uranyl ions to form a coating on the bacteria. This coating is magnetic, and so the uranyl coating can be separated from the rest of the sample with a magnetic field, decontaminating the sample.

In bioremediation processes, special strains of common bacteria such as *E. coli* that are resistant to radiation are added to hazardous waste to transform contaminants into forms that can be easily removed. These bacteria incorporate radioactive atoms of elements such as uranium or thorium dissolved in water into compounds that are not soluble in water, which can then be easily removed from the water. Such bacteria are very useful because they perform chemical reactions that would otherwise be expensive and time-consuming to carry out artificially.

Once radioactive material has been removed from the environment, it still needs to be sealed off for a long period of time while it is still radioactive. One approach to doing this is glass vitrification. In this process, radioactive waste is combined with glass powder, and the mixture is heated to a high enough temperature to melt it. The liquid glass is cooled, producing a solid, glassy material with the radioactive material locked within it. The glass material can then be stored underground. Environmental engineers are working to determine glass compositions that will best hold different types of radioactive waste. They also need to address concerns about the glass becoming cracked over time.

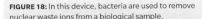
FIGURE 18: In this device, bacteria are used to remove nuclear waste ions from a biological sample.

 Chemistry in Your Community Scientists from diverse backgrounds are responsible for many of the advances in the field of environmental science, such as remediation of radioactive waste. Research an environmental engineer whose work has benefited your community. These may include, but are not limited to, the jobs of health and safety engineer, chemical engineer, microbiologist, and mining engineer. Integrate multiple sources to write a blog post that describes how this person's work has improved the environment in your area and assesses their solution.

| NUCLEAR DISASTERS | HALF-LIFE AND RADIOMETRIC DATING | NUCLEAR MEDICINE | Go online to choose one of these other paths. |

Collaborate

You may choose to assign this activity or direct students to the Interactive Online Student Edition, where they can choose from all available paths. These activities can be assigned individually, to pairs, or to small groups.

 ETS1.B Developing Possible Solutions

Hazardous Waste Removal Removing hazardous waste contamination from the environment is an engineering design challenge. As waste moves through natural cycles, it can concentrate in some areas, such as in the leaves of plants or in the bodies of top predators. Have students research how waste is removed or managed in your area.

Chemistry in Your Community

Provide guidance for students in choosing an environmental engineer to research. Students may want to contact the person to learn more about the work and its impact on the community.

Explore Online ▶

Nuclear Disasters

Students research the meltdown of a nuclear power plant and analyze what went wrong.

Half-Life and Radiometric Dating

Students learn about applications of half-life in unstable nuclei in radiometric dating.

Nuclear Medicine

Students research the use of radioisotope tracers to observe processes in the body.

EVALUATE Lesson Self-Check

Can You Explain the Phenomenon?

Claims, Evidence, and Reasoning

Have students clearly state their claim—their explanation for the phenomenon they have been investigating throughout this lesson. They should present their reasoning for making this claim, along with evidence such as facts, examples, and statistics that support their claim.

You may want to have students present their arguments orally, in writing, or as a debate. Refer students to the **English Language Arts Handbook** for more information on evaluating claims and presenting arguments.

Cultivating Student Questions

Assessing Student Growth Review the list of questions students generated at the beginning of the lesson. Have volunteers select any unanswered questions and suggest how they could be investigated. After approving student plans, have small groups conduct the investigations and report back to the class.

Evidence Notebook

1 Students' answers should explain the different types of nuclear reactions. They should identify radioactive decay as the reaction that is used to produce the medical image and explain that instability in the nucleus is responsible for this process. The types of particles that are detected indicate the type of nuclear reaction that has occurred and the forces that caused the reactions. Radioactive decay occurs when the ratio of neutrons to protons in the nucleus produces an unstable nucleus that decays to produce a more stable nucleus. Fusion occurs when smaller nuclei combine to produce a larger nucleus. Fission occurs when a large nucleus breaks apart to form smaller nuclei.

Lesson Self-Check

CAN YOU EXPLAIN THE PHENOMENON?

FIGURE 19: In a PET scan, small amounts of radioactive nuclides are injected into the bloodstream to produce images of the body.

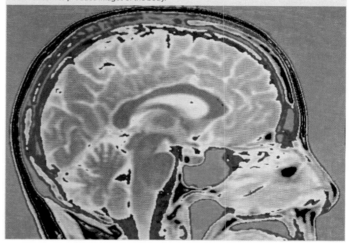

Medical images can be produced using a variety of techniques and processes. In one process, x-ray radiation moves through the body, and a detector on the opposite side of the body produces an image. In a PET scan, however, a medical image is generated from instruments that detect radiation emitted from within the body. Radioactive nuclides are introduced into the body either by injection or by having the patient drink a solution containing the nuclides.

 Evidence Notebook Refer to your notes in your Evidence Notebook to make a claim about why some atoms give off radiation that can be detected in a medical image. Your explanation should include a discussion of the following points:

Claim What types of nuclear reactions would cause atoms to give off radiation that can be detected in a medical image, and how do forces within the nuclei cause these reactions?

Evidence What evidence supports a claim of whether the nuclear reactions are a form of radioactive decay, fission, or fusion? What evidence supports a claim of the types of forces within the nuclei that cause the reactions?

Reasoning Explain how the evidence you cited supports your claim.

 Formal Assessment Go online for student self-checks and other assessments.

CHECKPOINTS

Check Your Understanding

1. Select the correct terms to complete the statement.

   In fission, nuclei break apart | join. This reaction is found spontaneously in nuclides with few | many nucleons.

   In fusion, nuclei break apart | join. This reaction is possible when energy is added to | released from nuclei with few | many nucleons.

2. Which force repels like charges from each other?
   - ○ **a.** gravitational
   - ○ **b.** electrostatic
   - ○ **c.** strong
   - ○ **d.** weak

3. Which of the following are conserved in all nuclear reactions? Select all correct answers.
   - ☐ **a.** mass
   - ☐ **b.** charge
   - ☐ **c.** number of protons
   - ☐ **d.** number of neutrons
   - ☐ **e.** number of nucleons

4. Select the correct terms to complete the statement.

   When nucleons come together to form a nucleus, they gain | lose mass and gain | lose energy. This difference in energy is absorbed | released if the nucleus comes apart.

5. How would you expect the nuclide $^{17}_{7}N$ to decay to result in a more stable nuclide?
   - ○ **a.** alpha decay
   - ○ **b.** beta decay of an electron
   - ○ **c.** beta decay of a positron
   - ○ **d.** gamma decay

6. Which properties might a nuclide on the band of nuclear stability have?
   - ○ **a.** atomic number 10 and 15 neutrons
   - ○ **b.** atomic number 30 and 30 neutrons
   - ○ **c.** atomic number 52 and 78 neutrons
   - ○ **d.** atomic number 86 and 128 neutrons

7. Match each type of radioactive decay with the decay particle it produces.

alpha decay	○	○	γ
beta decay	○	○	$^{4}_{2}He$
gamma emission	○	○	$^{0}_{+1}e$

8. When uranium-235 undergoes fission in nuclear power plants, thorium-231 is produced, which soon decays to protactinium-231. Protactinium-231 has a half-life of 32 760 years. Complete the sentences to describe the decay of a 5.00-g sample of protactinium-231 over time.

   After 32 760 years, the sample will contain about _____ grams of the radioactive nuclide.

   After 65 520 years, the sample will contain about _____ grams of the radioactive nuclide.

   After 98 280 years, the sample will contain about _____ grams of the radioactive nuclide.

9. What are some disadvantages of using nuclear energy to produce electricity compared to a coal-fired power plant? Select all correct answers.
   - ☐ **a.** It has a lower power output.
   - ☐ **b.** It requires larger amounts of fuel.
   - ☐ **c.** It requires more water.
   - ☐ **d.** It produces waste products that require long-term storage.
   - ☐ **e.** It requires mining operations and processing that are more costly.

Answers

1. break apart, many, join, added to, few
2. b
3. b, e
4. lose, gain, released
5. b
6. c
7. alpha decay: $^{4}_{2}He$; beta decay, $^{0}_{+1}e$; gamma emission: γ
8. 2.50, 1.25, 0.625
9. c, d, e

© Houghton Mifflin Harcourt Publishing Company

Answers

10. The conservation of energy holds for nuclear reactions if the energy bound in atomic nuclei is taken into account. The quantity of this energy can be found by taking the mass deficit—the difference between the masses of individual particles and a bound nucleus—and applying $E = mc^2$.

11. Sample answer: A submarine is often submerged, making combustion and solar energy unusable. Long trips favor power sources that do not need to be replenished. Passive designs (such as hydroelectric and tidal generators) don't work for a vehicle that needs to move.

Make Your Own Study Guide

Have students create a study guide that helps them organize and visualize the important information from the lesson. Their study guide should focus on the main ideas from the lesson and tie multiple ideas together. Students can make an outline, a concept map, a graphic organizer, or another representation.

EVALUATE

CHECKPOINTS (continued)

10. Explain how the conservation of energy applies to nuclear reactions.

_____

_____

_____

_____

_____

_____

11. Nuclear submarines use a process similar to the process used in thermoelectric power plants, using the heat of fission to generate steam from water and spin turbines. Explain why nuclear energy might be a practical power source for a submarine.

_____

_____

_____

_____

_____

_____

_____

_____

_____

_____

MAKE YOUR OWN STUDY GUIDE

In your Evidence Notebook, design a study guide that supports the main ideas from this lesson:

A stable atomic nucleus is held together primarily by the strong nuclear force.

Unstable nuclei spontaneously decay, releasing radiation in the form of energy and particles.

Large nuclei may undergo nuclear fission, and small nuclei may undergo nuclear fusion.

Nuclear energy can be harnessed for practical applications.

Remember to include the following information to your study guide:
• Use examples that model main ideas.
• Record explanations for the phenomena you investigated.
• Use evidence to support your explanations. Your support can include drawings, data, graphs, laboratory conclusions, and other evidence recorded throughout the lesson.

Consider the costs and benefits that nuclear technology has for society and the environment.

UNIT 2 Connections

Physical Science Connection

Subatomic Particles The properties of subatomic particles smaller than protons, neutrons, and electrons are studied by observing high-energy interactions of particle beams at large accelerator facilities such as CERN, the European Organization for Nuclear Research. Institutes from many countries use the equipment at CERN to run studies. CERN employs over 2500 people to build and maintain equipment, run experiments, and interpret data.

> Research recent discoveries about subatomic particles and the scientists and engineers that work at facilities such as CERN. Write a news article explaining how one discovery was made, the importance of that discovery, and the team responsible for making the discovery.

FIGURE 1: The CMS detector at CERN

Literature Connection

Nuclear Reactions in Literature After atomic bombs saw use in World War II, books and films began exploring story lines about the new nuclear age. Villains and superheroes alike were depicted as creations of nuclear radiation's effect on the human body. Nuclear disasters, such as the accidents at Chernobyl in 1986 or Fukushima Daiichi in 2011, have been the basis for fiction and nonfiction works on the possible dangers of nuclear energy.

> Select a piece of literature influenced by nuclear energy, nuclear weapons, or nuclear disasters. Research how the author was influenced by the perceptions of nuclear energy at the time. Synthesize your findings in a book report, including a plot synopsis of your selection.

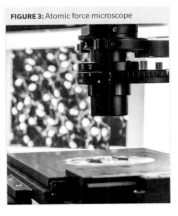

FIGURE 2: Chernobyl nuclear power station after the accident in 1986.

Technology Connection

Imaging Molecules Light microscopes allow scientists to research cells that range in size from 10^3–10^5 nanometers and therefore can reflect visible light. But molecular structures ranging in size from 0.1 to 10 nanometers are so much smaller that new imaging techniques had to be developed to render them visible. Today, scientists have a variety of techniques for imaging molecules. For example, the atomic force microscope can produce a three-dimensional image with a resolution less than one nanometer by measuring the force between a probe and the sample surface.

> Make a multimedia presentation about a molecule that was imaged using a molecular imaging technique. Explain how the molecule was imaged, and what scientists and engineers learned from being able to image the molecule you researched.

FIGURE 3: Atomic force microscope

Support for Unit Connections

Physical Science Connection

Discoveries about subatomic particles and their properties continue in laboratories around the world. A major discovery was the Higgs boson in 2012. These discoveries are the work of numerous scientists and engineers, each of whom plays a critical role. Students' news article about a discovery should explain its importance in aiding understanding of subatomic particles and their interactions. Articles should identify the researchers and their affiliations and explain how this discovery builds on or relates to previous work. Articles can also discuss future investigations the researchers may be planning.

Literature Connection

Due to the ethical, economic, emotional, and energy-related factors and policies associated with nuclear energy and nuclear weapons, students will need guidance to study and discuss this topic. Consider collaborating with your literature and social studies colleagues to compile a short list of appropriate books for students to read and research for their book report. The focus of the report should be on how the plot of the novel—or the topic of the book if nonfiction—was influenced by nuclear reactions and people's concern about or misunderstanding of them. Encourage students to research the decade in which the book was written to learn about the intended audience's familiarity with nuclear reactions. Some of these books have been popularized in science fiction movies or documentaries.

Technology Connection

Objects such as molecules with structures less than a nanometer in size cannot be imaged by light waves because the wavelengths are hundreds of nanometers. Instead, scientists use imaging techniques that rely on measurements of force or changes in electric fields. Such instruments include the atomic force microscope, the scanning tunneling microscope, and the scanning electron microscope. Many carbon-based compounds have been imaged using atomic force microscopes and scanning tunneling microscopy. Presentations should describe a molecule that has been imaged using this type of technology and the importance of this imaging.

THING EXPLAINER BY RANDALL MUNROE

A BOOK EXPLAINING COMPLEX IDEAS USING ONLY THE 1,000 MOST COMMON WORDS

THE PIECES EVERYTHING IS MADE OF
A table for putting small pieces in order

You know that the periodic table is an arrangement of the elements in order of their atomic numbers so that elements with similar properties fall in the same column. Here's a look at how this arrangement of elements helps us understand the world on an atomic scale.

RANDALL MUNROE

RANDALL MUNROE
XKCD.COM

THE STORY OF PUTTING THINGS IN ORDER

PEOPLE USED TO THINK THAT EVERYTHING AROUND US WAS BUILT FROM FOUR KINDS OF STUFF: EARTH, AIR, FIRE, AND WATER.

THEY WERE ALMOST RIGHT—BUT INSTEAD OF FOUR KINDS OF PIECES, THERE ARE MORE LIKE TEN DOZEN.

ALL THE THINGS WE CAN TOUCH (BUT NOT THINGS LIKE LIGHT) ARE MADE FROM THESE PIECES.

DON'T TOUCH MY FOOD!

THERE HE GOES TOUCHING THINGS AGAIN . . .

THERE ARE ALMOST TEN DOZEN THAT WE'VE FOUND SO FAR, BUT THERE ARE PROBABLY MORE.

THIS TABLE PUTS THE PIECES IN ORDER BY WEIGHT, AND PUTS GROUPS OF PIECES THAT ARE LIKE EACH OTHER IN SOME WAY ABOVE AND BELOW EACH OTHER.

I GOT 4 NEW ONES!

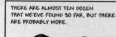

PIECES OF PIECES

These pieces are made of even smaller pieces. Different kinds of pieces have different numbers of those smaller parts. There are three main kinds of these smaller parts—two heavy ones and a light one.

Light pieces

Heavy pieces

Over the past hundred years, we've learned that the idea of "where" doesn't always work well for very small things.

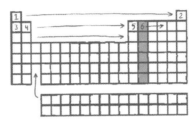

TABLE SHAPE

The boxes in this table are in order from left to right and top to bottom. It has this strange shape because pieces are in groups with other pieces that are a lot like them.

(The reason those groups are like each other has to do with the number of light parts around the outside of the piece—which is mostly the same as the piece's center number—and the way different numbers of light parts sort themselves around the outside of the piece.)

NAMES

Some of the things on this table have had names for a long time (like gold) but some of them were only found in the last few hundred years.

Many of the pieces in this table are named after people or places—and especially for people who helped to learn about them or the places where those people worked.

Here are a few of the things these pieces are named after.

CENTER NUMBER

We number the pieces by counting how many of one kind of heavy part they have in their center, and use that number to put pieces in boxes in the table. The other heavy part doesn't matter to the count, so pieces with different numbers of that part may share the same box in the table.

  #1 #2 #3

SHORT LIVES, STRANGE HEAT

Some kinds of pieces don't last very long, slowly breaking down into other pieces over time by throwing away bits of their centers in all directions, which makes them give off a kind of strange heat.

We count how long a kind of piece lasts by timing how long it takes for half of it to break down. We call this the piece's "half-life."

© Houghton Mifflin Harcourt Publishing Company

Teacher Notes

_____

_____

_____

_____

_____

_____

_____

_____

_____

_____

_____

_____

_____

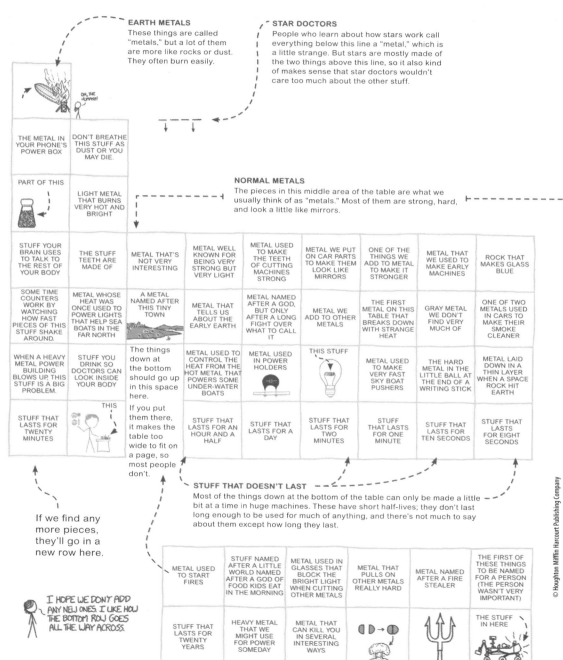

THE PIECES EVERYTHING IS MADE OF

NOT METAL

The things toward the top right part of the table are things that aren't metal. Most of these things are very different from each other. Many of them come in the form of air. A few of them look like a kind of rock or water instead of air. They usually turn to air easily, and most of them are not very strong.

THE LINE

People don't agree exactly where the line between "metals" and "not metals" is, but it's somewhere around here, and runs down and to the right.

AIR, WATER, AND FIRE

The things in this area of the table do a lot of things. When you put them near things from the other end of the table, they can turn to different kinds of water, start fires, or make everything blow up.

QUIET AIR

This end of the table is pretty quiet. When you put these kinds of air with other things, they usually don't seem to notice.

THE AIR IN HERE

| | | THE STUFF THAT KEEPS KITCHEN GLASS FROM BREAKING WHEN HOT | THE STUFF ALL KNOWN LIFE IS MADE FROM | THE PART OF AIR WE DON'T NEED TO BREATHE TO STAY ALIVE | THE PART OF AIR WE DO NEED TO BREATHE TO STAY ALIVE | GREEN BURNING AIR THAT KILLS | AIR IN BRIGHT SIGNS MADE FROM COLORED LIGHT |

| | | THIS METAL | THE ROCK THAT MAKES UP BEACHES, GLASS, AND COMPUTER BRAINS | BURNING WHITE ROCKS | SMELLY YELLOW ROCKS — LIKE THIS | THE STUFF THEY PUT IN POOLS SO NOTHING BAD CAN GROW IN THEM | AIR THAT DOESN'T DO MUCH OF ANYTHING |

| THE GRAY METAL AT THE CENTER OF THE EARTH | BROWN METAL WE USE TO CARRY POWER AND VOICES | METAL USED TO MAKE THE BROWN METAL STRONGER (NOW USED FOR MANY OTHER THINGS) | WATERY METAL THAT MAKES DRINK CANS TEAR LIKE PAPER | METAL NAMED AFTER THIS PLACE | THE ROCK MOST WELL KNOWN FOR KILLING YOU IF YOU EAT IT | A ROCK THAT CAN CHANGE ONE KIND OF POWER INTO ANOTHER | RED WATER | AIR USED BY DOCTORS TO MAKE THIN BRIGHT LIGHTS FOR CUTTING EYES |

| ONE OF TWO METALS USED IN CARS TO MAKE THEIR SMOKE CLEANER | | METAL USED IN PAINT UNTIL WE REALIZED IT MADE PEOPLE SICK | PART OF THE SILVER METAL YOU CAN HEAT UP AT HOME TO STICK PARTS TOGETHER | METAL PUT ON FOOD CANS TO KEEP WATER FROM MAKING HOLES IN THEM | METAL PUT IN THINGS TO KEEP THEM FROM BURNING | METAL THAT CAN BE FOUND IN LOTS OF PLACES, BUT MOST OF THEM AREN'T EARTH | STUFF THEY ADD TO THIS — SO YOUR BRAIN GROWS RIGHT | AIR USED IN CAMERA FLASHES |

| A ROCK THAT PEOPLE WILL PAY AS MUCH FOR AS GOLD | GOLD | THIS | METAL WE USED FOR KILLING ANIMALS BUT STOPPED USING BECAUSE IT WAS TOO GOOD AT IT | METAL WELL KNOWN FOR BEING HEAVY | ROCK THAT LOOKS LIKE A COOL TINY CITY | THIS | STUFF NO ONE HAS SEEN CLEARLY BECAUSE IT BURNS UP TOO FAST | AIR THAT COMES FROM ROCKS UNDER HOUSES AND CAN MAKE YOU SICK |

| STUFF THAT LASTS FOR TEN SECONDS | STUFF THAT LASTS FOR HALF A MINUTE | STUFF THAT LASTS FOR A THIRD OF A MINUTE | STUFF THAT LASTS THREE SECONDS | STUFF THAT LASTS FOR LESS THAN A THIRD OF A SECOND | STUFF THAT LASTS FOR THE TIME IT TAKES YOU TO CLOSE AND OPEN YOUR EYES | STUFF THAT LASTS FOR THE TIME IT TAKES SOUND TO TRAVEL ONE FOOT |

MONEY METAL

We use a lot of the things in this group as money—although not the bottom one, since it disappears very fast.

(Some people who know a lot about money actually think that having money that disappears over time could be good, but they probably don't mean quite this quickly.)

FEEL BETTER

This stuff is made from the rock that looks like a tiny city. If you feel like food is going to come out of your mouth, you can eat or drink some of this, and it might help you feel better.

SO MANY DIFFERENT PARTS OF THE WORLD!

| METAL NAMED AFTER THIS PLACE | METAL THAT PULLS ON OTHER METALS WHEN IT GETS JUST A LITTLE COLDER THAN NORMAL AIR | ANOTHER METAL NAMED AFTER THIS TINY TOWN | METAL WHOSE NAME MEANS "HARD TO GET" | METAL NAMED AFTER THIS PLACE | ANOTHER METAL NAMED AFTER THIS TINY TOWN | THE NAME PEOPLE HERE USED FOR PEOPLE HERE | I'M SURE THIS IS A NICE TOWN, BUT COME ON. | METAL NAMED AFTER THIS PLACE |

| STUFF IN THE BOXES THAT TELL YOU WHEN YOUR HOUSE IS ON FIRE | METAL NAMED FOR HER | METAL NAMED AFTER THIS PLACE | METAL NAMED AFTER THIS PLACE | METAL NAMED FOR HIM | METAL NAMED FOR A MAN WHO HELPED BUILD THE FIRST HEAVY METAL POWER BUILDING | METAL NAMED FOR HIM — THIS WAS MY IDEA | METAL NAMED FOR HIM | METAL THAT LASTS FOR FOUR MINUTES |

NAMED FOR THIS PLACE

Teacher Notes

_____

_____

_____

_____

_____

_____

_____

_____

_____

_____

_____

_____

_____

_____

_____

_____

_____

_____

THING EXPLAINER BY RANDALL MUNROE

A BOOK EXPLAINING COMPLEX IDEAS USING ONLY THE 1,000 MOST COMMON WORDS

THING EXPLAINER
COMPLICATED STUFF IN SIMPLE WORDS

RANDALL MUNROE

RANDALL MUNROE
XKCD.COM

HEAVY METAL POWER BUILDING
Making heat from heavy metals

You know that nuclear reactors use controlled-fission chain reactions to produce energy and radioactive nuclides—and that nuclear power plants use heat from nuclear reactors to produce electrical energy. Here's a look at the process that turns nuclear fission into electric current.

THE STORY OF THE HEAVY METAL POWER BUILDING

THESE BUILDINGS USE SPECIAL KINDS OF HARD-TO-FIND HEAVY METAL TO MAKE POWER. SOME OF THE METALS THEY USE CAN BE FOUND IN THE GROUND, BUT ONLY IN A FEW PLACES. OTHER KINDS CAN BE MADE BY PEOPLE—BUT ONLY WITH THE HELP OF A POWER BUILDING THAT'S ALREADY RUNNING.

THESE METALS MAKE HEAT ALL THE TIME, EVEN WHEN THEY'RE JUST SITTING. THEY MAKE TWO KINDS OF HEAT: NORMAL HEAT—LIKE HEAT FROM A FIRE—AND A DIFFERENT, SPECIAL KIND OF HEAT. THIS SPECIAL HEAT IS LIKE LIGHT THAT YOU CAN'T SEE. (AT LEAST, YOU CAN'T SEE IT MOST OF THE TIME. IF THERE'S A WHOLE LOT OF IT, ENOUGH TO KILL YOU QUICKLY, YOU CAN SEE IT. IT LOOKS BLUE.)

NORMAL HEAT CAN BURN YOU, BUT THE SPECIAL HEAT FROM THESE METALS CAN BURN YOU IN A DIFFERENT WAY.

ME TOO
I'M ON FIRE!

IF YOU SPEND TOO MUCH TIME NEAR THIS HEAT, YOUR BODY CAN START GROWING WRONG. SOME OF THE FIRST PEOPLE WHO TRIED TO LEARN ABOUT THESE METALS DIED THAT WAY.

I'M BURNING UP
RIP

THE SPECIAL HEAT IS MADE WHEN TINY PIECES OF THE METAL BREAK DOWN. THIS LETS OUT A LOT OF HEAT, FAR MORE THAN ANY NORMAL FIRE COULD. BUT FOR MANY KINDS OF METAL, IT HAPPENS VERY SLOWLY. A PIECE OF METAL AS OLD AS THE EARTH MIGHT BE ONLY HALF BROKEN DOWN BY NOW.

WITHIN THE LAST HUNDRED YEARS, WE LEARNED SOMETHING VERY STRANGE: WHEN SOME OF THESE METALS FEEL SPECIAL HEAT, THEY BREAK DOWN FASTER. IF YOU PUT A PIECE OF THIS METAL CLOSE TO ANOTHER PIECE, IT WILL MAKE HEAT, WHICH WILL MAKE THE OTHER PIECE BREAK DOWN FASTER AND MAKE MORE HEAT.

IF YOU PUT TOO MUCH OF THE METAL TOGETHER LIKE THIS, IT GETS HOTTER AND HOTTER SO FAST THAT IT CAN ALL BREAK DOWN AT ONCE, LETTING OUT ALL ITS HEAT IN LESS THAN A SECOND. THIS IS HOW A SMALL MACHINE CAN BURN AN ENTIRE CITY.

BOOM!

TO MAKE POWER, PEOPLE TRY TO PUT PIECES OF THIS METAL CLOSE ENOUGH TOGETHER THAT THEY MAKE HEAT FAST, BUT NOT SO CLOSE THAT THEY GO OUT OF CONTROL AND BLOW UP. THIS IS VERY HARD, BUT THERE IS SO MUCH HEAT AND POWER STORED IN THIS METAL THAT SOME PEOPLE HAVE WANTED TO TRY ANYWAY.

OUTSIDE POWER LINE

Even though the building makes power, without outside power it will stop running.

This is important, because it means that if there's a very big problem, you can stop things from the outside by turning off the power.

POWER BUILDING

This building holds the metal and makes power. Water comes in, and it uses the metal to heat the water, then makes power from the hot water. (There's a bigger picture of it on the next page.)

COOLING BUILDING

After they're done with it, the sea water is very hot. They put it in this building to let it cool down a little so it's not too hot when they put it back in the sea.

They pour the water out into the air, where it falls like rain. As it falls, the air cools it down. This warms up the air, which makes it rise, and new cold air moves in from the outside to take its place.

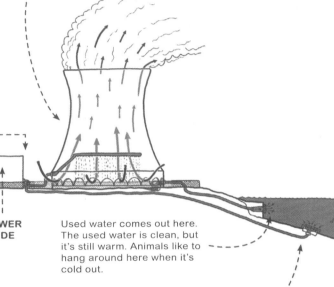

HOT METAL SIDE   **POWER SIDE**

POWER LINE BOX

Sometimes animals get in here and break something, and it makes the entire building stop working.

Used water comes out here. The used water is clean, but it's still warm. Animals like to hang around here when it's cold out.

Cold water gets pulled in here. Sometimes fish get stuck in it and they have to turn off the power building to figure out what's wrong.

MAKING POWER WITH WATER

The building makes power by heating water. This means they need lots of cold water, which is why they're usually built near the sea or a big river.

They don't let the water from the sea touch the water that goes near the hot metal itself. Instead, they let the metal heat up water that runs through metal lines. Then the heat from those lines heats water in another water carrier, which goes over to the other part of the building. Then *that* water heats the water from the sea.

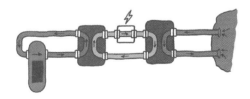

Teacher Notes

_____

_____

_____

_____

_____

_____

_____

_____

_____

_____

_____

_____

_____

_____

_____

_____

_____

_____

Teacher Notes

_____

_____

_____

_____

_____

_____

_____

_____

_____

_____

_____

_____

_____

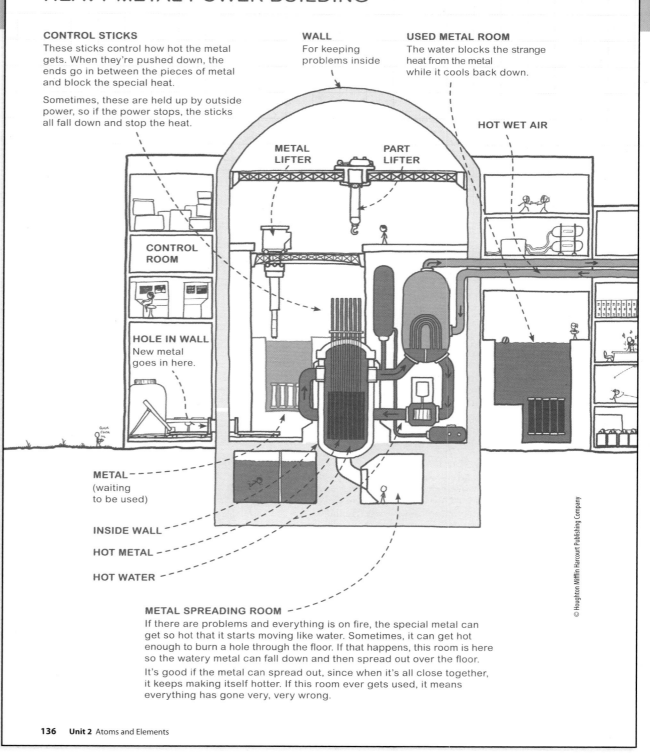

HEAVY METAL POWER BUILDING

CONTROL STICKS
These sticks control how hot the metal gets. When they're pushed down, the ends go in between the pieces of metal and block the special heat.

Sometimes, these are held up by outside power, so if the power stops, the sticks all fall down and stop the heat.

WALL
For keeping problems inside

USED METAL ROOM
The water blocks the strange heat from the metal while it cools back down.

HOT WET AIR

METAL LIFTER

PART LIFTER

CONTROL ROOM

HOLE IN WALL
New metal goes in here.

METAL
(waiting to be used)

INSIDE WALL

HOT METAL

HOT WATER

METAL SPREADING ROOM
If there are problems and everything is on fire, the special metal can get so hot that it starts moving like water. Sometimes, it can get hot enough to burn a hole through the floor. If that happens, this room is here so the watery metal can fall down and then spread out over the floor.

It's good if the metal can spread out, since when it's all close together, it keeps making itself hotter. If this room ever gets used, it means everything has gone very, very wrong.

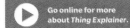
Go online for more about *Thing Explainer*.

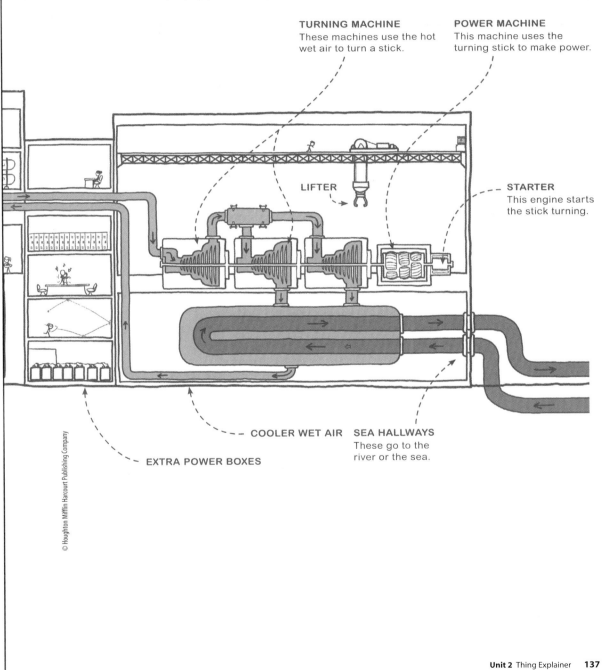

TURNING MACHINE
These machines use the hot wet air to turn a stick.

POWER MACHINE
This machine uses the turning stick to make power.

LIFTER

STARTER
This engine starts the stick turning.

COOLER WET AIR

SEA HALLWAYS
These go to the river or the sea.

EXTRA POWER BOXES

© Houghton Mifflin Harcourt Publishing Company

Teacher Notes

UNIT PERFORMANCE TASK

👥 Small Groups ⏱ 90 minutes

Identifying Elements Using Patterns

SEP Developing and Using Models

Students use a model to identify elements according to repeating patterns on the periodic table.

Answers

1. **Sample answer:** I will determine the identity of the unknown elements based on the given properties of the sample. I will need to know the groups and periods on the periodic table and how many energy levels and electrons the elements have.

2. Students' research should include various methods of identifying elements such as reactivity, density, mass, and number of electrons. Types of equipment used to gather this information could include mass spectrometers and x-ray spectrometers.

3. Unknown 1 is strontium, Unknown 2 is potassium, Unknown 3 is chlorine, Unknown 4 is arsenic, and Unknown 5 is oxygen.

4. Students should develop a table that is incorporated into their final presentation and shows the reasoning behind their identification.

5. Students should share their final presentations with the class. In their conclusion, they should compare their approach with that of a scientist, including the equipment the scientist would use. For example, a scientist would use a mass spectrometer to determine the different isotopes for Unknown 3.

Performance Task Scoring Rubric

Points	Criteria
	Plan is clearly based on using information in the periodic table.
	Table correctly identifies the location on the periodic table of the five elements.
	Presentation includes process and equipment used to determine the unknown elements in samples.
	Presentation includes images and data that support the student's reasoning.

Identifying Elements Using Patterns

You are an analytical chemist for a company that provides reference materials for industrial analytical labs. During a company financial audit, the auditors bring samples from stock supplies to confirm that the inventory is correct. You analyze the samples to confirm that the products are correctly labeled and accounted for. The table shows some information you collected about properties for each sample. Your job now is to use the periodic table to infer the identity of each sample based on its description. Then, present the auditors with a report identifying each of the samples.

Unknown	Description	Element Identity
1	It is an alkaline earth metal with two valence electrons and relatively low electronegativity. It has the same number of electron energy shells as iodine.	
2	It is a highly reactive metal in Period 4 of the periodic table. Its atoms bond in a one-to-one ratio with elements in the group that have the highest electron affinities of any elements on the periodic table.	
3	It is a highly reactive nonmetal with two isotopes. One has a mass of 35 u and an abundance of 75.78%. The other has a mass of 37 u and an abundance of 24.22%.	
4	It is a metalloid with five valence electrons. It has the same number of electron energy shells as calcium.	
5	Its electron-dot structure has six dots, and its atoms bond in a one-to-one ratio with magnesium. It has the highest electronegativity in its group.	

1. PLAN AN INVESTIGATION

With your team, formulate a plan for analyzing the data. Decide how you will compare the data to trends in the periodic table as a way of identifying the five elements.

2. CONDUCT RESEARCH

With your team, research ways that scientists identify unknown elements in samples. Consider the types of questions they ask about the element, the instruments they use to test the sample, and the approaches they use to analyze the data collected. How can this information be used by other scientists and engineers who are interested in using similar materials?

3. EVALUATE DATA

With your team, analyze the description of each unknown element in the table. Compare these descriptions to what you know about the properties of different groups and trends in the periodic table.

4. CONSTRUCT AN EXPLANATION

Describe the location of each unknown element on the periodic table. Explain how you inferred the identity of each element. Then, record the identity of each element in the table.

5. COMMUNICATE

Make a multimedia presentation to describe the process you and your team used to identify each unknown element. Explain how your approach is similar or different to how a scientist in a lab would determine the identity of an unknown element.

 CHECK YOUR WORK

Once you have completed this task, you should have the following:

- a plan for identifying the five elements using the periodic table
- a completed table identifying the location on the periodic table of the five unknown elements
- a presentation explaining the process used to determine the unknown elements
- images and data that further support your explanation

UNIT 2 Practice and Review

Name _____   Date _____

SYNTHESIZE THE UNIT

In your Evidence Notebook, make a concept map, other graphic organizer, or outline using the Study Guides you made for each lesson in this unit. Be sure to use evidence to support your claims.

When synthesizing individual information, remember to follow these general steps:
- Find the central idea of each piece of information.
- Think about the relationships among the central ideas.
- Combine the ideas to come up with a new understanding.

DRIVING QUESTIONS

Look back to the Driving Questions from the opening section of this unit. In your Evidence Notebook, review and revise your previous answers to those questions. Use the evidence you gathered and other observations you made throughout the unit to support your claims.

PRACTICE AND REVIEW

1. Select the correct terms to complete the statement about chlorine.

   Chlorine is often used as an oxidizing agent and disinfectant in large pools. It is very reactive because it has a small | large electronegativity value. The atomic number for chlorine is 17. This means it has 17 electrons and protons | electrons and neutrons | protons and neutrons. There are two stable isotopes of chlorine, and both are used to study environmental pollution. Chlorine-35 has seventeen | eighteen | nineteen | twenty neutrons, and chlorine-37 has seventeen | eighteen | nineteen | twenty neutrons.

2. If numbered consecutively, what describes the relationship of group number to valence electrons? Select all correct answers.
   - ☐ a. For Groups 1 and 2, the number of valence electrons is equal to the group number.
   - ☐ b. For Groups 1 and 2, the number of valence electrons is twice the group number.
   - ☐ c. For Groups 13–18, the number of valence electrons is the group number minus 5.
   - ☐ d. For Groups 13–18, the number of valence electrons is the group number minus 10.

3. Complete these statements about trends in ionization energy on the periodic table.

   As you move from left to right across a period, the ionization energy tends to increase | decrease. As you move down a group, the ionization energy tends to increase | decrease.

   For example, lithium is in Group 1, Period 2, and boron is in Group 13, Period 2. Based on these locations, you would expect boron | lithium to have a higher ionization energy.

4. Which of the following are true of stable nuclei? Select all correct answers.
   - ☐ a. The electromagnetic force between nucleons is stronger than the strong force.
   - ☐ b. The nucleus has a low binding energy.
   - ☐ c. For a midsize nucleus, the nucleus contains slightly more neutrons than protons.
   - ☐ d. For a small nucleus, the nucleus has equal numbers of protons and neutrons.

5. Carbon has 6 protons, and nitrogen has 7 protons. Fill in the following information about the decay of carbon-14 to nitrogen-14.
   - a. The charge of the particle emitted: _____
   - b. The final number of neutrons: _____
   - c. The total number of nucleons: _____

Synthesize the Unit
Suggest that students begin by writing the titles of the lessons and the explorations in each unit as well as any associated vocabulary. Encourage students to recognize relationships between concepts introduced in different lessons.

Driving Questions
Students may wish to use pens with different ink colors to extend their previous answer to each question and visualize how their understanding has changed since the start of the unit.

Practice and Review
SUMMATIVE ASSESSMENT
Answers
1. **DOK 2** large, electrons and protons, eighteen, twenty
2. **DOK 2** a, d
3. **DOK 2** increase, decrease, boron
4. **DOK 2** c, d
5. **DOK 2** −1, 7, 14

3D Item Analysis	1	2	3	4	5
SEP Developing and Using Models		•	•		
SEP Constructing Explanations and Designing Solutions	•		•	•	
DCI PS1.A Structure and Properties of Matter	•	•	•	•	•
DCI PS1.C Nuclear Processes				•	•
CCC Patterns	•	•	•	•	
CCC Energy and Matter				•	•

Answers

6. **DOK 3** The relative distance between the size of the nucleus and the outer shell electrons cannot be shown to scale in most models because of the relative size of protons, neutrons, and electrons and the limitations of the size of a page and human vision. If a nucleus was drawn to be the size of a grain of sand, the electron cloud would be the size of a baseball stadium. By modeling the number of atomic particles and their relative locations to one another, but not the size of the particles or the distances between them, the model becomes more useful. When using the model, this tradeoff in accuracy must be kept in mind.

7. **DOK 3** If the electronegativities of two bonded elements are slightly different, one atom will attract electrons more strongly and have a slightly negative charge. The other will have a slightly positive charge. If there is a large difference in electronegativity, the element with higher electronegativity accepts one or more electrons from the element with lower electronegativity.

8. **DOK 3 Sample answer:** Once the nuclear fuel is mined and processed, nuclear fission reactions do not produce any carbon dioxide as they generate energy, unlike standard fossil fuel power plants. Fossil fuels are used to mine and purify the uranium, but nuclear power plants still produce far less greenhouse gas than fossil fuel power plants do. A drawback is that nuclear energy produces radioactive waste that must be properly stored for hundreds to thousands of years. Also, safety risks are higher for running nuclear power plants, as various accidents have demonstrated. All energy alternatives involve both benefits and risks, and the tradeoffs may vary at different geographic locations.

3D Item Analysis	6	7	8
SEP Developing and Using Models	•	•	
SEP Constructing Explanations and Designing Solutions	•	•	•
DCI PS1.A Structure and Properties of Matter	•	•	
DCI PS1.C Nuclear Processes			•
DCI ETS1.B Developing Possible Solutions			•
CCC Patterns	•	•	
CCC Influence of Engineering, Technology, and Science on Society and the Natural World			•

6. Visual atomic models do not represent the relative scale of the atom. Explain why they are still useful, even though they may be inaccurate.

_____

_____

_____

_____

_____

_____

7. Explain how patterns in electronegativity on the periodic table can be used to predict bond formation.

_____

_____

_____

_____

_____

_____

8. Discuss two benefits and two drawbacks of nuclear-fueled electric power plants compared to conventional fossil fuel power plants. How and why have the relative tradeoffs of these two sources of electricity changed in the last fifty years?

_____

_____

_____

_____

_____

_____

_____

UNIT PROJECT

Return to your unit project. Prepare a presentation using your research and materials, and share it with the class. In your final presentation, evaluate the strength of your hypothesis, data, analysis, and conclusions.

Remember these tips while evaluating:

- What atomic properties were best illustrated by your models?
- How did you incorporate the patterns of the periodic table into your models?
- Were you able to demonstrate radioactive decay, fission, and fusion with your models?

Integrating the NGSS* Three Dimensions of Learning

Building to the Performance Expectations

The learning experiences in this unit prepare students for mastery of

Matter and Its Interactions

HS-PS1-1 Use the periodic table as a model to predict the relative properties of elements based on the patterns of electrons in the outermost energy level of atoms.

HS-PS1-3 Plan and conduct an investigation to gather evidence to compare the structure of substances at the bulk scale to infer the strength of electrical forces between particles.

Motion and Stability: Forces and Interactions

HS-PS2-6 Communicate scientific and technical information about why the molecular-level structure is important in the functioning of designed materials.

Engineering Design

HS-ETS1-2 Design a solution to a complex real-world problem by breaking it down into smaller, more manageable problems that can be solved through engineering.

Additional supported standards include **Matter and Its Interactions PS1-2** and **Engineering Design ETS1-1, ETS1-3, and ETS1-4.**

Assessing Student Progress

The **Unit Project: Designing Detergents** and the **Unit Performance Task: Testing Water-Repellent Fabrics** provide opportunities to practice aspects of the Performance Expectations.

Unit Storyline Students consider why substances such as paint and diamonds have different properties. They gather evidence to explain how properties of compounds are related to their atomic structure. Students also learn about mixtures and solutions and the effect of intermolecular forces on their properties. They then apply what they have learned to engineered materials and consider how they could optimize the properties of a polymer.

Lesson 1
Investigating Chemical Compounds

In Lesson 1, students investigate the relationship between the structure of a compound and its melting point (SEP Planning and Carrying Out Investigations, DCI PS1.A). They explore patterns of electronegativity on the periodic table and use those patterns as evidence to support claims about observations of the interactions of matter at the bulk scale (SEP Constructing Explanations and Designing Solutions, DCI PS1.A, CCC Patterns). Students learn that these patterns demonstrate the relationship between the structure and interactions of matter at the bulk scale and electrical forces within and between atoms (SEP Developing and Using Models, DCI PS2.B).

Lesson 2
Analyzing the Properties of Compounds and Solutions

In Lesson 2, students plan an investigation to gather evidence that structure and interactions of matter at the bulk scale are determined by electrical forces within and between atoms (SEP Planning and Carrying Out Investigations, DCI PS1.A, CCC Patterns). They use what they learn about forces of attraction and repulsion between electric charges at the atomic scale to investigate the properties of solutions (SEP Constructing Explanations and Designing Solutions, CCC Patterns).

Lesson 3
Engineering Materials

In Lesson 3, students investigate how properties of matter relate to interactions at the molecular level (SEP Obtaining, Evaluating, and Communicating Information; DCI PS1.A). They analyze the structure and function of several materials and explore how the materials can be part of designed solutions for real-world problems (SEP Constructing Explanations and Designing Solutions, DCI ETS1.B, DCI ETS1.C, CCC Structure and Function). Students plan and carry out an investigation of physical and chemical properties and extend their learning in a case study about shape memory alloys (SEP Planning and Carrying Out Investigations, DCI PS1.A, DCI PS2.B, CCC Influence of Engineering, Technology, and Science on Society and the Natural World).

 You Solve It Go online to access two interactive simulations.

Integrating the NGSS, continued

NGSS across This Unit

▶ Explore Online

Next Generation Science Standards	Unit Project	Lesson 1	Lesson 2	Lesson 3	Unit Performance Task	You Solve It
SEP Constructing Explanations and Designing Solutions	•	•	•	•	•	
SEP Planning and Carrying Out Investigations	•	•	•	•	•	• •
SEP Asking Questions and Defining Problems		•	•	•		
SEP Obtaining, Evaluating, and Communicating Information	•			•	•	
DCI PS1.A Structure and Properties of Matter	•	•	•	•	•	• •
DCI PS2.B Types of Interactions	•	•	•	•	•	•
DCI ETS1.B Developing Possible Solutions	•			•	•	• •
DCI ETS1.C Optimizing the Design Solution	•			•	•	
CCC Patterns	•	•	•	•	•	•
CCC Structure and Function	•			•	•	
CCC Influence of Engineering, Technology, and Science on Society and the Natural World	•	•	•	•	•	

NGSS across the Grades

Middle School

MS-PS1-1 Develop models to describe the atomic composition of simple molecules and extended structures.

MS-PS1-3 Gather and make sense of information to describe that synthetic materials come from natural resources and impact society.

MS-ETS1-2 Evaluate competing design solutions using a systematic process to determine how well they meet the criteria and constraints of the problem.

Grades 9–12

HS-PS1-1

HS-PS1-3

HS-PS2-6

HS-ETS1-2

 Trace Tool to the NGSS Go online to view the complete coverage of standards across lessons and units.

Differentiate Instruction

Differentiate with Technology

Video Conference with a Chemist
Contact a molecular chemist at a university or research facility and arrange a real-time video discussion with the class. Explain the topics that students are studying in this unit so the chemist can prepare to discuss how those topics relate to the research the chemist is doing. Make sure students are prepared with questions to ask the chemist.

3D Molecular Models
Many molecular models are available online that allow students to explore the three-dimensional structure of molecules. Students can rotate the models, zoom in, and even assume the view from inside some models.

Molecule-Building App
Apps are available for downloading or online that allow students to construct molecules. Have students work with one of the apps to explore how interactions between atoms constrain the structures.

Key Word Support

Key Words
ionic bond *Lesson 1*
covalent bond *Lesson 1*
molecule *Lesson 1*
metallic bond *Lesson 1*
polyatomic ion *Lesson 1*
intermolecular forces *Lesson 2*
polarity *Lesson 2*
hydrogen bond *Lesson 2*
solution *Lesson 2*
solvent *Lesson 2*
solute *Lesson 2*
solubility *Lesson 2*
concentration *Lesson 2*
electrolyte *Lesson 2*
colligative property *Lesson 2*
materials science *Lesson 3*
polymers *Lesson 3*
hydrocarbons *Lesson 3*
composite *Lesson 3*

Reinforcing Key Words
To help students build key word knowledge for this unit, have them make a word triangle for each term by writing the term and definition in one point of a triangle, a sentence using the term in a second point, and an illustration in the third point.

Academic Vocabulary
Point out to students that chemists use terms that have very specific scientific meanings. This deliberate practice ensures clear communication among scientists around the world. As an example of the value of this practice, ask students to come up with alternative definitions for particular words that are not precise, such as defining *molecule* only as "a particle." Discuss the pitfalls of such incomplete and inaccurate definitions, such as confusing a molecule with other particles in discussions or reports.

English Language Learners
Have students synthesize key topics by taking combination notes as they read. Students divide their notes into two columns with the notes about content in the left-hand column and drawings in the right-hand column. This can help students better understand how scientists study bonding and how they model it.

ELL
ELL teaching strategies in this unit include

Lesson 1 p. 150
Lesson 2 pp. 171, 178, 183, 191
Lesson 3 p. 211

MTSS/RTI
Strategies for students who need extra support in this unit include

Lesson 1 pp. 147, 149, 156, 165
Lesson 2 pp. 175, 179, 189
Lesson 3 p. 199

Extension
Strategies for students who have mastered core content in this unit include

Lesson 1 pp. 150, 159
Lesson 2 pp. 174, 179, 180, 191
Lesson 3 p. 203

Making Connections

Connections to Community

Use these opportunities for informal science
learning to provide local context and to extend and enhance unit concepts.

At Home

COMPOUNDS IN THE HOME Ask students to investigate different compounds used at home by reading the labels of at least a dozen products. Caution them to exercise care when handling cleaning products and other household chemicals. Students can work in pairs to search for compounds and identify those found in several products. Suggest that partners compare their lists with others in the class. *Use with Lesson 1.*

FOOD PREPARATION Explain that some foods are prepared according to their polarity. In many cases, recipes are built on the ability of one ingredient to mix with or dissolve another ingredient. Have students research and make a list of five dry ingredients and how they mix with either oil or water. For example, salt will not dissolve in oil but will dissolve in water. Have students examine recipes, paying attention to how the steps are sequenced and how this sequence affects the properties of the ingredients. Have students compile a list of ingredients that are usually found together and then identify which ones are solvents and which are solutes. Students can also suggest which ones are polar and which are nonpolar. *Use with Lesson 2.*

In the Community

COMMUNITY IMPACT Having a clean water supply depends on a community's ability to filter out harmful compounds contained in the local water source. Water-purification plants usually employ a number of techniques, depending on the specific pollutants in the local water. Have students investigate to learn more about the water and procedures used at the local facility to keep the water clean. Have them discuss how interactions and structures of particles make these processes possible. *Use with Lesson 2.*

Culture

HOW ENGINEERING AFFECTS CULTURES As new technology is developed, the compounds needed to produce various parts can have either beneficial or adverse affects on areas of the world where the compounds are mined. Have students research an example of how new engineering methods have produced a significant effect on a culture—and how the people responded to that effect. *Use with Lesson 3.*

 Home Letters Use these letters to engage family members with unit concepts.

Collaborate

Opportunities for students to work collaboratively in this unit:

Discussion pp. 152, 175, 186, 197, 211, 213

Gallery Walk p. 205

Graffiti p. 147

Ranking Ladder p. 202

Think-Pair-Share, Draw-Pair-Share pp. 172, 181

Connections to Other Disciplines

Opportunities to connect to other content areas in this unit:

Biology Connection p. 187

Environmental Science Connection pp. 178, 206

Math Connection pp. 160, 182, 209

Language Arts Connection pp. 153, 154, 158, 165, 188, 189, 208, 210, 215

3D Unit Planning

Lesson 1 Investigating Chemical Compounds pp. 145–168

Overview

Objective Students gather evidence about the properties of compounds and explain how these properties are related to atomic structure.

SEP Developing and Using Models
SEP Planning and Carrying Out Investigations
SEP Constructing Explanations and Designing Solutions
DCI **HS-PS1.A** Structure and Properties of Matter
DCI **HS-PS2.B** Types of Interactions
CCC Patterns
CCC Influence of Engineering, Technology, and Science on Society and the Natural World

Math and **English Language Arts** standards and features are detailed on lesson planning pages.

Print and **Online** Student Editions

Explore Online ▶

ENGAGE	**Investigative Phenomenon** p. 145 **Can You Explain the Phenomenon?** How do you think the properties of sodium and chlorine change when they are combined to make sodium chloride?	**ELA Handbook** **Video** Reaction of Sodium and Chlorine
EXPLORE/ EXPLAIN	**Analyzing the Properties of Compounds** p. 146 **Describing Chemical Bonds** p. 149 🔬 Producing Salts **Predicting the Structure of Compounds** p. 156 **Math Connection** Writing Ionic Formulas 🔬 **Modeling the Shapes of Molecules** p. 162	**Math Handbook** **Hands-On Lab Worksheets** **Hands-On Lab Teacher Support** **Lab Safety Handbook** **Video** Melting Point **Animation** Metallic Bonding
ELABORATE	**Take It Further** p. 165 Asking Questions about Minerals	**Take It Further** More Practice with Formulas Teaching Types of Bonding 🔬 Types of Bonding in Solids **Hands-On Lab Worksheet** **Hands-On Lab Teacher Support** **Lab Safety Handbook**
EVALUATE	**Lesson Self-Check** p. 166	**Lesson Quiz**

🧪 Hands-On Lab Planning

Analyzing the Properties of Compounds

🕐 45 minutes
👥 Small Groups

Objective Students observe and compare several substances as they are heated to see how their properties change. They use their observations as evidence to support a claim about which of the substances has the highest melting point.

Materials
- aluminum foil
- Bunsen burner
- citric acid, small amount
- paraffin wax, small amount
- permanent marker
- ring stand, ring, and clamp
- salt, small amount
- spatula or scoop
- striker
- wire gauze

Modeling the Shapes of Molecules

🕐 90 minutes
👥 Individuals or Small Groups

Objective Students make models of the molecular shapes of carbon tetrachloride, oxygen difluoride, carbon disulfide, phosphorus tribromide, methanal, and silicon dioxide. They research properties of each compound and use evidence from their investigation to support a claim about the shape of each molecule they model.

Materials
- foam spheres
- modeling clay, various colors
- molecular modeling kit
- pompoms, various colors
- sticks, craft
- toothpicks

3D Unit Planning, continued

Lesson 2 Analyzing the Properties of Compounds and Solutions pp. 169–194

Overview

Objective Students investigate how intermolecular forces influence the properties of compounds, mixtures, and solutions.

SEP Asking Questions and Defining Problems
SEP Planning and Carrying Out Investigations
SEP Constructing Explanations and Designing Solutions
DCI **HS-PS1.A** Structure and Properties of Matter
DCI **HS-PS2.B** Types of Interactions
DCI **HS-ETS1.A** Defining and Delimiting Engineering Problems
CCC Patterns
CCC Influence of Engineering, Technology, and Science on Society and the Natural World

Math and **English Language Arts** standards and features are detailed on lesson planner pages.

Print and **Online** Student Editions

ENGAGE	**Investigative Phenomenon** p. 169 **Can You Explain the Phenomenon?** How is water important in the Earth system?

**EXPLORE/
EXPLAIN**
	Exploring Intermolecular Forces in Liquids p. 170
	Explaining Intermolecular Forces p. 172
	    Math Connection Calculating Force
	Describing Solutions p. 177
	    Problem Solving Measuring Solution Concentration
	 Measuring the Electrical Conductivity of Solutions p. 184
	Analyzing the Behavior of Solutions p. 186

ELABORATE	**Take It Further** p. 191 **Careers in Engineering** Water Supply Engineer
EVALUATE	**Lesson Self-Check** p. 192

Explore Online ▶

ELA Handbook

🧪 Temperature and Solubility

🧪 Testing Water for Ions

🧪 Diffusion and Cell Membranes

Hands-On Lab Worksheets
Hands-On Lab Teacher Support
Lab Safety Handbook
Math Handbook

Take It Further
Reverse Osmosis
Paper Chromatography
🧪 Separating Salt Mixtures

Hands-On Lab Worksheet
Hands-On Lab Teacher Support

Lesson Quiz

 ### Hands-On Lab Planning

Exploring Intermolecular Forces in Liquids

🕐 90 minutes
👥 Small Groups

Objective Students design a procedure to analyze intermolecular forces in liquids found in everyday phenomena. They collect evaporation rate and surface tension data.

Materials
- acetone in dropper bottle
- flasks with stoppers (4), each containing water, acetone, isopropy alcohol, or glycerol
- glycerol in dropper bottle
- isopropyl alcohol in dropper bottle
- marker
- stopwatch or clock with second hand
- wax paper (1 sheet)

Measuring the Electrical Conductivity of Solutions

🕐 45 minutes
👥 Small Groups

Objective Students plan and conduct an investigation to explore patterns of conductivity in solutions. They learn that electrical conductivity results from electrical forces within and between atoms.

Materials
- beaker, 100 mL (8)
- conductivity tester
- paper towels
- wash bottle
- aluminum chloride, $AlCl_3$, solution, 0.05 M (50 mL)
- calcium chloride, $CaCl_2$, solution, 0.05 M (50 mL)
- distilled water (300 mL)
- ethanol, C_2H_5OH, (50 mL)
- sodium chloride, NaCl, solution, 0.05 M (50 mL)
- sugar water (50 mL)
- tap water (50 mL)

Lesson 3 Engineering Materials pp. 195–218

Overview

Objective Students investigate the properties of materials and explain how those properties relate to interactions at the molecular level.

SEP	Planning and Carrying Out Investigations
SEP	Obtaining, Evaluating, and Communicating Information
SEP	Constructing Explanations and Designing Solutions
DCI	**HS-PS2.B** Types of Interactions
DCI	**HS-ETS1.B** Developing Possible Solutions
DCI	**HS-ETS1.C** Optimizing the Design Solution
CCC	Structure and Function
CCC	Influence of Engineering, Technology, and Science on Society and the Natural World

Math and **English Language Arts** standards and features are detailed on lesson planner pages.

Print and Online Student Editions

Explore Online ▶

| **ENGAGE** | **Investigative Phenomenon** p. 195 **Can You Solve the Problem?** How would understanding the properties of different materials be useful for selecting the best material for each part of a car? | **ELA Handbook** |

| **EXPLORE/ EXPLAIN** | **Exploring Materials Science and Design** p. 196   Collecting Water from Fog   **Experimenting with Polymers** p. 201 **Analyzing Types of Materials** p. 205 **Case Study: Shape Memory Alloys** p. 211 | **Hands-On Engineering Worksheet** **Hands-On Engineering Teacher Support** **3D Model** Space Shuttle **3D Model** Artificial Hip **Video** Shape Memory Glasses **Video** Shape Memory Tires |

| **ELABORATE** | **Take It Further** p. 215 **Careers in Science** Organic Chemist | **Take It Further** Career: Biomedical Engineer Applications of Materials Science Evaporation and Ink Solvents **Hands-On Lab Worksheet** **Hands-On Lab Teacher Support** |

| **EVALUATE** | **Lesson Self-Check** p. 216 | **Lesson Quiz** |

Hands-On Lab Planning

Experimenting with Polymers

🕐 90 minutes
👥 Small Groups

Objective Students design, test, and optimize a polymer to meet defined criteria and constraints for a toy.

Materials
- food coloring, assorted colors
- graduated cylinder, 50 mL
- plastic cup, 4 oz
- polyvinyl alcohol (PVA), 5% solution
- ruler, 30 cm
- sodium tetraborate, 4% solution
- wooden dowel, 1/4-in. diameter, 8 in. long

Additional Downloadable Lab Option
Evaporation and Ink Solvents

🕐 90 minutes
👥 Small Groups

Objective Students design an experiment to investigate the influence of chemical structure and intermolecular forces of attraction on evaporation time. Students then use evidence from their investigation to make a claim about which substance would work best for a fast-evaporating ink.

 **You Solve It**

Go online for an additional
interactive activity and teacher support.

Which Planetary-Rover Materials Are Suitable?

This interactive activity offers practice in support of **HS- PS1-1, HS-PS1-2,** and **HS-ETS1-4**.

SEP Planning and Carrying Out Investigations

SEP Using Mathematics and Computational Thinking

DCI PS1.A Structure and Properties of Matter

DCI ETS1.B Developing Possible Solutions

Learning Objective

Students use simulations to investigate how metals and metal alloys chemically react with water, sulfuric acid, and sea water.

Activity Problem

Students imagine they are engineers tasked with selecting metals or metal alloys for a planetary rover that must be able to withstand environmental conditions on Venus and on Europa, one of Jupiter's moons. Students use a simulation to observe and to analyze simple chemical reactions between metals and chemical reactants. Students make a claim about which material will best withstand the conditions of both Venus's atmosphere and Europa's ocean. Students explain the reactivity of the metals with respect to their positions on the periodic table, as well as the reactivity of alloys with respect to their parent metals. Students support their claims with evidence and notes collected from their simulations. Then students explain their reasoning about how the evidence supports their claims.

Interaction Summary

This You Solve It offers students the opportunity to choose a material and a reactant from the menu and evaluate the impact of the reactant on the material. Students then analyze data generated by the simulation on the gases produced, color changes, and changes to mass. Students will construct an explanation of how that material could be used in the construction of a planetary rover.

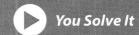 **You Solve It** Go online for an additional interactive activity and teacher support.

How Can You Change the Properties of a Substance?

This interactive activity offers practice in support of **HS-PS1-3** and **HS-ETS1-4**.

SEP Planning and Carrying Out Investigations
SEP Using Mathematics and Computational Thinking
DCI PS1.A Structure and Properties of Matter
DCI PS2.B Types of Interactions
DCI ETS1.B Developing Possible Solutions
CCC Patterns

Learning Objective

Students use a model of an adhesive additive process to analyze the changing properties of substances.

Activity Problem

Students are given a scenario in which they assist a company in testing additives to change the properties of their water-based adhesive product to meet the criteria of a possible new customer. The customer wants the adhesive to have a lower surface tension, to have a stable temperature range, and to keep a strong and rigid bond. Students use simulations to experiment with additives to analyze changes to surface tension, thermal profile, and tensile strength. Students make a claim recommending the additive that changes the properties of the stock adhesive to meet the customer's criteria. Students support their claims with evidence from their simulations and with the data they collect. Students then explain their reasoning about how the evidence supports their claims.

Interaction Summary

This You Solve It offers students the opportunity to manipulate variables (additives) to discover which additive best meets the criteria established for a water-based adhesive. As students toggle between Surface Tension, Thermal Profile, and Tensile Strength tabs, they learn about the properties of the stock adhesive and the additives. Students select an additive, run the simulation, save the results, and try another additive.

Assessment Planning

Preassessment
Assessment Guide, Unit Pretest

Formative Assessment
Interactive Worktext: Explorations, Lesson Self-Check

Summative Assessment
Assessment Guide, Lesson Quiz

Interactive Worktext: Unit Performance Task, p. 224

Interactive Worktext: Unit Practice and Review, p. 225

Assessment Guide, Unit Test and Modified Unit Test

  HMH Field Trips
powered by
Google Expeditions

Go to **HMH Google Expeditions** in the Resources tab on Ed: Your Friend in Learning for 3D, 360-degree experiences to share with your students and a Teacher Guide for you.

Unit Project

Overview and Planning

Designing Detergents

3D Learning Objective

Students plan and conduct an investigation into how detergents work and how they can be optimized for desired properties.

Students make a homemade detergent and conduct an investigation to compare their detergent with a liquid soap and commercial detergent using evidence observed through the cleaning abilities of the solutions. They conduct research to learn more about how detergents affect the environment and consider what chemicals in their homemade detergents could negatively affect the environment. Students learn how different types of bonding, molecular structure, and intermolecular forces can affect the properties of a material.

NGSS Focus

The project supports building student mastery of **Performance Expectations HS-PS1-3, HS-PS2-6, HS-ETS1-2,** and **HS-ETS1-3.** Students plan and conduct investigations to collect evidence to compare various performance criteria of soaps and detergents. They design and test a solution to improve a specified criterion of a detergent. Students communicate scientific and technical information about the chemical properties of soaps and detergents.

Science and Engineering Practices
- Planning and Carrying Out Investigations
- Constructing Explanations and Designing Solutions
- Obtaining, Evaluating, and Communicating Information

Disciplinary Core Ideas
- **PS1.A** Structure and Properties of Matter
- **PS2.B** Types of Interactions
- **ETS1.B** Developing Possible Solutions
- **ETS1.C** Optimizing the Design Solution

Crosscutting Concepts
- Patterns
- Structure and Function
- Influence of Engineering, Technology, and Science on Society and the Natural World

Classroom Management

👥 Small Groups

🕐 Three 45-minute class periods

Suggested Materials
- See the procedure for detailed materials list for the lab.

- In advance, prepare small, oil-stained fabric squares. Each group will require a minimum of 10 if only one trial is completed for each solution. If you allow students to run more than one trial for each solution, then more fabric squares will be needed. Use a medicine dropper to apply the same amount of an oil (such as olive oil) to each fabric square. Make sure the oil stain is clearly visible on the fabric square.

- Ask if any students have allergies to particular soap and detergent brands. If any students have sensitive skin or allergies, consider having them be the Recorder for their group and not mix or test any of the solutions to avoid contact with the soap or detergents.

- You may need to provide additional amounts of soap, sodium carbonate, or sodium tetraborate for students to make their optimized detergents.

Safety
- Make sure students exercise the appropriate cautions when handing the materials, making detergent, and testing the soap and detergent solutions. Tell them to clean up any spills immediately.

Suggested Resources
- **ACI:** American Cleaning Institute has numerous articles and scientific literature on detergents.

- **ACS:** American Chemical Society has numerous resources on detergent and surfactant chemistry.

▶ Go Online

Go online to download the teacher version of the student worksheet for this unit project, which includes additional questions, sample answers, and additional scaffolding to help students use evidence and reasoning to support their claims.

Introducing the Project

Prepare students for their investigation by asking the following questions:

- **How do soaps and detergents work?**
- **How do different environmental conditions affect soaps and detergents?**
- **How do soaps and detergents affect the environment?**
- **How does the concentration of soap affect its performance?**
- **What does *synthetic* mean?**
- **What intermolecular forces are involved to make a detergent function?**

Student Deliverables

A **student worksheet** is available to help students in planning and completing the project. Students can turn in their worksheets, or they can be assessed on a final lab report, their models, and/or final presentations explaining their project. Evidence Notebook prompts throughout the unit refer to the Unit Project to help keep its connection to the investigative phenomenon present in students' minds.

In addition to the worksheet, students should make a presentation that describes the process of designing an optimal detergent mix based on an established design criteria and provide data to support their findings for their final detergent formulation.

Scoring Rubric for Unit Project	
	The worksheet and presentation describe observations that are used to determine if their data support their claims.
	The plan has a way of measuring and documenting the various performance criteria by comparing test results using qualitative or quantitative data.
	The results of the testing procedures are collected and analyzed, showing similarities and differences between the performance criteria of the different solutions.
	An optimized detergent mixture is developed based on specified expectations and compared to previous types of solutions tested.

Guiding Students on Project Planning

Once students understand the project goals and their deliverables, the next step is for students to conduct research and develop presentations. Ask questions that spur their thinking about ways they might proceed in designing and implementing their project. Consider asking the following questions:

- **How will you collect data?**
  Students should consider how they will measure the effects of the specific factors they have selected in terms of their design criteria. For example, how will they qualitatively and quantitatively measure stain removal?

- **How will you record your data?**
  Explain that data should be recorded in a data table. Data collection should be consistent and contain control and experimental groups. Having a good control is essential when observing how changing formulations can affect stain-removal properties.

- **Which might affect the cleaning ability of the homemade detergent?**
  Students might identify factors such as water hardness, solution temperature, or solution concentration. Solution temperature and concentration are factors they could optimize during their project.

Be sure to review and approve project plans before students begin. The Unit Project Worksheet can be used for formal approval.

Differentiate Instruction

MTSS/RTI Have students work collaboratively in pairs. Assign each pair one or two variables to test in their models. For example, partners might design and test how water temperature or salinity affects different formulations. Encourage students to discuss and describe their design and how they plan to proceed before beginning. Afterward, have pairs combine their observations to draw conclusions about the factors that affect detergent design. Encourage students to offer constructive criticism about their own and other pairs' tests.

Teacher Notes

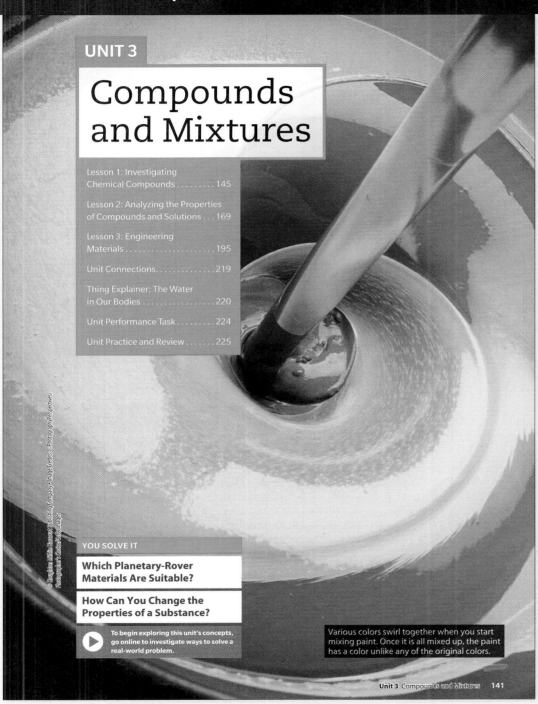

YOU SOLVE IT

**Which Planetary-Rover
Materials Are Suitable?**

**How Can You Change the
Properties of a Substance?**

To begin exploring this unit's concepts,
go online to investigate ways to solve a
real-world problem.

Various colors swirl together when you start
mixing paint. Once it is all mixed up, the paint
has a color unlike any of the original colors.

The learning experiences in this unit prepare students for the mastery of

Performance Expectations

HS-PS1-1 Use the periodic table as a model to predict the relative properties of elements based on the patterns of electrons in the outermost energy level of atoms.

HS-PS1-3 Plan and conduct an investigation to gather evidence to compare the structure of substances at the bulk scale to infer the strength of electrical forces between particles.

HS-PS2-6 Communicate scientific and technical information about why the molecular-level structure is important in the functioning of designed materials.

HS-ETS1-2 Design a solution to a complex real-world problem by breaking it down into smaller, more manageable problems that can be solved through engineering.

HS-ETS1-3 Evaluate a solution to a complex real-world problem based on prioritized criteria and trade-offs that account for a range of constraints, including cost, safety, reliability, and aesthetics, as well as possible social, cultural, and environmental impacts.

Explore Online

In addition to the print resources, the following resources are available online to support this unit.

Lesson 1 Investigating Chemical Compounds
- Interactive Online Student Edition
- Lesson Quiz

Lesson 2 Analyzing the Properties of Compounds and Solutions
- Interactive Online Student Edition
- Lesson Quiz

Lesson 3 Engineering Materials
- Interactive Online Student Edition
- Lesson Quiz

You Solve It Which Planetary-Rover Materials Are Suitable?

You Solve It How Can You Change the Properties of a Substance?

Unit Performance Task

Unit Practice and Review

Unit Prerequisite Knowledge

Students should understand these concepts before starting the unit:

- Atoms regroup during a chemical reaction to form new substances.
- Subscripts show the number of atoms of each element in a chemical formula. No subscript indicates one atom of the element.
- Compounds are ionic if valence electrons are transferred from one atom to another and covalent if valence electrons are shared by atoms.

Collaborate

Driving Questions You may wish to have partners discuss their initial thoughts about the Driving Questions for this unit before you discuss the questions as a class. Encourage students to record the questions and their initial responses in their Evidence Notebook, where they can revise and add to their answers as they work through the unit.

Anchoring Phenomenon

Project Based Learning

Designing Detergents

SEP **Obtaining, Evaluating, and Communicated Information**

An anchoring phenomenon connects student learning across the lessons in a unit. The Unit Project serves as an anchoring phenomenon as students apply what they learn about relating properties of compounds to atomic structure and bonding in the lessons to produce a detergent mixture and evaluate its effectiveness.

Tips on Cultivating Questions Have students read and discuss the Driving Questions with a partner. Tell students that although they probably will not know the answers to the questions, they should record their initial responses in their Evidence Notebook, where they can revise and add to their answers as they move through the unit.

 Sample answer: Scientists have to know what elements the substance is made of and how the atoms of the substance are arranged. They may also need to know how the substance forms in nature.

FIGURE 1: The cutting edge of this drill bit is coated with diamonds to protect it from wearing out too quickly when it is used to cut into hard metals.

Diamond is a form of pure, elemental carbon and is one of the hardest substances found in nature. Because it is so hard, it can scratch or cut most other substances and is used in a variety of industries. For example, tools that are used to cut, shape, or smooth metal, rock, or other hard substances are sometimes coated with diamonds. Natural diamonds are not easy to mine from Earth. Diamond mining techniques include digging large pits and drilling into the ocean floor. Because of diamond's industrial importance, engineers developed methods of producing synthetic diamonds. One method of making diamonds involves subjecting graphite, which is another form of elemental carbon, to extremely high pressures and temperatures. A second method of producing synthetic diamonds involves growing diamond crystals in a chamber filled with carbon-rich gases. Both processes are reliable, cost less than mining, and have been used to make industrial-quality diamonds. However, the second method has advantages: very high pressures are not needed and diamonds can be grown on larger surfaces.

1 **PREDICT** Diamond is not the only naturally-occurring substance that scientists and engineers have made in laboratories. For example, scientists have made a synthetic form of indigo, which is the dye used to color jeans. What information do you think scientists need in order to make a substance in a laboratory?

_____

_____

_____

DRIVING QUESTIONS

As you move through the unit, gather evidence to help you answer the following questions. In your Evidence Notebook, record what you already know about these topics and any questions you have about them.

1. How can different kinds of bonding affect the properties of substances?
2. How can you use the periodic table to predict the types of bonds atoms will form?
3. How can interactions between particles be modeled?
4. How do forces between particles affect the properties of materials?

UNIT PROJECT

Go online to download the Unit Project Worksheet to help plan your project.

Designing Detergents

A detergent is a cleansing agent that cleans materials by bonding with dirt and oil so that they can be dissolved and washed away. Investigate properties of soaps and detergents. What is the difference between the two and does it affect how they work? Develop a plan to optimize the effectiveness of a homemade detergent mixture.

Language Development

Use the lessons in this unit to complete the chart and expand your understanding of the science concepts.

TERM: ionic bond

Definition	Example

Similar Term	Phrase

TERM: covalent bond

Definition	Example

Similar Term	Phrase

TERM: metallic bond

Definition	Example

Similar Term	Phrase

TERM: polarity

Definition	Example

Similar Term	Phrase

Language Development

The summary chart graphic organizer allows students to practice using unit vocabulary to convey meaning and to communicate clearly. The chart shown, which is continued on the next page, may not include every unit vocabulary term.

Using the Chart As you encounter a highlighted vocabulary term, direct students to fill in the corresponding boxes in the summary chart. Students should always fill in the Definition box, but they need not fill in all others. Students can write a cognate from their home language in the Similar Term box. Students whose home language is English can fill in a synonym or word with the same root (such as *atomic* for the word *atom*). Accept all reasonable answers.

If desired, hand out to students a blank summary chart. Provide the starting words or have students select their own from the list of unit vocabulary. Work with students to complete the charts for each word. You may also ask students to work in pairs and then share and compare their work with that of their classmates.

Students can explore all vocabulary terms in the Online Glossary. A multilingual glossary is also available online.

SAMPLE ANSWERS

ionic bond: a force that attracts electrons from one atom to another, which transforms a neutral atom into an ion; the bond between a metal and a nonmetal; positive and negative ions; enlace iónico; The ions in sodium chloride are bound together by an ionic bond.

covalent bond: a bond formed when atoms share one or more pairs of electrons; bond between carbon and hydrogen; enlace covalente; The atoms in a water molecule are bound together by covalent bonds.

metallic bond: a bond formed by the attraction between positively charged metal ions and the electrons around them; the type of bonds in iron; enlace metálico; Metallic bonds make metals conductive.

polarity: uneven distribution of charge in a molecule; the polarity in water molecules; polaridad; Water is able to dissolve many substances because of the strong polarity of its molecules.

hydrogen bond: the intermolecular force occurring when a hydrogen atom that is bonded to a highly electronegative atom of one molecule is attracted to two unshared electrons of another molecule; the intermolecular force between a hydrogen atom bonded to an oxygen atom in one molecule and the unshared electrons in a neighboring molecule; enlace de hidrógeno; Hydrogen bonding is responsible for water's strong surface tension.

solution: a homogeneous mixture of two or more substances uniformly dispersed throughout a single phase; salt water; solución; Many salts easily dissolve in water to form solutions.

solubility: the ability of one substance to dissolve in another at a given temperature and pressure, expressed in terms of the amount of solute that will dissolve in a given amount of solvent to produce a saturated solution; sugar has a high solubility in water; solubilidad; In order to increase the solubility of some materials in water, you have to heat the water.

composite: a designed material made from combining two other materials with complementary properties; carbon fiber; compuesto; Fiberglass is a composite made of glass fibers and plastic.

TERM: hydrogen bond

Definition	Example

Similar Term	Phrase

TERM: solution

Definition	Example

Similar Term	Phrase

TERM: solubility

Definition	Example

Similar Term	Phrase

TERM: composite

Definition	Example

Similar Term	Phrase

Investigating Chemical Compounds

Building to the Performance Expectations

The learning experiences in this lesson prepare students for mastery of

HS-PS1-1 Use the periodic table as a model to predict the relative properties of elements based on the patterns of electrons in the outermost energy level of atoms.

HS-PS1-2 Construct and revise an explanation for the outcome of a simple chemical reaction based on the outermost electron states of atoms, trends in the periodic table, and knowledge of the patterns of chemical properties.

 Trace Tool to the NGSS

Go online to view the complete coverage of standards across lessons, units, and grade levels.

 **Science & Engineering Practices**

Developing and Using Models
Use a model to predict the relationships between systems or between components of a system.

 VIDEO Developing and Using Models

Constructing Explanations and Designing Solutions
Construct and revise an explanation based on valid and reliable evidence obtained from a variety of sources (including students' own investigations, models, theories, simulations, peer review) and the assumption that theories and laws that describe the natural world operate today as they did in the past and will continue to do so in the future.

 VIDEO Constructing Scientific Explanations

 **Disciplinary Core Ideas**

PS1.A Structure and Properties of Matter
Each atom has a charged substructure consisting of a nucleus, which is made of protons and neutrons, surrounded by electrons. (HS-PS1-1)

PS1.A Structure and Properties of Matter
The periodic table orders elements horizontally by the number of protons in the atom's nucleus and places those with similar chemical properties in columns. The repeating patterns of this table reflect patterns of outer electron states. (HS-PS1-1) (HS-PS1-2)

 VIDEO Bonds

PS1.A Structure and Properties of Matter
The structure and interactions of matter at the bulk scale are determined by electrical forces within and between atoms. (HS-PS1-3)

PS2.B Types of Interactions
Attraction and repulsion between electric charges at the atomic scale explain the structure, properties, and transformations of matter, as well as the contact forces between material objects. (HS-PS1-1)

 **Crosscutting Concepts**

Patterns
Different patterns may be observed at each of the scales at which a system is studied and can provide evidence for causality in explanations of phenomena.

Influence of Engineering, Technology, and Science on Society and the Natural World
New technologies can have deep impacts on society and the environment, including some that were not anticipated. Analysis of costs and benefits is a critical aspect of decisions about technology.

MATH STANDARDS

MP.2 Reason abstractly and quantitatively.

HSN-Q.A.3 Choose a level of accuracy appropriate to limitations on measurement when reporting quantities.

ELA STANDARDS

WHST.9-12.2 Write informative/explanatory texts, including the narration of historical events, scientific procedures/ experiments, or technical processes.

WHST.11-12.8 Gather relevant information from multiple authoritative print and digital sources, using advanced searches effectively; assess the strengths and limitations of each source in terms of the specific task, purpose, and audience.

Supporting All Students, All Standards

Integrating the Three Dimensions

In this lesson, students carry out an investigation in which they relate the structures of compounds to their melting points **(SEP Planning and Carrying Out Investigations, DCI PS1.A).** Students learn about electronegativity, which measures forces of attraction and repulsion between electric charges at the atomic scale, and relate those forces to structure and interactions of matter at the bulk scale **(DCI PS1.A).** Students use the periodic table to predict the behavior of matter and the outcomes of chemical reactions **(SEP Constructing Explanations and Designing Solutions, SEP Developing and Using Models, DCI PS1.A).** Students also identify patterns in the periodic table and use these patterns to make predictions about the behavior of matter at different scales **(CCC Patterns).**

Preassessment

Have students complete the unit pretest or see the Assessment Guide.

Build on Prior Knowledge

Point out that although atoms of some elements form common substances, such as gold or copper, most substances are made of atoms of different elements that form compounds. Ask students to describe what they already know about the arrangement of atoms in compounds, and discuss their ideas as a class.

You may want to review the following concepts:
- Each element on the periodic table is composed of atoms that have the same number of protons.
- Subatomic particles are bound together by different forces.
- Protons in the nucleus are positively charged, and electrons surrounding the nucleus are negatively charged. The protons and electrons are attracted to each other.
- Atoms can form bonds by gaining, losing, or sharing their valence electrons—the outermost electrons within an atom.

 *Professional Development* Go online to view **Professional Development videos** with strategies to integrate CCCs and SEPs, including the ones used in this lesson.

Content Background

Electrostatic attractions within and among atoms are a key part of chemical bonding. Because protons in the nucleus are positively charged and electrons surrounding the nucleus are negatively charged, an attractive force exists between them. This force holds electrons within an atom, but the protons within a nucleus are also attracted to the electrons of nearby atoms. The number of protons within the nucleus helps determine how strong the attraction is for electrons within the same atom and for electrons of nearby atoms. Because each type of atom has a different number of protons (and a different number of neutrons and electrons), the strength of the attractions varies. The tendency of an atom to attract electrons is the atom's electronegativity value.

Different types of models are used to show the structures of compounds. Ionic compounds are often represented by a three-dimensional crystal lattice that shows the bonding of the positive and negative ions. Metallic compounds are shown as many protons with the negatively charged electrons scattered among them to illustrate the delocalized electrons that move among the atoms. For covalent compounds, molecules are often represented by three-dimensional geometries with areas that represent where electrons are located around the atoms in the molecules. Electron-dot structures show an element's symbol surrounded by dots that represent valence electrons, which may participate in bonding.

Differentiate Instruction

KEY WORDS
- ionic bond
- covalent bond
- molecule
- metallic bond
- polyatomic ion

ELL SUPPORT

Engage students in a discussion of how forces and the properties of atoms relate to the structure of chemical bonds and the strength of bonds. Relate the topic to **everyday phenomena,** such as a tug-of-war, in which different forces are exerted on an object in opposite directions.

ENGAGE: Investigative Phenomenon

3.1

Investigating Chemical Compounds

A fiery reaction occurs when sodium metal is exposed to chlorine gas.

CAN YOU EXPLAIN THE PHENOMENON?

Sodium is an essential element required by the human body to function. In the United States, about 11% of a person's daily sodium intake comes from adding table salt to food. Table salt is a perfectly safe material made from two elements that can be highly hazardous by themselves: sodium and chlorine. Sodium metal is toxic, corrosive, and reacts vigorously with water to produce hydrogen, a flammable gas. Exposure to elemental chlorine gas can result in poisoning and health complications. Chlorine was weaponized during World War I. Today, chlorine is a commonly manufactured chemical in the United States and is a key component of bleach.

FIGURE 1: Sodium chloride (left) is the product of the reaction of sodium metal (center) and chlorine gas (right).

1 **PREDICT** How do you think the properties of sodium and chlorine change when they are combined to make sodium chloride?

_____

_____

_____

_____

2 📓 **Evidence Notebook** As you explore the lesson, gather evidence to explain why the properties of sodium chloride are so different from the properties of sodium and chlorine.

Lesson Objective

Students gather evidence about the properties of compounds and explain how these properties are related to atomic structure.

Cultivating Student Questions

Have students look at the photo of sodium metal in chlorine gas. Prompt them to ask all questions that come to mind about why the metal reacts so strongly when exposed to chlorine gas. Record the questions on chart paper, and then sort the questions based on their focus. With students, narrow the questions down to ones that directly relate to the learning objective. Have students reflect on this list throughout the lesson and check off questions as they are answered.

Can You Explain the Phenomenon?

The Investigative Phenomenon is the focus of the lesson. Students are asked to record their initial thoughts about how the properties of sodium and chlorine change when combined to make sodium chloride.

Students will collect evidence related to this phenomenon throughout the lesson and revisit the question at the end of the lesson to use what they have learned to explain how chemical properties relate to atomic structure.

1 Accept all reasonable answers, even if incorrect. **Sample answer:** Sodium and chlorine both change from very volatile to very stable. This must be caused by the way they combine at the atomic level.

📓 **Evidence Notebook**

2 The topic of differences in properties of compounds and the elements they are composed of will be revisited throughout this lesson.

EXPLORATION 1   Analyzing the Properties of Compounds

3D Learning Objective

Students **plan and carry out an investigation** to show patterns in the melting points of three substances. These patterns provide evidence that the structure and interactions of matter at the bulk scale are determined by electrical forces within and between atoms.

Everyday phenomena discussed through the Explorations of the lesson can often be used to connect the science content to students' personal experiences.

Hands-On Lab 👥 Small Groups ⏱ 45 minutes
Analyzing the Properties of Compounds

SEP **Planning and Carrying Out Investigations**

Students observe and compare several substances as they are heated to see how their properties change. They use their observations as evidence to support a claim about which of the substances has the highest melting point and which has the lowest melting point.

Advance Preparation   Before the investigation, prepare small amounts of salt, wax, and citric acid for each group.

Safety Information   Remind all students that indirectly vented chemical splash goggles, a nonlatex apron, and nonlatex gloves are to be worn during the setup, hands-on, and takedown segments of the activity. Remind them not to eat any food items used in a lab activity. Instruct students to use caution when working with Bunsen burners because this heat source can seriously burn skin and clothing. Remind them not to pour chemicals, either used or unused, back into the original container. Instruct students how to dispose of chemicals.

❶ Sample answer: I predict salt will have the highest melting point because I have never seen salt melt. I predict wax will have the lowest melting point because it melts even in very warm rooms.

Hands-On Lab

Analyzing the Properties of Compounds

Differences in the structures of compounds at the atomic level cause the differences that are observed at the macroscopic scale. One physical property that varies widely among different materials is melting point. As such, melting point is an example of a physical property that scientists can use to identify an unknown compound. Other physical properties, such as density, boiling point, and electrical conductivity, can also be analyzed to help verify the identity of the compound.

Knowing physical properties of compounds also allows scientists to identify possible uses of the compound. Additionally, knowing these properties allows scientists to properly store and handle compounds and can help determine how to clean up or dispose of the material in the event of a spill.

RESEARCH QUESTION   How does a compound's atomic-level structure influence its use in natural or human-designed systems?

❶ MAKE A CLAIM

In this lab you will compare the melting points of three common substances: citric acid, $C_6H_8O_7$; paraffin wax, $C_{31}H_{64}$; and table salt, NaCl. Which one do you think will have the highest melting point? Which one will have the lowest? Explain.

_____

_____

_____

MATERIALS

- indirectly vented chemical splash goggles, nonlatex apron, nitrile gloves
- aluminum foil
- Bunsen burner

- citric acid, small amount
- paraffin wax, small amount
- permanent marker
- ring stand, ring, and clamp
- salt, small amount

- spatula or scoop
- striker
- wire gauze

SAFETY INFORMATION

indirectly vented chemical splash goggles

- Wear indirectly vented chemical splash goggles, a nonlatex apron, and nitrile gloves during the setup, hands-on, and takedown segments of the activity.
- Secure loose clothing, wear closed-toe shoes, and tie back long hair.
- Never eat any food items used in a lab activity.
- If you get a chemical in your eye, use an eyewash station immediately.
- Never pour chemicals, either used or unused, back into their original containers. Dispose of chemicals according to your teacher's instructions.

Student Lab Worksheet and complete Teacher Support are available online.

COLLECT DATA

Construct a data table in your Evidence Notebook to record the findings from your investigation. Your data table will record the melting order of the three substances. It should do so with both qualitative and quantitative data. Consider how you will determine when a substance begins to melt and whether or not it matters how long it takes to melt completely. Have your teacher approve your data table and data-collection plans.

FIGURE 2: Experimental setup

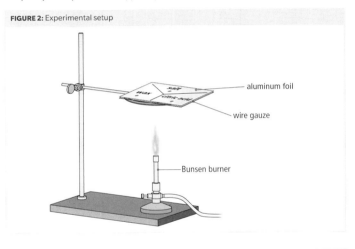

aluminum foil

wire gauze

Bunsen burner

CARRY OUT THE INVESTIGATION

1. Use a marker to divide a square piece of aluminum foil into three sections. Label the sections *salt, wax,* and *citric acid.* Fold the edges up to keep melted wax from spilling.

2. Use a spatula to transfer a very small (pea-sized) amount of each substance onto the foil. Be sure to clean and dry the spatula between each substance.

3. Set up a ring stand as shown in Figure 2. Adjust the ring's height so that the Bunsen burner can fit under it.

4. Place a piece of wire gauze on top of the ring, and carefully place the aluminum foil on top of the gauze.

5. Secure loose clothing and tie back hair. Light the Bunsen burner, and carefully place it under the wire gauze. Observe the order in which the substances melt. Record the melting order in the data table.

6. Turn off the Bunsen burner when the substances have melted. Dispose of your materials as instructed by your teacher.

Differentiate Instruction

MTSS/RTI Tape a tennis ball to each end of a short string to model the bond between particles in a substance. Gently move the balls back and forth and explain that the attractive force between particles remains intact as long as the particles do not move much. Ask a volunteer to move the balls vigorously so that the string connection breaks. Remind the student to be respectful of others in the group and not allow the balls or their hands to hit anyone. Ask another volunteer to explain how the movement of the tennis balls and the breaking of the string connection relate to particles. Guide students to understand that at the melting point, heating adds energy that causes particles to move enough to overcome the attractive forces between particles.

Collaborate

Graffiti Provide each group with a large piece of paper and felt pens of different colors. Have students generate ideas, in the form of "graffiti" on the paper, about how the structures of compounds influence the functional uses of compounds in natural or human-designed systems. Groups can share their ideas and graffiti with the class.

CCC Patterns

Ask students to consider what must happen in order for a substance to melt. Have them consider why this might occur at different temperatures for different substances.

DCI PS1.A Structure and Properties of Matter

Display images of the chemical structures of citric acid, paraffin wax, and sodium chloride. After students make observations about which compound has the highest melting point and which has the lowest melting point, encourage them to start thinking about how the structures of the compounds are different and how these differences might relate to the differences in melting point. Explain to students that they will learn throughout this lesson more about these structures and the ways that the chemical structure of compounds affects the properties of compounds.

Claims, Evidence, and Reasoning

Point out to students that they can use **everyday phenomena** as part of the evidence to support their claim. As students are drawing conclusions about the results of their investigation, have them discuss with a partner what happens at the particle level to the substances as they are heated. Emphasize to students that the macroscopic (or macroscale) properties of matter are explained by attractions and interactions at the subatomic scale.

1 Sketches should show particles of the substance in three forms. One view should show the particles close together as they exist in a solid. A second view should indicate some movement and should show space between particles as they are being heated. A final view should show the particles farther apart and freer to move about, as in a liquid.

2 **Sample answer:** The salt did not melt when it was heated, so it has the strongest attractive forces between particles. The attraction between the particles was too strong to be overcome by the addition of energy in the form of heat. Wax was the first substance to melt, so it has the weakest attractive forces between particles.

Evidence Notebook

3 Answers may vary. Students may suggest that sodium chloride has the strongest forces between atoms because it is the most stable of the three substances. Students may suggest testing properties such as melting point, boiling point, or other physical properties to learn more about the bonding between the atoms.

FORMATIVE ASSESSMENT

3-2-1 Have students write three things they learned while completing this investigation, two things they found interesting, and one question they still have about the results they obtained during the investigation.

---

1 **ANALYZE**
Choose one of the substances tested in the lab, and sketch the particles in the substance before, during, and after being heated.

2 **DRAW CONCLUSIONS**
The melting point of a substance is related to the strength of attractive forces between the particles that make up that substance. Write a conclusion that addresses each of the points below.

Claim Which substance tested in this investigation has the strongest attractive forces between its particles? Which substance has the weakest?

Evidence Give specific examples from your data to support your claim.

Reasoning Explain how the evidence you gave supports your claim. Describe, in detail, the connections between the evidence you cited and the argument you are making.

3 **Evidence Notebook** As you have seen, sodium metal, chlorine gas, and sodium chloride have different properties. What conclusion can you make about the forces holding the atoms of these substances together? What tests could you run to learn more about each substance?

© Houghton Mifflin Harcourt Publishing Company

EXPLORATION 2 Describing Chemical Bonds

EXPLORATION 2

Describing Chemical Bonds

The electron arrangement of most atoms causes them to have a high potential energy. Recall that a chemical bond forms when atoms gain, lose, or share valence electrons and end up with a full outer shell, or octet. A full outer shell has lower potential energy than a partially filled shell, so the full shell is a more stable arrangement. Therefore, when atoms form chemical bonds, the compound formed typically has a lower potential energy than the total potential energy of the individual atoms.

 4 **Collaborate** Like a ball rolling down a hill, systems tend to naturally change toward lower, more stable energy states. The ball at the top of the hill represents a large amount of stored, or potential, energy. That potential energy is converted to kinetic energy as the ball rolls down the hill to a more energetically stable position. With a partner, make your own analogy to explain how chemical bond formation leads to more stable energy states.

Making Predictions about Bonding

Electronegativity is a measure of the tendency of an atom to attract electrons. Differences in electronegativity can be used to predict the types of chemical bonds atoms will form.

FIGURE 3: Patterns in electronegativity can be observed on the periodic table.

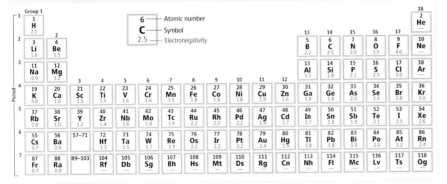

5 **EXPLAIN** Using Figure 3, select the correct terms to complete the statement.

As you move from left to right across a row in the periodic table, the electronegativity of the elements increases | decreases | does not show a pattern. As you move down a column, the electronegativity of the elements increases | decreases | does not show a pattern. The more electronegative elements can be found in the upper right | upper left | lower right | lower left of the periodic table.

3D Learning Objective

Students learn about electronegativity as a way to describe forces of attraction between electric charges at the atomic scale and predict the interactions of matter at the bulk scale. Students investigate patterns in the periodic table and use the periodic table as a model to predict the outer electron states of atoms and explain types of interactions.

Differentiate Instruction

MTSS/RTI Involve kinesthetic learners in a demonstration to better understand the relationship between bonds and energy. Have two students hold hands, imagining that this represents a chemical bond joining two atoms. Ask a third student to "break the bond" by unclasping the hands between the two students. Point out that the student used energy to break the bond. Emphasize that energy is always required to break a chemical bond. Ask students to explain what happens to the energy when a bond forms.

Praise students, as appropriate, for managing themselves well and for showing respect for others as they act out forming and breaking bonds.

DCI **PS1.A Structure and Properties of Matter**

Emphasize to students that electronegativity is a property of each atom because of its atomic structure. Electronegativity *differences*, however, are a property of two bonded atoms. It is the difference in electronegativities that determines the ionic or covalent character of a bond.

4 Analogies should be logical. **Sample answers:** an acorn, apple, or similar item falling from a tree; a house of cards collapsing; an elastic band that is stretched and then let go

5 increases, decreases, upper right

Preconception Alert

Bond Type Students may think that bond types can be classified as completely ionic or completely covalent. Emphasize that bond types are a spectrum that depends on the electronegativity of the two bonded elements. In all cases, the sharing of electrons produces a mutual attraction between two nuclei. Bonds are described as ionic when the transfer of electrons is complete enough that the particles are more appropriately described as charged ions.

Differentiate Instruction

Extension Point out to students that the discussion in this Exploration describes polar and nonpolar bonds, but it does not address the overall polarity of a molecule. Have students work in pairs to research and write an explanation of why some molecules that contain polar covalent bonds are polar and some are nonpolar. Students should find that in some molecules, such as carbon dioxide, the effects of the polar bonds cancel.

ELL Support Point out the terms *ionic* and *covalent*. Discuss the root words, *ion* and *valent,* and how they relate to the meanings of the terms. *Covalent* is composed of *co-*, which means "together" or "sharing," and *-valent,* which refers to valence electrons, which are the electrons shared in bonding. After discussing the parts, have students tell a partner the meaning of each term.

1 C and S: 0.0, nonpolar covalent, same, carbon disulfide, CS_2
O and H: 1.4, polar covalent, O, water, H_2O
Na and Cl: 2.1, ionic, Cl, sodium chloride, NaCl
Mg and O: 2.3, ionic, O, magnesium oxide, MgO

When there is a large electronegativity difference between two atoms—between about 1.7 and about 3.3—their bonding pattern is best explained as a transfer of electrons from the less electronegative atom to the more electronegative atom. An ionic bond is formed by the transfer of one or more electrons. A greater difference in electronegativity corresponds to a more complete transfer of electrons from one atom to the other.

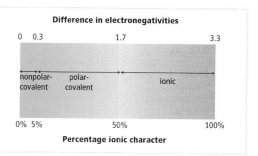

FIGURE 4: Bond types fit into a continuous range that is related to the difference in electronegativities of the two atoms that form the bond.

Difference in electronegativities

0   0.3   1.7   3.3

nonpolar-covalent   polar-covalent   ionic

0% 5%   50%   100%

Percentage ionic character

As the electronegativity difference decreases, so does the tendency of either atom to attract or "let go" of valence electrons. The two atoms share their valence electrons, forming what is called a covalent bond. If there is a small difference in electronegativity, atoms share electrons unevenly, forming a *polar covalent bond*. If two atoms are from the same element, their electronegativity difference is 0, and they form a *nonpolar covalent bond*. The diatomic elements of hydrogen, nitrogen, oxygen, and the halogens are examples of this type of bond, and the electrons are shared equally between the atoms.

There is a spectrum of bond types between completely ionic and nonpolar covalent bonds, as shown in Figure 4. All bonds result from the mutual attraction between positively charged and negatively charged particles across two atoms.

1 **ANALYZE** Using Figures 3 and 4, fill out the table to describe how the listed elements will react with each other when forming a chemical bond.

Elements Bonded	Electronegativity Difference	Bond Type	More Electronegative Atom	Example Compound
C and O	1	polar covalent	0	carbon dioxide, CO_2
C and S				
O and H				
Na and Cl				
Mg and O				

A difference in electronegativity between two bonding atoms indicates how much, if any, sharing of electrons will occur. As this difference increases, the sharing of electrons becomes more uneven. If the electronegativity difference becomes great enough, the unequal pull on valence electrons will result in the transfer of electrons to the more electronegative element, forming an ionic bond. For this reason, we can discuss bonds as having a percentage ionic character.

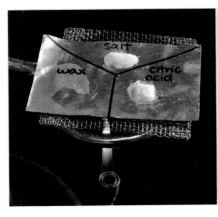

Patterns

Patterns in Bonding

You can find patterns in the ways some categories of elements form compounds. In general, metallic elements do not attract electrons, and they have low electronegativities. Nonmetals have higher electronegativities that increase toward the top right of the periodic table. The noble gases are an exception, as they do not attract electrons.

2 **INFER** Complete the statement about how different elements bond.

Metals tend to have relatively high | low electronegativities, and nonmetals have relatively high | low electronegativities. When a metal bonds with a nonmetal, electrons will most likely be transferred, and a covalent | an ionic bond will form. When a nonmetal bonds with a nonmetal, the difference in electronegativity values is relatively low. Therefore, electrons will be shared between the two nonmetals, and a covalent | an ionic bond will form.

Explore Online ▶

FIGURE 5: Melting point can be used to determine the relative strength of interactions between particles in various compounds in the solid state.

3 **APPLY** The chemical formulas for salt, citric acid, and paraffin wax are NaCl, $C_6H_8O_7$, and $C_{31}H_{64}$, respectively. Use this information and data you collected earlier in this lesson to determine which statements below are true. Select all that apply.

☐ **a.** Salt has a high melting point and there is a high electronegativity difference between sodium and chlorine, so, salt contains ionic bonds.

☐ **b.** Salt and citric acid both have high melting points, and there are high electronegativity differences between the atoms, so, both contain ionic bonds.

☐ **c.** Citric acid and wax both have relatively low melting points, and there are low electronegativity differences between the atoms, so, both contain covalent bonds.

Notice that none of the examples above involve bonds between metal atoms. Metal atoms do not interact with one another to form ionic or covalent bonds. The interactions between metals will be discussed in another section.

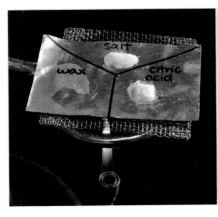

© Houghton Mifflin Harcourt Publishing Company • Image Credits: ©Houghton Mifflin Harcourt

---

ccc **Patterns**

As students work through the Infer activity, they should be able to explain the reason for each of their answers. Encourage them to include "because . . ." or "which means . . ." statements to explain each of the sentences they complete. For example, they might say, "Metals tend to have relatively low electronegativities, which means they have a weak attraction to their valence electrons."

Explore Online ▶

Encourage students to go online to watch a video demonstrating the differences in melting point of salt, citric acid, and wax.

DCI **PS1.A Structure and Properties of Matter**

Collaborate Make sure students understand the reason that metals have low electronegativities, nonmetals have higher electronegativities, and noble gases do not attract electrons. Divide the class into small groups. Assign each group one metal, one nonmetal, and one noble gas, and have them draw the electron arrangement of each element. Then have them discuss why these arrangements produce the electronegativity differences of the elements.

2 low, high, an ionic, a covalent

3 a, c

Collaborate

Discussion Have students work in groups of three to develop a mnemonic for remembering the difference between a cation and an anion. For example, the *t* in cation looks like a plus sign, which is a way to remember that cations have positive charge. Afterward, have groups share their ideas with the class.

 Influence of Engineering, Technology, and Science on Society and the Natural World

Point out to students that the strength of the ionic bond makes ionic compounds useful for many industrial and manufacturing applications. Have students research an application of an ionic compound and give a short presentation to the class describing it.

Evidence Notebook

1 Magnesium stearate contains ionic bonds (between Mg and the stearate ion) and covalent bonds (between H, O, and C within the stearate ion). Students should realize that compounds that dissolve in water might contain ionic bonds (salt), covalent bonds (sugar), or both (sulfuric acid), so the type of bonding involved must not fully explain the insolubility of soap scum.

2 sodium ion: +, cation; chloride ion: −, anion

Describing Ionic Bonding

Elements with very different electronegativity values generally form ionic bonds. Sodium chloride is an example of an ionically bonded compound. Recall that a mixture of sodium metal and chlorine gas reacts to form sodium chloride. Each sodium atom loses an electron, and each chlorine atom gains an electron. The attraction between positive and negative ions holds the ions together in an ionic bond. The ionization of the atoms and the formation of the ionic bond increase the stability of the system. The reaction releases energy as light and heat, resulting in a much lower energy state for the compound as compared to the sum of the energy states of the individual atoms.

1 **Evidence Notebook** When soaps are used in hard water, ions such as calcium or magnesium in the water form soap scum, which is made up of insoluble compounds such as magnesium stearate, $Mg(C_{18}H_{35}O_2)_2$. What bond types are present in this compound? How might bond type explain the properties of the soap you are investigating in your unit project?

When an atom loses one or more electrons, it becomes a positive ion, or *cation*. Cations have more protons than electrons and so have an overall positive charge. When an atom gains electrons, it becomes a negative ion, or *anion*. Anions have more electrons than protons and so have an overall negative charge. A sodium atom has one valence electron, and chlorine has seven valence electrons.

2 **ANALYZE** Sodium transfers an electron to chlorine when forming sodium chloride. Write either a positive sign or a negative sign as a superscript by each ion formed in this bond. Then, label each as either a *cation* or an *anion* below the chemical symbol.

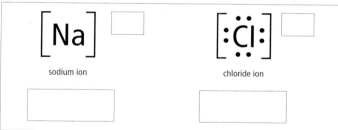

sodium ion   chloride ion

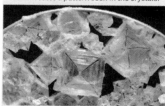

FIGURE 6: The regular arrangement of ions in salt creates a pattern seen in the crystals.

When sodium donates one electron to chlorine, both the negative chloride ion and the positive sodium ion end up with stable octet configurations. Thus, this ionic compound is more stable than either of its highly reactive elements.

An ionic compound consists of many bonds between positive and negative ions, which form repeating patterns in the solid state of the compound. This gives the compound a regular, geometric shape, as shown in Figure 6. As solids, ionic compounds do not conduct electric current, but they do conduct electric current when dissolved in water. They are also very hard and brittle, and they have high melting and boiling points.

The structure formed by atoms in a solid ionic compound like the one in Figure 6 is called a *crystal*. The repeating, symmetrical arrangement of atoms in a crystal is called a *crystal lattice*. In the model of a sodium chloride crystal lattice shown in Figure 7, attractions between ions are represented with solid lines.

Notice that each ion is attracted to more than one ion of opposite charge. The chemical formula of an ionic compound represents the simplest ratio of its ions in an electrically neutral crystal. A neutral compound has equal amounts of positive and negative charge.

3 **GATHER EVIDENCE** Observe sodium chloride with a hand lens. How is the relatively high melting point of sodium chloride related to its structure at the atomic scale? Use your observations and the model in Figure 7 to support your claim.

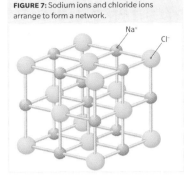

FIGURE 7: Sodium ions and chloride ions arrange to form a network.

Na^+

Cl^-

Engineering

Producing Salts

Salts are ionic compounds made of metal and nonmetal ions. They are important for human life and activities. Salts can be mined from deposits left by natural evaporation of ancient oceans. As the water evaporated, the ions in solution formed new ionic bonds, producing a crystalline ionic compound. Salts can also be produced by evaporating water from seawater. For example, some of the lithium metal used in batteries comes from lithium salts harvested by evaporation of brine deposits, as shown in Figure 8.

Long-lasting, recyclable lithium batteries are essential to many consumer products. They are also used to store renewable energy from sources such as solar and wind power. Chemical engineers must weigh tradeoffs to minimize the economic and environmental costs of producing lithium salts and maximize the benefits. As current lithium deposits become exhausted and demand for lithium continues to increase, costs and environmental concerns will continue to be considerations for engineers searching for and mining new deposits of lithium.

FIGURE 8: Lithium salts are isolated by solar evaporation of water from brine.

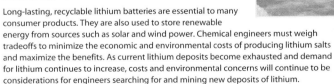

4 **Language Arts Connection** Research the development of lithium batteries, the increased demand for lithium, and how and where this demand is currently being met. Make a news article or presentation explaining how the need for lithium is related to modern technologies.

© Houghton Mifflin Harcourt Publishing Company • Image Credits: (tr) ©Florian Neukirchen/Alamy

---

SEP Developing and Using Models

Have students make a list of properties of ionic compounds that are explained by the model in **Figure 7.** Students should recognize that although sodium chloride is described as having a bond between a sodium ion, Na^+, and a chloride ion, Cl^-, an ionic compound is actually a network of ions that are bonded (attracted) to each of their neighboring ions. Ensure that students realize the bars shown in the model are not physical structures. They are shown only to represent forces between the particles.

Language Arts Connection
WHST.9-12.2 Write informative/explanatory texts, including the narration of historical events, scientific procedures/experiments, or technical processes.

Students should explain that new technologies that use lithium batteries, including cell phones, laptops, and electric cars, continue to grow, keeping the demand for lithium high. Articles or presentations should include documented sources.

Information Literacy Skills Have students ask themselves the following questions when obtaining information: *Do I know how to organize information using key words and metadata? Which technology tools should I use for specific purposes? Do I use ethical and legal behavior when I'm sharing information?* Use written or verbal responses as needed to assess students' information literacy skills.

3 Students should note that sodium chloride viewed through a hand lens looks like tiny cubes and that these cubes reiterate the structure shown in the model in **Figure 7.** Sodium chloride has a high melting point because it takes a lot of energy to overcome the attractive forces between particles in the crystal structure.

4 Students should explain that new technologies that use lithium batteries—including cell phones, laptops, and electric cars—continue to grow, keeping the demand for lithium high. Articles or presentations should include documented sources.

Lesson 1 Investigating Chemical Compounds 153

Preconception Alert

Students may assume that all chemically bonded particles are molecules. They may have heard sodium chloride incorrectly referred to as a molecule. Use the discussion and the models on this page and the next to emphasize that the term *molecule* refers only to the smallest particle of a covalent compound. The smallest particle of an ionic compound, such as sodium chloride, is a *formula unit*. Also emphasize that each molecule is composed of atoms that are neutral because they have neither gained nor lost electrons. An ionic compound is composed of ions, not neutral atoms. Each ion has either a positive charge or a negative charge.

Exploring Visuals

In **Figure 9,** students can observe the overlap of two electron clouds as the atoms approach each other and form a molecule. ***Ask:*** *What do the light- and dark-colored regions represent?* Both regions represent areas where electrons have a probability of being located. The darker the region, the greater the probability of electrons being located there. *How would the diagram be the same and how would it be different for ionic bonding?* The electron clouds would still overlap, but the dark-colored region would be mostly around the more electronegative atom.

Language Arts Connection

Explain to students that until recently sugar was thought to melt when heated. Investigations have shown, however, that sugar instead undergoes a complex process of thermal decomposition. Remind students that melting is a physical change in which a solid turns into a liquid. Sugar experiences a chemical change in which it caramelizes at the same time as or, in some cases, before it liquefies, so it does not strictly melt. Have students research more about the thermal decomposition of sugar and write one or two paragraphs about the process. Have them identify other examples of **everyday phenomena** in which a familiar substance changes by thermal decomposition. **(WHST.9-12.2)**

1 share, strong, less, weaker

Describing Covalent Bonding

In a covalent bond, neither atom exerts sufficient attractive force to cause an electron to transfer between atoms, so electrons are shared. A molecule is a neutral group of atoms that are held together by covalent bonds. A fluorine molecule is shown in Figure 9.

FIGURE 9: Two fluorine atoms share a pair of electrons equally.

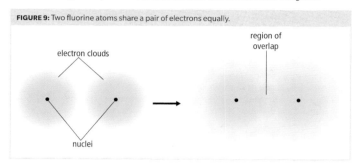

electron clouds

region of overlap

nuclei

A single molecule of a chemical compound is an individual unit that functions, in many ways, as a single particle. A molecule consists of two or more atoms bonded together by covalent bonds. Some molecules, such as diatomic oxygen, shown in Figure 10a, are made up of atoms of only one element. Other molecules, such as water and sugar, shown in Figure 10b and Figure 10c, are made of atoms of two or more elements. A chemical compound in which the simplest units are molecules is called a *molecular compound*. Molecular compounds have different properties from ionic compounds.

FIGURE 10: Molecules consist of two or more covalently bonded atoms.

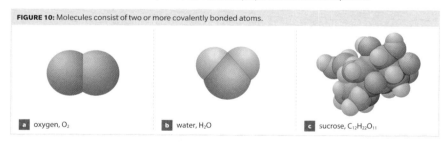

a oxygen, O_2 b water, H_2O c sucrose, $C_{12}H_{22}O_{11}$

1 **EXPLAIN** In general, the melting and boiling points of molecular compounds are much lower than those of ionic compounds. What can explain this difference?

Molecular compounds such as those in Figure 10 are formed when one or more atoms transfer | share | release electrons to form molecules. The covalent bonds *within* a molecule are very strong | weak. However, it requires more | less energy to melt a molecular compound than an ionic compound such as the one in Figure 7. This is because the attractive forces *between* individual molecules are weaker | stronger than the forces between ions in an ionic compound.

In general, properties of molecular compounds result from their structure as molecules. In addition to having lower melting and boiling points than ionic compounds, some of them are gases at room temperature. Because molecules are neutral, covalently bonded compounds do not conduct electric current in either their solid or liquid state.

Explore Online ▶

Hands-On Lab

Types of Bonding in Solids
Analyze conductivity, solubility, and melting point to determine the bonding type present in solids.

Describing Metallic Bonding

Metal atoms have low electronegativity values. They do not attract additional electrons, and their own outer electrons are loosely held. Inside a sample of metal, the positive metal ions are surrounded by delocalized valence shell electrons. Delocalized electrons are not tightly held by any one atom, so they can move about within the sample. The chemical bonding that results from the attraction between metal atoms and the surrounding sea of electrons is called metallic bonding.

2 ANALYZE Mercury is a liquid at room temperature, gallium will melt if held in your hand, and aluminum is a solid that has a high melting point. All three are metals. How can you explain these observations using information about the strength of metallic bonds?

_____

_____

_____

FIGURE 11: Electrons are able to move freely within a metal substance.

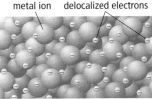

metal ion   delocalized electrons

a The delocalized electrons interact with the metal ions resulting in metallic bonding.

b A metal spoon can complete a circuit because the delocalized electrons move when a current is applied.

As with all substances, the properties of metals are related to the bonds they form. Metals are malleable, or easily hammered into sheets. The delocalized electrons around the positive ions form relatively weak links within the substance, making it easy to bend and shape metal. The mobile electrons moving easily throughout the substance allow metals to conduct electric current and contribute to their ability to conduct energy as heat. Gold is used in solid-state electronic devices due to the low voltage and currents that these devices operate under, which might cause other metals to oxidize or corrode. However, copper is still the choice for wiring in a home, as it is more cost effective. In both cases, delocalized electrons allow an electric current to flow through the circuits.

3 **Evidence Notebook** What types of bonds form within a sample of sodium metal, chlorine gas, and sodium chloride crystals? How does the electron structure of each substance affect the properties of compounds that it forms?

Explore Online ▶

Hands-On Lab 👥 Small Groups 🕐 45 minutes
Types of Bonding in Solids

SEP **Planning and Carrying Out Investigations**

In this lab, students analyze conductivity, solubility, and melting point to determine the bonding type present in solids. _Student lab worksheet and teacher support available online._

DCI **PS1.A Structure and Properties of Matter**

Show students a piece of aluminum foil. Allow them to hold it and explore the properties of the foil. Then engage students in a class discussion of how the structure of the aluminum is responsible for the properties they observe, as well as properties they know from having used the foil in cooking.

Explore Online ▶

Encourage students to go online to watch a video about the movement of electrons in a metal.

2 Students should point out that metallic bonding holds atoms of a metal together, and if this bonding is not strong, certain properties such as melting point will be affected. The weaker the metallic bonding, the lower the melting point.

Evidence Notebook

3 Metallic bonds form in sodium metal. The delocalized electrons make sodium metal easy to bend. Chlorine gas consists of pairs of covalently bonded chlorine atoms. Chlorine gas does not conduct electric current because the molecules are neutral. Ionic bonding occurs in sodium chloride. The strong attractive forces between sodium and chlorine give sodium chloride crystals a regular, geometric shape, low reactivity, and a high melting point.

FORMATIVE ASSESSMENT

Debriefing Ask students to name ways that ionic bonds, covalent bonds, and metallic bonds are alike and ways they are different. Use students' responses to make a Venn diagram on the board.

EXPLORATION 3 Predicting the Structure of Compounds

3D Learning Objective

Students use the periodic table to **predict relationships** between atoms in compounds. Students relate patterns in the periodic table to patterns in the **structure and properties of matter** and use these as **evidence** to **construct explanations.**

Differentiate Instruction

MTSS/RTI Help students work collaboratively to review how to use the periodic table to identify the number of valence electrons of each main group element and then how to use this number to determine whether an atom will gain or lose electrons when forming an ionic bond.

DCI **PS1.A Structure and Properties of Matter**

Have students think about how the structures of the calcium and fluorine atoms shown in **Figure 12** contribute to their charge before and after the ionic compound forms. ***Ask:*** *Why are the calcium and fluorine atoms neutral before the compound forms?* The number of protons and electrons in each atom is equal. *How do the numbers of protons and electrons of each atom compare after the compound forms?* The calcium ion has two fewer electrons than it has protons, so its overall charge is 2+. Each fluorine ion has one more electron than it has protons, so the overall charge on each ion is 1−.

1 Examples of other Group 2 and Group 17 compounds are BeF_2, $MgCl_2$, and BaF_2. The ratio of Group 2 atoms to Group 17 atoms is always 1:2. The compounds form two ionic bonds. Group 1 and Group 17 atoms always combine in a 1:1 ratio; they form compounds with one ionic bond. Group 2 and Group 16 atoms always combine in a 1:1 ratio; they form compounds with one ionic bond. Group 1 and Group 16 atoms always combine in a 2:1 ratio; they form compounds with two ionic bonds.

2 two, one, CaF_2

3 c

Predicting the Structure of Compounds

Every molecule of a covalently bonded substance has the same number and type of atoms in the same arrangement as other molecules of the substance. Ionic compounds have a fixed ratio of ions, and this ratio determines their three-dimensional arrangement within the substance. For example, calcium and fluorine always combine in a ratio of one calcium ion to two fluoride ions. Calcium fluoride occurs naturally as the mineral fluorite. Calcium fluoride is used to make hydrofluoric acid, which is used to produce pharmaceuticals and other materials.

1 **Collaborate** With a partner, research other compounds formed when Group 2 and Group 17 atoms combine. What do you notice about the ratio of atoms in the compound? How many bonds form, and what types of bonds? Do other groups, such as Group 1 and Group 16, show a pattern when their atoms combine?

Analyzing Chemical Formulas for Ionic Compounds

When an ionic bond forms, metal atoms transfer electrons to nonmetal atoms. A nonmetal atom accepts enough electrons to fill its outer shell, and a metal atom loses enough electrons to empty its outer shell. This transfer determines the ratio of the elements in the ionic compound. Figure 12 shows the transfer of electrons from calcium to fluorine to form calcium fluoride.

2 **APPLY** Complete the statement about the chemical formula of calcium fluoride.

Calcium is located in the second column of the periodic table, so a calcium atom has one | two | three valence electron(s), which it loses to form a calcium ion. Each fluorine atom has seven valence electrons, so each fluorine atom accepts one | two | three electron(s) to form a fluoride ion. Therefore, the formula for calcium fluoride is CaF | CaF_2 | Ca_2F.

FIGURE 12: Two valence electrons transfer from calcium to fluorine.

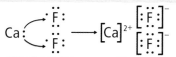

The chemical formula of an ionic compound indicates the relative numbers of atoms of each element in the compound, using atomic symbols and subscript numerals. The formula for calcium fluoride indicates that the simplest unit of the compound contains a ratio of two fluoride ions to one calcium ion.

3 **EXPLAIN** Calcium chloride, $CaCl_2$, and potassium chloride, KCl, are also ionic compounds. Which of the following statements is likely to be true based on this information?

○ **a.** Calcium and potassium ions require the same relative number of chloride ions to empty their outer electron shells.

○ **b.** Ionic compounds never contain more than two ions of an atom.

○ **c.** $CaCl_2$ has three atoms in its simplest unit, and KCl has two atoms in its simplest unit.

Patterns

Ionic Formulas

The table below shows some chemical formulas for binary ionic compounds, which are compounds containing one metal and one nonmetal element. The elements are all found in Period 3 of the periodic table.

Compounds containing sodium	Na_3P	Na_2S	$NaCl$
Compounds containing magnesium	Mg_3P_2	MgS	$MgCl_2$
Compounds containing aluminum	AlP	Al_2S_3	$AlCl_3$

4 **Collaborate** With a partner, discuss the patterns you see in the chemical formulas. How does the placement of the elements on the periodic table appear to relate to the numbers in the chemical formula?

Describing Patterns in Ionic Bonding

In order to determine the formula for an ionic compound, the number of valence electrons for each atom in the compound must be known. Previously, you learned to determine the number of valence electrons using an element's electron configuration. You can also use the periodic table to determine the number of valence electrons of any main group element.

5 **MODEL** Draw the dot diagrams for the elements in each group. When you see a pattern, draw an electron-dot diagram around the X that represents the entire group.

X 1								**2** **He:**
1 **H** 1	**X·** 2		**X** 13	**X** 14	**X** 15	**X** 16	**X** 17	**X** 18
3 **Li**	**4** **Be**		**5** **·B·**	**6** **C**	**7** **N**	**8** **O**	**9** **F**	**10** **:Ne:**
11 **Na**	**12** **Mg**		**13** **·Al·**	**14** **Si**	**15** **P**	**16** **S**	**17** **Cl**	**18** **Ar**
19 **K**	**20** **Ca**		**31** **Ga**	**32** **Ge**	**33** **As**	**34** **Se**	**35** **Br**	**36** **Kr**
37 **Rb**	**38** **Sr**		**49** **In**	**50** **Sn**	**51** **Sb**	**52** **Te**	**53** **I**	**54** **Xe**
55 **Cs**	**56** **Ba**		**81** **Tl**	**82** **Pb**	**83** **Bi**	**84** **Po**	**85** **At**	**86** **Rn**
87 **Fr**	**88** **Ra**		**113** **Nh**	**114** **Fl**	**115** **Mc**	**116** **Lv**	**117** **Ts**	**118** **Og**

Patterns

Collaborate Have students work in groups to make a diagram that describes the pattern by which elements in Groups 1 and 2 form ionic compounds with elements in Groups 16, 17, and 18.

Sports Medicine Connection

Relate ionic compounds to **everyday phenomena** by asking students if they have seen athletes with sports drinks during a game or if students have ever had a sports drink themselves. Explain that sports drinks contain ionic compounds that are essential to the proper functioning of the body. They are often used by athletes to replenish ions such as sodium, magnesium, and calcium lost by sweating during intense workouts.

4 **Sample answer:** Students should notice that as the group number of the metal increases, the ratio of metal to nonmetal atoms decreases. At the same time, an increase in group number of the nonmetal also causes the ratio of metal to nonmetal atoms to decrease.

5 Students should identify that elements in Group 1 have one valence electron, elements in Group 2 have two valence electrons, elements in Group 13 have three valence electrons, and so on. So for elements in Groups 1 and 2, the number of valence electrons is equal to the group number. For elements in groups 13–18, the number of valence electrons is equal to the group number minus 10.

ccc Patterns

Point out to students that the pattern in the number of valence electrons from left to right across a period of the periodic table corresponds to the pattern in electronegativity of the elements. Across a period, as the number of valence electrons increases, the electronegativity increases. Ask students to consider the octet rule in thinking about this correlation. They should realize that for elements with just one or two valence electrons, the closest octet is achieved by losing one or two electrons, and their electronegativity is low. For elements with six or seven valence electrons, the closest octet is achieved by gaining electrons, and their electronegativity is high.

Language Arts Connection

WHST.11-12.8 Gather relevant information from multiple authoritative print and digital sources, using advanced searches effectively; integrate information into the text selectively to maintain the flow of ideas, avoiding plagiarism and overreliance on any one source and following a standard format for citation.

Show students examples of paraphrasing and quotation from sources and contrast those with examples of plagiarism or improper citation. You can also use this writing activity as an opportunity to explain the process in which scientists publish their research results. Explain that articles submitted to a peer-reviewed journal are first reviewed by several experts in the field. Careful scrutiny is given to the research procedures and whether the results are reliable and contribute to the understanding of the topic. Articles are sometimes sent back to the researchers to provide more information or to explain procedures or content. Bring in examples of several peer-reviewed articles for students to observe. Draw their attention to the abstracts and the list of sources.

 Row 1: Group 1, Li_2O
Row 2: Group 16, MX
Row 3: Group 13, Group 16, B_2O_3
Row 4: Group 1, MX
Row 5: MX_2, $CaCl_2$
Row 6: Group 13

 b

All of the elements found in Group 1 have one valence electron, those in Group 2 have two valence electrons, those in Group 13 have 3 valence electrons, and so on through Group 18. Based on this pattern, scientists know that the ratio of atoms will be the same when an element from Group 1 bonds with an element from Group 17, regardless of which elements bond.

1 EXPLAIN Use the valence electron pattern you found in the periodic table to determine the pattern between group numbers in the chemical formula for each example.

| Group 1 | Group 13 | Group 16 | MX | MX_2 | $CaCl_2$ | Li_2O | B_2O_3 |

Group Number	Group Number	Chemical Formula	Example
	Group 16	M_2X	
Group 2			MgO
		M_2X_3	
	Group 17		KCl
Group 2	Group 17		
	Group 17	MX_3	$AlCl_3$

The locations of elements on the periodic table allows their compound formulas to be determined. For example, aluminum is in Group 13 and oxygen is in Group 16. Based on the patterns you observed, the resulting compound has the formula Al_2O_3.

> **Language Arts Connection** Elements in Group 17, known as the halogens, are highly reactive, whereas elements in Group 18, the noble gases, have very low chemical reactivity. Use multiple authoritative sources to research these two groups of elements. What explains the difference in reactivity? How do the valence electron patterns in these groups affect how elements in each group are used? Write up your findings as a summary report. Be sure to include a full list of sources you referenced.

Writing Chemical Formulas for Ionic Compounds

The patterns in ionic formulas result from the charges of the ions of an element. Because the most stable ions have either a completely empty or a completely filled outer shell, the charges on ions are related to their group on the periodic table. Metal elements in Group 1 lose an electron to form a 1+ charge. Metal elements in Group 2 lose two electrons to form a 2+ charge. The chemical symbol of an ion consists of its element symbol followed by its charge as a superscript. For example, a magnesium ion has the symbol Mg^{2+}. If the charge is 1+ or 1−, the numeral 1 is not written, as in Cl^-.

2 PREDICT Aluminum is a metal with three valence electrons. What is the correct symbol for an aluminum ion?

○ **a.** Al^{5+} ○ **b.** Al^{3+} ○ **c.** Al^{3-} ○ **d.** Al^{5-}

Nonmetals typically have 5, 6, 7, or 8 valence electrons, and nonmetals have higher electronegativities than metals. The most stable arrangement occurs when these elements gain electrons when forming ionic bonds. Noble gases in Group 18 beyond helium, such as neon and argon, do not typically bond with other elements because they already possess a full outer shell.

3 **ANALYZE** Write in the charges you would expect elements in each group to form. Then, choose an example element from that group, and write its ion symbol in the next row.

Group	1	2	13	14	15	16	17	18
Charge	___	2+	___	4+/4−	___	2−	___	0
Example ion	___	___	Al^{3+}	Si^{4+}	N^{3-}	___	___	N/A

The transition metals, Groups 3–12 of the periodic table, do not follow the same predictable pattern of ion formation as do the main group elements. The valence electron structure of transition metals is more complex than those of the metals in the main groups. Many of the transition metal elements can form several different stable cations, depending on the number of electrons lost.

For example, an iron atom can lose two electrons to form Fe^{2+}, or it can lose three electrons to form Fe^{3+}. The ratio of iron ions to nonmetal ions in an ionic iron compound depends on which iron ion is present. For example, iron and oxygen form iron oxide in two different forms, FeO and Fe_2O_3, shown in Figure 13. When you write the name of a compound of a metal that can form more than one ion, the charge on the metal is indicated by a roman numeral in parentheses. The reddish-brown compound, which you may recognize as rust, is designated as Fe_2O_3, or iron(III) oxide, because the iron ion has a 3+ charge.

FIGURE 13: Iron and oxygen can combine to form two different compounds with different chemical and physical properties.

a Iron(II) oxide, FeO, is used as a pigment.

b Iron(III) oxide, Fe_2O_3, is the rust that forms when iron is exposed to air.

4 **APPLY** What differences do you notice between iron(II) oxide and iron(III) oxide in Figure 13? How does the charge of the iron ions result in different chemical formulas?

_____

_____

_____

_____

Differentiate Instruction

Extension Another iron oxide is magnetite, Fe_3O_4. Have students carry out research to determine the charge of the ions that form this compound, as well as properties of the compound. Students should find that Fe_3O_4 is produced from two Fe^{2+} ions, one Fe^{3+} ion, and four O^{2-} ions. The result is magnetite, a ferromagnetic compound.

SEP **Constructing Explanations and Designing Solutions**

Ask questions to ensure that students understand the reasons for the charges of bonding atoms from each main group on the periodic table. **Ask:** *Why do metals mostly form cations and nonmetals mostly form anions in ionic bonding?* Metals are in lower-numbered groups on the periodic table, which indicates that they have fewer valence electrons. In order to form an octet, they lose electrons, giving them a positive charge. Nonmetals are in higher-numbered groups on the periodic table, which indicates they have more valence electrons. In order to form an octet they gain electrons, giving them a negative charge.

DCI **PS1.A Structure and Properties of Matter**

Explain to students that a copper atom can lose one electron to form Cu^+, lose two electrons to form Cu^{2+}, or lose three electrons to form Cu^{3+}. Have students write chemical formulas for the following compounds: copper(I) sulfide, Cu_2S; copper(I) bromide, CuBr; copper(II) oxide, CuO; copper(II) fluoride, CuF_2; and copper(III) oxide, Cu_2O_3.

3 Charge: 1+, 3+, 3−, 1−; Example Ion: Li^+, Ca^{2+}, O^{2-}, Br^-

4 The two iron oxides are different colors. Oxygen has a 2− charge. When iron has a 2+ charge, the ions come together in a one-to-one ratio, and the compound has the formula FeO. When iron has a 3+ charge, there are two iron ions for every three oxygen ions. The formula for this compound is Fe_2O_3.

Math Connection

MP.2 Reason abstractly and quantitatively.

Students will learn the crisscross method for writing the formula of an ionic compound. As students study **Figure 14,** point out that the cation and the anion must first be determined using the group number of each element on the periodic table. The magnitude of each charge, but not the sign, can then be placed as the subscript for the other ion in the chemical formula. If the subscripts have a common denominator, divide both subscripts by that denominator to simplify the formula. For example, using the crisscross method, the formula for calcium oxide is Ca_2O_2. The subscripts have a common denominator of 2, so the formula will simplify to CaO.

SEP Developing and Using Models

Ask questions to ensure that students understand the formation of bonds as represented in **Figure 15.**

Ask: *What do the dots around the atoms show in the first step of the diagram?* Each hydrogen atom has one valence electron, and the carbon atom has four valence electrons.

Ask: *What happens in the second step of the diagram?* Each hydrogen atom shares its valence electron with the carbon atom, and the carbon atom shares each of its four valence electrons with a hydrogen atom, forming four covalent bonds.

Ask: *How is the third part of the diagram different from the second part of the diagram?* They show the same thing in a different way. Instead of representing each bond as two dots, the third part represents each bond as a line segment.

As students consider the models, emphasize that they are only a way of visualizing bonding and do not imply that a chemical bond is a separate physical structure with its own mass. Explain that these kinds of models are merely a method of "atomic accounting" by counting valence shell electrons.

1 Lithium and phosphorus: Li^+, P^{3-}, Li_3P
   Calcium and sulfur: Ca^{2+}, S^{2-}, CaS
   Aluminum and oxygen: Al^{3+}, O^{2-}, Al_2O_3
   Aluminum and nitrogen: Al^{3+}, N^{3-}, AlN

Math Connection

Writing Ionic Formulas

FIGURE 14: Crisscross method

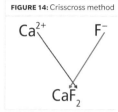

CaF$_2$

The crisscross method, shown in Figure 14, is a shortcut for determining the formula of an ionic compound. Using this method, the charge for each ion becomes the subscript for the other ion in the formula. For example, to write the formula for calcium fluoride, first determine the charges on each ion. Calcium has a 2+ charge, and fluorine has a 1− charge. Using this method, calcium has a subscript of 1, which is not written, and fluorine has a subscript of 2. This shortcut is useful, but the chemical formula might need to be reduced to its simplest ratio. For example, the formula for iron(II) oxide obtained by the shortcut is Fe_2O_2, which can be reduced to FeO.

1 **ANALYZE** Write the ion of each element in the combination. Then use the crisscross method to determine the chemical formula.

Elements	Positive ion	Negative ion	Chemical formula	Chemical name
Magnesium and chlorine	Mg^{2+}	Cl^-	$MgCl_2$	magnesium chloride
Lithium and phosphorus				lithium phosphide
Calcium and sulfur				calcium sulfide
Aluminum and oxygen				aluminum oxide
Aluminum and nitrogen				aluminum nitride

A polyatomic ion is a group of covalently bonded atoms that has a charge and behaves as an ion. To determine the chemical formula for compounds containing a polyatomic ion, follow the same rules about making the compound neutral as with a single-atom ion. For example, when ammonium, NH_4^+, bonds with sulfate, SO_4^{2-}, the resulting compound is ammonium sulfate, $(NH_4)_2SO_4$, a common ingredient in fertilizers.

Analyzing Covalent Compounds

Working with formulas for covalent compounds is more complex than it is for ionic compounds. Many covalent compounds have large and complex molecules, and the arrangement of atoms affects the properties of the molecules. We start our formula work by considering how many electrons atoms must share in order to obtain full energy levels.

FIGURE 15: These models show that four pairs of electrons are shared in a methane molecule.

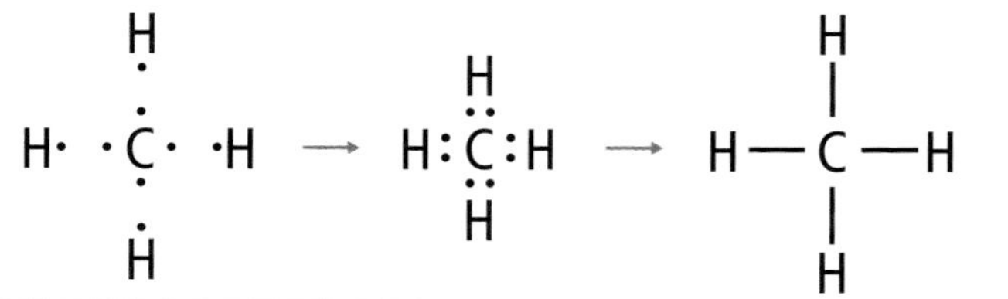

As in ionic bonding, each atom in a covalent molecule obtains a stable outer shell, usually in the form of an octet. For example, the carbon atom in Figure 15 shares its four valence electrons with four hydrogen atoms, which each contribute one electron. Each pair of electrons forms a single covalent bond, represented by two dots or a line. This way, the carbon atom obtains an octet. Hydrogen is an exception to the octet rule because a hydrogen atom only needs two electrons to fill its outer shell.

FIGURE 16: Each oxygen atom obtains an octet by forming a double covalent bond.

$$:\overset{..}{O}\cdot\cdot\overset{..}{O}: \longrightarrow :\overset{..}{O}::\overset{..}{O}: \longrightarrow :\overset{..}{O}=\overset{..}{O}:$$

In some cases, covalent bonds occur as double or triple bonds. A double bond represents four shared electrons, and a triple bond represents six shared electrons. Figure 16 shows an electron-dot diagram of the covalent bond formed between two oxygen atoms. Each oxygen atom has six valence electrons. In order to obtain an octet, the atoms must share four electrons. This results in a double covalent bond, represented by two lines between the atoms. A triple bond is represented by three lines. Triple bonds are the strongest and shortest type of covalent bond, while single bonds are the weakest and longest.

2 **MODEL** Model the structure of carbon tetrafluoride, a low-temperature refrigerant and greenhouse gas. It contains one carbon atom and four fluorine atoms.

3 **EXPLAIN** How many valence electrons are present in carbon and fluorine, and how are they shared in carbon tetrafluoride? How many bonds are present? Why are the bonds considered covalent?

All models have advantages and limitations. This type of model does not show the actual three-dimensional shape of the carbon tetrafluoride molecule, and real bonds are not made of dots or lines. A more accurate model would consider the size of the atoms and the dynamic structure of the molecule.

4 **Evidence Notebook** Determine the chemical formulas for sodium metal, chlorine gas, and sodium chloride. How can you use the electron-dot structures of chlorine gas and sodium metal to predict their reactivity levels and the compound they form when they react?

History of Science

Electron-dot structures were introduced in 1916, when Gilbert N. Lewis at the University of California, Berkeley, published a paper in which he used the diagrams to explain his ideas about the role of electrons in chemical bonding. Have students conduct research to learn how Lewis's electron-dot structures (often called "Lewis structures") have changed since they were first described.

2 Students' models should show a central carbon atom bonded to four fluorine atoms, similar to the structure for methane, CH_4.

3 **Sample answer:** A carbon atom has four valence electrons, and a fluorine atom has seven valence electrons. Carbon and fluorine form covalent bonds because these atoms are similar in electronegativity. Because carbon tetrafluoride has covalent bonds, the atoms will share electrons. The carbon atom shares one electron pair with each of the fluorine atoms, giving each atom a full outer shell. The straight lines between the central carbon atom and each fluorine atom model the electron sharing.

Evidence Notebook
4 **Sample answer:** Na, Cl_2, NaCl. Each sodium atom has one valence electron, and each chlorine atom has seven valence electrons. Using electron-dot structures, I can see that sodium and chlorine each have one unpaired electron, so they are very reactive alone and will combine in a stable one-to-one ratio to form NaCl.

FORMATIVE ASSESSMENT
One-Sentence Summary Have students look back through the Exploration. Then, have them write a one-sentence summary of the text under each heading.

EXPLORATION 4 Modeling the Shapes of Molecules

3D Learning Objective

Students explore VSEPR theory and **use models to predict relationships** between atoms in compounds. They investigate how **repulsion between electric charges at the atomic scale** affects the shapes of molecules and look for **patterns** in atomic-level structure and macroscopic properties of different substances.

Hands-On Lab 👥 Individuals or Small Groups ⏱ 90 minutes
Modeling the Shapes of Molecules

SEP Developing and Using Models

Students make models of the molecular shapes of carbon tetrachloride, oxygen difluoride, carbon disulfide, phosphorus tribromide, methanal, and silicon dioxide. They research properties of each compound and use evidence from their investigation to support a claim about the shape of each molecule they model.

Advance Preparation Collect materials, including the possible materials listed on the student page, that students can use to make their models. You may wish to provide students with the addresses of several reliable websites where they can learn about the properties and structures of the compounds they will model.

Safety Information Remind all students that indirectly vented chemical splash goggles and a nonlatex apron are to be worn during the setup, hands-on, and takedown segments of the activity. Remind them to use caution when using sharp tools, which can cut or puncture skin. Have students wash their hands with soap and water immediately after completing this activity.

1 **Sample answer:** I can determine the shape of a molecule by using VSEPR theory and determining the valence electrons of each atom in the molecule.

Hands-On Lab

Modeling the Shapes of Molecules

Electron-dot diagrams help to explain bonding patterns in molecules and compounds, but they do not represent the actual three-dimensional shapes of these compounds. However, you can use such diagrams to predict the three-dimensional structures. Pairs of valence electrons of an atom in a molecule repel other pairs of valence electrons, because like charges repel. Therefore, the three-dimensional structure of a molecule results from the electron pairs arranging themselves as far apart as possible.

FIGURE 17: Ammonia can be modeled using an electron-dot diagram or VSEPR theory.

a electron-dot diagram

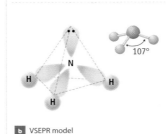

b VSEPR model

This idea is known as valence-shell electron-pair repulsion, or VSEPR. In this lab, you will use electron-dot structures and the VSEPR theory to predict the three-dimensional structures of several covalently bonded molecules.

Consider the example of ammonia shown in Figure 17. The electron-dot diagram shows that ammonia consists of a nitrogen atom bonded to three hydrogen atoms, with one pair of lone electrons. VSEPR theory predicts that the four pairs of electrons surrounding the nitrogen atom will arrange themselves as far apart as possible. Because of the lone pair, there is no atom at one apex of the resulting arrangement of electron pairs. The shape of the molecule is a pyramid with three hydrogen atoms spread apart on one side of the nitrogen atom.

There are a number of shapes that molecules can have, such as linear, pyramidal, or tetrahedral. You will explore some of these shapes in this lab.

The first step in determining molecular shape using VSEPR is to draw an electron-dot diagram of the molecule. Use the periodic table to find the number of valence electrons for each atom. Then, draw a structure that shows the pairs of shared electrons, how many bonds form, and any unshared electrons. The unshared electrons should be indicated in pairs.

RESEARCH QUESTION What shapes can molecules take on, and why is this important in understanding the behavior of substances?

1 MAKE A CLAIM
How can you determine the shape of a molecule?

_____

_____

_____

_____

_____

 Student Lab Worksheet and complete Teacher Support are available online.

POSSIBLE MATERIALS

- indirectly vented chemical splash goggles, nonlatex apron
- foam spheres
- modeling clay, various colors
- molecular modeling kit
- pompoms, various colors
- sticks, craft
- toothpicks

SAFETY INFORMATION

- Wear indirectly vented chemical splash goggles and a nonlatex apron during the setup, hands-on, and takedown segments of the activity.
- Use caution when using sharp materials, which can cut or puncture skin.
- Wash your hands with soap and water immediately after completing this activity.

indirectly vented chemical splash goggles

PLAN THE INVESTIGATION

In this activity, you will model the molecular shapes of six substances: carbon tetrachloride, oxygen difluoride, carbon disulfide, phosphorus tribromide, methanal, and silicon dioxide. You will need to plan how you will build your models, including the materials that you will use to model the atoms, the bonds, and the lone electron pairs. Write your procedure and a safety plan in your Evidence Notebook. Be sure to include enough detail that someone reading your procedure would be able to replicate your models. Have your teacher approve your procedure and your safety plan.

COLLECT DATA

Once your teacher has approved your plans, construct a data table to record the following information for each molecule you model: chemical formula, electron-dot diagram, and a drawing of the model showing its molecular shape. Any other types of information that will aid in your understanding of the models you build should also be included in the data table. Now, build your models.

CONDUCT RESEARCH

Research each molecule in this investigation to find out its applications and whether the shape of the molecule is an important factor in these applications. Be sure to research the safety data sheet (SDS) for each molecule and record any safety implications or other important concerns for storage, handling, and disposal for each substance.

ANALYZE

1. Research the shape of each of the six molecules. How close were your models to the actual shapes?

© Houghton Mifflin Harcourt Publishing Company

Collaborate

Jigsaw Divide the class into six groups, and assign each group one of the six substances that they are modeling in this lab. Have each group research their assigned substance to learn about one or more examples of **everyday phenomena** that involve the substance. Have a representative of each group describe the phenomena to the class.

CCC Patterns

After students complete their models, have them spend time considering the patterns in the structures. Have them think about how structures are alike and different, and then have them consider how the difference affects the shape. Encourage students to suggest generalizations about the patterns they observe.

DCI PS1.A Structure and Properties of Matter

Emphasize the importance that lone pairs have on the structure of the molecular shapes that students are producing. Make sure students realize that lone pairs repel other electrons and that structures with two lone pairs experience an even stronger repulsion.

Analyze

1. carbon tetrachloride, CCl_4, tetrahedral; oxygen difluoride, OF_2, bent; carbon disulfide, CS_2, linear; phosphorus tribromide, PBr_3, pyramidal; methanal (formaldehyde), H_2CO, trigonal planar; silicon dioxide, SiO_2, bent

   Students' answers should reflect how accurate their electron-dot diagrams were and how well they were able to interpret those diagrams into models.

Analyze (continued)

2. Students' answers should reflect how their research helps them point out the problems they had with their models and determine a way to improve the models that were incorrect.

3. Students' answers should relate the properties of compounds to their structures—for example, by thinking about the locations of unshared electrons and how that might affect the molecule's polarity. Physical properties, such as solubility and the ability to dissolve other substances, as well as a compound's physical state at room temperature and pressure, relate to the three-dimensional shape of the molecules, as does chemical reactivity.

1 **Sample answer:** Using VSEPR theory and electron-dot diagrams, I was able to determine the expected shape of a molecule based on the valence electrons of each atom that make up the particular molecule. The research I did to find out the actual shape showed that the shapes I determined were correct.

2 The shape of a molecule that has one atom of a Group 15 element and three atoms of a Group 17 element should be a pyramid. This shape minimizes the repulsions of the valence electrons. This is the same shape as the ammonia molecule shown in **Figure 17**.

Evidence Notebook

3 Sodium has one valence electron, and that electron is transferred to chlorine, which has seven valence electrons and a much higher electronegativity than sodium. The structure of NaCl is determined by the strong attractive forces between the sodium and chlorine ions. In this lab, the valence electrons are shared, not transferred.

FORMATIVE ASSESSMENT

3-Minute Pause Have students pause to think of what they have learned while researching the compounds and producing their models. Have them respond to the following prompts:

I became more aware of . . .
I didn't realize that . . .
I still don't understand . . .

Have volunteers share their responses with the class.

---

2. How could you revise your models to be more accurate based on your research?

3. How might the shape of the compound influence how it behaves?

1 **DRAW CONCLUSIONS**

Write a conclusion that addresses each of the points below.

Claim How can you determine the shape of a molecule?

Evidence What evidence from your investigation supports your claim?

Reasoning How does your evidence support or refute your claim?

2 **EXTEND**

Based on your results, what should the shape of a molecule be that consists of one atom of a Group 15 element and three atoms of a Group 17 element? Explain your answer.

3 **Evidence Notebook** How do valence electrons in sodium chloride determine its structure as an ionic compound? How does that compare to the valence electrons in the molecular structures you investigated in this lab?

TAKE IT FURTHER Guided Research

TAKE IT FURTHER

Guided Research

Asking Questions about Minerals

If you pick up a rock and look at it closely using a hand lens, you can often detect crystal shapes in its structure. Occasionally, you might even find a rock that is itself a single crystal. Rocks are made up of one or more minerals. Minerals are naturally occurring solid materials with a definite chemical composition and a crystalline structure.

What kind of chemical compounds would you expect minerals to be composed of? In general, minerals are composed of ionic compounds. Most minerals consist of compounds of one or more metallic elements bonded to nonmetallic elements or polyatomic ions composed of nonmetallic elements.

A familiar use of minerals is for decoration. Gems are minerals that are especially popular in jewelry. A key part of the attractiveness of many gems is their color. The color is caused by the ways different minerals reflect or absorb light. In many cases, the color of a mineral is determined by the metal atoms it contains. The addition of a small amount of different metal atoms in the crystal lattice can change the appearance of the mineral. This occurs because the electrons of each element interact with other atoms in specific ways. Differences in electron interactions affect how the mineral interacts with light, as shown in Figure 18.

Quartz, for example, is an ionic compound of silicon and oxygen that is colorless and transparent. However, the addition of a small amount of iron to the quartz forms amethyst, a mineral with a violet color.

Transition metals generally produce minerals with strong colors. Minerals containing copper ions are blue or green. Chromium causes red and green colors, depending on other components. For example, red rubies consist mostly of aluminum oxide, but their color comes from the presence of chromium compounds in the crystal. Small amounts of iron and titanium in sapphires give them a rich blue color. In other minerals, iron imparts a reddish color.

 Language Arts Connection Research minerals that are found in your area. Consider the following when conducting your research:

- What features about different minerals stand out to you?
- How are the features related to the chemical composition of the mineral?
- How have people manipulated mineral structure for their own needs?

Present your information as a slide show, photo gallery, or live presentation. Prepare a list of sources used in your research.

FIGURE 18: The color of a mineral is often determined by metal ions in the crystal.

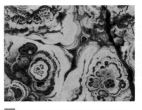

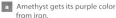 Amethyst gets its purple color from iron.

Copper causes the green bands in malachite.

The transition metal vanadium makes vanadinite red.

 MORE PRACTICE WITH FORMULAS | TYPES OF BONDING IN SOLIDS | TEACHING TYPES OF BONDING | Go online to choose one of these other paths.

Collaborate

You may choose to assign this activity or direct students to the Interactive Online Student Edition, where they can choose from all available paths. These activities can be assigned individually, to pairs, or to small groups.

Differentiate Instruction

MTSS/RTI Help students identify minerals in your area by having them visit a variety of websites. Compile links to such sites as state or local governmental natural resources divisions or environmental protection departments. Provide mineral samples for students to observe, if possible. Then, engage students in a discussion in which they describe the minerals and their properties. Ask them to take notes and to be respectful as others speak. Have pairs work together and, referring to their notes, list where the minerals they discussed might be used in homes, industries, or communities. Call on volunteers to share their lists. Encourage students to build on volunteers' lists with items from their own lists.

 Language Arts Connection
SL.11-12.5 Make strategic use of digital media.
Students make a presentation, slide show, or photo gallery about the features, composition, and uses of local minerals

Explore Online ▶

More Practice with Formulas

Students practice writing ionic and covalent formulas.

Types of Bonding in Solids

Students analyze the properties of solids to determine the type of bonding present in each.

Teaching Types of Bonding

Students develop a lesson plan that relates physical properties to types of bonding.

Lesson 1 Investigating Chemical Compounds   165

EVALUATE   Lesson Self-Check

Can You Explain the Phenomenon?

Claims, Evidence, and Reasoning

Have students clearly state their claim—their explanation for the phenomenon they have been investigating throughout this lesson. They should present their reasoning for making this claim, along with evidence such as facts, examples, and statistics that support their claim. You may want to have students present their arguments orally, in writing, or as a debate. Refer students to the **English Language Arts Handbook** for more information on evaluating claims and presenting arguments.

Cultivating Student Questions

Assessing Student Growth   Review the list of questions students generated at the beginning of the lesson. Have volunteers select any unanswered questions and suggest how they could be investigated. After approving student plans, have small groups conduct the investigations and report back to the class.

As the year progresses, the number of volunteers for this task will likely increase. The sophistication of the means of investigation also may increase. Both outcomes are measures of positive growth that are essential to the scientific mindset and demonstrate that students are beginning to understand that the correct answer is much less important than the means used to investigate the question. You will find that students are more engaged and more willing to take the risk of being "wrong," which indicates positive growth in scientific thinking.

 Evidence Notebook

1 **Sample answer:** Na has one valence electron, and Cl has seven valence electrons. Because atoms that do not have full outer shells have high potential energy and tend to be unstable and reactive, both Na and Cl are highly reactive. When they are combined, Na transfers an electron to Cl to form NaCl, in which both atoms have more stable outer shell configurations. Because of the high electronegativity difference between Na and Cl, NaCl is an ionic compound.

EVALUATE

Lesson Self-Check

CAN YOU EXPLAIN THE PHENOMENON?

FIGURE 19: The reaction between sodium metal and chlorine gas produces sodium chloride.

a Sodium reacting in a beaker of chlorine gas   **b** Samples of sodium chloride, sodium metal, and chlorine gas

Chlorine is a versatile element. It is used as a disinfectant and to make many household products, and it has even been developed as a chemical weapon. Sodium metal is used as a coolant in nuclear reactors, but sodium salts are used more commonly than the metal itself. Sodium salts are used in a variety of applications, including deicing roads and softening water. One of the most common sodium salts is sodium chloride, also known as table salt. Unlike its individual components, sodium chloride is extremely stable and does not readily react with other substances.

1 **Evidence Notebook**   Refer to your notes in your Evidence Notebook to explain why sodium metal and chlorine gas are dangerous and reactive on their own but combine to form the stable compound sodium chloride. Your explanation should include a discussion of the electrical forces within and between atoms in each substance. Using this information, address the following:

Claim   Make a claim about why the compound sodium chloride has properties that are so different from the properties of sodium and chlorine.

Evidence   What evidence supports your claim? For example, what differences in chemical structure could explain the differences in reactivity among the three substances?

Reasoning   Explain how the evidence you gave supports your claim about why sodium chloride is different from sodium metal and chlorine gas.

 Formal Assessment   Go online for student self-checks and other assessments.

Name _____ Date _____

CHECKPOINTS

Check Your Understanding

1. Which of the following best explains why ionic crystals are brittle?

○ **a.** They have low melting points.

○ **b.** They have high melting points.

○ **c.** The strong ionic bonds do not allow flexibility within the structures.

○ **d.** The forces of attraction between positive and negative ions are weak, so they break easily.

2. Categorize each compound as exhibiting ionic bonding or covalent bonding.

a. LiF _____

b. Cl_2 _____

c. NH_3 _____

d. $CaCl_2$ _____

e. NaOH _____

f. FeO _____

g. NO_2 _____

h. H_2O _____

3. A student tests a solid sample of a compound and determines that it does not conduct an electric current. When the compound is dissolved in water, the solution does conduct an electric current. What type of bonding does the compound have?

○ **a.** covalent

○ **b.** ionic

○ **c.** metallic

4. A long, thin sample of a substance bends easily. When the substance is placed in an electric circuit and the switch is closed, an LED light turns on. What type of bonding holds the particles of the substance together?

○ **a.** covalent

○ **b.** ionic

○ **c.** metallic

5. Select the correct terms to complete the statement about bonding.

A nitrogen molecule, N_2, has less | more potential energy than two separate nitrogen atoms, so the molecule is less | more stable. Each nitrogen atom has five valence electrons, so a nitrogen atom needs one | two | three electron(s) to reach maximum stability. Therefore, the diatomic nitrogen molecule has three | six electrons that are shared between the atoms, forming a triple covalent bond.

6. Use the crisscross method and the periodic table to determine the values of x and y in the formula for aluminum sulfide, Al_xS_y.

$x =$ _____

$y =$ _____

7. Which statements correctly describe the compound potassium bromide? Select all correct answers.

□ **a.** The compound is considered a salt.

□ **b.** It contains potassium and bromide ions in a one-to-one ratio.

□ **c.** Potassium bromide likely has a higher melting point than does candle wax.

□ **d.** The electronegativities of the two component atoms are very similar.

8. The electronegativities of carbon and sulfur are almost the same. Both elements form covalently bonded compounds with oxygen. Why are the molecular shapes of carbon dioxide, CO_2, and sulfur dioxide, SO_2, different?

○ **a.** Carbon has a smaller atomic radius than sulfur.

○ **b.** A molecule of SO_2 has a lone pair of electrons, but CO_2 does not.

○ **c.** A molecule of CO_2 has one single and one double bond, but SO_2 does not.

○ **d.** A molecule that contains carbon cannot have a linear shape.

Answers

1. c

2. a. ionic, b. covalent, c. covalent, d. ionic, e. ionic, f. ionic, g. covalent, h. covalent

3. b

4. c

5. less, more, three, six

6. 2, 3

7. a, b, c

8. b

Answers

9. Students should recognize from the periodic table that aluminum and chlorine have a higher difference in electronegativity (1.5) than phosphorus and chlorine (0.9). Aluminum trichloride is a polar covalent compound, and phosphorus trichloride is a covalent compound. Because melting point is related to how strong the attractive forces are between atoms in a compound, aluminum trichloride probably has a higher melting point.

10. The electron-dot structure has oxygen in the center, with one hydrogen on either side of the O. Oxygen has six valence electrons, and hydrogen has one, so one electron from the oxygen atom is shared with each hydrogen (forming two single bonds between O and H), and leaving two lone pairs of electrons on the O. Based on the electronegativity difference between hydrogen and oxygen, the bonds are polar covalent. The two lone pairs of electrons from the oxygen are opposite each other (on the top and bottom of the O) in the electron-dot structure.

11. Potassium is in Group 1 and has one valence electron, which it tends to lose when bonding with another element. Argon is in Group 18 and has eight valence electrons. This is a full outer shell, and argon will not accept an electron from potassium. Potassium and chlorine would react to form potassium chloride, KCl. K has an electronegativity much lower than that of Cl, so KCl is an ionic compound. Potassium is in group 1 of the periodic table, so it loses an electron to become K+, and chlorine gains an electron to become Cl−. That means that K and Cl combine in a one-to-one ratio to give KCl.

Make Your Own Study Guide

Have students create a study guide that helps them organize and visualize the important information from this lesson. Their study guide should focus on the main ideas from this lesson and tie multiple ideas together. Students can make an outline, a concept map, a graphic organizer, or another representation.

EVALUATE

CHECKPOINTS (continued)

9. Which compound likely has a higher melting point—aluminum trichloride, AlCl₃, or phosphorus trichloride, PCl₃? Use the periodic table to support your claim, and explain your reasoning.

_____

_____

_____

_____

10. Water, H₂O, consists of a central oxygen atom bound to two hydrogen atoms. Draw an electron-dot structure of water. Below, explain how you determined the number of bonds and unpaired electrons, the types of bonds, and, if applicable, where the unpaired electrons are located.

_____

_____

_____

11. Potassium metal is mixed with argon gas in one flask and with chlorine gas in another flask. Use the periodic table to explain what happens in each flask. If you predict that a reaction will occur, describe the type of compound that forms.

_____

_____

_____

_____

_____

MAKE YOUR OWN STUDY GUIDE

 In your Evidence Notebook, design a study guide that supports the main ideas from this lesson:

Patterns in the periodic table can be used to predict the types of bonds that will form between atoms.

The properties of substances are related to the atomic structures of the substances.

Patterns in valence electrons can be used to predict the structure of substances.

Remember to include the following information in your study guide:
- Use examples that model main ideas.
- Record explanations for the phenomena you investigated.
- Use evidence to support your explanations. Your support can include drawings, data, graphs, laboratory conclusions, and other evidence recorded throughout the lesson.

Consider how patterns of atomic structure, as shown in the periodic table, can provide evidence for explanations of properties of chemical compounds at the bulk scale.

Analyzing the Properties of Compounds and Solutions

Building to the Performance Expectations

The learning experiences in this lesson prepare students for mastery of

HS-PS1-3 Plan and conduct an investigation to gather evidence to compare the structure of substances at the bulk scale to infer the strength of electrical forces between particles.

 Trace Tool to the NGSS

Go online to view the complete coverage of standards across lessons, units, and grade levels.

 SEP Science & Engineering Practices

Planning and Carrying Out Investigations
Plan and conduct an investigation individually and collaboratively to produce data to serve as the basis for evidence, and in the design: decide on types, how much, and accuracy of data needed to produce reliable measurements and consider limitations on the precision of the data (e.g., number of trials, cost, risk, time), and refine the design accordingly.

▶ **VIDEO** Planning and Carrying Out Investigations

Constructing Explanations and Designing Solutions
Apply scientific ideas, principles, and/or evidence to provide an explanation of phenomena.

▶ **VIDEO** Constructing Scientific Explanations

 **DCI** Disciplinary Core Ideas

PS1.A Structure and Properties of Matter
The structure and interactions of matter at the bulk scale are determined by electrical forces within and between atoms. (HS-PS1-3)

▶ **VIDEO** Equilibrium

PS2.B Types of Interactions
Attraction and repulsion between electric charges at the atomic scale explain the structure, properties, and transformations of matter, as well as the contact forces between material objects. (HS-PS2-6) (secondary to HS-PS1-1) (secondary to HS-PS1-3)

 **CCC** Crosscutting Concepts

Patterns
Different patterns may be observed at each of the scales at which a system is studied and can provide evidence for causality in explanations of phenomena.

Scientific Knowledge Assumes an Order and Consistency in Natural Systems
Science assumes the universe is a vast single system in which basic laws are consistent.

MATH STANDARDS

MP.2 Reason abstractly and quantitatively.

MP.4 Model with mathematics.

HSN-Q.A.3 Choose a level of accuracy appropriate to limitations on measurement when reporting quantities.

ELA STANDARDS

WHST.9-12.7 Conduct short as well as more sustained research projects to answer a question (including a self-generated question) or solve a problem; narrow or broaden the inquiry when appropriate; synthesize multiple sources on the subject, demonstrating understanding of the subject under investigation.

Supporting All Students, All Standards

Integrating the Three Dimensions

In this lesson, students develop and use models based on evidence (**SEP Developing and Using Models**) to show that the structure and interactions of matter at the bulk scale are determined by electric forces within and between atoms (**DCI PS1.A, CCC Structure and Function**). Students use the knowledge of forces of attraction and repulsion between electric charges at the atomic scale (**DCI PS2.B**) to conduct investigations and produce data that can serve as the basis for evidence (**SEP Planning and Carrying Out Investigations**). These investigations can provide evidence for causality in explanations of phenomena (**CCC Patterns**).

Preassessment

Have students complete the unit pretest or see the Assessment Guide.

Build on Prior Knowledge

Have students consider what they know about the composition of the atom in terms of the charges and locations of subatomic particles within the atom. Remind students that negatively charged electrons are attracted to the positively charged nucleus and that electrons repel other electrons. Revisit the concept of molecular geometry and remind students that molecules can have different shapes. The shape of a molecule depends on the number and type of atoms present in the molecule.

You may want to review the following concepts:
- An atom is the smallest unit of an element, made up of protons, neutrons and electrons.
- Protons are positively charged, neutrons are neutral, and electrons are negatively charged.
- A chemical bond forms when valence electrons are shared or transferred between atoms.
- An ionic compound is made up of positive and negative ions held together by strong attractive forces.
- A molecule is made up of one or more atoms held together by covalent bonds.

Professional Development

Go online to view **Professional Development videos** with strategies to integrate CCCs and SEPs, including the ones used in this lesson.

Content Background

Any two charged objects at a distance from each other will experience a force that is governed by Coulomb's law. The force will be attractive if the two charges are opposite (one positive and one negative) and repulsive if the two charges are the same (positive and positive or negative and negative). Because electrons are negatively charged and protons are positively charged, an electron in one atom, ion, or molecule (particle) will be attracted to a proton in another particle. These coulombic forces of attraction determine how strongly the atoms of a material are held together and are reflected in the properties of the material.

Materials with strong attractive forces between their particles require that a lot of energy be added to separate the particles. Intermolecular forces therefore determine properties of a material such as melting and boiling point.

When particles of different substances are mixed together, the intermolecular forces of electrical attraction between the particles determines the extent to which they can mix. Substances with separated positive and negative charges, such as salt and water, can mix completely to form a solution because positive and negative charges in particles of the different substances attract each other.

Differentiate Instruction

KEY WORDS
- intermolecular forces
- polarity
- hydrogen bond
- solution
- solvent
- solute
- solubility
- concentration
- electrolyte
- colligative property

ELL SUPPORT

Before students encounter each new key term in their reading, pause to pronounce and explain each one. Help students connect the term to words and concepts they have already learned and to cognates in their home language, as appropriate.

ENGAGE: Investigative Phenomenon

3.2

Analyzing the Properties of Compounds and Solutions

Undersea organisms depend on substances that are dissolved in ocean water.

CAN YOU EXPLAIN THE PHENOMENON?

There is more than just salt (sodium chloride) in the ocean. There are many different salts, minerals, and gas molecules dissolved in ocean water that undersea organisms of all kinds require for life. You know that oxygen is a gas, but fish do not get oxygen from bubbles of oxygen in the water. Rather, individual oxygen molecules are mixed together with, and dissolved in, the water molecules. Water molecules have unique properties that allow it to dissolve many different substances. In particular, attractive forces between water molecules, and also between water molecules and dissolved substances, allow them all to mix freely with one another.

1 EXPLAIN How is water important in the Earth system?

_____

_____

_____

_____

_____

2 📓 **Evidence Notebook** As you explore the lesson, gather evidence to explain why water has unique properties and provide examples of how these properties are important in the Earth system.

Lesson 2 Analyzing the Properties of Compounds and Solutions   **169**

Build on Prior Lessons

In Lesson 1, students learned that the properties of compounds are related to atomic structure. Lesson 2 builds on this concept as students explore how intermolecular forces influence properties.

Lesson Objective

Students investigate how intermolecular forces influence the properties of compounds, mixtures, and solutions.

Cultivating Student Questions

Have students look at the photo of undersea life. Prompt them to ask all questions that come to mind about the substances present in the photo and the properties of these substances. Record the questions on chart paper, and then sort the questions based on their focus. With students, narrow the questions down to the ones that directly relate to the learning objective. Have students reflect on this list throughout the lesson and check off questions as they are answered.

Can You Explain the Phenomenon?

The Investigative Phenomenon is the focus of the lesson. Students are asked to record their initial thoughts about water's importance to the Earth system. Encourage them to relate this to water's properties. Students will collect evidence related to this phenomenon throughout the lesson and revisit the question at the end of the lesson to use what they have learned to explain how properties are influenced by intermolecular forces.

1 Accept all answers. Students may describe how water's ability to dissolve substances is related to the survival of life on Earth.

📓 **Evidence Notebook**
2 The topic of intermolecular forces and the unique properties of water will be revisited throughout this lesson.

EXPLORATION 1 Exploring Intermolecular Forces in Liquids

3D Learning Objective

Students plan and carry out an investigation to collect evidence showing patterns of physical properties due to intermolecular forces. They learn that the structure and interactions of matter are determined by electrical forces.

Everyday phenomena discussed throughout the Explorations of the lesson can often be used to connect the science content to students' personal experiences.

Hands-On Lab 👥 Small Groups ⏱ 90 minutes

Exploring Intermolecular Forces in Liquids

SEP **Planning and Carrying Out Investigations**

Students design a procedure that can be used to analyze intermolecular forces in liquids found in **everyday phenomena.** They collect evaporation rate and surface tension data.

Safety Information This lab is best completed using a fume hood. Students can place a piece of wax paper in the fume hood, add a drop of each substance, and then time the rate of evaporation.

Materials Alert Do not use the household/drugstore versions of these chemicals—for example, nail-polish remover, rubbing alcohol—as they are commonly diluted with water, which will affect the lab results.

1 Sample answer: I predict that water will have the strongest intermolecular forces, followed by glycerol, isopropyl alcohol, and then acetone with the weakest. This is because water is the most polar compound and acetone the least polar.

Hands-On Lab

Exploring Intermolecular Forces in Liquids

Patterns in how liquids behave can be explained in terms of patterns in the intermolecular forces between their molecules. Intermolecular forces are the forces of attraction between molecules. When a substance has strong intermolecular forces, that substance requires more energy than a substance with weaker intermolecular forces requires to go from the solid state to the liquid state, or from the liquid state to the gas state. Intermolecular forces also affect surface tension, which is a force that tends to pull adjacent parts of a liquid's surface together.

In this lab, you will design a procedure to analyze intermolecular forces in four common household chemicals—water, acetone, isopropyl alcohol, and glycerol. Figure 1 shows the structures of these substances. You will collect data on the evaporation rates and surface tensions of these compounds.

RESEARCH QUESTION How do intermolecular forces determine the uses of commonly-used molecular compounds?

FIGURE 1: The molecular structures of water, acetone, isopropyl alcohol, and glycerol

Water	Acetone	Isopropyl Alcohol	Glycerol

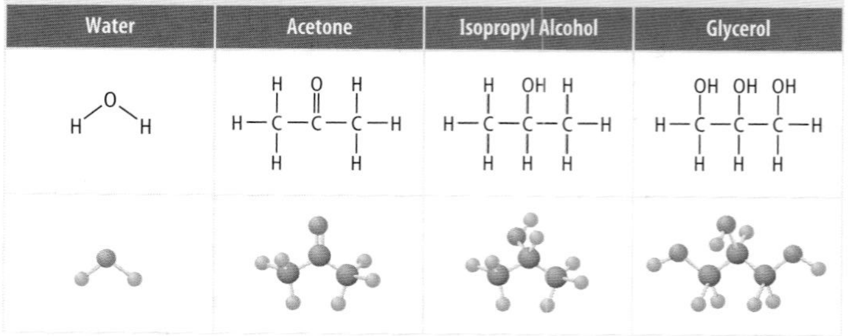

1 MAKE A CLAIM

Which substance do you think will have the strongest intermolecular forces, and which the weakest? Explain your reasoning.

_____

_____

MATERIALS

- indirectly vented chemical splash goggles, nonlatex apron, and nitrile gloves
- acetone in dropper bottle
- flasks with stoppers (4), each containing water, acetone, isopropyl alcohol, or glycerol
- glycerol in dropper bottle
- isopropyl alcohol in dropper bottle
- marker
- stopwatch or clock with second hand
- water in dropper bottle
- wax paper (1 sheet)

 Student Lab Worksheet and complete Teacher Support are available online.

SAFETY INFORMATION

- Wear indirectly vented chemical splash goggles, a nonlatex apron, and nitrile gloves during the setup, hands-on, and takedown segments of the activity.
- All operations in which noxious or poisonous gases or flammable vapors are used or produced must be carried out in the fume hood.
- Never pour chemicals, either used or unused, back into their original container. Dispose of chemicals according to your teacher's instructions.
- Use caution when working with glassware, which can shatter and cut skin.
- Wash your hands with soap and water immediately after completing this activity.

PLAN THE INVESTIGATION

1. In your Evidence Notebook, develop a procedure and safety plan to test the surface tension and the rate of evaporation of water, acetone, isopropyl alcohol, and glycerol.
2. Draw a data table in your Evidence Notebook for recording your observations and data. When designing your data table, consider what types of data would be appropriate for analyzing surface tension and rate of evaporation.
3. Have your teacher approve your plans before you begin your work. If you need additional materials to complete your procedure, discuss these with your teacher.
4. Clean up your lab area and dispose of your lab materials as instructed by your teacher.

indirectly vented
chemical splash
goggles

2 DRAW CONCLUSIONS

Write a conclusion that addresses each of the points below.

Claim Based on the patterns you observed in the surface tension and evaporation rate of the compounds, how would you rank the strength of the intermolecular forces in the compounds from strongest to weakest?

Evidence Give specific examples from your data to support your claim.

Reasoning Explain how the evidence you gave supports your claim. Describe, in detail, the connections between the evidence you cited and the argument you are making.

_____
_____
_____
_____
_____
_____
_____
_____
_____

3 **Evidence Notebook** What did you discover from this investigation about the properties of water that make it different from the other substances?

Differentiate Instruction

ELL Support Have students look at the key term *intermolecular forces*. Explain that the prefix *inter-* means "between, among, together, in the midst of." Ask how this helps them understand the term's meaning.

CCC Patterns

Students may observe that glycerol is a larger molecule than water, so the increased number of electrons results in greater intermolecular forces. Isopropyl alcohol and acetone are polar due to their containing strongly electronegative oxygen atoms. Both molecules contain a nonpolar region that somewhat weakens the intermolecular force.

2 **Sample answer:** Claim—Glycerol has the strongest intermolecular forces, followed by water, isopropyl alcohol, and acetone. Evidence—The evaporation rate and surface tension of a liquid are affected by intermolecular forces, which are forces of attraction between molecules. Glycerol has the slowest evaporation rate and highest surface tension. Water has the next slowest rate and noticeable surface tension. Isopropyl alcohol evaporated quickly and had minimal surface tension. Acetone evaporated fastest and had very little surface tension. Reasoning—Stronger intermolecular forces result in more energy being required for evaporation. They also pull on the molecules at the surface of a liquid more, causing greater surface tension.

Evidence Notebook

3 Students should discover that the surface tension of water is unusually high, and the evaporation rate is unusually low. These properties are due to strong forces between water molecules. However, glycerol has the strongest intermolecular forces due to the three H–O bonds, which allow for the formation of many hydrogen bonds between individual glycerol molecules.

FORMATIVE ASSESSMENT

One-Sentence Summary Ask students to answer the following question in a single sentence: *What two factors determine the strength of most intermolecular forces?*

Lesson 2 Analyzing the Properties of Compounds and Solutions   171

EXPLORATION 2 Explaining Intermolecular Forces

3D Learning Objective

Students explore scenarios related to charge and electric force to **construct explanations** for how attractive and repulsive forces are related to the **structure and properties of matter.** Students apply **patterns** in types of intermolecular forces to different contexts to make predictions about the properties of materials.

 CCC Patterns

Explain that different materials have different affinities for electrons, and then ask students how this idea might apply to the **everyday phenomenon** of static cling. Ask students what should happen as one material is rubbed over another material with a different affinity for electrons. (Electrons will be transferred to the material with a higher affinity for electrons.) Elicit from students the idea that opposite charges attract, so in the balloon scenario, negative charge on the balloon is attracted to positive charge on the hair. This consistent pattern of opposite charges attracting each other is found everywhere in nature and applies in the same way to forces within and between molecules.

 Collaborate

Think-Pair-Share Have student pairs work together to write one statement explaining why an increase in charge increases electric force and an increase in distance decreases electric force. Explain that the formulas for gravitational and electric forces are similar. Have pairs predict similarities and differences between the two formulas.

① **Sample answer:** While electrically neutral overall, water molecules have a charge imbalance with a slightly positive end that is attracted toward the negatively charged balloon. The water molecules turn their positive side toward the charged balloon, and the water stream is bent accordingly.

② The charges are in the numerator of the equation; the distance is in the denominator and is squared. Because the distance is doubled, the magnitude of the force is decreased by a factor of four.

Explaining Intermolecular Forces

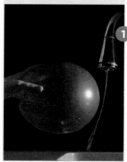
FIGURE 2: Static charges on a balloon affect water molecules.

Rubbing a balloon with a cloth generates "static" that attracts certain substances, such as the stream of water shown in Figure 2. Similarly, you may have noticed that when clothes are first taken out of a dryer, they stick to each other, a phenomenon known as "static cling."

① **INFER** What do you think is happening at the atomic scale that causes the water in Figure 2 to bend toward the balloon?

Forces between Particles

Most materials have no overall charge because they have equal numbers of protons and electrons. When you rub a balloon with a cloth, however, electrons are transferred from the cloth to the balloon. This transfer makes some atoms in the cloth positively charged and some atoms in the balloon negatively charged. Because opposite charges attract, positively charged particles will stick to the negatively charged balloon. Phenomena related to static electricity are caused by forces between electric charges that attract or repel each other, as seen in Figure 3. Repulsions and attractions due to electric charge are known as electric forces. Another name for electric force is the Coulomb force.

FIGURE 3: Charged particles may attract or repel each other.

opposite charges attract

like charges repel

The attractive forces that exist between the particles of a substance affect the physical and chemical properties of that substance. Ionic compounds have strong attractive forces that hold ions tightly together. Thus, these compounds typically have relatively high melting points.

Math Connection

Calculating Force

Coulomb's law describes how to calculate electric force. This law states that the magnitude of the electric force ($F_{electric}$) between two point charges (q_1 and q_2) is directly related to the product of the charges and inversely related to the square of the distance (d) between them. The Coulomb constant (k_C) is a constant used in the calculation of electric force. The equation for Coulomb's law is:

$$F_{electric} = k_C \frac{q_1 q_2}{d^2}$$

② **Collaborate** As charge increases, electric force increases. However, if the distance between two charges doubles, electric force decreases by a factor of four. With a partner, discuss how the equation for this law demonstrates these relationships between charge, distance, and force.

Uneven Molecular Charges

Why do different molecular compounds exhibit different intermolecular forces? The answer has to do with the type of atoms in a molecule and how they are arranged in the 3-dimensional space of the molecule relative to each other. Recall that electronegativity is the tendency of an atom to pull electrons toward itself. As Figure 4 shows, a *nonpolar covalent bond* forms when the bonding electrons are evenly shared between two atoms. On the other hand, if one of the atoms has a higher electronegativity than the other atom, the more electronegative atom attracts the bonding electrons more strongly than does the other atom. This results in the formation of a *polar covalent bond*. This uneven distribution of charges in a molecule is known as polarity.

The ball-and-stick model shown in Figure 5 represents the polar molecule iodine monochloride, ICl. The chlorine end of the molecule has a partial negative charge, and the iodine end has a partial positive charge. These two ends are called poles, and a molecule with two poles is said to have a *dipole*. Its dipole is represented by an arrow with a head that points toward the negative pole and a crossed tail near the positive pole. Partial charges are represented by the lowercase Greek letter delta, δ. A partial positive charge is shown as $\delta+$, and a partial negative charge is shown as $\delta-$.

FIGURE 4: In a nonpolar covalent bond, the electron cloud is evenly dispersed. In a polar covalent bond, it is not.

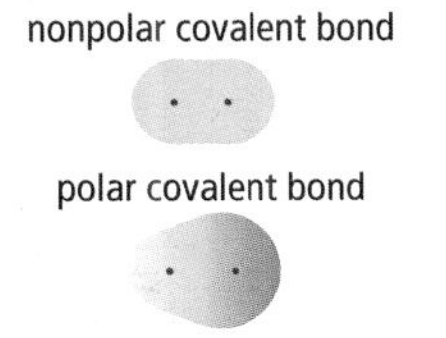

nonpolar covalent bond

polar covalent bond

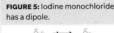

FIGURE 5: Iodine monochloride has a dipole.

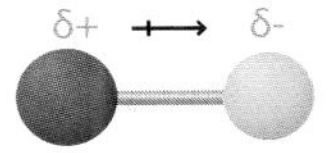

 $\delta+$ ⟶ $\delta-$

3 **EXPLAIN** Select the correct terms to complete the statement.

Water is a polar molecule. The oxygen atom is more | less electronegative than the hydrogen atom, so the oxygen atom has a partial negative | positive charge, and each hydrogen atom has a partial negative | positive charge. The oxygen atom of a water molecule is attracted to a hydrogen | an oxygen atom of another water molecule.

The polarity of diatomic molecules such as ICl is determined by just one bond. For molecules that contain more than two atoms, polarity is determined by both the polarity of the individual bonds and the three-dimensional arrangement of the molecule. The ball-and-stick models in Figure 6 show how the three-dimensional arrangement of bonds in a molecule affects the overall polarity of the molecule.

FIGURE 6: The three-dimensional arrangement of a molecule affects the overall polarity of the molecule.

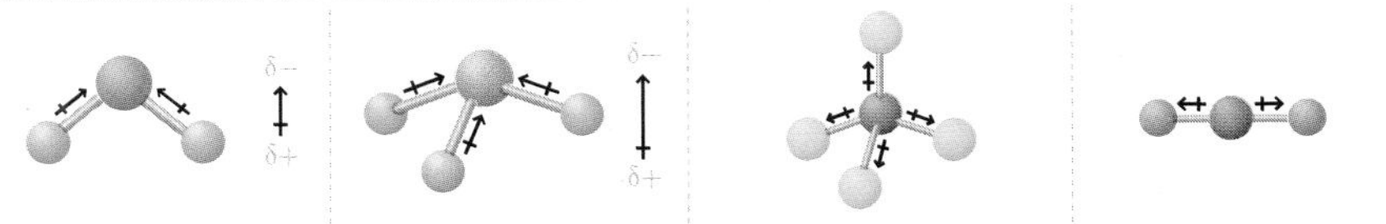

a Water, H₂O   **b** Ammonia, NH₃   **c** Carbon tetrachloride, CCl₄   **d** Carbon dioxide, CO₂

Since H_2O and NH_3 have a bent shape, the bond polarities in each molecule combine to give one end of the molecule a partial positive charge and the other end a partial negative charge. Thus, these molecules are polar. Carbon dioxide, by contrast, is nonpolar, even though it has two polar bonds. The carbon dioxide molecule is linear, so polarities of the two bonds cancel each other out, and there is no net dipole in the molecule.

4 **Evidence Notebook** How can understanding the polarity of water help you design detergents in your unit project?

Lesson 2 Analyzing the Properties of Compounds and Solutions **173**

DCI **PS1.A Structure and Properties of Matter**

Ask students to describe differences between the molecules in **Figure 6**. Have students calculate the differences in the electronegativities of the two atoms in each bond. Equate the bond dipoles in a molecule to forces—like a tug of war among atoms as they unevenly pull on electrons in the bonds. Then have students examine the shape of each molecule to determine whether each is symmetrical or asymmetrical. Use physical models to help students better visualize the three-dimensional shapes of the molecules. Explain that the shape of the molecule, the polarity of the bonds, and the presence of lone pairs are all factors that must be considered when determining the net molecular dipole of a molecule. For example, water has two lone pairs of electrons on the oxygen atom. This, combined with the fact that the bond polarities in a water molecule combine (because the molecule is bent), results in a partial negative charge on the oxygen atom.

SEP **Developing and Using Models**

Develop a physical model of a water molecule using three students and two bungee cords. Have one student act as the oxygen atom and the other two act as the hydrogen atoms. The angular shape of the molecule followed by the pull in the bungee cords will help students understand the nature of the net molecular dipole.

3 more, negative, positive, a hydrogen

Evidence Notebook
4 **Sample answer:** Oil and grease are made up of nonpolar molecules and will not mix with, or dissolve in, polar water molecules unless a long molecule such as detergent, which has both a polar end and a nonpolar end, is present.

Differentiate Instruction

Extension Challenge student pairs to determine why liquid water and its solid form, ice, make one of the few liquid-solid pairs in which the solid floats in its liquid. Guide students to make a model to show how the density of water changes as its temperature and its state of matter change. Have students write a brief summary of their findings.

DCI PS2.B Types of Interactions

Students should recognize that while the interaction between two atoms in a bond must be considered, it must also be understood that the interactions extend to all other atoms, molecules, and ions that are within a very small distance from an atom in a bond. Remind students that these are forces-at-a-distance values that can be found using Coulomb's law.

Nature of Science

Chemists often use ball-and-stick models such as those shown on this page. Using this type of model allows a chemist to observe the three-dimensional position of the atoms in a substance to better determine the bonds that form between atoms. Understanding the type of bonds that form also helps a chemist determine the kind of intermolecular forces that form between particles. Give students foam balls and either toothpicks or drinking straws. Ask them to make a ball-and-stick model of a compound of their choice. Students should list the compound's features that can be determined from their model.

1 polar, nonpolar, higher, positive and negative

2 A dipole-induced dipole interaction is weaker than a dipole-dipole interaction because the electrons in the nonpolar atom are shifted to one side of the molecule only temporarily, so a dipole-induced attraction between molecules can change.

Dipole-Dipole Forces

In the molecule iodine monochloride, the highly electronegative chlorine atom has a partial negative charge, and the iodine atom has a partial positive charge. As Figure 7 shows, the partially negative and partially positive ends of neighboring iodine monochloride molecules attract each other.

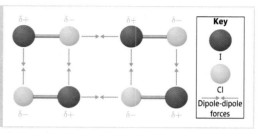

FIGURE 7: The arrows show the dipole-dipole forces between the positive and negative ends of neighboring ICl molecules.

When a liquid is heated, energy is added to the system. The kinetic energy of the liquid's molecules increase, and they move faster. As the temperature approaches the boiling point, the molecules move fast enough to overcome the attractive forces between molecules. They pull away from each other and enter the gaseous state. The stronger the forces are between molecules, the higher the boiling point will be. Boiling point is a good measure of the attractive forces between molecules of a liquid.

1 **APPLY** Select the correct terms to complete the statement.

ICl is a polar | nonpolar molecule, whereas Br_2 is polar | nonpolar. The boiling point of ICl is likely to be higher | lower than the boiling point of Br_2. This is due to dipole-dipole intermolecular interactions between two positive | two negative | positive and negative portions of polar molecules.

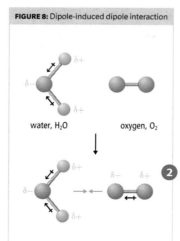

FIGURE 8: Dipole-induced dipole interaction

water, H_2O oxygen, O_2

A polar molecule also can induce the formation of a dipole in a nonpolar molecule by temporarily attracting the electrons in the nonpolar molecule. This results in a short-term intermolecular force. For example, the positive pole of a polar water molecule causes a temporary change in the electron distribution of an adjacent nonpolar oxygen molecule. The temporary negative pole induced in the side of the oxygen molecule closest to the water molecule is attracted to the positive pole of the water molecule. This shift of electrons in the oxygen molecule then causes an induced positive pole on the opposite side of the oxygen molecule, as shown in Figure 8. This induced dipole attraction allows oxygen to be dissolved in water, which is important for sustaining life in aquatic environments.

2 **EXPLAIN** Do you think a dipole-induced dipole interaction is stronger or weaker than a dipole-dipole interaction? Explain your answer.

_____

_____

_____

Hydrogen Bonding

Some dipole-dipole interactions can be especially strong. For example, in some hydrogen-containing compounds such as hydrogen fluoride, HF; water, H_2O; and ammonia, NH_3; a special kind of dipole-dipole interaction exists.

Molecules that contain a hydrogen atom bonded to the highly electronegative atoms fluorine, oxygen, or nitrogen are strongly polar. Particularly strong dipole-dipole intermolecular forces, called hydrogen bonds, exist between molecules of these compounds. The highly electronegative atom attracts the electrons in the bond away from the hydrogen atom and toward itself. Consequently, the highly electronegative atom has a partial negative charge and the hydrogen atom has a partial positive charge. The partial positive charge on one molecule is attracted to a partial negative charge on a nearby molecule.

3 **MODEL** Label the partial negative and partial positive charges on the water molecules. Red spheres indicate oxygen atoms, blue spheres hydrogen atoms. Then, draw dotted lines to represent hydrogen bonds.

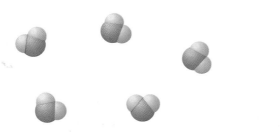

Surface Tension

The attraction between molecules of the same substance is known as cohesion. Cohesion between neighboring water molecules is especially noticeable at the surface of water. These water molecules form many hydrogen bonds with the water molecules beneath them and beside them, but not with the molecules in the air above them. This causes the surface water molecules to be drawn together, forming a spherical shape. This cohesion at the surface of a liquid is known as surface tension. Figure 9 shows liquids that have different amounts of surface tension. The stronger the intermolecular forces in a liquid are, the greater its surface tension will be.

FIGURE 9: Droplets of mercury, water, dimethyl sulfoxide, and acetone have different amounts of surface tension.

Surface tension explains how some small insects such as water striders can stand on water's surface even though they have greater density than water. The surface tension of water also lowers its rate of evaporation. In general, a substance with strong intermolecular forces will have high surface tension and require more energy to disrupt those interactions. Therefore, substances with high surface tension also have a high boiling point.

4 **Collaborate** With a partner, explain how hydrogen bonding at the molecular scale explains surface tension in water.

Collaborate

Discussion Have student pairs discuss how polarity might affect the properties of a substance, such as boiling point and adhesion.

Preconception Alert

Students may incorrectly assume that any compound with bond dipoles will have a net molecular dipole. Emphasize that when all bond dipoles are considered in a molecule, they can add as vectors to give an overall molecular dipole of zero. Have students think about a tug of war in which two teams pull with equal force in opposite directions. The rope will not move. Likewise, a net molecular dipole combines all bond dipoles. For a molecule with one central atom, a net molecular dipole will exist (assuming bond dipoles exist) only when there are either lone electron pairs around the central atom or if different atoms surround the central atom, creating different strengths of bond dipoles around the central atom.

Differentiate Instruction

MTSS/RTI Students most likely have observed the **everyday phenomenon** of water forming a downward meniscus in a container (due to water in the center attracting itself via cohesion and water on the perimeter being attracted via adhesion to the cylinder's glass walls). This creeping up a tube is more dramatic the narrower the diameter of the tube. Less well known is the fact that an upward meniscus will form in any glass or plastic cup when it is filled to the top and either additional drops are added slowly from a short height or paper clips or pennies are added. Challenge students to count the drops of water that will fit on top of a penny without spilling over.

3 Partial negative charges are located by the oxygen atoms in the water molecules. Partial positive charges are located by the hydrogen atoms in those same molecules. Dotted lines should connect each oxygen atom in the molecules to a hydrogen atom in another molecule.

4 The surface of water consists of molecules that are strongly hydrogen bonded to each other and are, therefore, more attracted to each other than they are to objects next to them, causing surface tension.

Lesson 2 Analyzing the Properties of Compounds and Solutions 175

CCC Structure and Function

Elicit from students the idea that chemical processes in living systems are influenced by attractive and repulsive forces.

 Language Arts Connection
WHST.9-12.7 Conduct short as well as more sustained research projects to answer a question.

Students are to research the biological molecule that is responsible for our genetic makeup: the DNA molecule. The hydrogen bonds that hold together the two strands of DNA allow the double helix to "unzip" so that it can be copied or transcribed into RNA. Encourage students to expand their research to include tRNA, mRNA, and rRNA and compare and contrast these molecules with the DNA molecule.

1 greater, less, float

 Evidence Notebook
2 **Sample answer:** Highly polar water molecules have hydrogen bonds between them, which gives water a relatively high boiling point and high surface tension. This keeps its evaporation rate low and allows water to absorb a lot of heat. Hydrogen bonds also cause water molecules to form a less dense structure when water freezes. Therefore, ice floats on liquid water. Because water freezes from the top down, aquatic plants and organisms that depend on them do not freeze.

FORMATIVE ASSESSMENT
Four Corners Have students place themselves into four corners based on their confidence in the material. Corner 1 feels least confident, and Corner 4 feels most confident. ***Ask:*** *What creates a bond dipole, and how can you tell if a bond dipole exists?* Give students time to discuss their answers with other groups, and then pair students from Corner 1 with Corner 3 and Corner 2 with Corner 4 to explain and help each other with content. A bond dipole exists when there is an uneven sharing of electrons in a chemical bond. When the difference in electronegativity between atoms is great enough, electrons are shared unevenly enough for the bond to be polar.

The Low Density of Ice

If you have ever frozen a full container of water you have discovered that, unlike most other substances, water expands when it freezes. Like many of water's unusual properties, this is related to the formation of hydrogen bonds. When water freezes, the molecules lose kinetic energy and slow down, so more hydrogen bonds form between them. The water molecules form a network structure in which each water molecule is held away from nearby molecules at a fixed distance.

FIGURE 10: Water molecules are arranged differently in solid water than in liquid water.

a Icebergs float in liquid water. **b** solid water **c** liquid water

 INFER Complete the statement to explain why icebergs float in liquid water.

The amount of space between molecules in solid water is less | greater than that in liquid water. As a result, the density of solid water is less | greater than that of liquid water. Because substances with lower density float | sink in substances with higher density, ice floats in liquid water. This explains why icebergs float, instead of sink, in liquid water.

Patterns

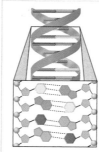

FIGURE 11: Hydrogen bonds in DNA

Living Systems

Hydrogen bonds play an important role in living organisms. For example, DNA molecules are held together by hydrogen bonds. Patterns of DNA at the molecular scale determine the traits of an organism. A DNA molecule looks like a long twisted ladder, with two chains of sugar molecules and phosphate groups making up the sides of the ladder and nitrogen bases sticking into the center like steps of the ladder. DNA is stabilized by millions of pairs of nitrogen bases that are held together by hydrogen bonds. Because individual hydrogen bonds are relatively weak, they can break to allow the chains to separate during DNA replication and protein synthesis.

 Language Arts Connection Research the structure of DNA. Why is it important that hydrogen bonds, not ionic or covalent bonds, hold the two strands of DNA together? Develop a presentation answering this question, citing specific textual evidence.

 2 **Evidence Notebook** How do the intermolecular forces between water molecules explain the unique properties of water, and how do they make water important in the Earth system?

EXPLORATION 3 Describing Solutions

Describing Solutions

If you've ever looked at a bottle of oil and vinegar, you probably noticed that the oil settles in a layer above the vinegar, which is a mixture of acetic acid and water. You can mix the oil and vinegar by shaking the bottle, but they quickly separate into layers again. This is what people mean when they say that "oil and water don't mix." Figure 12 shows what happens when you try to mix oil and water.

There are many substances that do mix easily. For example, both salt and sugar readily dissolve in water. Heating or cooling the water can also have a strong effect on whether a substance will dissolve in water and the speed at which it dissolves.

FIGURE 12: Cooking oil being poured into water

3 👥 **Collaborate** Discuss with a partner why some compounds dissolve in water while others do not. What properties of water do you think contribute to its ability to dissolve some compounds?

Vinegar, salt water, and sugar water are examples of solutions. A **solution** is a homogeneous mixture, which means that two or more substances are uniformly dispersed at the molecular level. Solutions contain both a solvent and a solute. The **solvent** is the substance in which the **solute** dissolves. The solvent usually makes up the greatest amount of the solution. Solute particles may be atoms, molecules, or ions. They are so small that they maintain their even distribution without settling. One substance is **soluble** in another if it can dissolve in that substance.

A solution that contains the maximum amount of dissolved solute is *saturated*. If you increase the amount of solvent in a saturated solution, the solution becomes *unsaturated* and you can dissolve more solute. For any given solution, there is a maximum ratio of solute to solvent that the solution can contain at a given temperature.

The Dissolving Process

Table salt, NaCl, is made of tiny, cubic-shaped crystals. When stirred into water, however, salt does not keep this crystal shape. The crystals quickly begin to break apart into separate sodium and chloride ions. When a substance dissolves and becomes a solute, it breaks into smaller and smaller pieces until it is thoroughly mixed with the solvent at the particle level.

4 **PREDICT** Why do you think stirring, shaking, or heating a mixture help a solute dissolve more quickly?

_____

_____

_____

_____

© Houghton Mifflin Harcourt Publishing Company • Image Credits: ©Jose A. Bernat Bacete/Moment Open/Getty Images

3D Learning Objective

Students **apply scientific ideas, principles, and evidence to explain** the behavior of solutions. They relate **patterns** in solubility to **electrical forces within and between atoms.**

SEP **Developing and Using Models**

Have students make a model of the solution process and use it to teach another student the difference between a solvent, a solute, and the rate of dissolution. Students should take turns using their models to teach each other. They should discuss differences in their models and identify any portions of their model that were unclear. Students should give their partner suggestions on how to improve their model.

Exploring Visuals

Students should note that the particle models in this lesson represent the homogeneous nature of solutions. Use the models to establish the difference between solutions that can conduct electricity and those that cannot conduct electricity.

DCI **PS1.A Structure and Properties of Matter**

Obtain three pieces of iron(II) chloride, $FeCl_2$, of equal mass and shape and three different beakers containing water. Add one piece of $FeCl_2$ to a beaker, and stir the contents. Pulverize another piece of $FeCl_2$, and let it sit in the second beaker. Add the last piece to the third beaker, and allow it to stand still. As an introduction to the principles of this Exploration, ask students to write questions they may have about how the particles of matter behave differently in each beaker.

3 Students may suggest that compounds with electric charges, such as ionic compounds and molecules that form hydrogen bonds, dissolve in water because water is polar.

4 **Sample answer:** Stirring, shaking, or heating a mixture causes the particles to move around. Particles that may be clumped together can be separated, exposing a greater number of the particles to the solvent in a shorter amount of time, so the solute dissolves faster.

Environmental Science Connection

Have student groups research why some natural sources of water are unfit for drinking. Have them present a case study to the class, tying their information to the concepts of solutes, solvents, and the solution process. Students should use these concepts to outline the steps that have been taken to remedy the effects and to propose additional steps that might be taken.

Differentiate Instruction

ELL Support Students may have difficulty distinguishing among the words *solute, solvent*, and *solution* because all three begin with the same syllable. Suggest that students sketch a diagram in their notebooks to which they can refer as needed. Their diagrams could show a container of liquid with a spoonful of sugar or salt being added. Students should label each part of their diagram with the appropriate word.

CCC Patterns

The fact that large volumes of some solutes such as oxygen, salt, and sugar can be added to water without any noticeable change in volume is one of many simple observations of **everyday phenomena** that support the atomic and kinetic molecular theory. Help students understand that the simplest explanation for this observation is that there is a significant number of ever-moving "holes" or "empty spaces" in pure water and that the solute molecules (or ions) "fill in" without increasing the initial volume of water. In fact, when dissimilar pure liquids are added to each other, there may be an observable loss in volume. For example, if 50.00 mL of 98% alcohol of almost any variety is added to 50.00 mL of water, the solution will have a combined volume of 96–97 mL.

1 Diagrams should show solute particles in a large block of solute mixing only with the solvent particles around the outside of the block. They should also show powdered solute as smaller pieces with greater surface area allowing more solute particles to mix with the solvent particles.

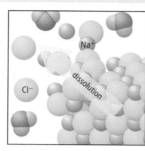 

FIGURE 13: Dissolution occurs in a system when the particles of a solute move away from each other and become mixed in with the solvent particles.

a At the molecular scale, solute particles become mixed evenly with the solvent particles.

b At the observable scale, the solute will seem to disappear after it is thoroughly mixed with the solvent.

Figure 13a shows what happens at a particle scale when sodium chloride dissolves in water. For any soluble compound, there is a limit to how much of it can dissolve in the solvent. The amount of solute that can dissolve depends on the volume of the solvent and on the temperature of the solution. For gases, it also depends on pressure. Solubility is the extent to which a solute can dissolve in a solvent at a given temperature and pressure. Increasing the temperature of a solution generally increases the solubility of a solute in the solvent. Decreasing the temperature generally decreases the solubility, which might cause some of the dissolved solute to come out of solution and form a crystalline solid again.

Because dissolution happens at the interface between the dissolving substance and the solvent, the surface area of the solute affects how fast dissolution happens. Think about what happens to a single crystal of salt when it is placed into water. As the salt dissolves, only the particles on the surface of the crystal touch the water. The rate of dissolving depends on the surface area of the crystal. If you were to break the single salt crystal into smaller crystals before mixing, the salt would dissolve faster. The separate crystals have a greater surface area that can interact with the water.

1 MODEL Draw a model on the particle scale showing how patterns in the interaction of solvent particles with a large block of solute are different from patterns in the interaction of solvent particles with finely powdered solute.

The solvent of a solution can be either a solid, a liquid, or a gas. The same is true for the solute. The table gives examples of solute and solvent combinations in various solutions.

 Collaborate Examine the table showing different kinds of solutions. With a partner, discuss other common examples of solutions you can think of.

Examples of Solutions		
Example	Solute State	Solvent State
oxygen in nitrogen	gas	gas
carbon dioxide in water	gas	liquid
alcohol in water	liquid	liquid
mercury in silver and tin	liquid	solid
sugar in water	solid	liquid
copper in nickel	solid	solid

Factors Affecting Solubility

Many solutions used in chemistry have liquid solvents. A solution in which the solvent is water is called an *aqueous solution*. Chemical formulas of solutes in water are sometimes labeled (*aq*) to identify them as solutes in an aqueous solution.

Solubility and Polarity

Recall that water molecules are polar. Oxygen atoms have a slightly stronger attraction for electrons than hydrogen atoms do. When crystals of an ionic solid, such as sodium chloride, NaCl, dissolve in water, the electrical forces in the positive and negative ends of water molecules separate the sodium and chloride ions. The negatively-charged parts of water molecules attract and surround the positive ions of the ionic solid. The positively-charged parts of water molecules attract and surround the negative ions of the ionic solid. This process, called *hydration*, is how ionic compounds dissolve in water.

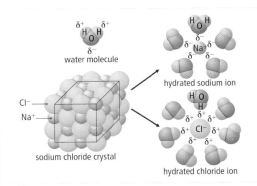

FIGURE 14: Water's polarity allows it to hydrate the positive and negative ions of an ionic solid. This conceptual model shows that the partial negative charge of water is attracted to the positive ion. The partial positive charge of water is attracted to the negative ion.

Although not all substances dissolve in water, water is sometimes referred to as "the universal solvent." The ability to dissolve many different covalent and ionic compounds is unique to polar solvents such as water.

3 **INFER** Complete the statement about the behavior of nonpolar solvents.

Ionic compounds would generally be soluble | not soluble in nonpolar solvents.

Nonpolar solvents have | do not have the charges necessary to draw the ions out of the crystal and into solution.

Differentiate Instruction

MTSS/RTI Ask students to fold a piece of paper in half to form two columns. Have them label one half of the paper "Polar Compounds" and the other half of the paper "Nonpolar Compounds." Have students list various compounds under each heading. Compounds and their polarities can be found in reference books. To reinforce the concept, discuss with students whether combinations of various compounds would dissolve in each other.

State the directions for this activity clearly, and encourage students to ask for and receive help from others as needed.

Extension Challenge students to think about why the direct temperature-solubility relationship is generally true for solid solvents but inversely true for gaseous solids. Raising the temperature decreases the solubility of a gas in a liquid, such as when a carbonated drink goes flat if warmed.

DCI **PS2.B Types of Interactions**

Have students explain in their own words why water is able to hydrate both positive and negative ions of an ionic solid. The explanation might take the form of a skit with some students representing cations, other students representing anions, and others representing water molecules with positive and negative portions labeled.

Exploring Visuals

Remind students that Na^+ and Cl^- ions are surrounded by water molecules in three dimensions, which is difficult to represent in a two-dimensional textbook or on a flat screen.

2 Answers may vary. Students may mention oxygen dissolved in water, salts dissolved in water, carbon dioxide dissolved in nitrogen, combinations of metals in Earth's crust.

3 not soluble, do not have

Differentiate Instruction

Extension When flour is suspended in water in a glass, it appears to be blue instead of the white color you might expect. This color is due to the scattering of light known as the Tyndall effect. Have students research and report on how scattering effects are also responsible for **everyday phenomena** such as the blue color of the sky, blue eyes, and the opalescence of some gemstones. Students can also report on how phenomena such as Rayleigh scattering is different from the Tyndall effect.

CCC Energy and Matter

Have students examine the graph in **Figure 15**. *Ask: In terms of the kinetic energy of the particles, why are gases less soluble at higher temperature than at lower temperature?* At high temperatures, the gas particles have greater kinetic energy and escape the liquid more easily.

Explore Online ▶

Hands-On Lab 👥 Small Groups ⏱ 60 minutes
Temperature and Solubility

SEP Planning and Carrying Out Investigations

Students investigate the effect of changing temperature on the amount of solute that will dissolve in a given amount of water and then plot a solubility curve using their data.

Student lab worksheet and teacher support available online.

1 Students should suggest that polar solutes are usually soluble in polar solvents but insoluble in nonpolar solvents. Nonpolar solutes are usually insoluble in polar solvents but soluble in nonpolar solvents.

2 No bubbles appear in carbonated water when a bottle is unopened. The pressure inside the bottle is high enough that the CO_2 is soluble in the water. After the bottle is opened, the pressure is released, resulting in lower pressure, so the CO_2 begins to come out of solution, forming bubbles of gas in the water.

Explore Online ▶

Hands-On Lab

Temperature and Solubility
Investigate how temperature affects the solubility of a substance.

Nonpolar substances, such as fats, oils, and greases, do not easily dissolve in polar liquids because the forces between the polar molecules are stronger than the forces between polar and nonpolar molecules. This is why oil and water form layers instead of mixing. Liquids that are not soluble in each other are called *immiscible*. Nonpolar substances generally do dissolve in nonpolar liquids, such as gasoline and carbon tetrachloride. The intermolecular forces are weak in nonpolar solvents, so solvent and solute particles can mix freely. Liquids that dissolve freely in one another in any proportion are called *miscible*.

1 👥 **Collaborate** A common way to remember the relationship between polarity and solubility is the phrase "like dissolves like." With a partner, explain how this description is useful for determining the solubility of substances.

Solubility and Pressure

Because the particles in liquids and solids are already very close together, pressure has little effect on the solubility of substances in these states. Changes in pressure, however, do affect the solubility of gases. Imagine you have a closed container containing a liquid and a gas, as shown in Figure 15. The liquid is the solvent and the gas above it is the solute. When the pressure on the system is increased, the gas and liquid particles collide more often than they did at the original pressure. As a result, more gas dissolves in the liquid.

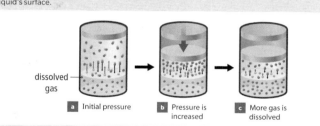

FIGURE 15: A change in pressure affects the rate at which gas particles encounter the liquid's surface.

dissolved gas

a Initial pressure   **b** Pressure is increased   **c** More gas is dissolved

2 **APPLY** It may appear that an unopened bottle of carbonated water does not contain any gases, but when you open it the water fizzes. How can the large-scale behavior of this system be explained in terms of pressure and the solubility of particles at a small scale?

_____

_____

_____

_____

_____

Carbonated beverages, those with dissolved carbon dioxide gas, CO_2, demonstrate how pressure affects the solubility of a gas. During production of the beverage, CO_2 gas is forced into the liquid under high pressures. When the bottle is opened, the pressure of the gas suddenly decreases. The CO_2 can now escape from the liquid, causing the drink to fizz.

Solubility and Temperature

Temperature has a different effect on the solubility of gases in water from its effect on the solubility of solids in water. Figures 16 and 17 show how the solubility of different solids and gases change when the temperature is increased.

3 **ANALYZE** Based on the patterns in Figure 16, what effect does temperature have on the solubility of a solid in water?

○ **a.** Solubility always increases with an increase in temperature.

○ **b.** Solubility always decreases with an increase in temperature.

○ **c.** Solubility generally increases with an increase in temperature, but sometimes decreases.

○ **d.** Solubility generally decreases with an increase in temperature, but sometimes increases.

For a solid dissolved in a liquid, increasing the temperature generally increases its solubility. The effects shown in Figure 16 on an observable scale can be explained on the scale of particles. When the temperature is increased, the particles of the solution have more kinetic energy. The increased movement allows the solvent particles to surround and dissolve the solute particles more effectively.

The effect of temperature on solubility is different for a gas dissolved in a liquid. As shown in Figure 17, as temperature increases, the gas particles have more kinetic energy and are better able to escape from the liquid solvent. For all gases, increasing temperature decreases the solubility of the gas. As with liquids and solids, polarity also affects the solubility of the gas particles.

4 **INFER** Would you expect an opened can of carbonated water to go "flat" more quickly if it was cold or warm? Use evidence from the graph to support your claim.

_____

_____

_____

_____

_____

_____

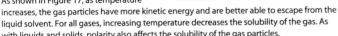

Solubility of Solids in Water

FIGURE 16: Effect of temperature on the solubility of a solid in water

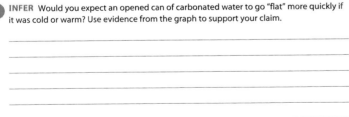

Legend: CaCl₂, Pb(NO₃)₂, NaCl, KCl, Ce₂(SO₄)₃, KNO₃, KClO₃

Solubility of Gases in Water

FIGURE 17: Effect of temperature on the solubility of a gas in water

Legend: NO, O₂, CO, CH₄, N₂

© Houghton Mifflin Harcourt Publishing Company

SEP Developing and Using Models

The regions found above and below each solubility curve in **Figures 16** and **17** represent saturated and unsaturated solutions, respectively. Ask students to describe the type of solution represented by any point above a solubility curve. For example, have them identify the point on the solubility curve for NaCl represented by the values 60 °C and 40 g NaCl/100 g H₂O. Students should recognize that this value represents a saturated solution. Then repeat the exercise by asking which type of solution is represented by any point found below a solubility curve.

Collaborate

Draw-Pair-Share Describe for students the phenomenon known as the "bends." Have pairs of students make a labeled sequence of diagrams showing why scuba divers can develop this condition if they ascend too rapidly after diving. You may want to have students describe the process in a paragraph to accompany their diagrams. Have pairs compare their diagrams and note similarities and differences.

Ecology Connection

Nearly 70 percent of the world is covered by water. Only 2.5 percent of it is fresh, and only 1 percent of that is accessible. Given water's ability to dissolve so many different substances, society needs to conserve and recycle this limited resource. Have students research and report on how fresh water can be conserved or recycled.

3 c

4 Students should hypothesize that an opened can of carbonated water would go flat much faster when warm than when cold. Gases are less soluble in liquid at high temperature, so they escape more readily when the pressure is released. **Sample answer:** The carbonated water would lose carbon dioxide faster because the increased kinetic energy of the carbon dioxide molecules would enable it to leave the solution more readily.

Preconception Alert

Concentration and Volume Some students may believe that the concentration of a solution is proportional to the amount of solution. Remind them that the molar concentration of a solution is independent of the volume.

Math Connection
HSN-Q.A.1 Use units as a way to understand problems.
Ask students how they would change the Sample Problem if it read, "You have 350 mL of solution containing 90.0 g of sodium chloride, NaCl." Help them understand that molarity is expressed in terms of liters, so they must convert 350 mL to 0.350 L to solve the problem.

SEP **Using Mathematics and Computational Thinking**

Explain to students that because the molarity of a solution relates the moles of the solute to the volume of the solution, the concentration term can be used as a conversion factor. This makes using dimensional analysis practical in solving many kinds of chemistry problems. For example, a 6.0 M solution of K_2CrO_4 can be expressed as the following conversion factors:

$$\frac{6.0\ mol\ K_2CrO_4}{1.0\ L}\ or\ \frac{1.0\ L}{6.0\ mol\ K_2CrO_4}\ or\ \frac{6.0\ mol\ K_2CrO_4}{1000\ mL}\ or\ \frac{1000\ mL}{6.0\ mol\ K_2CrO_4}$$

Then, to find the volume of solution that contains 0.120 mol of solute,

$$0.120\ \cancel{mol\ K_2CrO_4} \times \frac{1.0\ L}{6.0\ \cancel{mol\ K_2CrO_4}} = 0.020\ L\ K_2CrO_4.$$

Practice Problem Answer

1 210.1 mol H_2O

Problem Solving

Measuring Solution Concentration

Just as objects are sometimes counted in dozens, chemical amounts are expressed in units of *moles* (mol). Given the incredibly small size of atoms, the number of atoms in a sample large enough to be visible is very large. A mole is 6.02×10^{23}, and represents the number of particles, whether they are atoms, ions, or molecules. It is used to convert mass to number of particles. For example, because an atom of potassium has greater mass than an atom of sodium, one gram of potassium has fewer atoms than one gram of sodium.

The periodic table shows the atomic mass of each element, which is the mass of one mole of atoms of that element. For example, using the periodic table, you will find that one mole of oxygen atoms has a mass of 15.999 grams, whereas one mole of iron atoms has a mass of 55.85 grams.

The molar mass of a compound is the mass of one mole of molecules or formula units of that compound. To find the molar mass of a compound, you add up the molar masses of the atoms of each element in the compound.

If you know the mass of a sample and its molar mass, you can use the following equation to find the amount in moles.

$$\text{amount (mol)} = \frac{\text{mass (g)}}{\text{molar mass (g/mol)}}$$

SAMPLE PROBLEM	Suppose you have a 5.00-g sample of calcium chloride, $CaCl_2$. How many moles of calcium chloride is this?
ANALYZE	**Known:** mass = 5.00 g $CaCl_2$
	Unknown: moles of $CaCl_2$
SOLVE	Obtain the atomic masses of calcium and chlorine from the periodic table. Calcium chloride has one atom of calcium and two atoms of chlorine per formula unit, so the molar mass of calcium chloride is 40.08 g/mol + (2 × 35.45 g/mol) = 110.98 g/mol.

To find the amount of calcium chloride in your sample in moles, divide the mass by calcium chloride's molar mass.

$$\frac{5.00\ \cancel{g}}{110.98\ \cancel{g}/mol} = 0.0451\ mol\ CaCl_2$$

1 **PRACTICE PROBLEM**   **SOLVE** One gallon is about 3.785 liters, and this volume of water has a mass of about 3785 grams. Use the space below to calculate how many moles of water are in one gallon. Report your final answer using the correct number of significant figures.

_____ mol H_2O

The concentration of a solution is the amount of solute in a given amount of solution. The concentration of a solution is usually expressed by the molarity of the solution. *Molarity* (M) is the number of moles of solute in one liter of solution, as shown in the following equation.

$$\text{Molarity (M)} = \frac{\text{amount of solute (mol)}}{\text{volume of solution (L)}}$$

For example, a one-molar solution of sodium hydroxide, NaOH, contains one mole of NaOH in every liter of solution. The concentration of a one-molar solution of sodium hydroxide is written as 1 M NaOH.

SAMPLE PROBLEM An IV saline solution commonly found in hospitals contains 9.00 grams of NaCl dissolved in enough solvent to form a solution with a volume of 1.00 L. What is the molarity of the saline solution?

ANALYZE **Known:** solute mass = 9.00 g NaCl

solution volume = 1.00 L

Unknown: molarity of NaCl solution

SOLVE Use the periodic table to compute the molar mass of NaCl as 58.44 g/mol. Calculate the molarity using the molar mass of NaCl as a conversion factor.

$$\frac{9.00 \text{ g NaCl}}{1.00 \text{ L solution}} \times \frac{1 \text{ mol NaCl}}{58.44 \text{ g NaCl}} = 0.154 \text{ M NaCl}$$

---

2 PRACTICE PROBLEM **SOLVE** A scientist wants to test the effects of different potassium chloride, KCl, solution concentrations. Potassium chloride is sometimes used to treat conditions that result from potassium depletion, such as cardiac or kidney disease. The scientist dissolves 255 g KCl to make a 3.20 L solution. Use the space provided to calculate the molarity of the potassium chloride solution. Report your final answer using the correct number of significant figures.

_____ M KCl

 3 Evidence Notebook How does water's ability to dissolve substances make it important in the Earth system?

Differentiate Instruction

ELL Support Display the key word *concentration*, say it aloud, and have students repeat it. Elicit the word's two common meanings: "the act of focusing attention or mental effort on something" and "a large amount in one place." In chemistry, *concentration* refers to a solution's strength. Have students write sentences using each meaning.

Classroom Practice

What is the molarity of 2.00 L of a solution that contains 14.6 g NaCl?
0.125 M NaCl

What is the molarity of an HCl solution that contains 6.25 g HCl in 0.300 L of solution? 0.571 M HCl

How many moles of NaCl are present in 1.25 L of a 0.330 M solution?
0.413 mol NaCl

How many moles of KI are present in 0.250 L of a 2.30 M solution?
0.575 mol KI

What volume of a 0.500 M solution of HBr is needed for a reaction that requires 32.5 g of HBr? 0.803 L HBr

Practice Problem Answer

 1.07 M

For the complete solutions to the Practice Problems and Classroom Practice, see the online Problem Solutions.

 Evidence Notebook

3 Sample answer: Because water can dissolve gases, aquatic organisms can obtain oxygen from the water they live in. Organisms also rely on many other substances dissolved in water.

FORMATIVE ASSESSMENT
One-Sentence Summary Ask students to look back through the Exploration. Have them read each heading, look at the photographs, and then write a one-sentence summary of the text under each heading.

EXPLORATION 4 Measuring the Electrical Conductivity of Solutions

3D Learning Objective

Students **plan and conduct an investigation** to explore **patterns** of conductivity in solutions. They learn that electrical conductivity results from **electrical forces within and between atoms.**

Hands-On Lab 👥 Small Groups 🕐 45 minutes

Measuring the Electrical Conductivity of Solutions

SEP **Planning and Carrying Out Investigations**

When planning the procedure, student groups should discuss how they can evaluate the electrical conductivity of solutions found in **everyday phenomena,** determine data they will record for each solution, and determine the conditions for the measurements. Remind students to have their procedures approved by you before they begin. Students should suspend the conductivity probe from a ring-stand clamp and bring the solutions to the probe for measurements. Explain what a conductivity tester is. Calibrate the conductivity probe. Demonstrate how to use it according to the manufacturer's instructions. Tell students to swirl the solution gently and be sure the hole near the end of the probe is completely submerged before taking a reading. They should have an empty beaker or tub to catch any runoff. Have them use a wash bottle to rinse the probe with distilled water after each reading.

Materials Alert Large test tubes can replace the beakers. You can construct a conductivity meter easily with a 9V battery.

1 Students may predict that any substance that is not pure will conduct electricity or that only dissolved ionic compounds will conduct electricity. Substances that are made up of only nonpolar covalent bonds have no charge separation that would allow electricity to flow. Substances that are polar covalent and/or ionic would have charge separation in aqueous solution, allowing electricity to flow.

2 Students should suggest that they measure the conductivity of each solution in two trials and make the procedure as uniform as possible for each solution.

Hands-On Lab

Measuring the Electrical Conductivity of Solutions

Conductivity is a measure of how well a solution can carry an electric current. The presence of anions, cations, and pollutants can alter the conductivity of water. Thus, water quality can be determined by measuring its conductivity. You will explore the electrical conductivity of solutions containing various covalent and ionic compounds as solutes.

RESEARCH QUESTION Why might some solutions be better conductors of electrical charge than others?

1 MAKE A CLAIM

Which of the test solutions will conduct electricity well and which will not? How might the physical and chemical properties of each solution affect their conductivity?

_____

_____

_____

MATERIALS

- indirectly vented chemical splash goggles, nonlatex apron, nitrile gloves
- beaker, 100 mL (8)
- conductivity tester
- paper towels
- wash bottle

Test Solutions
- aluminum chloride, $AlCl_3$, solution, 0.05 M (50 mL)
- calcium chloride, $CaCl_2$, solution, 0.05 M (50 mL)
- distilled water (300 mL)
- ethanol, C_2H_5OH, (50 mL)
- sodium chloride, NaCl, solution, 0.05 M (50 mL)
- sugar water (50 mL)
- tap water (50 mL)

indirectly vented chemical splash goggles

SAFETY INFORMATION

- Wear indirectly vented chemical splash goggles, a nonlatex apron, and nitrile gloves during the setup, hands-on, and takedown segments of the activity.
- Never pour chemicals, either used or unused, back into their original container. Dispose of chemicals according to your teacher's instructions.

PLAN THE INVESTIGATION

In your Evidence Notebook, write a procedure to test the electrical conductivity of the seven test solutions. Consider the accuracy you could achieve based on the limitations of your materials. Your procedure should also include safety considerations and any additional materials you may need. Have your procedure and safety plan checked by your teacher before you begin.

2 COLLECT DATA

Decide what data to record, the conditions for the measurements, and how many trials you will need to complete. Develop a data table in your Evidence Notebook.

Student Lab Worksheet and complete Teacher Support are available online.

ANALYZE

1. Did the result you found for distilled water match your result for tap water? Explain why the results do or do not make sense.

_____

_____

_____

2. Compare the results you found for NaCl solution and sugar water. Considering the intermolecular forces that exist between the atoms of these molecules, why do you think the results were the same or different?

_____

_____

_____

3. Compare your results for AlCl₃, CaCl₂, and NaCl. How do you think the intermolecular forces associated with these compounds affect their conductivity?

_____

_____

_____

3 DRAW CONCLUSIONS

Write a conclusion that addresses each of the points below.

Claim Compare how well each of the solutions you tested conducted electricity. What about their physical or chemical properties could influence this ability?

Evidence Give specific examples from your data to support your claim.

Reasoning Explain how the evidence you gave supports your claim. Describe, in detail, the connections between the evidence you cited and the argument you are making.

_____

_____

_____

_____

_____

_____

_____

_____

_____

_____

_____

4 **Evidence Notebook** What did you learn from this experiment about the unique properties of water?

Analyze

1. **Sample answer:** Distilled water was not conductive, and tap water was slightly conductive. Distilled water is a pure substance and contains no charged particles that conduct electric current. Tap water contains charged particles from dissolved ionic compounds, so it will conduct an electric current.

2. **Sample answer:** The results were different. NaCl is an ionic compound that dissolves to form ions in solution, which then can conduct electric current. Sugar is a covalent compound. It is not composed of ions, so it cannot conduct electric current.

3. From lowest to highest conductivity: NaCl, CaCl₂, AlCl₃. Students may infer that in solution, NaCl produces the fewest number of charged particles and AlCl₃ the largest number. Because each solution was 0.05 M, it contained the same number of moles of the compound, so the concentration of each solution did not impact the conductivity.

3 The number of ions produced by a compound in solution determines how well it can conduct electricity. The covalent compounds did not conduct electricity. The degree to which the ionic compounds conducted electricity in solution was, from lowest to highest: NaCl, CaCl₂, AlCl₃. This is because NaCl produces two ions in solution, CaCl₂ produces three, and AlCl₃ produces four. This matches the order of increasing strength of conductivity, so the number of ions in solution may indicate how well an ionic compound can conduct electricity.

Evidence Notebook

4 **Sample answer:** Although pure water does not conduct electricity, it can dissolve ionic compounds, and the resulting solution can conduct electricity.

FORMATIVE ASSESSMENT

3-2-1 Have students write three things they learned in the experiment, two things they found interesting, and one question they still have about the concepts presented in the experiment.

EXPLORATION 5 Analyzing the Behavior of Solutions

3D Learning Objective

Students **construct explanations** of how chemical properties of solutions are determined. They learn that the **structure and interactions of matter** form a **pattern** that is **determined by electrical forces within and between atoms.**

Collaborate

Discussion Have students read the section on the dissociation of ionic compounds, and then discuss these questions:

- How can you predict whether a certain compound will form a precipitate?
- How is dissociation different from ionization?
- What compounds do you expect to conduct electricity? Why?

DCI **PS1.A Structure and Properties of Matter**

Display a colored crystalline salt, such as $CuSO_4\cdot5H_2O$, in its solid form alongside a large beaker or flask containing an aqueous solution of the same salt. Ask students to compare the composition and arrangement of particles in the crystals with those in the solution. After groups have generated their responses, have one member from each group move to a new group to share and compare information.

CCC **Patterns**

Have students research the solubility of as many ionic compounds as possible. Then have them make a table formulating general guidelines that will be useful in predicting which combinations of ions will dissolve when mixed. For example, compounds containing sodium ions are soluble in water, while most compounds containing sulfide ions are insoluble.

1 Strong conductors: aluminum chloride, calcium chloride, sodium chloride; Weak conductor: tap water; nonconductors: distilled water, ethanol, sugar

---

Analyzing the Behavior of Solutions

You have learned how the formation of solutions is affected by the electric forces between solute and solvent particles. Properties of solutions at the observable scale, such as electrical conductivity, product formation, and changes in freezing point and boiling point, can often be explained by describing the effects of electric forces between particles.

Strong and Weak Electrolytes

You previously tested the conductivity of different solutions. An **electrolyte** is a substance that conducts an electric current when dissolved in solution because it yields ions. A *nonelectrolyte* is a substance that does not conduct an electric current when dissolved in solution because it does not yield ions. As shown in Figure 18, the strength with which substances conduct an electric current is related to their ability to form ions in solution.

FIGURE 18: Sugar is a nonelectrolyte, while sodium chloride and hydrochloric acid are electrolytes.

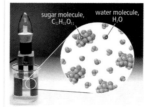 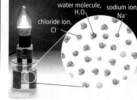 

a Sucrose (sugar) solution   **b** Sodium chloride (salt) solution   **c** Hydrochloric acid solution

All soluble ionic compounds are considered *strong electrolytes*, whose dilute aqueous solutions conduct electricity well. A few molecular compounds, such as HCl, also yield only ions when they dissolve and are therefore strong electrolytes. A *weak electrolyte* forms only a few ions in water, so it is not a good conductor of electric current. Ammonia, NH_3, is an example of a weak electrolyte. When ammonia is dissolved in water, only about one out of every hundred ammonia molecules interacts with water molecules to produce ions.

1 **APPLY** Classify each substance you tested in the conductivity lab according to its ability to conduct electric current.

aluminum chloride, $AlCl_3$ calcium chloride, $CaCl_2$ distilled water

ethanol, CH_3CH_2OH sodium chloride, NaCl   sugar   tap water

Strong electrolyte	Weak electrolyte	Nonelectrolyte

Modeling the Dissociation of Ionic Compounds

Ionic and covalent substances often behave differently when dissolved in an aqueous solution. Suppose you dissolve an ionic substance, such as sodium chloride, in a polar solvent, such as water. Sodium chloride contains ionic bonds, which means sodium ions and chlorine ions already exist before the substance is added to the water.

Explore Online ▶

🧪 **Hands-On Lab**

Testing Water for Ions
Investigate the ion content of various substances.

Similarly, a solution of manganese bromide, $MnBr_2$, contains the ions Mn^{2+} and Br^-. A chemical equation can be used to model the fact that a total of three moles of ions are produced for each mole of $MnBr_2$.

$$MnBr_2(s) \rightarrow Mn^{2+}(aq) + 2Br^-(aq)$$

| | 1 mole | 1 mole | 2 moles |

The "(s)" indicates that manganese bromide is solid, and "(aq)" is placed next to the ions to indicate that they are dissolved in aqueous solution. The "2" before "Br^-" means that for every 1 mole of manganese bromide dissolved, there are 2 moles of bromide ions in solution.

When dissolved in a solvent, ionic compounds dissociate completely into their separate ions. For example, if you dissolve silver nitrate, $AgNO_3$, in water, the solution does not actually contain $AgNO_3$. It contains only Ag^+ and NO_3^- ions. For each mole of $AgNO_3$ that you dissolve, the solution will contain a total of two moles of ions, one mole of Ag^+ ions and one mole of NO_3^- ions.

$$AgNO_3(s) \rightarrow Ag^+(aq) + NO_3^-(aq)$$

| | 1 mole | 1 mole | 1 mole |

② **PREDICT** Sodium nitrate and ammonium chloride are soluble in water. Sodium chloride and ammonium nitrate are also soluble in water. What ions will be present in a solution that results when solutions of sodium nitrate and ammonium chloride are mixed?

Ionic compounds dissociate completely up to their solubility limit. But if the amount of compound exceeds its solubility in the solution, some of the compound will not dissociate and so will remain undissolved. Some ionic compounds' solubilities are so low that they are considered *insoluble*.

If the mixing of two solutions results in a combination of ions that forms an insoluble compound, a precipitation reaction will occur. Precipitation occurs when the attraction between the ions is greater than the attraction between the ions and surrounding water molecules. Precipitation reactions can be used for making pigments, for removing salts from water in water treatment, and in chemical analysis to measure the amounts of substances in solution.

For example, potassium iodide and lead nitrate are each soluble in water, and form colorless solutions. But when you mix them, a bright yellow solid forms, as shown in Figure 19. The yellow precipitate is lead iodide, PbI_2, which is not soluble.

FIGURE 19: A precipitation reaction of aqueous lead nitrate and aqueous potassium iodide

③ 👥 **Collaborate** With a partner, discuss which ions are present in solution after potassium iodide and lead nitrate are mixed.

Explore Online ▶

Hands-On Lab 👥 Small Groups 🕐 45 minutes
Testing Water for Ions

SEP **Engaging in Argument from Evidence**

Students use evidence gathered during a series of chemical reactions to infer the presence of ions in different aqueous solutions. *Student lab worksheet and teacher support available online.*

DCI **PS1.A Structure and Properties of Matter**

Ask students to explain how dissociation and ionization relate to what they learned from the lab in Exploration 1 about strong and weak electrolytes and the ability of a solution to conduct electricity. Students should suggest that if the number of ions that are dissolved either through dissociation or ionization is high, the solution will be a strong electrolyte and will conduct electricity well. If the number is low, the solution will be a weak electrolyte and will not conduct electricity well. The greater the number of ions that dissolve, the stronger the electrolyte will be and the better the solution will conduct electricity.

Biology Connection

Electrolytes are vital for the normal functioning of cells in the bodies of living things. Sodium and potassium in particular are cations that are required for electrical conduction in muscles. Calcium is required for blood clotting, bone structure, and muscle function. Chloride is an essential anion. Have students choose one ion and research its function in the human body.

② Because sodium chloride and ammonium nitrate are both soluble, the resulting solution will contain all four ions: Na^+, Cl^-, NH_4^+, and NO_3^-.

③ K^+, NO_3^-

© Houghton Mifflin Harcourt Publishing Company • Image Credits: ©HMH

Collaborate

Debate Most of the palladium that is mined today is used in catalytic converters of vehicles. These devices convert the toxic gases in exhaust (hydrocarbons, carbon monoxide, and nitrogen dioxide) into safer gases (nitrogen, carbon dioxide, and water vapor). Palladium is also used in the manufacture of dental fixtures, fuel cells, and electronic components, such as conductors, semiconductors, and insulators. Have student groups research where palladium is mined and debate whether the United States should buy this rare metal from countries that may not have ethical mining practices.

Language Arts Connection

Suggest that students research a few rare earth metals that are widely used in **everyday phenomena** but are rare. Almost all rare earth metals come from China, and China has become extremely protective of these rich resources in the past few years. There is more utilization of rare earth metals in the manufacture of LED/LCD screens than in chips or cell phone components. Mobile phones utilize europium, cerium, neodymium, yttrium, and terbium, which are toxic. They also use lithium for batteries. Have student groups choose one rare earth metal, research its uses, and give a class presentation. **(WHST.9-12.7)**

Exploring Visuals

Explain to students that a hydrogen ion is never represented in a diagram such as that shown in **Figure 21**, because almost as soon as an acid dissociates or ionizes, the hydrogen atom becomes bound to a water molecule, which then becomes a hydronium ion, H_3O^+. Therefore, hydronium ions always represent the product of the dissociation of an acid in an aqueous solution.

1 Students' newspaper articles may describe the recycling of tungsten catalysts by precipitation. Articles should show that students understand how the tungsten is recycled and how this process offsets the impact of mining tungsten.

2 The strength of the bonds in a molecular compound determines whether the compound will ionize. If the bonds are strong, water molecules will not be able to pull the compound apart.

 Scientific Knowledge Assumes an Order and Consistency in Natural Systems

Recycling Palladium

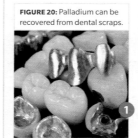

FIGURE 20: Palladium can be recovered from dental scraps.

Dental fixtures often include precious metals because of their low reactivity. If the fixtures are removed, the metal can be recovered by dissolving the scrap in a carefully chosen solvent in which the metal precipitates. Palladium in dental scrap can be retrieved by dissolving the scrap in hydrochloric acid and adding a compound to precipitate out the palladium from the solution. This kind of recycling saves energy compared to mining and processing new raw palladium ore. It also conserves a limited valuable resource from going to a landfill.

Language Arts Connection Using multiple sources, research other precipitation reactions used to recycle rare materials. How do these reactions offset the impacts of mining? Write a newspaper article describing your findings. **1**

Modeling the Ionization of Molecular Compounds

FIGURE 21: HCl completely ionizes in water. $HC_2H_3O_2$ partially ionizes in water.

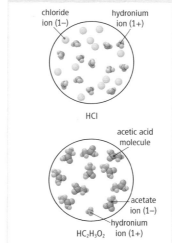

chloride ion (1−)

hydronium ion (1+)

HCl

acetic acid molecule

acetate ion (1−)

hydronium ion (1+)

$HC_2H_3O_2$

Some molecular compounds, such as sugar, dissolve in water but do not form ions. But when the polar covalent compound hydrogen chloride is dissolved in water, it forms an ionic solution called hydrochloric acid. The process by which polar covalent solute molecules form ions in solution is called *ionization*. Hydrogen chloride completely ionizes in water, so it is a strong electrolyte. The attraction of the hydrogen atom to the water molecules breaks the H—Cl bond, forming a hydrogen ion, H^+, and a chloride ion, Cl^-. This ionization can be modeled by a chemical equation:

$$HCl(aq) \xrightarrow{H_2O} H^+(aq) + Cl^-(aq)$$

Molecular compounds such as HCl that have a hydrogen atom covalently bonded to a highly electronegative atom can release H^+ ions in an aqueous solution. An H^+ ion, however, is so strongly attracted to other charged particles that it bonds covalently with a water molecule to form a *hydronium ion*, H_3O^+. The presence of hydronium ions is what makes a solution acidic at the bulk scale.

$$H_2O(l) + H^+(aq) + Cl^-(aq) \rightarrow H_3O^+(aq) + Cl^-(aq)$$

Some molecular compounds have stronger bonds to their hydrogen atoms. Acetic acid, $HC_2H_3O_2$, is a weak electrolyte. It ionizes less readily than hydrochloric acid because hydrogen is bonded more strongly to the $HC_2H_3O_2$ molecule. A small proportion of acetic acid molecules ionize in water, but most remain un-ionized.

2 **EXPLAIN** What determines whether a molecular compound will ionize in water?

Colligative Properties

A solution made by dissolving a solute in a liquid will have different physical and chemical properties than those of the solvent alone. Pure water cannot conduct electricity, freezes at 0 °C, and boils at 100 °C. Salt water does conduct electricity, freezes at a slightly lower temperature than pure water, and boils at a slightly higher temperature than pure water.

Some of the properties of solutions are affected by the presence of solutes (either molecules or ions) regardless of whether they are electrolytes or not. Such properties are referred to as colligative properties, which are dependent only on the concentration of solute particles, not on the identity of the solute particles. The greater the concentration of solute particles in a certain mass of solvent, the greater the change in the colligative property of the substance.

3 **APPLY** Select the correct terms to complete the statement about the colligative properties of sodium chloride, NaCl, and calcium chloride, $CaCl_2$, solutions.

One mole of NaCl dissolves to give one | two | three dissolved particles per formula unit. One mole of $CaCl_2$ dissolves to give one | two | three dissolved particles per formula unit. Therefore, NaCl will have a lesser | greater effect than $CaCl_2$ when added to water.

Changing Freezing Point and Boiling Point

Two important colligative properties are the changes in freezing point and boiling point of a liquid when substances are dissolved in the liquid. The boiling point and freezing point of a solution differ from those of the pure solvent. For example, ethylene glycol, also known as antifreeze, is miscible in water. Adding antifreeze to a car's radiator forms a solution that has a freezing point that is lower than the freezing point of water, preventing freezing in cold weather. This change is called *freezing-point depression*. Antifreeze also increases the boiling point of water in the radiator, which prevents overheating. This change is called *boiling-point elevation*.

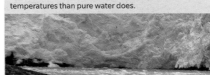

FIGURE 22: Ocean water remains liquid at lower temperatures than pure water does.

Another example of freezing point depression is seen when salt is added to icy sidewalks or roads to melt the ice. The salt lowers the freezing point of the water so that ice melts at a lower temperature than it normally would. Freezing point depression also plays an important role in ocean water, as shown in Figure 22.

4 **ANALYZE** Imagine what would happen if ocean water froze each time the temperature reached the freezing point of pure water, 0 °C. The constant movement of the water partly explains why the ocean water remains liquid. How does freezing-point depression also explain the behavior of ocean water?

_____

_____

_____

_____

Differentiate Instruction

MTSS/RTI Use the following flow chart showing cause-and-effect relationships to help students understand colligative properties:

increased number of solute particles → fewer solvent molecules at solution surface → fewer solvent molecules escape to form vapor → vapor pressure decreases → solution remains liquid over a wider temperature range → lower freezing point and higher boiling point

If some students appear to struggle with understanding, ask a more able student to help explain the flow chart.

MTSS/RTI Share this visual analogy to help explain boiling point elevation: a football line of scrimmage with a full, half-full, and nearly empty line of defenders to prevent the movement of the offensive team "trying to escape" to the other side.

Collaborate

Take and Pass At the beginning of class, fill two containers with the same amount of ice. Add a large handful of rock salt to one, and stir the mixture. During class, have students observe the containers and note the rate at which the ice melts in each. Ask students to write a response explaining why the ice mixed with NaCl melts faster. Have students pass their responses to the right. Each student should then add his or her response to the paper received and continue passing papers until the student's paper returns. Discuss the results.

Language Arts Connection

Have students research why calcium chloride is often used instead of sodium chloride to melt snow and ice from slick roads and sidewalks. Students should use scientific texts to find evidence and cite specific textual evidence to support their claims. (RST.11-12.1)

3 two, three, lesser

4 **Sample answer:** Ocean water contains dissolved salts and other minerals, which contribute to freezing-point depression and keep ocean water from freezing at 0 °C.

SEP ## Constructing Explanations and Designing Solutions

Be sure students understand that osmosis stops when the water column on the more concentrated side is high enough to exert a pressure equal to the osmotic pressure. Explain that if additional water pressure were applied to the less concentrated side of the tube so that the pressure on that side equaled the osmotic pressure, osmosis would stop. If this applied pressure is greater than the osmotic pressure, reverse osmosis would occur and the height of the pure-water side would rise.

Explore Online ▶

Hands-On Lab Small Groups   2 to 3 45-minute class periods
Diffusion and Cell Membranes

Students use eggs with a dissolved shell as a model for a living cell and then predict the results of an experiment that involves the movement of water through a membrane. *Student lab worksheet and teacher support available online.*

Preconception Alert

Students may have misconceptions about osmosis as a special case of diffusion. In diffusion, a substance moves from a region of higher concentration (solute) to a lower one. In osmosis, water (the solvent) moves from a region of higher concentration to a lower *water* concentration (or, inversely, higher solute concentration).

1 The level of the more concentrated side rose because more water particles passed through the membrane from the lower to the higher solute concentration.

 **Evidence Notebook**

2 Water allows many substances to ionize and dissociate, such as electrolytes that organisms need. Dissolved substances also keep water from freezing at lower temperatures.

FORMATIVE ASSESSMENT
Quick Write Have students make a table comparing osmosis and reverse osmosis.

Freezing point depression and boiling point elevation are explained by changes in vapor pressure, the pressure caused by solvent molecules in the gas phase directly above the solution. Increasing the concentration of solute particles means fewer solvent particles are able to escape from the liquid to enter the gas phase. This lowers the vapor pressure, which keeps the solution in a liquid state over a larger temperature range.

Explore Online ▶
Hands-On Lab

Diffusion and Cell Membranes
Investigate osmosis across a semipermeable membrane.

Osmotic Pressure

Figure 23 shows a U-tube containing sucrose solutions of different concentrations. The solutions are separated by a semipermeable membrane that blocks the passage of certain particles but allows others to pass through. In this case, the larger sucrose molecules are blocked, but the smaller water molecules can pass through freely.

1 🧑 **Collaborate** With a partner, discuss what is happening in the U-tube that would cause the levels of the solutions to change. Why did the level of the more highly concentrated solution rise? Use evidence from Figure 23 to support your ideas.

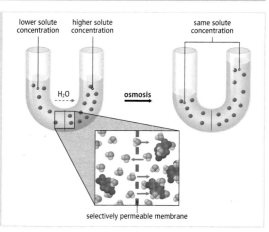

FIGURE 23: Osmosis is the movement of solvent molecules from the solution with lower solute concentration to the solution with higher solute concentration.

lower solute concentration   higher solute concentration   same solute concentration

H_2O osmosis

selectively permeable membrane

A higher concentration of solute particles in the solution allows fewer water molecules to strike the membrane than on the side with the lower solute concentration. So, the rate of water molecules moving into the higher concentration solution is greater than the rate moving in the opposite direction. *Osmosis* is the diffusion of a solvent through a semipermeable membrane to the side of higher solute concentration. As the difference in the heights of the solutions increases, an increasing pressure difference will develop. Eventually, the rate of solvent molecules moving each way across the membrane will become equal. *Osmotic pressure* is the external pressure that must be applied to stop osmosis. Osmotic pressure is dependent on the concentration of solute particles, not on the type of solute particles, so it is also a colligative property.

 Evidence Notebook How are the properties of pure water different from the properties of water when dissolved solutes are present in it? How do you think this affects the importance of water in the Earth system?

TAKE IT FURTHER Careers in Engineering

Careers in Engineering

Water Supply Engineer

When you turn on a faucet, you expect a flow of clean, drinkable water. If you are confident in the purity of your water supply, you can thank a water supply engineer. Water supply engineers identify and develop water sources, produce and maintain water purification systems, and develop water distribution systems.

The water you drink may originate in a lake or a river, or it may come from groundwater. Groundwater is usually pumped to the surface from drilled wells that are sometimes hundreds or thousands of feet deep. Regardless of its source, the water must be cleaned and purified before it can be sent to homes, schools, and businesses.

A water supply engineer develops the water purification processes, designs the equipment, and plans the methods for testing the water to make sure it is fit for consumption. Screening is the first step in the purification process. During screening, water passes through a screen to remove larger objects such as trash, leaves, and twigs.

The water then flows into large sedimentation pools where residual solid material settles. To remove any remaining small particles, chemicals such as aluminum sulfate, $Al_2(SO_4)_3$, or soluble iron salts are added. This causes small particles, unwanted ions, and residual chemicals to clump together. These precipitates are removed through different filtration processes.

Typically, the last step in water purification is to disinfect the water. Chlorine gas is the cheapest and most common substance used to disinfect water on a large scale. However, an unanticipated result of this method is that chlorine can react to form chlorine-containing organic byproducts that may cause cancer. As a result, engineers modified the process to minimize chlorine treatment and supplement it with chloramine, NH_2Cl. Chloramine is also an effective disinfectant, and it does not form harmful byproducts.

FIGURE 24: A water supply engineer collecting a sample

 Chemistry in Your Community Imagine you are a water supply engineer. Develop a plan for a water treatment plant for a community that is located away from developed areas. After researching this issue, write a report describing criteria and constraints for the task of identifying and developing a suitable source of water for this community. Define the components and the boundaries of the system. When writing your report, consider how the diverse needs of the community might be met by the water treatment system you develop, and what costs and benefits you would anticipate. How will you address their demand for water while keeping the stress on the water resource low? In addition, analyze the need for drinking water as a major global challenge.

SEPARATING SALT MIXTURES | PAPER CHROMATOGRAPHY | REVERSE OSMOSIS | Go online to choose one of these other paths.

Collaborate

You may choose to assign this activity or direct students to the Interactive Online Student Edition, where they can choose from all available paths. These activities can be assigned individually, to pairs, or to small groups.

Differentiate Instruction

ELL Support Advances in water sanitation have resulted in the greatest reduction in disease of any modern invention, but clean water is still a problem in some parts of the world. Ask students who have lived in other countries to share with the class any problems they may have experienced getting access to clean water.

Extension Have interested students research what happened in Flint, Michigan, when government agencies failed to adequately test the water supply. Students can share their findings with the class.

③ Student reports should incorporate information they learn from the reading and from independent research about water-treatment facilities that are appropriate for undeveloped areas.

Explore Online ▶

Separating Salt Mixtures

Students use differences in solubility to separate a mixture of salts in an aqueous solution.

Paper Chromatography

Students learn about the uses of paper chromatography and design an investigation.

Reverse Osmosis

Students investigate how reverse osmosis can be used to purify water.

EVALUATE Lesson Self-Check

Can You Explain the Phenomenon?

Claims, Evidence, and Reasoning

Have students clearly state their claim—their explanation for the phenomenon they have been investigating throughout this lesson. They should present their reasoning for making this claim, along with evidence such as facts, examples, and statistics that support their claim. You may want to have students present their arguments orally, in writing, or as a debate. Refer students to the **English Language Arts Handbook** for more information on evaluating claims and presenting arguments.

Cultivating Student Questions

Assessing Student Growth Review the list of questions students generated at the beginning of the lesson. Have volunteers select any unanswered questions and suggest how they could be investigated. After approving student plans, have small groups conduct the investigations and report back to the class.

 Evidence Notebook

1 Student answers may vary. Organisms could not survive in the ocean if ocean water did not contain dissolved ionic substances. Blood and other body fluids are water solutions. Because water is a polar solvent, ionic compounds can easily dissolve in it. Ionic compounds are electrolytes that dissociate into ions in water. These ions conduct the electricity that nerves and muscles need to function. If blood were a nonpolar solvent, the ionic solutes in the ocean could not dissolve, and aquatic life could not exist.

EVALUATE

Lesson Self-Check

CAN YOU EXPLAIN THE PHENOMENON?

FIGURE 25: Ocean water contains a number of dissolved solutes that are important for living organisms.

Not every interaction of substances is a chemical reaction. In some interactions, changes take place, but the identity of the substances involved remains the same. One example of this type of interaction is the dissolution of a solute into a solvent as a solution forms. An understanding of intermolecular forces makes it possible to predict which interactions will take place and to explain what happens during these interactions. The interactions that take place in ocean water affect many parts of the Earth system, including the organisms that live in and near the ocean. Understanding these interactions starts with a consideration of how intermolecular forces affect interactions between water and the ionic and molecular compounds that are dissolved in the ocean.

1 **Evidence Notebook** Refer to your notes in your Evidence Notebook to make a claim about water. Your explanation should include a discussion of the following points:

Claim Why does water have unique properties and what are some examples of how these properties are important in the Earth system?

Evidence Give specific evidence to support your claim.

Reasoning Describe, in detail, the connections between the evidence you cited and the claim you are making.

 Formal Assessment Go online for student self-checks and other assessments.

CHECKPOINTS

Check Your Understanding

1. Water, H_2O, and hydrogen sulfide, H_2S, are both molecules with a bent structure, but the melting point of H_2O is much higher than the melting point of H_2S. Why is this?
   - ○ **a.** The intermolecular forces in H_2S are much greater than those in H_2O.
   - ○ **b.** H_2O molecules have hydrogen bonds between them.
   - ○ **c.** The three-dimensional arrangement of H_2O makes it a nonpolar molecule.
   - ○ **d.** H_2S has a lower molar mass than H_2O.

2. Select the correct terms to complete the statement about charged particles.

   The pattern that electrical forces show is that like charges attract | repel and opposite charges attract | repel. According to Coulomb's law, as the distance between two charged particles decreases, the force between the particles decreases | increases. As the magnitude of the charges decreases, the force decreases | increases.

3. If solutions are produced from each of these compounds, which solutions would most likely conduct an electrical current? Select all correct answers.
   - ☐ **a.** aluminum chloride, $AlCl_3$
   - ☐ **b.** chromium trioxide, CrO_3
   - ☐ **c.** ethanol, C_2H_5OH
   - ☐ **d.** glucose, $C_6H_{12}O_6$
   - ☐ **e.** sodium azide, NaN_3

4. Which statement correctly describes the effect of an increase in temperature on the solubility of gases dissolved in a liquid?
   - ○ **a.** Solubility increases for all gases.
   - ○ **b.** Solubility decreases for all gases.
   - ○ **c.** Solubility increases for most gases but decreases for some.
   - ○ **d.** Solubility decreases for most gases but increases for some.

5. Which statement best explains why oil and water do not mix?
   - ○ **a.** Water molecules are polar and oil molecules are nonpolar.
   - ○ **b.** Oil molecules are polar and water molecules are nonpolar.
   - ○ **c.** Water molecules are carbon-based and oil molecules are not.
   - ○ **d.** Oil and water both have covalent bonds and repel one another.

6. Which of the following types of compounds is most likely to be a strong electrolyte?
   - ○ **a.** a polar compound
   - ○ **b.** a nonpolar compound
   - ○ **c.** a covalent compound
   - ○ **d.** an ionic compound

7. Select the correct terms to complete the statement.

   The freezing point of water when a solute is dissolved in the water is higher | lower than the freezing point of pure water. The change in the freezing point occurs because the vapor pressure of the solution is higher | lower than that of the pure water. This change in vapor pressure also causes the boiling point of the solution to be higher | lower than the boiling point of pure water. The change in boiling point is directly proportional to the number of | identity of the solute particles.

8. A 3.25 L solution is prepared by dissolving 285 g of $BaBr_2$ in water. Use the space provided to determine the molarity. Report your final answer using the correct number of significant figures.

   _____ M $BaBr_2$

Answers

1. b
2. repel, attract, increases, decreases
3. a, b, e
4. b
5. a
6. d
7. lower, lower, higher, number of
8. 0.295

Answers

9. HF shows stronger intermolecular forces because it contains fluorine, a highly electronegative element. As shown by periodic trends, the electronegativity of chlorine is less than that of fluorine, so chlorine does not pull electrons away from hydrogen as strongly. Both HF and HCl form hydrogen bonds. Because F is more electronegative than Cl, the bonds formed between HF molecules are stronger than those between HCl molecules. The boiling point and surface tension of HF will be greater because of these forces.

10. **Sample answer:** At the bulk scale, as the $CaBr_2$ begins to dissolve, the solid disappears as the solution forms. At the particle level, water molecules are polar. The oxygen part has a slightly negative charge, and the hydrogen part has a slightly positive charge. $CaBr_2$ is an ionic compound. When it dissolves, water hydrates its ions. The oxygen parts of water molecules surround the Ca^{2+} ions, and the hydrogen parts of water molecules surround the Br^- ions.

Make Your Own Study Guide

Have students create a study guide that helps them organize and visualize the important information from this lesson. Their study guide should focus on the main ideas from this lesson and tie multiple ideas together. Students can make an outline, a concept map, a graphic organizer, or another representation.

EVALUATE

CHECKPOINTS (continued)

9. Explain whether HCl or HF shows the stronger intermolecular forces and how this is related to trends in the periodic table. Then, explain which of these compounds would have a higher boiling point based on differences in intermolecular forces.

10. A student makes a solution by dissolving $CaBr_2$ in water. Describe what happens at the bulk scale and at the particle level as the $CaBr_2$ dissolves.

MAKE YOUR OWN STUDY GUIDE

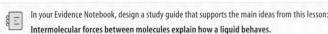 In your Evidence Notebook, design a study guide that supports the main ideas from this lesson:

Intermolecular forces between molecules explain how a liquid behaves.

Polarity results when there is an uneven distribution of charges in a molecule.

The solubility of a substance depends on the forces that exist between the solute particles and the solvent particles.

Solutions of charged particles can conduct electric current.

Remember to include the following information in your study guide:
- Use examples that model main ideas.
- Record explanations for the phenomena you investigated.
- Use evidence to support your explanations. Your support can include drawings, data, graphs, laboratory conclusions, and other evidence recorded throughout the lesson.

Consider how patterns may be observed in the intermolecular forces that exist between compounds.

Engineering Materials

Building to the Performance Expectations

The learning experiences in this lesson prepare students for mastery of

HS-PS2-6 Communicate scientific and technical information about why the molecular-level structure is important in the functioning of designed materials.

HS-ETS1-2 Design a solution to a complex real-world problem by breaking it down into smaller, more manageable problems that can be solved through engineering.

 Trace Tool to the NGSS
Go online to view the complete coverage of standards across lessons, units, and grade levels.

 SEP **Science & Engineering Practices**

Planning and Carrying Out Investigations
Plan and conduct an investigation individually and collaboratively to produce data to serve as the basis for evidence, and in the design: decide on types, how much, and accuracy of data needed to produce reliable measurements and consider limitations on the precision of the data (e.g., number of trials, cost, risk, time), and refine the design accordingly.

▶ **VIDEO** Planning and Carrying Out Investigations

Obtaining, Evaluating, and Communicating Information
Communicate scientific and technical information (e.g., about the process of development and the design and performance of a proposed process or system) in multiple formats (including oral, graphical, textual and mathematical).

DCI **Disciplinary Core Ideas**

PS1.A Structure and Properties of Matter
The structure and interactions of matter at the bulk scale are determined by electrical forces within and between atoms. (HS-PS1-3) (secondary to HS-PS2-6)

PS2.B Types of Interactions
Attraction and repulsion between electric charges at the atomic scale explain the structure, properties, and transformations of matter, as well as the contact forces between material objects. (HS-PS2-6) (secondary to HS-PS1-1) (secondary to HS-PS1-3)

ETS1.B Developing Possible Solutions
When evaluating solutions, it is important to take into account a range of constraints, including cost, safety, reliability, and aesthetics, and to consider social, cultural, and environmental impacts. (HS-ETS1-3)

ETS1.C Optimizing the Design Solution
Criteria may need to be broken down into simpler ones that can be approached systematically, and decisions about the priority of certain criteria over others (tradeoffs) may be needed. (HS-ETS1-2)

▶ **VIDEO** Engineering: Chemistry

CCC **Crosscutting Concepts**

Patterns
Different patterns may be observed at each of the scales at which a system is studied and provide evidence for causality in explanations of phenomena.

Structure and Function
Investigating or designing new systems or structures requires a detailed examination of the properties of different materials, the structures of different components, and connections of components to reveal its function and/or solve a problem.

Influence of Science, Engineering, and Technology on Society and the Natural World
New technologies can have deep impacts on society and the environment, including some that were not anticipated. Analysis of costs and benefits is a critical aspect of decisions about technology.

MATH STANDARDS

HSN-Q.A.3 Choose a level of accuracy appropriate to limitations on measurement when reporting quantities.

ELA STANDARDS

RST.11-12.7 Integrate and evaluate multiple sources of information presented in diverse formats and media (e.g., quantitative data, video, multimedia) in order to address a question or solve a problem.

Supporting All Students, All Standards

Integrating the Three Dimensions

In this lesson, students investigate the properties of matter (DCI PS1.A) and explain how these properties relate to interactions at the molecular level. They analyze the structure and function of several materials (CCC Structure and Function) and explore how the different materials can be part of designed solutions for real-world problems (DCI ETS1.B). Students plan and carry out an investigation to optimize the physical properties of a polymer (SEP Planning and Carrying Out Investigations) and extend their learning in a case study about shape memory alloys.

Preassessment

Have students complete the unit pretest or see the Assessment Guide.

Build on Prior Knowledge

Have students consider what they know about states and properties of matter. Briefly review the properties of solids, liquids, and gases and the physical and chemical properties of metals and nonmetals. Review with students that an ionic compound is made up of positive and negative ions held together by strong attractive forces, while a molecule is made up of one or more atoms held together by covalent bonds. Revisit the concept of molecular geometry, and remind students that molecules can have different shapes. The shape of a molecule depends, in part, on the number and type of atoms present in the molecule.

Professional Development

Go online to view **Professional Development videos** with strategies to integrate CCCs and SEPs, including the ones used in this lesson.

Content Background

It will be helpful for students to have an understanding of the structure of metallic solids before beginning the lesson. While metals vary in their properties, as a class of materials they have high melting points and are good conductors of electrical energy and thermal energy. Many are ductile and malleable. Each of these characteristics relates to the metallic lattice structure. Electrons flow easily within the regular array of positive metal ions, which is why metals are good conductors. Because electrons are not held in rigid covalent bonds, the metal lattice can be deformed, allowing some metals to be particularly soft.

The lattice structure is also notably stable. The attraction between the positive ions and the "sea" of electrons within the lattice is very strong, so it takes a lot of energy to melt metallic solids.

Throughout the lesson, have students compare the internal structure and physical properties of pure metal solids with the more complex materials discussed in the lesson, such as alloys and ceramics.

Differentiate Instruction

KEY WORDS

- materials science
- polymer
- hydrocarbon
- composite

ELL SUPPORT

Before students encounter each new key term in their reading, pause to pronounce and explain each one. Help students connect the word to terms and concepts they have already learned and to cognates in their home language, as appropriate.

ENGAGE: Investigative Phenomenon

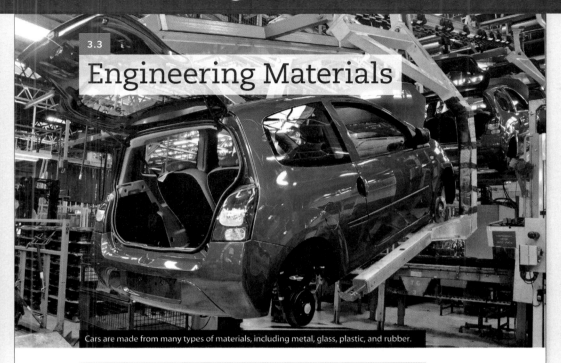

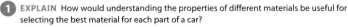

3.3
Engineering Materials

Cars are made from many types of materials, including metal, glass, plastic, and rubber.

CAN YOU SOLVE THE PROBLEM?

A car is a complex system with many parts, which have macro- and microscopic structures designed to serve specific functions. Engineers decide what materials to use for each part of a car using defined criteria and constraints. For example, the car frame provides basic structure and strength and absorbs energy during a collision. Frame materials must be strong but not too brittle. Windows let people see out. The windows must be able to withstand weather and flying pebbles and absorb the energy of a minor collision. The dashboard separates the passengers from the wiring and engine of the car. It must be easy to clean and tough enough to withstand daily life but as lightweight as possible to help increase fuel efficiency. Modern vehicles have on-board computers that control many functions. The materials for these systems are chosen for their electrical properties.

1 EXPLAIN How would understanding the properties of different materials be useful for selecting the best material for each part of a car?

_____

_____

_____

_____

  2 Evidence Notebook As you explore the lesson, gather evidence to determine what the best material (ceramic, metal, polymer, or semiconductor) would be for each car component: dashboard, frame, on-board computer, and windshield.

Lesson 3 Engineering Materials   **195**

Build on Prior Lessons

In Lesson 2, students investigated how intermolecular forces influence properties. In Lesson 3, they apply this understanding to evaluate how different materials might be used in engineering design solutions.

Lesson Objective

Students investigate the properties of materials and explain how those properties relate to interactions at the molecular level.

Cultivating Student Questions

Have students look at the photo of a car in a manufacturing plant. Prompt them to ask all questions that come to mind about the materials used in the car that is shown. Record the questions on chart paper, and then sort the questions based on their focus. With students, narrow the questions down to the ones that directly relate to the learning objective. Have students reflect on this list throughout the lesson and check off questions as they are answered.

Can You Solve the Problem?

The Investigative Phenomenon is the focus of the lesson. Students are asked to record their initial thoughts about how the properties of materials are useful when selecting the best materials for various car parts. Encourage critical thinking by asking students to list car parts, their functions, and the stresses on each one during use. Students will collect evidence related to this phenomenon throughout the lesson and revisit the question at the end of the lesson to use what they have learned to explain how the properties of materials affect their uses.

1 Students should explain that the properties of materials determine how they interact with other materials and to changes in energy, which affects how a material can be used.

Evidence Notebook

2 The topic of the best materials for different car parts will be revisited throughout this lesson.

EXPLORATION 1 Exploring Materials Science and Design

3D Learning Objective

Students explore the engineering design process and **evaluate criteria and constraints** used to develop and optimize new materials and solutions to complex problems. Students identify how new technology can affect society and the environment.

Everyday phenomena discussed throughout the Explorations of the lesson can often be used to connect the science content to students' personal experiences.

CCC Influence of Engineering, Technology, and Science on Society and the Natural World

Discuss with students that substances removed from nature may go through many processes that allow them to be converted into materials that benefit people. Have students research the types and sources of materials that can be found in an item they use.

Explore Online ▶

YOU SOLVE IT 👥 Small Groups ⏱ 20–45 minutes

How Can You Change the Properties of a Substance?

SEP Using Mathematics and Computational Thinking

Students use simulations to experiment with additives to optimize an adhesive. They analyze changes to surface tension, thermal profile, and tensile strength.

Student worksheet and teacher support available online.

1 Students should identify a material that could function better and the type of change that would improve its usefulness. **Sample answer:** I would make the fabric on my backpack more resistant to stains.

2 Phone glass could be tested for strength, resistance to scratches, being waterproof, sensitivity to touch, antiglare properties, and reflectivity.

EXPLORATION 1

Exploring Materials Science and Design

FIGURE 1: This apparatus is testing the flexibility of screen glass.

Have you ever wondered how smartphone glass was developed? To start, engineers had to understand the function that the part required, such as being resistant to cracks, as well as the properties that could help fulfill that function, such as being able to flex without breaking. To identify glass with this property, engineers can test the flexibility of glass samples, as shown in Figure 1. Engineers also had to find an efficient way to deliver the glass to manufacturers. To solve this problem, flexible glass is delivered in rolls and then cut into pieces. Materials science is the scientific study of the properties and applications of materials.

1 **PLAN** Consider a material that you use in your daily life. If you could improve it to make it function better, what would you change about it?

_____

_____

The Engineering Design Process

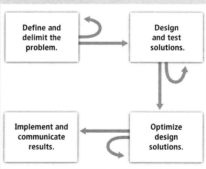
FIGURE 2: The engineering design process includes many iterations or cycles.

- Define and delimit the problem.
- Design and test solutions.
- Implement and communicate results.
- Optimize design solutions.

The engineering design process is used to develop and optimize solutions to problems. The process is iterative and can cycle through different parts of the process in various ways. Figure 2 shows a brief overview of the engineering design process.

The process begins by defining a problem that the solution will address. This includes listing criteria and constraints. At any stage in the process, engineers may discover new aspects of the problem and return to the initial definition to modify it. For example, an engineer working on a better cell phone cover might define the problem as the need to strengthen the glass face of the phone. If testing indicates that the glass is likely to crack when the phone lands on its edge, the problem might be redefined to include the need to protect the sides of the phone. Then, the criteria and constraints of the problem may need to be reevaluated as well.

When a potential solution to the defined problem is identified, the process is not over. Testing and evaluation of prototypes often lead to ideas for optimizing the design.

Explore Online ▶

YOU SOLVE IT

How Can You Change the Properties of a Substance?
Investigate the properties of five chemical additives that will be used to optimize an adhesive.

2 **Collaborate** With a partner, discuss what types of testing phone glass would undergo. Consider everything a phone might go through on a daily basis to help brainstorm ideas.

Engineering

Collecting Water from Fog

In some areas, it is common to see fog even though rain is rare and water is scarce. Engineers are developing ways to efficiently "harvest" water from the fog using engineered materials that collect water from the air.

Defining and Delimiting the Problem

Water needs vary greatly between communities and applications. Understanding how much water must be produced will determine whether fog harvesting can meet the water needs of an area. For example, a person in the United States might use 300 liters of water per day, while a person in Asia or Africa may use one-third or even one-sixth this much fresh water. In addition, fog is seasonal in many places and may not be a year-round solution for water needs. The social, cultural, and environmental impacts of a potential solution should be evaluated throughout this process. For example, many plants and animals depend on fog for water. Reducing the amount of water in the air may harm these organisms. Also, removing moisture from the air decreases the humidity. This may have unintended consequences that should be considered even if they cannot be fully predicted.

3 **DEFINE** Imagine you are designing a system to supply fog-harvested water to seedlings. Define the problem and break it down into smaller, more manageable sub-problems.

_____

_____

_____

4 **ANALYZE** Consider the sub-problem of designing a material that can harvest water from fog. Identify criteria and constraints for this problem.

_____

_____

_____

_____

Designing and Testing Solutions

Potential solutions can be brainstormed, modeled, and evaluated after the problem is defined. Engineers often research natural or human-designed solutions to similar problems as part of this step.

FIGURE 3: The Namib desert beetle can harvest water from the air.

One group of engineers took inspiration from living things as they designed water-collecting materials. The Namib desert is one of the driest environments on Earth. The Namib desert beetle, shown in Figure 3, survives in its desert home in southern Africa by drinking water that condenses on its hard, bumpy wing covers in early morning fog. A microscopic examination of the beetle's wings shows that they are covered with tiny bumps and grooves that are composed of different materials. The bumps are made of a material that attracts water from the air, and the material that makes up the grooves repels the water. Thus, the water flows along the grooves and is channeled into the beetle's mouth.

Lesson 3 Engineering Materials **197**

Collaborate

Discussion Have students consider what they have learned in terms of criteria and constraints. As a class, have them come up with a master list of criteria and constraints for a designed solution that collects water from fog.

Nature of Science

Scientific Investigations Use a Variety of Methods Scientists and engineers can learn from the diverse adaptations of organisms, which have resulted from natural selection. Some adaptations can help organisms survive in challenging environments. Biologically inspired engineering (also called bionics, biomimetics, and biomimicry) is the imitation of natural systems for the purpose of solving complex human problems. This field of engineering is a rapidly growing area of applied research. Have students conduct research about other engineered devices that were inspired by biological systems. For example, students might research how engineers have been inspired by camouflage in octopuses.

3 The overall problem is to supply fog-harvested fresh water to seedlings. Students may break this problem up in many ways, potentially including sub-problems of collecting, storing, and transporting the water.

4 Criteria for the material sub-problem could include how much water the material collects, how long the material will last, how much the material costs to produce, and how visually appealing the material is. Constraints could include whether fog harvesting will work in this particular location, whether it will collect enough water to meet specified needs, and whether the material is biodegradable.

DCI ETS1.C Optimizing the Design Solution

Ask students to consider the tradeoffs of fog-harvesting designs. For example, two criteria may be that it harvests enough fog to collect a specified amount of water each day and that it is easy to maintain. A certain design may harvest more than enough water, but dust, debris, and algae must be regularly removed from its nets, and tanks must be cleaned to reduce the growth of bacteria. Have students brainstorm ways the design could be optimized to reduce the need for this type of maintenance. Encourage students to research other types of materials that prevent bacterial growth.

Ask: *Which features of the design could be optimized to reduce the growth of algae and bacteria?* The mesh could be made from a material that resists algal growth. The collecting structures and tanks could be designed so that they are easy to clean.

Ask: *What materials do you know of that prevent the growth of microbes?* Some fabrics used in clothes and linens are designed to resist bacteria.

Ask: *How might an engineer weigh the importance of one criterion over another? For example, how might the need for bacterial resistance compare with the need for maximum water collection? How might the way these criteria are prioritized differ depending on the intended use?* The importance of the bacterial resistance criterion would depend on what the water was being used for. If the water is meant to be drinking water, bacterial resistance would be a higher priority than if the water is used for agriculture.

1 Students should evaluate the design based on the previously listed criteria and constraints. Tests that simulate the operating conditions for the intended design could be useful. For example, tests could be run in foggy conditions at different temperatures to see how the material performs at the range of temperatures in which the fog-collecting system will be used. Evaluations could include an analysis of costs, such as monetary costs per unit of water collected.

Engineers used observations from the Namib desert beetle to develop new materials that mimic the way the beetle's water-gathering system works. One material attracts and collects water from the air. Another material repels the collected water.

FIGURE 4: These nets are part of a fog-harvesting project in California.

Mesh nets that collect fog are usually nylon, polyethylene, or polypropylene. The density of the mesh can be varied to capture more or less water. Droplets that collect on the mesh may drip to the ground, providing water for plants, or they may flow into a gutter that channels the water into a storage tank. Dust, debris, and algae must be regularly removed from nets, and tanks must be maintained to prevent algal and bacterial growth.

1 **EVALUATE** Does the design in Figure 4 meet your criteria and constraints? How would you analyze the performance of this material? What tests would you run, and how would you evaluate the design?

Optimizing Design Solutions

After developing a new material, such as a water-collecting fabric, engineers test and analyze the material to make sure it has the properties to perform the desired function. A decision matrix can help determine how well a design meets important criteria. In a decision matrix, each criterion is given a number, or weight, based on its importance. Proposed designs are rated on how well they meet the identified criteria. The designs in the decision matrix on the next page are rated on a scale of 0–5. The score for each criterion in a decision matrix is multiplied by its respective weight, and the score for that design is the sum of those products. Engineers may choose to make additional prototypes of the design with the highest score, or they may choose to brainstorm new ideas if no designs meet the requirements satisfactorily.

Decision Matrix for Fog-Collecting Material				
Design criteria	Weight	Design 1	Design 2	Design 3
Durability	4	5	1	4
Water collected	3	2	3	4
Cost	2	1	2	1
Resists algae growth	1	1	4	0
Total Points		29	21	30

2 **ANALYZE** Select the correct terms to complete the statement.

According to the decision matrix, the most important criterion is durability |
water collected | cost | algae growth, which has a large effect on the total score. If
engineers decided to test only two of the designs further, they would likely eliminate
Design 1 | Design 2 | Design 3 from further consideration. Although it is not the most
durable, Design 3 scores better than the others in water collected | cost | algae growth.

A decision matrix also helps engineers consider tradeoffs, or the relative cost-benefit ratio
of different design solutions. If having a more durable product is more important than
minimizing costs, then durability can be given a higher weight in a decision matrix than
cost. This indicates which tradeoffs are acceptable for a particular problem. If a material,
product, or manufacturing process is inefficient or too costly, a new process may be
developed. The optimization process considers these tradeoffs.

Implementing the Solution and Communicating Results

Engineers are getting better at designing computer simulations and prototypes that are
more accurate models of how particular solutions will work at full-scale implementation.
As particular solutions are implemented, unanticipated outcomes, new technologies, or
new constraints may require further optimization or a new solution.

Fog collectors could provide an alternative source of fresh water in dry areas. This
technology works best in areas with frequent foggy periods, including areas in California,
Chile, Peru, and Guatemala. Prototypes have been tested in some areas as part of solution
optimization. Data from the evaluation of prototypes or fully implemented solutions can
be communicated to clients or the public through reports or scientific articles. These data
are valuable for further design optimization and for solving related problems in the future.

Often the final decision about whether a new device or process will be produced or
implemented is not made by the engineering team. There may be economic, political, or
cultural considerations unrelated to the technical performance of the design that must
be considered. For example, the environmental impacts of harvesting water from fog in
particular areas must be considered.

3 **Evidence Notebook** What are the environmental impacts of detergents? How might
these impacts compare to those of the homemade detergent from your unit project?

© Houghton Mifflin Harcourt Publishing Company

Differentiate Instruction

MTSS/RTI Students may benefit from an explanation of how the
total points in the decision matrix were calculated. For Design 1:
$29 = 5(4) + 2(3) + 1(2) + 1(1)$. Students may choose to add an extra
column for each design where they can write the product of the
weight and rating for each criterion before summing those products.
Have students work in pairs to verify the total points in the decision
matrix. They could also make up ratings for an imaginary design to
practice totalling the points.

SEP ## Constructing Explanations and Designing Solutions

Have students work in small groups to design a simple condensation
system to harvest water from the air to satisfy predetermined criteria
and constraints. For example, students might use an object removed
from a freezer to collect surface condensation and then design a
catchment system to collect drops of water. Consider having groups
exchange designs to make optimization suggestions, such as
increasing surface area to maximize amount of water collected.

2 durability, Design 2, water collected

Evidence Notebook

3 This Evidence Notebook question refers to the Unit Project.
Sample answer: The environmental impact of detergent
depends on how it is manufactured, packaged, and
distributed, as well as how it affects the environment after
entering wastewater systems or aquifers. Detergents may
be harmful to aquatic organisms, may cause eutrophication
of freshwater bodies, and may make wash water acidic. My
homemade detergent will contain fewer potentially harmful
substances than commercial detergents, which will reduce
environmental impacts. A homemade detergent may also
reduce packaging.

CCC Energy and Matter

Ask students to explain the 3Rs (Reduce-Reuse-Recycle) in terms of energy and environmental costs. Write their ideas on the board. Evaluate together the consequences of large amounts of material waste. Guide students to understand that the economic benefits related to the use of materials are often received by one nation, economic class, or generation of people, but that environmental costs resulting from the same use frequently pass on to other nations, economic classes, or later generations. Brainstorm **everyday phenomena** for which material waste is high, and then challenge students to list 3R ways to mitigate unintended environmental costs.

1 To completely evaluate the costs and benefits of a material or product, engineers must consider the financial and environmental costs of producing the product from raw materials and the costs of disposal or recycling of the product. If the beginning and end of the life cycle are not considered during a cost/benefit analysis, it will be impossible to understand the full financial and environmental impact of decisions regarding how a product is made and from what materials.

2 consumer use, obtaining resources, disposal, production, distribution

Evidence Notebook

3 The overarching problem is to identify suitable materials for different components in a car, based on the function of each component. Students should identify each car component (frame, windshield, dashboard, onboard computer) as a sub-problem that could be solved independently.

FORMATIVE ASSESSMENT

One-Sentence Summary Ask students to look back through the Exploration. Have them read each head and look at the images. Then have them write a one-sentence summary of the text under each head.

Life Cycle of Engineered Materials

Everything that we make or use requires materials. Because Earth is essentially a closed system with a finite supply of materials available, decisions about resource use should be carefully evaluated. For example, some resources, such as aluminum, are easily recycled and become materials for other products. Other resources, such as gasoline, exist in limited supply that cannot be reused. It takes many steps to manufacture and dispose of a consumer product, and each step has different impacts on society and the environment.

1 **Collaborate** With a partner, discuss why the entire life cycle of a material should be considered when analyzing costs and benefits.

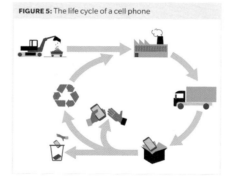

FIGURE 5: The life cycle of a cell phone

Figure 5 shows an example life cycle of a consumer product. Manufacturing begins with obtaining resources. These can be natural resources obtained by mining ores for metal, harvesting trees for lumber, or extracting fossil fuels from underground reservoirs. Resources may also come from recycled materials.

Raw resources are shaped into parts, assembled into a product, or manufactured into synthetic materials using chemical processes. Distribution of a consumer product may involve several transportation steps, such as moving the product to a warehouse then delivering to a retail outlet. Each input, such as worker time, fuel, or water usage, adds to the price of the product.

Some products may only be used once, such as food or a newspaper. Other products, such as a microwave or clothes, may be used many times. Eventually, consumers dispose of most products, which begins the final stage of the life cycle. This could consist of discarding the product as trash, reusing the product in a different way, or recycling it to use the materials in a new product.

2 **EVALUATE** Engineers reduce the impact of a product by optimizing various processes at different stages of its life cycle. Match the criteria engineers might optimize with the stage.

obtaining resources   production   distribution   consumer use   disposal

Engineering criteria	Life cycle stage
reduce the energy consumption of an appliance	
develop more efficient natural gas drilling techniques	
design a material that can be easily separated into recyclable components	
automate the assembly process for putting car parts together	
develop software systems to improve warehouse operations	

3 **Evidence Notebook** The dashboard, frame, on-board computer, and windshield in a car all serve different functions. How could you determine the best material from which to build each car component? Define this complex problem and divide it into multiple sub-problems using a diagram or flowchart.

EXPLORATION 2 Experimenting with Polymers

Engineering Lab

Experimenting with Polymers

You are a materials scientist who has been hired by a toy company to develop a toy made of a bouncy material. You will make an initial version of the material with a reaction of polyvinyl alcohol (PVA) and sodium tetraborate, also known as sodium borate or borax. In this reaction, borate ions link chains of PVA together, as shown in Figure 6. Then, you will test the properties of the material and optimize your design.

FIGURE 6: PVA and borate ions react to form a cross-linked polymer and water.

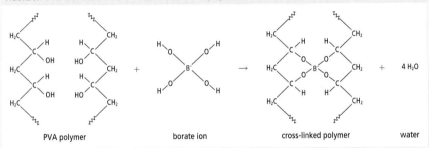

PVA polymer   borate ion   cross-linked polymer   water

DESIGN CHALLENGE

The company wants a colorful toy that is fun to look at and will bounce at least 15 cm high when dropped from a height of 30 cm onto a tile floor at room temperature. The toy should retain a spherical shape for several bounces and be stretchy and moldable by hand.

4 CONDUCT RESEARCH

Research the material you will be making from PVA and sodium tetraborate. This material is composed of very large molecules, called polymers, that are made up of repeating units, known as *monomers*. How do the monomers combine to form the polymer? How do the properties of the polymer influence the properties of the final material? As part of your research, look for information that could help you meet the criteria for a successful solution and maximize the bounciness of a toy made with this polymer.

5 DEFINE THE PROBLEM

Define the engineering problem you must solve and identify the criteria and constraints for the problem. Break the problem and criteria into smaller pieces as necessary.

_____

_____

_____

_____

_____

_____

Lesson 3 Engineering Materials   **201**

3D Learning Objective

Students **investigate** the structure and properties of a polymer and optimize the polymer to meet defined criteria and constraints.

Engineering Lab   Small Groups   90 minutes

Experimenting with Polymers

SEP Planning and Carrying Out Investigations

Students design, test, and optimize a polymer to meet defined criteria and constraints for a toy.

Safety Information Be sure students wear goggles, gloves, and an apron during this investigation. Some of the materials can be irritating to the skin and eyes. Remind students to add the borate solution rapidly, keeping safety in mind and stirring constantly to allow the polymer to form. If they find the odor too strong, the reaction can be carried out in a fume hood or in a well-ventilated room.

Materials Alert Students should use more PVA than sodium tetraborate. The sodium tetraborate should be added to the PVA and stirred briskly. Different teams might experiment with different ratios of sodium tetraborate to PVA. The collective data could be analyzed by the class to determine the optimal ratio for the intended results.

4 The material is a cross-linked polymer made by reacting polyvinyl alcohol (PVA) with sodium tetraborate. The borate ion makes weak bonds with the –OH groups on the PVA molecules, linking the PVA chains together. The degree of cross-linking depends on the borate concentration.

5 The engineering problem is to make a polymer with the characteristics the toy company has identified. Criteria include that the toy must bounce at least 15 cm high when dropped from a height of 30 cm onto a tile floor at room temperature, the toy must retain a spherical shape when it bounces, the toy must be stretchy and moldable by hand, and the toy must be colorful and fun to look at. Constraints include time, availability of materials, and safety and handling requirements.

Collaborate

Ranking Ladder Have design teams rank their criteria in order of most to least important. Next, have pairs of teams exchange design problems and criteria ladders. Ask each team to think about whether they would have listed the same criteria and constraints and if they would have prioritized the criteria in the same way. Encourage discussion of any differences.

DCI ETS1.C Optimizing the Design Solution

Students should recognize that once this polymer reaction reaches completion, it cannot be reversed. The rapid stirring and quick addition of reactants during a single reaction should show students the importance of that short period of time during which the reaction occurs. When students think about how to optimize the polymer, remind them that they need to focus on this primary reaction.

CCC Patterns

Have students identify why polymers are considered to have microscopic and macroscopic repeating patterns. They could circle the monomer unit to identify the piece that repeats in the polymer.

Test

1. Student assessment of the accuracy and precision of their data may vary, but students should recognize that taking careful measurements will improve their accuracy and repeating a test or measurement will evaluate their precision.

2. **Sample answer:** The toy bounced at least 10 cm each time it was dropped, and it was stretchy and moldable by hand. It is colorful and fun to look at. However, it did not bounce high enough and did not retain its spherical shape during the bouncing.

3. **Sample answer:** Our investigation is limited by time and materials and space to test the polymer. We gathered data for every criterion, but we decided to make the evaluation of stretchiness and moldability quantitative measurements instead of qualitative observations. This will allow us to more accurately assess our designs.

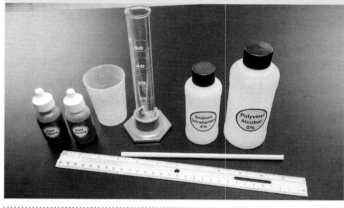

FIGURE 7: Polyvinyl alcohol, sodium tetraborate, and food coloring can be mixed together to make a colorful new material.

POSSIBLE MATERIALS

- indirectly vented chemical splash goggles, nonlatex apron, nitrile gloves
- food coloring, assorted colors
- graduated cylinder, 50 mL
- plastic cup, 4 oz
- polyvinyl alcohol (PVA), 5% solution
- ruler, 30 cm
- sodium tetraborate, 4% solution
- wooden dowel, ¼-in. diameter, 8 in. long

SAFETY INFORMATION

- Wear indirectly vented chemical splash goggles, a nonlatex apron, and nitrile gloves during the setup, hands-on, and takedown segments of the activity.
- If you get a chemical in your eye, use an eyewash station immediately.
- Never pour chemicals, either used or unused, back into their original container. Dispose of chemicals according to your teacher's instructions.
- Wash your hands with soap and water immediately after completing this activity.

indirectly vented chemical splash goggles

DESIGN SOLUTIONS

Your first step is to make a polymer and determine whether it is a suitable solution. In your Evidence Notebook, develop a procedure and safety plan and get your teacher's approval before proceeding. Include a plan for recording your initial observations. You will decide how much of each chemical to use. The total volume of reactants should be 35 mL.

TEST

In your Evidence Notebook, develop a procedure and safety plan for testing how well the polymer meets the criteria and constraints of the problem. Get your teacher's approval before proceeding. Include a table to record your data and quantitative measurements, and decide on an appropriate level of accuracy. Then, test your polymer in a safe area.

1. How accurate and precise are the data you collected? What could increase your accuracy and precision?

_____

_____

_____

2. Which criteria were met by the current toy design? Which criteria were not met?

_____

_____

_____

3. What are the limitations of your investigation? Are the data you gathered enough to accurately assess your design?

_____

_____

_____

4. Describe changes that will improve your testing procedure and investigation. Get approval from your teacher, and test your polymer again using the new procedure.

_____

_____

_____

_____

- -

OPTIMIZE

1. How do you think the recipe should change to optimize the polymer? Support your answer using information about how patterns in the polymer at the atomic scale cause changes to the properties of the polymer at the bulk scale.

_____

_____

_____

_____

2. You now need to optimize the design solution. You will need to consider certain tradeoffs. For example, if you try to optimize how high the toy can bounce, it might not be as stretchy and moldable. Rank the criteria in order of importance and explain the tradeoffs that you expect to make.

_____

_____

_____

_____

Differentiate Instruction

Extension Have students compare the macroscale properties and microscale structure of two different polymers. Challenge students to find examples of **everyday phenomena** in which each type of polymer might serve a useful role. For example, a rigid polymer may be well-suited to make plastic gears whereas a flexible polymer may be better suited for a squeeze bottle to hold condiments.

CCC **Structure and Function**

Have students consider how the criteria they choose to focus on will affect the structure of their polymer.

Test (continued)

4. **Sample answer:** We had problems accurately measuring the bounce height of the ball. To fix this, we taped a meterstick to the wall to make it easier to measure the height of each bounce. A person sat so that they could view the meterstick at eye level. Using this method resulted in bounce height measurements that were more accurate and precise and higher than the initial measurements.

Optimize

1. Students may suggest altering the ratio of PVA to sodium tetraborate. Students should support their answers with explanations, such as saying that changing the polymer to have more or less cross-linking at the microscopic scale will cause the ball to be firmer or softer, respectively.

2. **Sample answer:** Based on the engineering problem, I think the bounciness of the toy is the most important criterion, followed by keeping a spherical shape, being stretchy and moldable, and then being colorful and fun. When I optimize this design, I will focus on making the toy bouncier. The tradeoff might be that it is less moldable. The color should stay the same.

Optimize (continued)

3. Students' decision matrices should include bounce height, stretchiness, spherical shape, and color. Each criterion should be given a weight, with the most important criterion having the highest weight. Each design should be evaluated against each criterion using the same scale.

1 The polymer that formed when PVA and sodium tetraborate reacted has many cross-links, so the PVA molecules are connected in a network. The long PVA chains are still somewhat flexible, so the material is elastic, but they cannot move as freely as in liquid PVA.

2 Presentations should include data from the test phase of the process and an analysis of the performance of the design solution relative to criteria. Students should explain the properties of the material based on structural information obtained during their research and relate their observations to the structure.

3 Environmental impacts could include whether the toy is biodegradable and how cleanup of the materials might affect the environment. Students should write an argument either supporting or opposing the minimization of environmental impacts. Arguments should be well-reasoned and supported by evidence.

Evidence Notebook

4 Students should list the criteria and constraints that define an appropriate material for each part of the problem. For example, criteria for the dashboard include lightweight with an intermediate strength. Constraints include cost and ease of forming materials into specific shapes.

FORMATIVE ASSESSMENT

3-2-1 Have students write three things they found out in the lab, two things they found interesting, and one question they still have about the concepts explored in the lab.

3. Make a decision matrix and indicate the relative weight of each criterion. Evaluate your first design using the matrix. Then, make your optimized polymer and test it. As you test new designs, use your decision matrix to compare each iteration.

1 ANALYZE
Based on your research and observations, what is happening at the atomic scale to explain the function of your materials at the bulk scale?

2 COMMUNICATE
Develop a presentation that evaluates how well your final material worked, how you tested the design, and how you determined if the solution was suitable for the intended function. Include information about the structure and properties of the material based on your observations and research, and a mathematical display of your quantitative data.

3 EXTEND
List potential environmental impacts of your bouncy toy. Make sure to consider the entire life cycle of the product. Do you think minimizing environmental impacts should be prioritized over other criteria, such as cost or aesthetics? In your Evidence Notebook, write an argument supporting your position.

4 Evidence Notebook For the problem of material selection for automobile parts, identify criteria and constraints for each component (dashboard, frame, on-board computer, and windshield) based on its function.

EXPLORATION 3 Analyzing Types of Materials

EXPLORATION 3

Analyzing Types of Materials

Most complex objects consist of many parts made of different materials. Each part has a specific function and must be composed of materials that have the best properties for its function. An example of a very complex object is the space shuttle, shown in Figure 8. The space shuttle was used to ferry people and supplies to the International Space Station, carry repair crews to the Hubble telescope, and conduct many other missions. Shuttle engineers designed a vehicle that could travel into orbit using as little fuel as possible because fuel is heavy and expensive. To solve this problem, the shuttle body was built with aluminum, which is relatively light. To withstand the high temperatures caused by friction with the atmosphere upon the shuttle's return to Earth, the skin of the shuttle was covered with ceramic tiles. As the shuttle entered the atmosphere, these tiles became red hot, but the interior remained cool.

Explore Online ▶

FIGURE 8: The layers of the space shuttle give it strength and the ability to withstand high temperatures.

5 **Collaborate** Space vehicles operate in extreme conditions with limited ability for repairs. With a partner, discuss how safety and reliability considerations might affect cost-benefit analyses during the engineering design process for shuttle materials.

Metals: Applications and Properties

People first used the metal copper in a relatively pure form more than 10 000 years ago for ornaments and jewelry. Later, the development of bronze, which is a mixture of copper and tin, led to the invention of harder, more durable metal tools and weapons. Metal has been a part of human activities for thousands of years, and we continue to explore new ways to make and use metal products.

The properties of metals allow them to be used in numerous applications. Bridges and large buildings incorporate steel beams as structural support. In the form of nails, bolts, or screws, metal is an ideal fastener to hold other materials together. Metals are good conductors of electric current, so metal wires are common in electrical systems. Smooth metal surfaces are easy to clean, tolerate high temperatures, and are antimicrobial, making them ideal for medical uses, such as the titanium hip shown in Figure 9.

Explore Online ▶

FIGURE 9: Titanium metal is used for artificial hips.

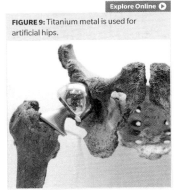

6 **EXPLAIN** What characteristics at the atomic scale determine the properties of metals at the bulk scale? Select all correct answers.

☐ **a.** ionic bonds

☐ **b.** sea of electrons

☐ **c.** low electronegativity

☐ **d.** interaction of cations and anions

3D Learning Objective

Students analyze the interactions between atoms at the molecular level to explain the structure and function of materials and communicate scientific information about material types.

Collaborate

Gallery Walk Tell students that carbon fiber provides a lot of strength with little weight—perfect for spacecraft! Have students research the variety of applications of carbon fiber and prepare a short report on one application. Have students leave their reports on a perimeter desk, and then allow time for students to do a gallery walk to learn about the various applications of this material.

Explore Online ▶

Encourage student pairs to go online to view the three-dimensional model of the space shuttle and the video of how metal is used in artificial hips. Have partners take turns explaining what they learned about the structure and function of materials from the model and video.

5 Because of the extreme conditions in which materials must function and the limited ability to replace parts, safety and reliability are generally more important considerations than cost for space applications.

6 b, c

Environmental Science Connection

Have small groups of students research the recycling of the various materials presented in this lesson. Groups should examine the environmental impact of each material and how recycling reduces this impact. Have students write a report and present their findings to the class.

Explore Online ▶

YOU SOLVE IT 👥 Small Groups 🕐 20–45 minutes

Which Planetary-Rover Materials Are Suitable?

SEP **Planning and Carrying Out Investigations, Using Mathematics and Computational Thinking**

Students are given a scenario in which they are engineers tasked with selecting metals or metal alloys for a planetary rover that must be able to withstand environmental conditions on Venus and on Europa, one of Jupiter's moons. Students use a simulation to observe and analyze simple chemical reactions between metals and chemical reactants. Provide Internet-ready devices so students can conduct the simulations.

Student worksheet and teacher support available online.

1 low, strong, electrons, high conductivity, ductile and malleable, hard

2 The pure metal should show a regular structure with the same positively charged metal ions throughout. The alloy should show a combination of different, positively charged metal ions. Both drawings should show the metal ions surrounded by smaller, negatively charged electrons. The different atom sizes in the alloy prevent the layers in the alloy from sliding as easily, making the alloy stronger than the pure metals from which it is composed.

Although a few metals, such as copper and gold, are found in small amounts in their pure form, almost all metal production begins with mining rock, known as an ore, that contains metal compounds. The extraction of metal from ore is an energy-intensive and expensive process. In general, it is much less expensive to recycle metal than to mine new metal. Thus, recycling is typically a positive for costs and the environment.

1 **INFER** Select the correct terms to complete the statement.

Due to the low | high electronegativity of metal atoms, the valence electrons form a "sea" of electrons that results in weak | strong metallic bonds. Copper is used for electrical wiring because the nuclei | protons | electrons are free to move, giving copper a low boiling point | high conductivity | high brittleness. Aluminum is brittle and soft | ductile and malleable and can be shaped into thin, flexible sheets through pressure. A lot of energy is needed to break metallic bonds, which makes many metals hard | soft.

Metals can be mixed with one another, and in some cases with nonmetals such as carbon, to form alloys. These alloys, such as bronze and steel, have different properties from the metals of which they are composed. Many alloys are, in fact, stronger and harder than the individual metals. That is why the development of bronze had a much greater effect on civilization than did the use of copper.

2 **MODEL** Draw the structure of a pure metal and an alloy at the atomic scale. Use your model to support an explanation of why alloys are typically stronger than pure metals.

Explore Online ▶

YOU SOLVE IT

Which Planetary-Rover Materials Are Suitable?
Investigate the effects of the extreme Venus environment on the metals and metal alloys used to build planetary rovers.

Consider how you use metals every day and how their useful properties relate to the atomic level arrangement of particles. For example, most tools are made of metal. The strong, delocalized bonds in metals make these tools hard and strong.

Many bicycle frames are made of steel or aluminum. These metals are strong and durable. The frame lasts for many years because the materials are hard but not brittle. Within a piece of metal, atoms can move a bit without breaking bonds because the electrons flow among the nuclei. This property keeps the frame from shattering when the bike runs over a bump or large pothole.

Ceramics: Applications and Properties

If you need a strong, durable material for a retaining wall, driveway, or building, concrete is a great choice. Concrete is made of cement, stone or sand, and water. When these components are mixed together, they form a solid material that is as hard and strong as rock. Concrete is a ceramic material. Ceramics are very stable and have been used for thousands of years. Roman concrete structures, such as the Colosseum, still stand today.

Ceramics are usually made up of bonded metal and nonmetal atoms and are typically inorganic, or not made mostly of carbon. They are produced by mixing earth materials, usually in the form of powder. For concrete, water is added to the earth materials to begin a reaction that forms the chemical bonds. In other ceramics, the chemical reaction occurs when the mixture is heated in an oven or kiln.

Ceramic materials have ionic or covalent bonds. Ionic bonds form between metal and nonmetal atoms. Covalent bonds form between nonmetal atoms. The atoms are linked by these bonds in a regular structure that is more complex than that of metals. Atoms in a ceramic may form a three-dimensional network with a rigid structure similar to the magnesia network in Figure 10. The bonds in ceramics are formed by the transfer or sharing of electrons between atoms, which is different from metallic bonding. As a result, the properties and applications of ceramics are different from those of metals.

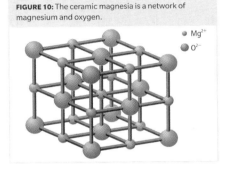

FIGURE 10: The ceramic magnesia is a network of magnesium and oxygen.

● Mg^{2+}
● O^{2-}

3 **ANALYZE** Select the correct terms to complete the statement.

In general, ceramics are hard and strong, but they are also brittle. If you drop a pottery vase and a metal vase on a hard surface, the metal | pottery is likely to bend while the metal | pottery shatters. Most ceramics are good | poor conductors of electric current because the electrons are locked into the chemical bonds and are free | unable to flow. Ceramics are good conductors | insulators of energy as heat because the atoms are held in place, so energy does not flow readily from one atom to another. For example, heat-resistant ceramic tiles protected the space shuttle during flight.

Ceramic often refers to pottery, but there are many other ceramic materials, including bricks, tiles, and glass. Glass consists mostly of silicon and oxygen atoms. When sand is melted and cooled, it forms glass. Like other ceramics, glass is hard, although brittle. Glass is often transparent to visible light, so glass has been used to make windows for many centuries.

4 **EXPLAIN** Why are insulators made of ceramics and not metals?

_____

_____

_____

_____

FIGURE 11: Porcelain or glass insulators may protect utility poles from high voltages.

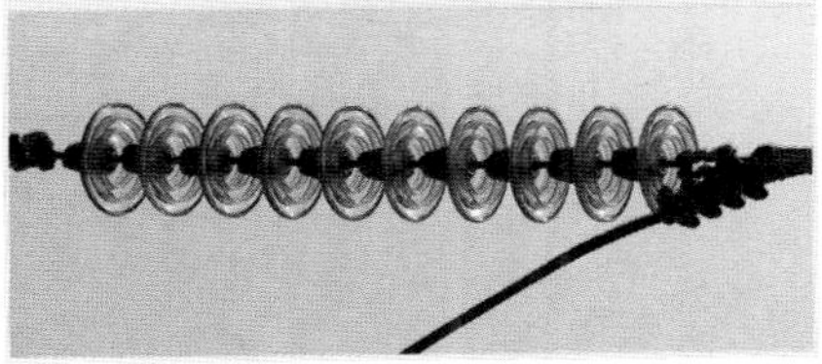

Preconception Alert

Concrete and Cement People often use the words *concrete* and *cement* interchangeably, but the two substances are actually different materials. Cement is made of compounds containing calcium, silicon, oxygen, and other elements. When mixed with water, cement forms a paste that binds together stone or sand to form concrete. Have students develop a mnemonic device to help them remember the relationship and difference between cement and concrete.

CCC Structure and Function

Work as a class to make a T-chart that compares metals and ceramics. Students should identify similarities and differences in the materials' molecular structures and their physical properties.

SEP Obtaining, Evaluating, and Communicating Information

Arrange students in small groups and have each group research a different ceramic. The groups should find out what materials are combined to form the ceramic, the process by which the ceramic is made, and the properties of the ceramic. If possible, the groups should also determine the microscale structure of the ceramic. Have the groups present their information in an oral presentation or as a poster to share with the class.

3 metal, pottery, poor, unable, insulators

4 Insulators are used to prevent or minimize the transfer of thermal or electrical energy. Metals are not a good choice for an insulator because the sea of electrons in metals readily conducts energy. Ceramics are a better choice for an insulator because the atoms are in a tight network and the electrons are transferred or shared between atoms. The fact that the electrons are not delocalized makes it more difficult for energy be transferred through a ceramic material.

SEP **Constructing Explanations and Designing Solutions**

Be sure students are aware of the "what if" that will often get asked once something new is found or discovered in science. While it is important that new materials are discovered or developed, it is not until someone asks, "What if we form this into . . ." or "What if we add some of this to . . ." that the designing of solutions in materials science occurs. Many suggestions are tested and do not work out, but a rare one will lead to a discovery or the development of something new.

DCI **ETS1.B Developing Possible Solutions**

Ask students to explain how they think the science and technology communities take into account constraints, tradeoffs, and environmental impacts when using materials for designing solutions to various issues. Students should understand that many people and organizations are involved in the process of developing new materials for use in society. Invite students to research the various organizations that would be involved in such processes.

Language Arts Connection
WHST.9-12.9 Draw evidence from informational texts to support analysis, reflection, and research.
Remind students that they can find tips on using informational texts in the online **English Language Arts Handbook.**

1 Claim: When phosphorus is added to a silicon crystal matrix, some electrons can move within it, increasing the system's conductivity. Evidence: Silicon atoms have four valence electrons and form four covalent bonds. Phosphorus atoms have five valence electrons, but the fifth electron is not involved in bonding in the silicon matrix, so it can move within the crystal. Reasoning: The movement of the free electrons from the phosphorus atoms increases the conductivity of the silicon. The free movement of electrons in a doped semiconductor is similar to the free movement of electrons in a metal, though not as strong.

Semiconductors: Applications and Properties

Semiconductors are materials that have electrical conductivity values between that of a conductor, such as copper, and that of an insulator, such as glass. Their conductivity increases as their temperature increases. Thus, they are not effective conductors at low temperatures, but they do conduct electrical current at temperatures above room temperature. The metalloid elements in pure form are semiconductors. They form crystals with covalent bonds. Electrons in metalloids do not flow as freely as they do in metals, but they are more mobile than the electrons are in ceramics.

The electrical properties of semiconducting elements, such as silicon, change when impurities are added to the crystal in a process called *doping*. These impurities are atoms of other elements, such as boron or phosphorus, that can take the place of silicon atoms in the crystal structure. Impurities affect the crystal by either donating or accepting electrons, which increases the conductivity of the semiconductor.

 MODEL A silicon atom has four valence electrons and bonds with four other silicon atoms. With a partner, explain using claims, evidence, and reasoning why adding small amounts of phosphorus to silicon makes it a conductor. Draw the structure of phosphorus-doped silicon to support your explanation.

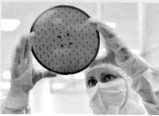

FIGURE 12: Clean room precautions at a computer-chip production facility

Silicon is the most widely-used semiconductor. Pure silicon makes up chips in virtually all electrical devices. Because impurities affect semiconductors at extremely low concentrations, chip production must be done in clean rooms with low concentrations of impurities. Figure 12 shows clean room conditions.

Semiconductor devices have had revolutionary effects on people's lives. Computers, which many people use on a daily basis, contain chips made of semiconductors. Semiconductors have many other applications, including solar cells, lasers, and LEDs. Modern LED light bulbs use a fraction of the power of incandescent light bulbs, which produce much more waste heat and emit much less light.

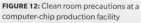 **Language Arts Connection** Semiconductors are a good example of the influence of society on science and engineering. Research the development and application of semiconductors. Analyze the costs and benefits of semiconductors and explain how this technology has affected society and the environment. Write a summary of your findings, drawing evidence from your research to support your analysis.

Polymers: Applications and Properties

Synthetic polymers are everywhere—from storage containers to contact lenses. DNA, spider silk, and proteins are natural polymers built by living organisms.

Plastic materials are manufactured polymers, mostly consisting of chains or networks of hydrocarbons that come from fossil fuels. Hydrocarbons are compounds that contain only carbon and hydrogen. Polymers have different structures, as shown in Figure 13. Structural patterns at the molecular scale cause polymers to have different properties.

FIGURE 13: Polymer structures

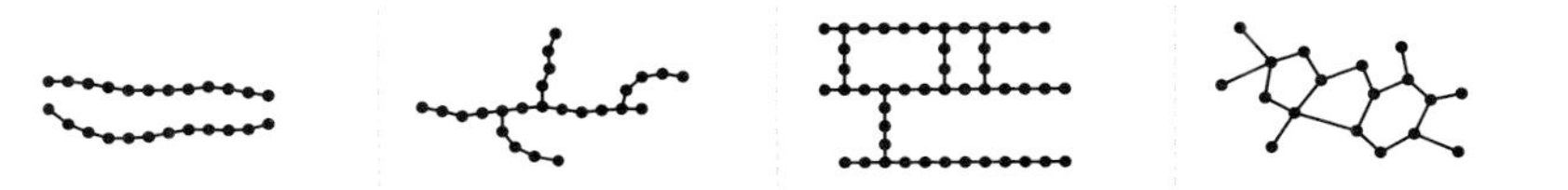

| a linear | b branched | c cross-linked | d networked |

2 ANALYZE Match each polymer description with the most likely structure from Figure 13.

Low-density polyethylene (LDPE) is a flexible polymer with many subunits as side chains. _____

Epoxy adhesives are strong and heat resistant. These polymers have so many connections between chains, an entire sample may be one molecule.

_____

Synthetic rubber is strong and stable. This polymer forms long chains with strong covalent bonds between the polymer chains. _____

Nylon is strong with high density and a high melting point. It is made of long polymer chains stacked closely together. _____

Thermoplastics are polymer materials that melt when heated. The covalent bonds within the polymer chains are very strong. There are no covalent bonds between chains. Instead, they are held together by weak attractive forces. The length of the chains can be controlled to influence properties, such as toughness. Density and the temperature at which it melts determine how easily a thermoplastic material can be recycled.

FIGURE 14: Thermoplastic

3 EXPLAIN Select the correct terms to complete the statement.

The greater the attractive forces are between molecules in a thermoplastic, the more flexible | tougher the material will be. Greater intermolecular forces between chains also means the plastic will melt at a lower | higher temperature. In Figure 14, the bottle with stronger intermolecular forces between its molecules is most likely the intact | melted bottle. The bottle that would be easier to recycle is most likely the intact | melted bottle. Recycling increases | reduces pollution and the need for raw materials and is typically less | more energy efficient than manufacturing new materials from scratch.

Math Connection

Hydrocarbon Ratios Tell students that simple hydrocarbons have a predictable ratio of carbon to hydrogen atoms. In molecules with only single bonds between hydrogen and carbon (called alkanes or saturated hydrocarbons), the ratio of carbon atoms to hydrogen atoms is n to $2n+2$, where n is the number of carbon atoms. Explain that this ratio is also expressed in the alkane's chemical formula, C_nH_{2n+2}. For example, if the alkane has 10 carbon atoms, then the ratio of carbon atoms to hydrogen atoms is 10 to 22, and its chemical formula is $C_{10}H_{22}$. **(MP.2)**

CCC Structure and Function

DNA is an example of a biological polymer built from four different monomers called nucleotides. Have students research how the polymer structure of DNA allows for its function as an information storage center in living cells. Consider having students make an infographic to summarize what they learn.

DCI PS1.A Structure and Properties of Matter

Demonstration Heat the side of an empty, clean plastic milk bottle with a heat gun, moving in a circular motion. The translucent plastic becomes transparent, or clear. When this occurs, blow into the milk bottle, and a bubble will form side of the bottle at the site where it was heated. The bubble will be similar to a polyethylene bag. Help students understand that this demonstrates the ease with which some plastics could be recycled.

2 b. branched, d. networked, c. cross-linked, a. linear

3 tougher, higher, intact, melted, reduces, more

EXPLORATION 3 *Analyzing Types of Materials, continued*

Language Arts Connection
RST.11-12.1 Cite specific textual evidence to support analysis of science and technical texts.
Direct students to the online **English Language Arts Handbook** for more information on conducting research and citing text evidence.

Information Literacy Skills Have students ask themselves the following questions when obtaining information: *Do I have permission to download this information? Can I find another source to verify this information? How will I organize the information I have found?* Use written or verbal responses as needed to assess students' information literacy skills.

1 **Sample answer:** Society benefits from single-use plastics, such as a plastic bag, because tasks are made easier. Society is also negatively affected because plastic bags can end up as litter and pollution in waterways, which is not pleasing to look at. Plastic bags are polymers formed from hydrocarbons. The environment is negatively affected by the extraction of fossil fuels and the use of energy throughout the production and distribution of plastic bags. The pollution caused by plastic bags also negatively affects the environment. There are alternatives to plastic bags, such as fabric bags. Based on this analysis, the use of plastic bags should be reduced or stopped to limit further negative effects.

Evidence Notebook
2 Students should propose two materials that could be used for each component. Then they should identify limitations that could be considered in deciding between the possible solutions. For example, the body panels could be made of steel or fiberglass. Limitations include rusting, cost, and weight for steel and likelihood of fracture for fiberglass.

FORMATIVE ASSESSMENT
Compare and Contrast Have students make a T-chart to compare and contrast the materials described in the lesson.

Petrochemical-based, human-designed plastics did not exist on Earth until the 1920s. Unfortunately, these plastics do not decompose readily in nature. In recent years, engineers have designed processes to recycle many types of plastics. Practical problems still remain, though, and overall plastic recycling rates are not yet optimized.

1 **EVALUATE** Some plastic objects, such as drinking straws or plastic bags, are designed to be used one time and then discarded. Describe the environmental and societal impacts of a single-use plastic. Should the production of single-use plastics be limited?

_____

_____

_____

_____

Structure and Function

Composite Materials in Prosthetic Limbs

FIGURE 15: Carbon fiber is a composite material that makes prosthetic limbs lightweight and durable.

In a composite, different materials are combined to form a new material with unique properties. One component of a composite typically surrounds and binds the other component. The original materials and the new material all exist separately in the final structure. Fiberglass is made of glass fibers and plastic. Glass is strong but brittle. The plastic holds glass fibers together to form a light, strong, and flexible fiberglass composite. Other composites include wood laminates, reinforced concrete, and waterproof clothing.

Composite materials have revolutionized prosthetic limbs. For example, "blade legs," such as the one shown in Figure 15, typically contain carbon fiber. This composite material was originally developed for use in aerospace technologies, but its use has expanded quickly due to its desirable properties. The advantages of using carbon fiber over more traditional materials include increased flexibility, greater durability and strength, and reduced weight.

Language Arts Connection Research composite materials used in prosthetic limbs. Write a blog post explaining the costs and benefits of these materials in terms of affordability, durability, and environmental impact. Use evidence from your research to analyze how the properties of these materials at the larger scale are related to their properties at the atomic scale.

2 **Evidence Notebook** For the automobile design problem, consider how the identified criteria and constraints and material limitations affect the choice of materials for each component (dashboard, frame, on-board computer, and windshield). Decide which criteria should have the highest priority, and propose two or more materials that could be considered as a solution for each component.

EXPLORATION 4 Case Study: Shape Memory Alloys

EXPLORATION 4

Case Study: Shape Memory Alloys

Eyeglass frames must be shaped just right to hold the lenses where they belong. Imagine wearing glasses with a metal frame and dropping them in gym class—where someone steps on them and bends the frame. Although you can adjust the shape of the metal to some degree, it is hard to get the frames back to the original shape.

3 **APPLY** What criteria would eyeglass frames need to meet to be able to bend but return to their original shape?

_____

_____

_____

_____

Shape Memory Alloys

Plasticity is the ability of an object to change shape permanently without breaking when a force is applied. Elasticity refers to the ability of an object to return to its original shape when a force is applied and then removed. Many objects have either elasticity or plasticity. Shape memory alloys (SMAs) are metal alloys that exhibit both properties.

When an SMA object is bent, it can take a new shape. However, it returns to its original shape when heated. The temperature change causes the alloy to become elastic. The eyeglass frames shown in Figure 16 are made from an SMA. While stepping on the frame might permanently bend or break eyeglass frames made from plastic or a different metal, frames made from an SMA will return to their original shape.

Shape memory alloys were first produced in the mid-20th century. Initial applications were in switches responsible for opening and closing valves or turning things on or off in response to applied forces and temperature changes.

Explore Online

FIGURE 16: The metal parts of these glasses are made of a shape memory alloy. They return to their original shape after being bent.

4 **ANALYZE** Based on the properties discussed, which type of device would be the best use of a shape memory alloy?

○ **a.** a device that can be bent into shape and then remain in position

○ **b.** a device that remains in the same shape during all operating conditions

○ **c.** a device that immediately returns to its original shape after being bent

○ **d.** a device that is easier to put into place in one shape but is used in another shape

SMAs are composed of two or three metal elements. The atoms are held together by metallic bonds in which valence electrons move freely among positively charged metal ions. These ions have a crystalline arrangement that can exist in different phases.

3D Learning Objective

Students analyze the **structure, properties, and transformations** of shape memory alloys and explore how the **structure of these metals leads to unique functions.** Students **evaluate and communicate scientific information** about the use and limitations of shape memory alloys.

SEP **Planning and Carrying Out Investigations**

Nitinol wire is an easily accessible SMA that students could use to plan and conduct an investigation into the phase changes in SMAs.

Collaborate

Discussion Demonstrate elasticity and plasticity using a rubber band and a metal paper clip. Then have students work in pairs or small groups to discuss applications when elastic materials are desirable and applications when plastic materials are desirable.

Differentiate Instruction

ELL Support Have English language learners work in pairs to tackle the vocabulary terms that relate to SMAs. First, have students look up the definition of _plasticity_ and _elasticity_ in their home language. Then have partners take turns writing a sentence in English that uses one of the words. Have partners identify and discuss (in English) **everyday phenomena** in which elastic and plastic materials are in use.

Explore Online ▶

Encourage students to go online to view the video of bendable glasses. Afterward, have the class brainstorm other real-world applications for shape memory alloys.

3 The frames would need to be able to bend without breaking and then automatically return to the original shape after being bent.

4 d

Exploring Visuals

Have students compare the austenite structure in **Figure 17** with the martensite structures in **Figure 18.**

Ask: *Why do scientists say that the twinned martensite structure has the same bulk shape as the austenite structure?* A line drawn around each structure would provide the same shape, a square or cube.

Ask: *Why is the detwinned martensite structure described as plastic, not elastic?* The detwinned martensite structure holds its new shape permanently. If it were elastic, it would return to its original shape when the deforming pressure is removed.

CCC **Structure and Function**

Have students look at the stent shown in **Figure 19.** Explain that the stent can be compressed and then returned to its original shape. To check understanding, ask students to write three to five sentences explaining how the internal structure of SMAs provides for this function.

1 austenite, martensite, can, austenite, original

2 Shape memory alloys have a crystalline structure that takes on different properties at different temperatures. The rigid structure in the austenite phase allows a shape memory alloy to maintain a certain shape above the transition temperature. The flexible structure of the martensite phase allows a shape memory alloy to be bent and hold the new shape. Once deformed, heating a shape memory alloy above the transition point makes the crystalline structure return to the original austenite structure, and the metal returns to its original shape. The properties of shape memory alloys make it possible to bend them and then return them to their original shape using temperature as a control.

3 Diagrams could show an SMA device that elongates through an applied force and contracts when heated. Something that expands and contracts regularly could be used to drive a generator that produces electrical energy.

Molecular Structure Leads to Macroscopic Function

The key to shape memory is the arrangement of atoms in the alloy. The austenite phase of an SMA, shown in Figure 17, occurs above a transition temperature, which varies among SMAs. In this phase, the atoms are tightly packed, and the metal is hard and rigid.

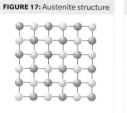

FIGURE 17: Austenite structure

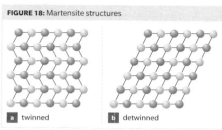

FIGURE 18: Martensite structures

a twinned   **b** detwinned

At lower temperatures, a phase change occurs. The layers in the crystal rearrange and form the martensite phase, shown in Figure 18. The twinned martensite phase has the same bulk shape as the austenite material, but the layers are not locked into place. When a force is applied, the layers shift and the material deforms. The deformed phase is detwinned martensite. Because the material in this phase is plastic, the object holds the new shape.

1 APPLY Select the correct terms to complete the statement.

Shape memory alloys exist in different phases, depending on the temperature. A wire formed of material in the austenite | martensite phase keeps its shape, even when heated. When the wire is cooled below the transition temperature, it enters the austenite | martensite phase. Applying a force to the wire at this point can | cannot change the shape of the wire. When the wire is heated after being deformed, it returns to the austenite | martensite phase and takes on the original | deformed shape.

 Collaborate As a group, discuss patterns in SMAs at the molecular scale that affect their properties at the macroscopic scale. How do the three phases affect the function of the metal?

2

Another property of SMAs that can be useful is superelasticity above the transition temperature. When a large force is applied to material in the austenite phase, the stressed area changes into the martensite phase, and the object bends. When the force is removed, the object returns to the austenite phase and the original shape. SMA eyeglass frames that spring back into shape after you step on them take advantage of this property.

3 MODEL Develop a diagram that shows how an SMA device could expand and contract. What problems might this function help solve?

Applications of Shape Memory Alloys

After the shape memory effect was discovered, engineers began looking for problems that SMAs could solve. One issue is that SMAs are more expensive than many other metals, so the applications of SMAs have to provide benefits that justify their higher price.

4 **EVALUATE** Propose a problem that could be solved through the phase change of an SMA that would provide a benefit that is worth the price of the SMA.

_____

_____

_____

_____

Consider the criteria and constraints for a medical device implanted in the human body. The device should have long-term stability and provide health benefits that outweigh its price. One constraint is size. In addition, the device must be compatible with the tissues that it touches. Based on this analysis, SMAs may be a good choice for biomedical devices. For example, arterial stents can be made of SMAs, as shown in Figure 19. A stent is implanted into a narrow artery to hold it open, restoring blood flow. A stent with shape memory can be manufactured and then cooled below the transition temperature to the martensite phase. In this phase, it is collapsed to a much thinner shape that is easier to slide into position in the artery. Once in place, the stent is warmed by the body and expands into its original austenite shape.

FIGURE 19: This stent can be collapsed in the martensite phase and will return to its original shape when warmed by the body.

5 **EXPLAIN** Place the steps of making and using a shape memory alloy as a medical stent in the correct order.

_____ **a.** Stent is compressed in its martensite form.

_____ **b.** Stent is cooled to below transition temperature.

_____ **c.** Stent is formed into its final shape in its austenite form.

_____ **d.** Stent is placed into the patient's artery.

_____ **e.** Stent undergoes transition from detwinned martensite form.

Applications of shape memory alloys can also be found in space. A common constraint is size, as room inside a space vehicle is very limited. For space telescopes, the arms that hold the solar panels can be manufactured with SMAs, cooled, and bent inward to fit inside the vehicle for launch. Once the telescope is in space and absorbing energy from the sun, the arms become warm enough to change phase. They expand and straighten to the original shape, effectively deploying the solar panels.

Other applications take advantage of the unusual properties of SMAs. For example, because the size and shape of an SMA device can change as temperature changes, it may be able to expand and contract. That motion could drive a generator to produce electrical energy. Although it is not yet commercially feasible, engineers have designed a prototype SMA device that generates electrical energy from waste heat in industrial processes.

Health Sciences Connection

Stents Ask if any students are familiar with stents. Stents are tiny scaffolds used to open blocked arteries in humans, such as the thin coronary arteries that feed the heart with blood.

Collaborate

Discussion Guide students in a class discussion about the creative and critical thinking that led to the use of SMAs as a designed solution to treat heart disease. Encourage interested students to conduct research about how stents changed health outcomes for patients with heart disease.

DCI **ETS1.B Developing Possible Solutions**

Have students work in small groups to complete the Evaluate activity. Encourage groups to identify an application in which SMAs might be useful, and then ask them to list criteria and constraints the SMA must meet for its use in the application to be considered successful. Remind students that justifying that a design solution has benefits that are worth the costs must include demonstrating that the design solution can meet criteria and constraints.

SEP **Obtaining, Evaluating, and Communicating Information**

Have students research balloon angioplasty and stainless steel stents. Then have them evaluate the differences between that method of opening clogged arteries and the use of SMA stents by making a pros and cons list for each method.

4 Students should consider how the phase transition could be applied. Examples could include temperature-activated switches, devices that would be easier to put in place in one form and function in another, and "self-healing" parts that regain their shape after being deformed.

5 c, b, a, d, e

Claims, Evidence, and Reasoning

Have students construct arguments to answer this question: *Are SMAs a good material choice for wristwatch bands?* Tell students that there is not a clear correct answer, but that they should consider possible criteria and constraints for wristwatch bands as they make claims and support their claims with evidence and reasoning from the lesson.

Explore Online ▶

Encourage students to go online to view the video about shape memory tires. Afterward, have the class brainstorm other real-world applications for shape memory alloys.

1 Students may argue that metal fatigue will not be an issue because each link can take on the strain of deformation individually. Additionally, each link touches the ground only a small percentage of the time, reducing the chance of the tire failing due to fatigue. Students could also argue that it would depend on how far the tire is expected to travel. Student arguments should be supported by evidence.

  Evidence Notebook

2 For each component in the car, students should consider the relative importance of each criterion. For example, the frame must be strong but not brittle. There may be a tradeoff between safety and cost, with a preference going to a stronger material even if it costs more because this would maximize safety. As another example, a windshield must be transparent and not break easily during a collision. A more expensive windshield that does not break into sharp pieces during a collision may be preferable to a less expensive windshield that is more dangerous. Overall, the lighter a vehicle can be safely made, the higher the mileage rating because less force is needed to accelerate lighter masses.

FORMATIVE ASSESSMENT

3-2-1 Have students write three things they found out in the lesson, two things they found interesting, and one question they still have about the concepts presented in the lesson.

Limitations of Shape Memory Alloys

A major limitation of shape memory alloys is metal fatigue due to repeated cycling between phases. Imagine what would happen if you bent the end of a paper clip back and forth repeatedly. The end would eventually break off due to metal fatigue. This is similar to fatigue in shape memory alloys. When an SMA is fatigued, its ability to change between phases decreases, and it may break or bend permanently.

Some applications, such as the arms that open solar panels in space, require only one phase change cycle. In other cases, a device may be required to undergo many phase changes. Currently, SMAs are not suitable solutions to these problems because they are limited by how many deformations they can undergo before breaking.

Explore Online ▶

FIGURE 20: NASA engineers conduct tests on the durability of shape memory alloy tires.

1 ARGUE The tire in Figure 20 is made of a shape memory alloy formed into many chains. Describe how the SMA in the tire will change as the tire is tested. Would you expect metal fatigue to be an issue in this situation? Use evidence to support your argument.

_____

_____

_____

_____

_____

_____

_____

_____

Materials scientists and engineers work to optimize the function of materials, including shape memory alloys. Scientists have developed a new alloy formula that is not limited by fatigue, even after many cycles between phases. Like most SMAs that have been used in commercial and medical applications, the new material consists mostly of titanium and nickel, but it also contains some copper and cobalt as well.

Although the research is not finished, scientists think that the copper atoms form tiny chunks within the alloy that act like bricks in a wall. The bricks bond with the surrounding atoms in both phases and function like a guide during transitions. This configuration helps the atoms jump back into place more reliably, avoiding the possibility of the bonds breaking and forming in ways that cause instability in the crystal. As scientists and engineers study this new shape memory alloy, they are looking for ways to produce it as a bulk material. Possible applications could include heart valve replacements that would need to open and close thousands of times each day. This application is currently not feasible due to metal fatigue in shape memory alloys.

2 **Evidence Notebook** Each material used to build a car has particular properties that add or detract from its usefulness for a particular purpose. Cost and availability of materials also vary. For each component, consider the tradeoffs that must be made when selecting a material type. Then use a decision matrix to evaluate your proposed materials for each component.

TAKE IT FURTHER Careers in Science

TAKE IT FURTHER

Careers in Science

Organic Chemist

Could you use your knowledge of intermolecular forces to help develop a cure for a disease? One person who is doing just that is James Nowick, a professor and organic chemist. Organic chemistry is the field of study that focuses on the chemistry of carbon-based molecules, especially those in living things. An organic chemist may study the structure and function of proteins, carbohydrates, DNA, or lipids. A person in this field might want to learn how these molecules are produced in the body, how they interact with other molecules, or how they affect a person's health.

Understanding the structure and function of proteins is an important part of finding cures for diseases such as Alzheimer's disease. Professor Nowick studies proteins involved in Alzheimer's and other neurodegenerative diseases. His research group is developing synthetic molecules that are similar in structure and function to these proteins. The purpose of developing these synthetic proteins is to model interactions between different parts of molecules. For example, a beta-pleated sheet is a zig-zag-shaped structure found in some proteins. When two beta-pleated sheets are near each other, hydrogen bonds form between the polar carbon-oxygen and nitrogen-hydrogen groups on the two sheets.

By using synthetic proteins as models, Nowick and his team are able to learn more about the forces that hold these molecules together and how changes in these interactions might lead to disease. The techniques his team uses include molecular modeling, spectroscopy, and x-ray crystallography. These tools allow the team to understand how the building blocks of proteins interact and how the team could possibly manipulate those interactions. The general process Nowick's team uses typically involves making new molecules that they think will interact through hydrogen bonding and other intermolecular forces. They can then analyze how the proteins fold and interact with other molecules and how they might operate in the human body.

FIGURE 21: Professor Nowick studies a model of an organic molecule.

James Nowick has been honored many times for his teaching, mentorship, and contributions to his community. He identifies as part of the LGBTQ+ community and has worked with organizations such as the Gay and Transgender Chemists and Allies subdivision of the American Chemical Society. This group works to promote inclusion, advocacy, and collaboration among LGBTQ+ chemists. Nowick's contributions to science and his community are numerous. His work will likely continue to drive important discoveries in this field and inspire others to pursue careers in science.

 Chemistry in Your Community Using multiple sources, research a scientist who works in the field of organic chemistry or biochemistry. Develop a profile for this person that explains the topics they study, what questions they hope to answer through their research, and how they collaborate with others in their field. Discuss the real-world applications of their research, and, if applicable, explain how intermolecular forces are related to their area of study.

| APPLICATIONS OF MATERIALS SCIENCE | EVAPORATION AND INK SOLVENTS | CAREER: BIOMEDICAL ENGINEER | Go online to choose one of these other paths. |

© Houghton Mifflin Harcourt Publishing Company • Image Credits: ©Daniel Do

Lesson 3 Engineering Materials   **215**

Collaborate

You may choose to assign this activity or direct students to the Interactive Online Student Edition, where they can choose from all available paths. These activities can be assigned individually, to pairs, or to small groups.

People in Science   James Nowick earned a Ph.D. in organic chemistry from the Massachusetts Institute of Technology. He joined the faculty at the University of California, Irvine in 1991.

DCI PS2.B Types of Interactions

Have students research and model a protein of their choice and explain how the structure and properties of the protein affect its function.

Language Arts Connection

As students conduct their research, encourage them to include diagrams to aid in the understanding of their research and to review the importance of credible references and resources. Inform students that information collected should be verified by at least one other source. The American Chemical Society and Royal Society are good places to find information. (WHST.9-12.9)

Explore Online ▶

Applications of Materials Science

Students research a material that has affected their lives in a significant way.

Evaporation and Ink Solvents

Students develop an ink that dries quickly at room temperature.

Career: Biomedical Engineer

Students explore designing human organs for transplantation and the structure and function of drugs used to aid patients with transplanted organs.

Lesson 3 Engineering Materials   215

EVALUATE Lesson Self-Check

Can You Solve the Problem?

Claims, Evidence, and Reasoning

Have students clearly state their claim—their explanation for the phenomenon they have been investigating throughout this lesson. They should present their reasoning for making this claim, along with evidence such as facts, examples, and statistics that support their claim.

You may want to have students present their arguments orally, in writing, or as a debate. Refer students to the **English Language Arts Handbook** for more information on evaluating claims and presenting arguments.

Cultivating Student Questions

Assessing Student Growth   Review the list of questions students generated at the beginning of the lesson. Have volunteers select any unanswered questions and suggest how they could be investigated. After approving student plans, have small groups conduct the investigations and report back to the class.

 Evidence Notebook

1 **Sample answer:** The dashboard should be made from a polymer, the car frame should be made from a metal, the onboard computer should be made from a semiconductor, and the windshield should be made from a ceramic. The main criterion for the car frame is to be strong in order to support the pieces of the car and protect the occupants of the car during a collision. There are strong metals and ceramics, but ceramics are brittle and may break during a collision. The structure of metals allows them to be shaped and to respond without breaking during a collision. Selecting a strong, suitable metal requires tradeoffs between higher strength and lower costs and between a heavier material and higher fuel efficiency.

The remaining components should be presented with similar supporting evidence and reasoning.

Lesson Self-Check

CAN YOU SOLVE THE PROBLEM?

FIGURE 22: Materials for car parts are designed and chosen based on the properties of the material, the function of the part, and defined criteria and constraints.

The choice of a material for a specific function depends on the properties of the material and how well it meets the defined criteria and constraints. Engineers decide what materials to use for each part of a car by analyzing the role of that part in the operation of the car and matching materials to the criteria determined for that role. The structural elements that give strength and bind together the rest of the vehicle have very different functions from the panels that provide the outer covering. Every material has specific properties that are based on its structure at the molecular level. Therefore, some materials are suitable for a particular function, but others are not.

1 **Evidence Notebook** What are the best materials to use for manufacturing different parts of a car? Refer to notes in your Evidence Notebook to propose a solution using a claim, evidence, and reasoning. Your solution should address the following points:

Claim What is the best material type (ceramic, metal, polymer, or semiconductor) for each car component: dashboard, frame, on-board computer, and windshield?

Evidence Summarize the evidence you have gathered to support your claim. Include information about the relationship between the molecular structure and properties of the material, and the function of each car component.

Reasoning Explain how the evidence you cited supports your claim.

 Formal Assessment Go online for student self-checks and other assessments.

Name _____ Date _____

CHECKPOINTS

Check Your Understanding

1. Why are metals generally ductile, or able to be pulled into wires?

- **a.** Metal ions form strong, rigid three-dimensional networks.
- **b.** Ions within the metal structure easily slide past one another.
- **c.** The bonds between metal atoms are very strong and they stick tightly together.
- **d.** Valence electrons can flow freely through the material when there is an electric potential.

2. How does the addition of an element that can donate electrons, such as phosphorus, into a silicon crystal change the electrical properties of the crystal?

- **a.** Conductivity is not affected by an increase in electrons.
- **b.** The donor atoms bond with all free electrons, increasing conductivity.
- **c.** The unbonded electrons from the donor atoms are mobile, increasing conductivity.
- **d.** Conductivity is lower at high concentrations of the donor atoms than at low concentrations of the donor atoms.

3. Select the correct terms to complete the statement about thermoplastic polymers.

The strength of intermolecular forces between polymer chains affects the properties of the material. The greater the intermolecular forces between adjacent molecules, the more | less rigid one would expect the material to be. As the strength of attractive forces between molecules increases, more | less energy is required to melt the material. Therefore, it would be easier to recycle a plastic with relatively strong | weak intermolecular forces between its molecules as compared to other types of plastics.

4. Which statements best describe a composite material? Select all correct answers.

- **a.** Composites all contain carbon, which makes them lightweight.
- **b.** A composite may have more desirable properties than its components.
- **c.** Composites form hydrogen bonds, which makes them stronger than their components.
- **d.** A brick made of mud and straw is an example of a composite; a brick made of mud is not.

5. Select the correct terms to complete the statement about how molecular patterns affect a shape memory alloy valve.

A temperature-sensitive valve is manufactured from a shape memory alloy in its austenite | twinned martensite | detwinned martensite phase. When the device is cooled, a phase change occurs, and the material's plasticity decreases | increases | remains stable. After being deformed, the material holds its new shape until it is bent | cooled | heated | stressed, which causes another phase change. The phase change from the deformed state to the original state is an example of the conductivity | elasticity | plasticity of shape memory alloys.

6. Given the constraint of metal fatigue, for which of these problems might SMA materials be a suitable solution? Select all correct answers.

- **a.** wires that hold teeth in place for a long time during orthodontic procedures
- **b.** automated pistons that move up and down in an automobile engine
- **c.** connectors between bones in a replacement knee joint
- **d.** sensors to open a sprinkler head during a fire
- **e.** landing gear on a robotic Mars lander

Answers

1. b

2. c

3. more, more, weak

4. b, d

5. austenite, increases, heated, elasticity

6. a, d, e

Answers

7. Sample answer: Defining the problem includes identifying the problem or need to be addressed and listing the criteria and constraints of the solution. When the criteria and constraints are known, engineers can use a decision matrix to choose materials based on how well they meet the criteria. They can also eliminate materials that do fall within the given constraints.

8. Sample answer: The properties of a material are determined by the electrical interactions of its atoms. Different bond types lead to different molecular structures, which determine properties such as reactivity, hardness, and electrical and thermal conductivity. These properties define the functions for which a particular material is suitable and are used to determine how well a material meets the criteria and constraints of the problem.

9. Sample answer: Most plastic is not biodegradable. An unintended consequence of using plastics is increasing pollution in waterways. Constraining plastic materials to those that can be recycled could reduce pollution.

Make Your Own Study Guide

Have students create a study guide that helps them organize and visualize the important information from this lesson. Their study guide should focus on the main ideas from this lesson and tie multiple ideas together. Students can make an outline, a concept map, a graphic organizer, or another representation.

EVALUATE

CHECKPOINTS (continued)

7. How does defining an engineering problem and identifying criteria and constraints help engineers determine the types of materials that are likely to be suitable for use in a device?

_____

_____

_____

_____

8. How do the electrical interactions of attraction and repulsion determine the properties of a material and how it can be applied to an engineering solution?

_____

_____

_____

_____

9. Describe a material that has had unintended consequences on society or the environment. What constraints could be considered when evaluating solutions that use this material?

_____

_____

_____

_____

MAKE YOUR OWN STUDY GUIDE

In your Evidence Notebook, design a study guide that supports the main ideas from this lesson:

The engineering design process is a way to determine the best material for a solution.

The properties of materials are determined by structure at the molecular level.

Different materials are used based on the required function of the part or product.

Remember to include the following information in your study guide:
- Use examples that model main ideas.
- Record explanations for the phenomena you investigated.
- Use evidence to support your explanations. Your support can include drawings, data, graphs, laboratory conclusions, and other evidence recorded throughout the lesson.

Consider how the structure and function of a system or product can be explained by examining how its components are connected and determining the molecular structure of materials used.

UNIT 3 Connections

Engineering Connection

Studying Volcanoes Scientists have limited, but ever-growing, knowledge about the conditions inside active volcano craters. These are places filled with toxic and corrosive gases, extreme heat, and unpredictable shifts of matter—not easy laboratories in which to work. Because scientists cannot enter a volcano themselves, they send in robots to collect data for them. The challenge for engineers is to design a robot or drone that can withstand those inhospitable conditions that keep humans out of volcano craters.

> Using a range of sources, prepare a poster presentation describing the processes used to engineer robots for extreme tasks, such as collecting data in an active volcano. Pay attention to the properties of the materials engineers use to build robots for these extreme tasks.

FIGURE 1: Conditions inside an active volcano crater are not suitable for humans, so research relies on robots and drones.

Social Studies Connection

Pigments Pigments are substances used for coloring. They have the ability to absorb and emit light at certain wavelengths, giving them distinct colors. Pigments derived from natural sources, such as plants or minerals, often have special significance for cultures where the natural source is located.

> Research ways that pigments are used in various cultures around the world. Write a report explaining how the pigments are used, how they are derived, and ways in which their production may have become more environmentally friendly or safe over time.

FIGURE 2: An array of different pigments

Life Science Connection

Cell Chemistry Cells in the nervous system called *neurons* rely on the charges of sodium and potassium ions in order to send signals through the nervous system. When a neuron receives a signal, sodium ions are quickly pumped into the inner membrane of the cell while potassium ions are slowly pumped out. This begins a chain reaction that moves the signal through the neuron. Eventually, the neuron releases neurotransmitters which then signal a different neuron to begin the cycle again.

> Choose another type of cell to investigate. Research the roles of ions, molecules, and chemical reactions in the cell. Using multiple sources as references, develop a comic strip or short animation that shows how the cell uses chemistry to function. Along with your comic strip or animation, provide a short description that briefly explains the process.

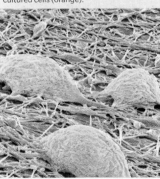

FIGURE 3: A false color scanning electron micrograph of a neuron (green) grown on cultured cells (orange).

Support for Unit Connections

Engineering Connection

Designing and engineering robots for data collection in volcano craters pushes engineering to its limits. Engineers have to use exotic alloys and materials for their robots to withstand the extreme heat as well as corrosive gases, all while gathering the data scientists need to better understand the thermal patterns within our planet. These technological advancements help engineers design products for the everyday consumer as well. Posters should address the robots' designs and materials, and how the technology has helped scientists understand thermal energy transfer within a volcano crater.

Social Studies Connection

Natural pigments are used by different cultures for decorations or in ceremonies. Pigments may be derived from mineral sources, but plants and animals can also be used as sources. Plant sources include seeds, fruit, leaves, and roots. Synthetic pigments, commonly derived from coal or petroleum, can be designed by chemical engineers to have a wider array of colors and better resist degradation from both sunlight and repeated cycles of washing and drying. Reports should provide details about how pigments are obtained and how they are used. Students can research the difference between natural and synthetic pigments and include their findings in their report.

Life Science Connection

Comic strips or animations should clearly show how the function of the cell is dependent on the movement of ions or molecules, or on specific chemical reactions. Students should find multiple credible sources and references and synthesize information from all of their sources. If sources have contradictory information, students should defend their reasoning for choosing the findings of one source over another. Examples could include the role of hormones in prompting cells in the pituitary or adrenal gland to perform an action or the chemical reactions that occur in digestive tissues or the liver.

Unit 3 Compounds and Mixtures 219

_____

_____

_____

_____

_____

_____

_____

_____

_____

_____

_____

_____

_____

THING EXPLAINER BY RANDALL MUNROE

A BOOK EXPLAINING COMPLEX IDEAS USING ONLY THE 1,000 MOST COMMON WORDS

THE WATER IN OUR BODIES

Blood and other kinds of watery stuff inside us

Plasma, the liquid part of blood, is made up of water, salts, and protein. Blood also contains some solids, such as red blood cells, white blood cells, and platelets. What makes up the other watery substances our bodies produce?

RANDALL MUNROE
XKCD.COM

THE STORY OF WATERY STUFF INSIDE OUR BODIES

OUR BLOOD, AND MOST OF THE WATER IN OUR BODIES, HAS THIS STUFF IN IT:

SO DOES THE SEA.

A WORLD LEADER ONCE SAID THAT THERE'S EXACTLY AS MUCH OF THAT STUFF IN OUR BLOOD AS THERE IS IN THE SEA, BECAUSE ALL LIFE CAME FROM THE SEA.

HE WAS RIGHT THAT LIFE COMES FROM THE SEA, BUT WRONG ABOUT OUR BLOOD. THERE'S MORE OF THAT WHITE STUFF IN THE SEAS THAN IN OUR BLOOD.

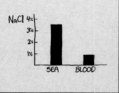

THANKS TO THE STUFF IN IT, THE WATER IN OUR BODIES CAN CARRY POWER. POWER MOVES THROUGH THE BODY BY PUSHING AND PULLING ON THE STUFF IN THE WATER.

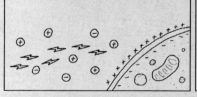

THIS WATER CAN CARRY MESSAGES IN OUR BODY THE WAY PHONE LINES CARRY VOICES, AND LETS OUR BODIES USE POWER TO PUSH AND PULL THINGS IN AND OUT OF OUR BLOOD.

PICK UP THOSE BOOKS.

OH, GREAT. NOW MY BRAIN HAS TO SEND A LOT OF MESSAGES TO MY HAND.

SO MANY STEPS!

IT MAY NOT BE EXACTLY THE SAME AS THE SEAS THAT LIFE CAME FROM, BUT THE WATER IN OUR BODIES IS LIKE A LITTLE SEA OF OUR OWN, FULL OF HIDDEN POOLS AND TINY WONDERS.

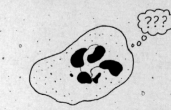

MOSTLY WATER

People often say that our bodies are mostly water, which is true. By weight, our bodies are about three parts water to two parts everything else. This water has all kinds of other things added to it. Your blood, the wet stuff in your mouth, the stuff that comes out of your eyes when you cry, and the stuff in your nose are almost all water; there's just a little other stuff in there too, and that stuff makes those kinds of water different from the normal clear water that you drink.

Since so much of our bodies are made of water, you might think that if you got a hole in your body, all your water would run out. It's true that your blood could come out—which is why people try not to get holes in them—but blood makes up only a small part of a human body's water. Most of the water is locked up in other parts of our body. Almost all the pieces we're made of have water in them—even our bones!

Most of our body parts, like all living things, are made of very tiny bags. Some of these bags hang around in our blood, while others stick together to make body parts like our hearts and skin. These bags are full of all kinds of things, but they're also full of water. If you get a hole in your body, a lot of the water is stuck in those bags—or in small spaces in between them—and won't go anywhere unless all the tiny bags break up.

WHERE IS ALL THE WATERY STUFF?

Here's what the different kinds of water in your bodies would look like if you put it in large bottles. (These are the size of bottles that people bring to parties to fill lots of people's cups from. They're often full of colorful drinks that make young people stay up all night.)

WATER IN OUR BLOOD BAGS

This is water that's locked inside the tiny bags in our body. Some of the bags are free to move around, like the red ones in our blood, but a lot of them are stuck together in certain shapes to make up body parts.

WATER OUTSIDE OUR BLOOD BAGS

This is the water that's not locked inside the tiny bags that make up our bodies. Some of it makes up the stuff in our blood, stomach, and eyes, but most of it is found in the tiny spaces between our bags. It helps the moving parts of our body move, keeps things from drying out, and acts like a road or river between different bags, carrying in the stuff they need and carrying away the stuff they're done with.

BLOOD

Most people have enough blood to fill between two and three of these bottles.

WATER IN THE RED BAGS IN OUR BLOOD

These bags are free to move around in our blood, and are what gives it that red color.

THE REST OF OUR BLOOD

This stuff is yellow-colored and almost all water. It's what things in our blood move around in.

© Houghton Mifflin Harcourt Publishing Company

Teacher Notes

_____

_____

_____

_____

_____

_____

_____

_____

_____

_____

_____

_____

_____

_____

_____

_____

Teacher Notes

_____

_____

_____

_____

_____

_____

_____

_____

_____

_____

_____

BLOOD

WATER INSIDE OUR BAGS

This is the water that's inside the red bags in our blood. These bags are red because they have a lot of metal in them.

A big plastic bottle, the kind used to fill smaller cups

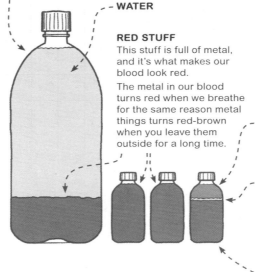

WATER

RED STUFF

This stuff is full of metal, and it's what makes our blood look red.

The metal in our blood turns red when we breathe for the same reason metal things turns red-brown when you leave them outside for a long time.

STUFF THAT STICKS TOGETHER TO COVER HOLES

If something makes a hole in your body, all your blood can fall out, which is bad. This stuff tries to fill those holes before you lose too much blood.

The hole-filling stuff is made of tiny flat circle-shaped bags. When they get near a hole, they stick together, making a thick layer that's strong enough to hold in your blood while your skin grows back over the hole.

BODY GUARDS

Some of the bags in your blood are there to keep you safe from attacks by tiny living things. Things that get into your body can make you sick. To stop them, these guards are always traveling around your body, looking for anything that's not supposed to be there. When they find something they don't like, they have all kinds of ways to mark it, attack it, and get rid of it.

SMALL-SIZE BOTTLES

These bottles are the largest size that you're allowed to carry on a flight in the US.

WATER OUTSIDE OF OUR BAGS

This is the part of our blood that's not locked up in the red bags. It's almost all water, and is kind of yellow in color if you take out all the red stuff.

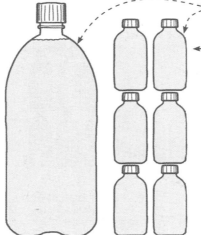

WATER

STUFF TO PUT ON CHIPS

This part of blood has the same stuff as on chips or in the sea.

METAL CARRIER

This stuff carries red metal in the blood. It can pick up metal and carry it into a bag.

WHITE STUFF

This is like the stuff in egg whites. Lots of things stick to it, and it carries them around the body.

STRONG STUFF

This is made of lots of long, thin pieces shaped like hairs. When the sticky bags in your blood are coming together to stop up a hole, these hairs help make them strong.

ROUND STUFF

This is like the white stuff, but made of bigger pieces. It does a lot of things , like carrying stuff around the body and sticking to things that shouldn't be there so your body guards can find and get rid of them.

OTHER WATERY STUFF

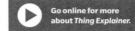 Go online for more about *Thing Explainer*.

SKIN WATER

This is the water that comes out of your skin when you get too hot. As your skin dries, the water carries away heat. This water comes from the clear part of your blood.

A normal person might make this much of it in a day, but they might make a lot more if they spend time in the heat.

KINDS OF SKIN WATER

One kind of skin water keeps you cool. It comes out of your skin all over your body, and it doesn't smell like much. It's mostly water, with just a little bit of stuff in it that makes it like the sea.

Another kind of water only comes out of certain parts of the body with hair on them, like under your arms. Your body makes it when you're worried or afraid, and it's thicker and less watery than the other kind. And after it's been there for a while, it starts to smell.

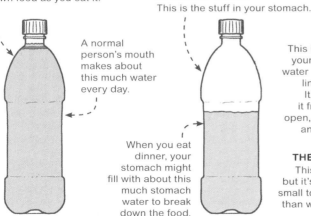

A drink bottle for one person

A tiny glass, the kind that holds drinks that you drink all at once

MOUTH WATER

The water in your mouth helps food slide down your throat. It's also full of stuff that starts breaking down food as you eat it.

A normal person's mouth makes about this much water every day.

STOMACH WATER

This is the stuff in your stomach.

When you eat dinner, your stomach might fill with about this much stomach water to break down the food.

BRAIN WATER

This is the layer of water that goes around the brain. It's very much like the yellow stuff in your blood, but it's more clean and clear, so nothing gets in the brain and hurts it.

When you hit your head, this water holds your brain in place and tries to keep it from running into the bone around it.

YELLOW WATER

This stuff holds all the watery things your body is getting rid of.

It's mostly water. The main other thing in it—which got its name because it's found in yellow water—carries stuff out of the body. It's full of the kind of stuff that makes trees and grass grow.

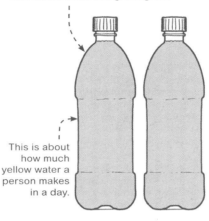

This is about how much yellow water a person makes in a day.

If you have a cold, this is how much of this stuff can fit in your nose.

NOSE STUFF

This is the stuff that comes out of your nose sometimes. It's mostly water and is a lot like the stuff that lines your throat and stomach. It helps keep the layers under it from drying out and breaking open, and catches and stops dust and things that you breathe in.

THE STUFF INSIDE YOUR EYE

This is almost completely water, but it's full of thin hairlike stuff, too small to see, which makes it thicker than water and helps the eye keep its shape.

Teacher Notes

_____

_____

_____

_____

_____

_____

_____

_____

_____

_____

_____

_____

_____

_____

_____

_____

_____

_____

UNIT 3 Performance Task

👥 Small Groups 🕐 Three 45-minute class periods

Testing Water-Repellent Fabrics

SEP **Constructing Explanations and Designing Solutions**

Students determine which fabric treatment will provide the best water-repellent, breathable solution for outdoor clothing.

Answers

1. Students should identify a readily available, nontoxic treatment that can be used to treat fabric. Criteria and constraints will vary based on the problem students define.

2. Students should discover in their research that *water-repellent* and *waterproof* are not the same. A water-repellent fabric does not easily let water through, but it does not keep water out completely or indefinitely. A waterproof fabric, however, is much more effective in keeping water out. The lotus plant, *Nelumbo*, is an example of a plant with leaves that repel water.

3. Students' choices for their investigations should be made based on research into existing treatments and the criteria and constraints of the design problem.

4. Students might suggest improvements to their procedure using different materials and equipment, and they likely will be able to use their test results to suggest a direction for further testing.

5. Presentations should relate test results to the problem, including the criteria and constraints.

Performance Task Scoring Rubric

Points	Criteria
	Problem statement is focused and clearly addressed in the final presentation.
	Research on water-repellent fabrics and how they work is presented clearly.
	Analysis of the test results is presented clearly.
	Presentation includes a description of how the testing procedure could be improved.

Hands-On Lab: *Student lab worksheet and teacher support available online.*

Testing Water-Repellent Fabrics

You are working for a company that makes water-repellent materials. Water-repellent fabrics are often used in tents, garments such as coats and shoes, and tarps that protect valuable materials. Your challenge is to develop a procedure to test a fabric that repels water. Not only should the material keep water out, but it should be breathable, or allow air to flow through.

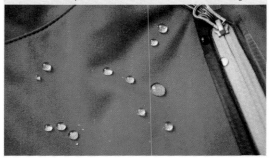

FIGURE 4: Water-repellent fabrics resist water but let air flow through.

1. DEFINE THE PROBLEM

Describe the problem you will address in this activity. Include criteria and any constraints that you will consider in your design. How will you determine how well your design repels water and how breathable it is?

2. CONDUCT RESEARCH

Research water-repellent fabrics and methods used for testing them. What is meant by the term *water-repellent*, and how is this different from waterproof? How do the adhesive and cohesive properties of water influence the way water-repellent fabrics are designed? Consider examples of plants that can also repel water and how these have influenced human-made designs.

3. CARRY OUT AN INVESTIGATION

Develop a plan for testing water-repellent fabric. Consider what materials and technology you will need, how you will safely collect and analyze data, and how you will properly dispose of waste materials.

 Explore Online ▶

🧪 **Engineering Lab**

Design Water-Repellent Fabrics Plan an investigation to design and test a water-repellent fabric. Develop a procedure to test how well the fabric repels water, as well as its breathability.

4. EVALUATE DATA

Explain which parts of your testing procedure worked well and which could be improved. How might the testing procedure differ if the tests were conducted in a facility with more advanced equipment? How would you use the results of your tests to suggest further improvements to water-repellent fabrics?

5. COMMUNICATE

With your team, develop a presentation including the problem you defined, your research on water-repellent fabrics, and the results of your tests. Explain how intermolecular forces are related to the results you obtained, and suggest areas for further research.

✓ CHECK YOUR WORK

A complete presentation should include the following information:

- a clearly defined problem that was addressed during the course of the investigation
- a description of water-repellent fabrics and how they work
- an analysis of your test results
- a description of possible improvements that could be made to the testing procedure

UNIT 3 Practice and Review

Name _____   Date _____

SYNTHESIZE THE UNIT

In your Evidence Notebook, make a concept map, other graphic organizer, or outline using the Study Guides you made for each lesson in this unit. Be sure to use evidence to support your claims.

When synthesizing individual information, remember to follow these general steps:

- Find the central idea of each piece of information.
- Think about the relationships among the central ideas.
- Combine the ideas to come up with a new understanding.

DRIVING QUESTIONS

Look back to the Driving Questions from the opening section of this unit. In your Evidence Notebook, review and revise your previous answers to those questions. Use the evidence you gathered and other observations you made throughout the unit to support your claims.

PRACTICE AND REVIEW

1. Which of these compounds would likely conduct an electrical current if dissolved in water? Select all correct answers.
   ☐ **a.** dioxygen, O_2
   ☐ **b.** magnesium bromide, $MgBr_2$
   ☐ **c.** gallium(III) nitrite, $Ga(NO_2)_3$
   ☐ **d.** carbon tetrabromide, CBr_4
   ☐ **e.** dinitrogen tetroxide, N_2O_4

2. A company wants to develop a plastic that can be used to hold food while it cooks in an oven. Complete the statement comparing different types of polymers the company could use.

   Linear polymers stack together neatly, whereas branched polymers do not. Linear polymers are held together less | more tightly by intermolecular forces. As a result, linear polymers typically have melting points that are lower than | higher than | the same as branched polymers. Therefore, a linear | branched polymer is best because the product will be used at high temperatures.

3. Which of these is a correctly written formula for the compound? Select all correct answers.
   ☐ **a.** aluminum bromide, $AlBr_3$
   ☐ **b.** strontium iodide, Sr_2I
   ☐ **c.** sodium fluoride, NaF
   ☐ **d.** barium phosphide, Ba_3P_2
   ☐ **e.** magnesium selenide, Mg_2Se

4. Scientists are conducting an experiment to determine the melting point of a substance. They find that the melting point is about 90 °C higher than they expected based on the size and molecular mass of the compound. What would explain their results? Select all correct answers.
   ☐ **a.** Dipole-induced dipole attractions strongly hold the molecules together.
   ☐ **b.** Temporary dipole-induced attractions form in the solid when it melts.
   ☐ **c.** The substance is strongly polar, so dipole-dipole attractions exist.
   ☐ **d.** Hydrogen bonding strongly holds the molecules together in the solid state.

5. A substance is dissolved in pure water, and both the freezing point and the boiling point of the liquid change. Which of these statements are true? Select all correct answers.
   ☐ **a.** The change in boiling point is directly proportional to the molarity of the solution.
   ☐ **b.** The freezing point of the pure water is higher than the freezing point of the solution.
   ☐ **c.** The change in the freezing point occurs because the vapor pressure of the solution is higher than that of the pure water.
   ☐ **d.** The change in vapor pressure causes the boiling point of the solution to be higher than the boiling point of the pure water.

Synthesize the Unit

Suggest that students begin by writing the titles of the lessons and the explorations in each unit as well as any associated vocabulary. Encourage students to recognize relationships between concepts introduced in different lessons.

Driving Questions

Suggest that students circle any parts of their original explanations that are wrong or incomplete and then write an improved explanation.

Practice and Review

SUMMATIVE ASSESSMENT

Answers

1. **DOK 2** b, c
2. **DOK 2** more, higher than, linear
3. **DOK 1** a, c, d
4. **DOK 2** c, d
5. **DOK 1** b, d

3D Item Analysis	1	2	3	4	5
SEP Constructing Explanations and Designing Solutions		•		•	•
SEP Obtaining, Evaluating, and Communicating Information	•		•	•	•
DCI PS1.A Structure and Properties of Matter	•	•	•	•	•
DCI PS2.B Types of Interactions				•	•
CCC Patterns	•	•	•	•	
CCC Structure and Function		•			

Answers

6. **DOK 2** 1.47 M; Each mole of calcium chloride produces 3 moles of ions compared with 2 for sodium chloride. The 1/3 more moles of ions for every mole of $CaCl_2$ means that the freezing point is depressed more. Therefore, calcium chloride can melt water at lower temperatures. Additionally, the dissolution of $CaCl_2$ is strongly exothermic compared with the dissolution of NaCl, so the dissolution of $CaCl_2$ serves as an extra deterrent to freezing.

7. **DOK 3 Sample answer:** Hydrogen bonding is a type of intermolecular force in which a hydrogen atom that is bonded to a highly electronegative atom, such as a fluorine, oxygen, or nitrogen atom, is attracted to an unshared electron pair of a nearby molecule. Approximately 70% of the mass of cells is water, so hydrogen bonding between H—O affects every chemical reaction inside and outside the cell membrane. The properties of proteins and DNA rely on hydrogen bonding between O—H and N—H.

8. **DOK 3** According to VSEPR theory, each pair of electrons, whether in a bond or not, repels all other pairs of valence electrons in the molecule. Electron pairs tend to be oriented as far apart as possible. The oxygen atom in a water molecule has two lone pairs that repel the hydrogen atoms, giving the molecule its bent shape.

3D Item Analysis	6	7	8
SEP Constructing Explanations and Designing Solutions		•	•
SEP Obtaining, Evaluating, and Communicating Information	•	•	
DCI PS1.A Structure and Properties of Matter	•	•	•
DCI PS2.B Types of Interactions	•	•	•
CCC Patterns	•	•	•

UNIT PRACTICE AND REVIEW

6. A 3.28 L solution is prepared by dissolving 535 g $CaCl_2$ in water. What is the molarity of the solution? Though more expensive than NaCl, $CaCl_2$ can prevent water from freezing and melt ice at lower temperatures than standard road salt. Explain why this happens.

_____

_____

_____

_____

_____

_____

7. Explain how hydrogen bonding is related to the properties of materials, such as water. Why is hydrogen bonding so important to biochemistry?

_____

_____

_____

_____

_____

_____

_____

8. A water molecule, H_2O, has a bent shape. Explain how the valence electrons of the atoms cause the molecule to have this shape.

_____

_____

_____

_____

_____

_____

_____

_____

UNIT PROJECT

Return to your unit project. Prepare a presentation using your research and materials, and share it with the class. In your final presentation, evaluate the strength of your hypothesis, data, analysis, and conclusions.

Remember these tips while evaluating:

- What structural features are common to all detergents, and how do they affect the properties of detergents?

- How can you model detergent and soap structures to help illustrate their functions?

- Why might different detergents be used for different applications?

- How do intermolecular forces facilitate the usefulness of detergents?

Integrating the NGSS* Three Dimensions of Learning

Building to the Performance Expectations

The learning experiences in this unit prepare students for mastery of

Matter and Its Interactions

HS-PS1-4 Develop a model to illustrate that the release or absorption of energy from a chemical reaction system depends upon the changes in total bond energy.

HS-PS1-7 Construct and revise an explanation for the outcome of a simple chemical reaction based on the outermost electron states of atoms, trends in the periodic table, and knowledge of the patterns of chemical properties.

Engineering Design

HS-ETS1-4 Use a computer simulation to model the impact of proposed solutions to a complex real-world problem with numerous criteria and constraints on interactions within and between systems relevant to the problem.

Assessing Student Progress

The **Unit Project: Modeling Heating Efficiency** and the **Unit Performance Task: Optimizing Heat Packs** provide opportunities to practice aspects of the Performance Expectations.

Unit Storyline In this unit about chemical reactions, students develop and use models to describe conservation of mass in chemical reactions by using chemical equations. They analyze how matter in reactions can be quantified and how changes in energy occur during reactions.

Lesson 1
Observing and Modeling Chemical Reactions

In Lesson 1, students plan and carry out investigations to gather evidence to determine if matter is conserved during chemical reactions that occur in open and closed systems **(SEP Planning and Carrying Out Investigations, CCC Energy and Matter).** They use mathematical representations to show that atoms are conserved and that their properties can be used to predict chemical reactions **(SEP Using Mathematics and Computational Thinking, DCI PS1.B, CCC Energy and Matter).** Students balance chemical equations and predict the outcome of different types of chemical reactions based on chemical properties **(SEP Using Mathematics and Computational Thinking, DCI PS1.B, CCC Patterns).**

Lesson 2
Analyzing Chemical Reactions

In Lesson 2, students use mathematical representations to explain that matter is conserved in chemical reactions and that reactions can be described in terms of particles, atoms, moles, or mass **(SEP Using Mathematics and Computational Thinking, DCI PS1.B, CCC Scientific Knowledge Assumes an Order and Consistency in Natural Systems).** They explain how chemical engineers optimize chemical processes to reduce side reactions, which lower the efficiency of reactions **(DCI ETS1.A, CCC Science is a Human Endeavor).** Students apply their knowledge of chemical reactions in a case study about the effects of greenhouse gas emissions **(CCC Science Addresses Questions About the Natural and Material World).**

Lesson 3
Investigating Energy in Chemical Reactions

In Lesson 3, students use equations and graphs as models to explain changes of energy and matter due to rearrangements of atoms during reactions **(SEP Developing and Using Models, DCI PS3.B, DCI PS3.D, CCC Systems and System Models).** They use models to describe how changes of energy and matter in reactions produce stable molecules **(DCI PS1.A, DCI PS1.B, CCC Energy and Matter).** Students consider how the sum of all bond energies relates to changes in energy and matter during endothermic and exothermic reactions **(DCI PS1.A, DCI PS1.B).** They identify criteria and constraints of combustion fuels and consider impacts on society and the environment from fossil fuel use **(SEP Constructing Explanations and Designing Solutions, DCI ETS1.A, DCI ETS1.B, CCC Influence of Engineering, Technology, and Science on Society and the Natural World).**

 You Solve It Go online to access an interactive simulation.

NGSS across This Unit

 Explore Online

Next Generation Science Standards	Unit Project	Lesson 1	Lesson 2	Lesson 3	Unit Performance Task	You Solve It
SEP Asking Questions and Defining Problems	•			•	•	
SEP Developing and Using Models	•			•		•
SEP Planning and Carrying Out Investigations		•	•	•	•	
SEP Using Mathematical and Computational Thinking	•	•	•	•	•	
DCI **PS1.A** Structure and Properties of Matter	•			•		•
DCI **PS1.B** Chemical Reactions	•	•	•	•	•	•
DCI **PS3.B** Conservation of Energy and Energy Transfer				•	•	
DCI **ETS1.A** Defining and Delimiting Engineering Problems	•		•	•	•	•
CCC Energy and Matter	•	•	•	•	•	•
CCC Scientific Knowledge Assumes an Order and Consistency in Natural Systems	•		•	•		

NGSS across the Grades

Middle School

MS-PS1-1 Develop models to describe the atomic composition of simple molecules and extended structures.

MS-PS1-2 Analyze and interpret data on the properties of substances before and after the substances interact to determine if a chemical reaction has occurred.

MS-PS1-4 Develop a model that predicts and describes changes in particle motion, temperature, and state of a pure substance when thermal energy is added or removed.

MS-PS1-5 Develop and use a model to describe how the total number of atoms does not change in a chemical reaction and thus mass is conserved.

Grades 9–12

HS-PS1-2
HS-PS1-4
HS-PS1-7
HS-PS3-4
HS-ETS1-4

▶ **Trace Tool to the NGSS** Go online to view the complete coverage of standards across lessons and units.

Differentiate Instruction

Differentiate with Technology

Computer Simulations
The study of chemical reactions can take several forms. Computer simulations can help students understand how reactions occur and can show the differences among different types of reactions. Many computer simulation programs are available on the Internet. Each program has a different emphasis, so be sure the program you choose to use for your class accomplishes your goals.

Photographs and Videos
Students may wish to take photographs of the reactions they observe in class. Color changes, formation of a precipitate, formation of gas bubbles, and release of energy as light are all indications that a chemical reaction has taken place. Phenomena can be recorded using cell phones. The progress of reactions can be recorded in videos for comparison purposes.

3D Modeling Software
Students can use free 3D modeling software to build models of molecules. Have students identify the atoms and their arrangements within molecules.

Key Word Support

Key Words
chemical reaction *Lesson 1*
law of conservation of mass *Lesson 1*
chemical equation *Lesson 1*
coefficient *Lesson 1*
mole *Lesson 2*
conversion factor *Lesson 2*
molar mass *Lesson 2*
limiting reactant *Lesson 2*
excess reactant *Lesson 2*
potential energy *Lesson 3*
kinetic energy *Lesson 3*
thermal energy *Lesson 3*
law of conservation of energy *Lesson 3*
specific heat capacity *Lesson 3*
exothermic reaction *Lesson 3*
endothermic reaction *Lesson 3*

Reinforcing Key Words
To help students build key word knowledge for this unit, have them use a Venn diagram to compare and contrast pairs of related terms, such as **endothermic reaction/exothermic reaction, potential energy/kinetic energy,** and **limiting reactant/excess reactant.**

Greek and Latin Word Parts
Encourage students to look for common Greek and Latin prefixes as they encounter new vocabulary. For this unit, point out the prefix *exo-* (outside) and *endo-* (inside). Have students develop a list of words that begin with *exo-* and *endo-*.

Academic Vocabulary
Ask students to make a graphic organizer to show how key words and academic vocabulary are related to one another. For example, students can pair *law of conservation of mass* with the concept of conservation as a saving. Encourage students to write a short definition for each term in their graphic organizer to help them recall the terms.

English Language Learners
Students may struggle with using vocabulary when participating in discussions or expressing thoughts in writing. Engage students by having them describe terms or processes in their own words.

ELL
ELL teaching strategies in this unit include

Lesson 1 p. 233
Lesson 2 pp. 254, 266
Lesson 3 pp. 285, 295

MTSS/ RTI
Strategies for students who need extra support in this unit include

Lesson 1 pp. 241, 244
Lesson 2 p. 257
Lesson 3 pp. 279, 289

Extension
Strategies for students who have mastered core content in this unit include

Lesson 1 pp. 233 , 246
Lesson 2 pp. 259, 263
Lesson 3 pp. 285, 292

Making Connections

Connections to Community

Use these opportunities for informal science learning
to provide local context and to extend and enhance unit concepts.

At Home

FOOD PREPARATION Many food products are prepared by chemical
reactions. For example, the making of cheese uses rennet to break down
proteins in milk. Sauerkraut and other fermented foods are made by
chemical reactions. Have students research and make a list of five chemical
reactions that take place during the production of food products. Chemical
reactions also take place when food is cooked. For example, baking soda
combines with weak acids in cake batter to produce carbon dioxide.
Chocolate, molasses, and buttermilk are all weakly acidic. The bubbles of carbon dioxide are
produced only when the mixture is heated. Have students determine whether cooking reactions
are endothermic or exothermic and explain their reasoning. *Use with Lessons 1 and 3.*

In the Community

CONSTRUCTION Students can investigate the role the law of conservation of mass plays during
a construction project, whether it involves putting together a piece of furniture or constructing
a building. Have students find out more about a current or recent construction project in the
community. How does building a structure relate to a balanced chemical equation? Ask students
to write down how to relate the construction process to the following terms: product, reactant,
coefficient, limiting reagent, and excess reagent. Have students identify how a construction
company's profit may be thought of in terms of chemical stoichiometry. *Use with Lessons 1 and 2.*

Culture

CONCEALING KNOWLEDGE Many cultures made discoveries in ancient alchemy, and they often
used stories to hide the knowledge from the "uninitiated." In stories such as those by the Arabic
alchemist Jabir ibn Hayyan's Kitab al-sab'in or the Chinese ancients' formula for fireworks, the
information was hidden out of order, in code, or in units and relationships that would be known
only to that culture. This provided not only an economic advantage but also a tactical one by
hiding knowledge from an enemy. Have students examine texts in early alchemy from different
cultures and report how they hid the stoichiometry. *Use with Lessons 1 and 2.*

Home Letters Use these letters to engage family members with unit concepts.

Collaborate

Opportunities for students to work collaboratively in this unit:

Discussion pp. 240, 256, 266, 283

Draw-Pair-Share, Think-Pair-Share pp. 245, 261

Take and Pass p. 239

Connections to Other Disciplines

Opportunities to connect to other content areas in this unit:

Biology Connection p. 286

Earth Science Connection pp. 246, 263, 276

Engineering Connection p. 290

Language Arts Connection pp. 234, 257, 269, 275, 287, 291

Math Connection pp. 239, 242, 255, 257, 258, 260, 275, 281

3D Unit Planning

Lesson 1 Observing and Modeling Chemical Reactions pp. 231–252

Overview

Objective Students develop and use models, including balanced chemical equations, to describe the conservation of mass in chemical reactions.

SEP Planning and Carrying Out Investigations
SEP Using Mathematics and Computational Thinking
SEP Constructing Explanations and Designing Solutions
DCI **PS1.B** Chemical Reactions
CCC Energy and Matter
CCC Patterns

Math and **English Language Arts** standards and features are detailed on lesson planning pages.

Print and Online Student Editions

		Explore Online ▶
ENGAGE	**Investigative Phenomenon** p. 231 **Can You Explain the Phenomenon?** Rusting is the corrosion of iron that appears as a reddish-brown deposit. Why might iron corrode more quickly than other metals? Why is rusting more pronounced in some environments than others?	**ELA Handbook**
EXPLORE/ EXPLAIN	🧪 **Evaluating Systems in Chemical Reactions** p. 232 **Exploring the Conservation of Mass** p. 237 **Modeling Chemical Reactions** p. 241 **Problem Solving** Balancing Chemical Equations	**Hands-On Lab Worksheet** **Hands-On Lab Teacher Support** **Lab Safety Handbook** **Math Handbook** **Video** Combustion Reaction
ELABORATE	**Take It Further** p. 248 🧪 **Modeling the Conservation of Mass**	**Take It Further** 🧪 The Composition of Hydrates **Hands-On Lab Worksheets** **Hands-On Lab Teacher Support** **Lab Safety Handbook** More Practice with Balancing Equations Fluoride and Your Teeth
EVALUATE	**Lesson Self-Check** p. 250	**Lesson Quiz**

🧪 Hands-On Lab Planning

Evaluating Systems in Chemical Reactions

⏱ 90 minutes
👥 Small Groups

Objective Students plan and carry out an investigation in which they describe and quantify changes in matter in chemical reactions and explore the conservation of matter in closed systems.

Materials
- balance
- balloon, nonlatex
- Bunsen burner
- calcium chloride (5–10 g)
- crucible with lid
- Erlenmeyer flask, 250 mL
- funnel
- graduated cylinder, 25 mL
- magnesium ribbon (5 cm)
- resealable plastic bag
- sodium bicarbonate (5–10 g)
- spoons or spatulas (2)
- tongs
- water, 25mL
- weighing boats or weighing paper (4)

Modeling the Conservation of Mass

⏱ 90 minutes
👥 Small Groups

Objective Students develop a model of a chemical reaction and use their model to demonstrate the conservation of matter.

Materials
- balance
- beads
- chemical modeling kit
- computer
- glue
- nuts and bolts
- paper clips
- paper
- polystyrene-foam balls
- scissors
- snap-together blocks
- string
- tape
- toothpicks
- trays, plastic (2)

Additional Downloadable Lab Option
Composition of Hydrates

⏱ 90 minutes
👥 Small Groups

Objective Students analyze how much water is released when varying amounts of copper sulfate pentahydrate are heated.

3D Unit Planning, continued

Lesson 2 Analyzing Chemical Reactions pp. 253–272

Overview

Objective Students analyze how matter in chemical reactions can be quantified.

SEP Planning and Carrying Out Investigations
SEP Using Mathematics and Computational Thinking
SEP Scientific Investigations Use a Variety of Methods
DCI **PS1.B** Chemical Reactions
DCI **ETS1.A** Defining and Delimiting Engineering Problems
CCC Scale, Proportion, and Quantity
CCC Energy and Matter
CCC Scientific Knowledge Assumes an Order and Consistency in Natural Systems
CCC Science Addresses Questions About the Natural and Material World

Math and **English Language Arts** standards and features are detailed on lesson planning pages.

Print and **Online** Student Editions

Explore Online ▶

ENGAGE

Investigative Phenomenon p. 253
Can You Solve the Problem? Suppose you wanted to optimize the fuel mixture used for a space flight in order to avoid the presence of excess fuel. What questions would you ask to get started?

ELA Handbook

EXPLORE/ EXPLAIN

Quantifying Matter in Chemical Reactions p. 254
    Problem Solving Calculating Molar Amounts
    Problem Solving Calculating Mass
Limiting and Excess Matter p. 259
    Problem Solving Determining Limiting and Excess Reactants
    Maximizing Percent Yield
Case Study: Greenhouse Gas Emissions p. 263
 Gravimetric Analysis p. 265

Math Handbook
Hands-On Lab Worksheet
Hands-On Lab Teacher Support
Lab Safety Handbook

ELABORATE

Guided Research p. 269
Redefining the Mole

Careers in Science: Atmospheric Scientist
Explaining Stoichiometry
More Practice with Stoichiometry

EVALUATE

Lesson Self-Check p. 270

Lesson Quiz

Hands-On Lab Planning

Gravimetric Analysis

🕐 Two 45-minute class periods
👥 Small Groups

Objective Students use gravimetric methods to measure the mass of an insoluble precipitate formed in a double-displacement reaction. Students then use stoichiometry to relate the mass of precipitate formed to the mass of reactants and explain to a company how to use this technique in the future.

Materials
- beaker tongs
- beakers, 250 mL (3)
- distilled water
- drying oven
- electronic balance
- filter paper
- glass funnel or Büchner funnel
- glass stirring rod
- graduated cylinder, 100 mL

- paper towel
- ring and ring stand
- rubber policeman
- sodium carbonate, Na_2CO_3, solution
- spatula
- strontium chloride, $SrCl_2$, solution, 0.30 M
- wash bottle

Advance Preparation Prepare the 0.30 M strontium chloride, solution by adding 47.56 g of to a final volume of 1.00 L of distilled water. Prepare the 0.50 M sodium carbonate, solution by adding 53.99g of to a final volume of 1.00 L of distilled water. When students calculate their percentage error, they may need help understanding the results. If their results are higher than the actual concentration, they will get a positive value. If their results are less than the actual concentration, they will get a negative value.

Lesson 3 Investigating Energy in Chemical Reactions pp. 273–298

Overview

Objective Students analyze changes in energy during chemical reactions and use different types of models to describe the changes that occur.

SEP Developing and Using Models
SEP Using Mathematics and Computational Thinking
SEP Constructing Explanations and Designing Solutions
DCI **PS1.A** Structure and Properties of Matter
DCI **PS1.B** Chemical Reactions
DCI **PS3.B** Conservation of Energy and Energy Transfer
DCI **PS3.D** Energy in Chemical Processes
CCC Systems and System Models
CCC Energy and Matter

Math and **English Language Arts** standards and features are detailed on lesson planning pages.

Print and Online Student Editions

Explore Online

ENGAGE | **Investigative Phenomenon** p. 273
Can You Explain the Phenomenon? What do you think is the source of the energy in a chemical reaction, such as the reaction that occurs when you light a sparkler?

ELA Handbook

EXPLORE/ EXPLAIN | **Investigating Thermal Energy and Heat** p. 274
 Math Connection Temperature Scales
 Exploring Thermal Energy and Temperature
 Measuring the Energy in Food p. 280
Exploring Reaction Energy p. 283
Case Study: Energy in Fuels p. 289
 Fuel Alternatives

Math Handbook
Video Energy Transfer
 Experimenting with Calorimetry
Videos Examples of Changes in Energy
 Investigating Energy in Chemical Processes
Hands-On Lab Worksheets
Hands-On Lab Teacher Support
Lab Safety Handbook

ELABORATE | **Take It Further** p. 295
Careers in Science Computational Chemist

Explaining Endothermic and Exothermic Processes
Photosynthesis and Respiration
Alternatives in Fuel Sources

EVALUATE | **Lesson Self-Check** p. 296

Lesson Quiz

Hands-On Lab Planning

Exploring Thermal Energy and Temperature

⏱ 30 minutes	**Objective** Students plan and carry out an investigation to explore the relationship between thermal energy and temperature of two systems of water.	**Materials**
👥 Pairs		• beaker, 500 mL (3)
		• thermometer (3)
		• water

Additional Downloadable Lab Options
Measuring the Energy in Food

⏱ 90 minutes	**Materials**	• snack foods with nutrition labels, two types (cheese puff, marshmallow, dry cereal, etc.)
👥 Small Groups	• aluminum foil, 30 cm × 30 cm sheet	
Objective Students investigate the concept of calories by combusting small samples of food using a simple calorimeter.	• balance	• soda can
	• beaker tongs	• spatula
	• evaporating dish	• thermometer
	• graduated cylinder, 100 mL	• thermometer clamp
	• matches or propane lighter	• three-finger clamp
	• ring and clamp	• water
	• ring stand	• weighing boat or weighing paper (2)
		• wire gauze

Experimenting with Calorimetry

| ⏱ 60 minutes | **Objective** Students build a calorimeter and test it by using it to determine the specific heat capacity of a known sample. Students explain that successful designs use materials that minimize the amount of energy lost to the surroundings. |
| 👥 Small Groups | |

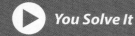 **You Solve It** Go online for an additional interactive activity and teacher support.

Why Use Diesel?

This interactive activity offers practice in support of **HS-PS1-4, ETS1-1,** and **ETS1-3.**

SEP Developing and Using Models
DCI **PS1.A** Structure and Properties of Matter
DCI **PS1.B** Chemical Reactions
DCI **ETS1.A** Defining and Delimiting Engineering Problems
DCI **ETS1.B** Developing Possible Solutions
CCC Energy and Matter

Learning Objective

Students use simulations to gather evidence and to analyze the factors that influence why alternative fuels have not replaced diesel fuel.

Activity Problem

Students are given a scenario in which they will investigate why cleaner, alternative fuels have not replaced diesel fuel. Students investigate the energy content of diesel, propane, and ethanol and evaluate them based on criteria such as pollution emission, cost, and availability. Students make a claim to explain why diesel fuel is still used more than alternative fuels and the characteristics of an ideal fuel. They support their claims with evidence from their simulations and the fuel data table. Students then explain their reasoning about how the evidence supports their claims.

Interaction Summary

This You Solve It offers students the opportunity to choose a fuel and to investigate the energy content of different hydrocarbon-based fuels and their environmental and economic impacts. Students then analyze data generated by the simulation, evaluating the energy content of the fuel versus its emissions and costs. Students construct an explanation of the best fuel to use based on these parameters.

Assessment Planning

Preassessment
Assessment Guide, Unit Pretest

Formative Assessment
Interactive Worktext: Explorations, Lesson Self-Check

Summative Assessment
Assessment Guide, Lesson Quiz

Interactive Worktext: Unit Performance Task, p. 304

Interactive Worktext: Unit Practice and Review, p. 305

Assessment Guide, Unit Test and Modified Unit Test

HMH Field Trips
powered by
Google Expeditions

Go to **hmhco.com/fieldtrips** for 3D, 360-degree experiences to share with your students. A Teacher Guide is also available to help you customize the experience.

Unit Project

Modeling Heat Efficiency

3D Learning Objective

Students apply their understanding of chemical reactions and heat transfer to design, test, and optimize a model of energy efficiency in heating a building.

Students model the chemical reaction of the combustion of methane to support the claim that atoms, and mass, are conserved during a chemical reaction. Then they design and build a model building to solve the problem of maximizing efficiency of energy use to reduce the negative effects of greenhouse emissions. They test and optimize their design based on the criteria and constraints of the engineering problem.

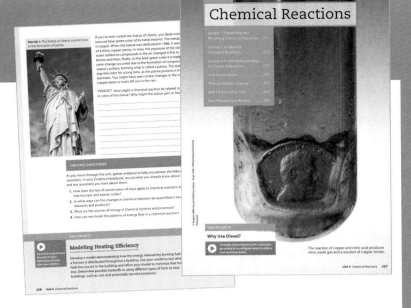

NGSS Focus

The project supports building student mastery of **Performance Expectations HS-PS1-2, HS-PS1-4, HS-PS1-7, HS-ETS1-1, and HS-ETS1-2.** Students construct explanations for the outcome of a simple chemical reaction and use mathematical representations to support the claim that atoms are conserved during a chemical reaction. Then they model energy flow and optimization of a heating system to solve the larger engineering problem of global warming.

Science and Engineering Practices

- Asking Questions and Defining Problems
- Developing and Using Models
- Using Mathematics and Computational Thinking
- Constructing Explanations and Designing Solutions

Disciplinary Core Ideas

- **PS1.A** Structure and Properties of Matter
- **PS1.B** Chemical Reactions
- **ETS1.A** Defining and Delimiting Engineering Problems
- **ETS1.C** Optimizing the Design Solution

Crosscutting Concepts

- Patterns
- Energy and Matter
- Scientific Knowledge Assumes an Order and Consistency in Natural Systems
- Influence of Engineering, Technology, and Science on Society and the Natural World

Classroom Management

- Small Groups
- Three 45-minute class periods

Suggested Materials

- See the procedure for detailed materials list for the lab. Students will also need a computer with Internet access.
- In addition to the materials on the list, you may wish to work with students to acquire easily obtainable materials that can be adapted and used in their designs. Encourage using discarded or previously used materials in the devices. Gather materials after the project is completed for reuse or recycling.

Safety

- Remind students to wear safety goggles during the setup, hands-on, and takedown parts of the activity.
- Remind students to use caution with sharp tools, which can cut or puncture skin.
- Have students pick up dropped items from the floor so they don't become a slip/fall hazard.
- Remind students to keep flammable materials away from heat sources, including light bulbs.

Suggested Resources

- **The U.S. Department of Energy** has numerous articles and scientific literature on heat distribution systems.
- **NBBI:** The National Board of Boiler and Pressure Vessel Inspectors has resources on the chemistry and safety of combustion reactions in furnaces.

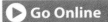

Go Online

Go online to download the teacher version of the student worksheet for this unit project, which includes additional questions, sample answers, and additional scaffolding to help students use evidence and reasoning to support their claims.

Unit Project, continued

Getting Started

Introducing the Project

Prepare students for their investigation by asking the following questions:

- **How is reducing heat loss from a building's heating system part of the engineering solution to a larger global problem?**
- **Do heating systems involve exothermic or endothermic reactions? Explain your answer.**
- **How could you use a physical model to test methods for reducing heat loss from a building's heating system?**

Student Deliverables

A **student worksheet** is available to help students in planning and completing the project. Students can turn in their worksheets, or they can be assessed on a final lab report, their models, and/or final presentations explaining their project. Evidence Notebook prompts throughout the unit refer to the Unit Project to help keep its connection to the investigative phenomenon present in students' minds.

Students should document the steps they take in designing, testing, and optimizing their heating system project to explain how the steps apply to the engineering design process.

Scoring Rubric for Unit Project	
	The combustion model (chemical equation) was correct and used to support claims.
	The model was designed to test the efficiency of heating.
	The student correctly used evidence in their reasoning for their claims.
	The student presentation is clear and logical.
	The student demonstrates conceptual understanding of the production of energy by combustion.

Guiding Students on Project Planning

Once students understand the project goals and their deliverables, they should conduct research and develop presentations. Ask questions that spur their thinking about ways they might proceed in designing and implementing their project. Consider asking the following questions:

- **How will you collect data?**
  Students should consider how they will measure the effects of the specific factors they have selected in terms of their design criteria. For example, how will they qualitatively and quantitatively measure heat and emission production?

- **What criteria and constraints will need to be addressed?**
  Remind students that criteria are things that the designer wants the solution to do and constraints are restrictions and limitations on the solution, including environmental and economic limitations.

- **What chemical reactions will take place in a furnace that is used to heat a building? What are the reactants? What are the products?**
  Students might identify a combustion reaction in which a fossil fuel such as natural gas or coal is burned. Students should recognize that carbon dioxide and sometimes toxic carbon monoxide are products of this type of reaction and that emission of these products is a factor students must consider in designing their heating system.

Be sure to review and approve project plans before students begin. The Unit Project Worksheet can be used for formal approval.

Differentiate Instruction

MTSS/RTI Encourage students to take on certain responsibilities as part of the team. For example, one student may be responsible for developing the project sketches, one responsible for organizing the construction of the model home, and the third could be responsible for developing the test procedure. Group members should discuss their plans with one another early and often.

Extension Have interested students explore heating systems that do not use energy from combustion reactions to produce heat. They might research solar energy, electrical energy, hydrothermal energy, or geothermal energy. Students should explore the source of the energy that heats each system and determine whether this energy comes from breaking of chemical bonds in substances or from other sources. Students may also wish to determine the efficiency, cost, and constraints of such systems.

UNIT 4

Chemical Reactions

© Houghton Mifflin Harcourt Publishing Company • Image Credits: ©Richard Megna-Fundamental Photographs

YOU SOLVE IT

Why Use Diesel?

 To begin exploring this unit's concepts, go online to investigate ways to solve a real-world problem.

The reaction of copper and nitric acid produces nitric oxide gas and a solution of copper nitrate.

The learning experiences in this unit prepare students for mastery of

Performance Expectations

HS-PS1-2 Construct and revise an explanation for the outcome of a simple chemical reaction based on the outermost electron states of atoms, trends in the periodic table, and knowledge of the patterns of chemical properties.

HS-PS1-4 Develop a model to illustrate that the release or absorption of energy from a chemical reaction system depends upon the changes in total bond energy.

HS-PS1-7 Use mathematical representations to support the claim that atoms, and therefore mass, are conserved during a chemical reaction.

HS-PS3-4 Plan and conduct an investigation to provide evidence that the transfer of thermal energy when two components of different temperature are combined within a closed system results in a more uniform energy distribution among the components in the system (second law of thermodynamics).

HS-ETS1-4 Use a computer simulation to model the impact of proposed solutions to a complex real-world problem with numerous criteria and constraints on interactions within and between systems relevant to the problem.

Explore Online ▶

In addition to the print resources, the following resources are available online to support this unit:

Lesson 1 Observing and Modeling Chemical Reactions
- Interactive Online Student Edition
- Lesson Quiz

Lesson 2 Analyzing Chemical Reactions
- Interactive Online Student Edition
- Lesson Quiz

Lesson 3 Investigating Energy in Chemical Reactions
- Interactive Online Student Edition
- Lesson Quiz

You Solve It Why Use Diesel?

Unit Performance Task

Unit Test

Unit Prerequisite Knowledge

Students should understand these concepts before starting the unit:

- One mole contains 6.022×10^{23} units of a substance.
- Energy can be stored in chemical and bonds.
- Chemical reactions follow the law of conservation of mass.
- Chemical reactions follow the law of conservation of energy.

Collaborate

Driving Questions You may wish to have students discuss their initial thoughts about the Driving Questions for this unit with a partner before you discuss the questions as a class. Encourage students to record the questions and their initial responses in their Evidence Notebook.

Anchoring Phenomenon

Modeling Heat Efficiency

SEP Developing and Using Models

An anchoring phenomenon connects student learning across the lessons in a unit. The Unit Project serves as an anchoring phenomenon as students synthesize what they learn about mass and energy in chemical reactions in Lessons 1–3 to make a model of a furnace and refine it using engineering design process principles.

Tips on Cultivating Questions Have students compare the size, the workings, and the fuels used in old furnaces with those of modern furnaces. If possible, display pictures of old furnaces. Have students ask questions and discuss how building heating has improved.

1 Encourage students to apply what they have learned about compounds and chemical changes. Students should mention how compounds in the air react with the metal, which can change the color of the statue or increase its mass. If something in air forms a compound with the metal without forming another product, such as a gas, the law of conservation of mass would indicate that the mass of the compound would be greater than that of the pure metal alone.

FIGURE 1: The Statue of Liberty is green due to the formation of patina.

If you've ever visited the Statue of Liberty, you likely noticed the unusual blue-green color of its metal exterior. The metal, however, is copper. When the statue was dedicated in 1886, it was the color of a shiny copper penny. In time, the exposure of the statue's outer surface to compounds in the air changed it first to a dull brown and then, finally, to the blue-green color it is today. This color change occurred due to the formation of compounds on the statue's surface, forming what is called a patina. The statue will stay this color for a long time, as the patina protects it from further reactions. You might have seen similar changes in the color of copper pipes or tools left out in the rain.

1 **PREDICT** How might a chemical reaction be related to the change in color of the statue? Why might the statue gain or lose mass?

_____

_____

_____

_____

_____

_____

_____

DRIVING QUESTIONS

As you move through the unit, gather evidence to help you answer the following questions. In your Evidence Notebook, record what you already know about these topics and any questions you have about them.

1. How does the law of conservation of mass apply to chemical reactions at both the macroscopic and atomic scales?
2. In what ways can the changes in chemical reactions be quantified in terms of reactants and products?
3. What are the sources of energy in chemical systems and processes?
4. How can we model the patterns of energy flow in a chemical reaction?

UNIT PROJECT

Go online to download the Unit Project Worksheet to help plan your project.

Modeling Heating Efficiency

Develop a model demonstrating how the energy released by burning fuel in a furnace is distributed throughout a building. Use your model to test where heat loss occurs in the building and refine your model to minimize that heat loss. Determine possible tradeoffs in using different types of fuels to heat buildings, such as cost and potentially harmful emissions.

Language Development

Use the lessons in this unit to complete the chart and expand your understanding of the science concepts.

TERM: chemical reaction

Definition	Example

Similar Term	Phrase

TERM: chemical equation

Definition	Example

Similar Term	Phrase

TERM: law of conservation of mass

Definition	Example

Similar Term	Phrase

TERM: mole

Definition	Example

Similar Term	Phrase

Language Development

The summary chart graphic organizer allows students to practice using unit vocabulary to convey meaning and to communicate clearly. The chart shown, which is continued on the next page, may not include every unit vocabulary term.

Using the Chart As you encounter a highlighted vocabulary term within the unit, direct students to fill in the corresponding boxes in the summary chart. Students should always fill in the Definition box, but they need not fill in all others. Students can write a cognate from their home language in the Similar Term box. Students whose home language is English can fill in a synonym or word with the same root (such as *atomic* for the word *atom*). Accept all reasonable answers. If desired, hand out to students a blank summary chart. Work with students to complete the charts for each word. You may also ask students to work in pairs and then share and compare their work with that of their classmates.

Students can explore all vocabulary terms in the Online Glossary. A multilingual glossary is also available online.

SAMPLE ANSWERS

chemical reaction: the process by which one or more substances change to produce one or more different substances; the reaction between lithium metal and water; reacción química; The process of burning wood is a chemical reaction between the wood and oxygen.

chemical equation: a representation of a chemical reaction that uses symbols to show the relationship between the reactants and the products; $2H_2 + O_2 \longrightarrow 2H_2O$; ecuación química; Chemists balance chemical equations using the law of conservation of mass.

law of conservation of mass: the law that states that mass cannot be created or destroyed but can be changed from one form to another; a chemical reaction; ley de la conservación de la masa; The mass of the reactants equals the mass of the products during a chemical reaction.

mole: the amount of a substance whose number of particles is the same as the number of atoms of carbon in exactly 12 g of carbon-12; a mole of water has a mass of 18 g; mol; The mole is a counting unit.

SAMPLE ANSWERS

specific heat capacity: the quantity of heat required to raise a unit mass of homogeneous material 1 K or 1 °C in a specific way given constant pressure and volume; the specific heat of liquid water is 4.18 J/(g·K); capacidad de calor específico; Water has a high specific heat capacity, so its temperature remains relatively stable when energy is applied.

law of conservation of energy: the law that states that energy cannot be created or destroyed but can be changed from one form to another; storing electrical energy in a battery; ley de la conservación de la energía; Energy is conserved when burning gas.

exothermic reaction: a chemical reaction in which energy is released to the surroundings as heat; a burning sparkler; reacción exotérmica; The burning of a piece of wood is an exothermic reaction that releases energy in the form of heat and light.

endothermic reaction: chemical reaction that requires energy input; the reaction used in a cold pack; reacción endotérmica; An endothermic reaction occurs when energy is absorbed by the system from its surroundings.

TERM: **specific heat capacity**

Definition	Example
Similar Term	Phrase

TERM: **law of conservation of energy**

Definition	Example
Similar Term	Phrase

TERM: **exothermic reaction**

Definition	Example
Similar Term	Phrase

TERM: **endothermic reaction**

Definition	Example
Similar Term	Phrase

Observing and Modeling Chemical Reactions

Building to the Performance Expectations

The learning experiences in this lesson prepare students for mastery of

HS-PS1-2 Construct and revise an explanation for the outcome of a simple chemical reaction based on the outermost electron states of atoms, trends in the periodic table, and knowledge of the patterns of chemical properties.

HS-PS1-7 Use mathematical representations to support the claim that atoms, and therefore mass, are conserved during a chemical reaction.

 Trace Tool to the NGSS

Go online to view the complete coverage of standards across lessons, units, and grade levels.

 **Science & Engineering Practices**

Using Mathematics and Computational Thinking
Use mathematical representations of phenomena to support claims.

Constructing Explanations and Designing Solutions
Construct and revise an explanation based on valid and reliable evidence obtained from a variety of sources (including students' own investigations, models, theories, simulations, and peer review) and the assumption that theories and laws that describe the natural world operate today as they did in the past and will continue to do so in the future.

 VIDEO Constructing Scientific Explanations

 **Disciplinary Core Ideas**

PS1.B Chemical Reactions
The fact that atoms are conserved, together with knowledge of the chemical properties of the elements involved, can be used to describe and predict chemical reactions. (HS-PS1-2) (HS-PS1-7)

 **Crosscutting Concepts**

Energy and Matter
The total amount of energy and matter in closed systems is conserved.

▶ **VIDEO** Matter

Patterns
Different patterns may be observed at each of the scales at which a system is studied and can provide evidence for causality in explanations of phenomena.

MATH STANDARDS

HSN-Q.A.2 Define appropriate quantities for the purpose of descriptive modeling.

HSN-Q.A.3 Choose a level of accuracy appropriate to limitations on measurement when reporting quantities.

MP.2 Reason abstractly and quantitatively.

ELA STANDARDS

WHST.9-12.2 Write informative/explanatory texts, including the narration of historical events, scientific procedures/experiments, or technical processes.

WHST.9-12.5 Develop and strengthen writing as needed by planning, revising, editing, rewriting, or trying a new approach, focusing on addressing what is most significant for a specific purpose and audience.

Supporting All Students, All Standards

Integrating the Three Dimensions

In this lesson, students demonstrate the conservation of atoms and mass in a chemical reaction (CCC Energy and Matter) using models and mathematical representations (SEP Using Mathematics and Computational Thinking). Students also use knowledge of the chemical properties of elements and the organization of elements on the periodic table to predict and explain (SEP Constructing Explanations and Designing Solutions) the outcome of chemical reactions (DCI PS1.B Chemical Reactions). These explanations of chemical reactions are based on patterns observed at the microscopic scale and the macroscopic scale (CCC Patterns).

Preassessment

Have students complete the unit pretest or see the Assessment Guide.

Build on Prior Knowledge

Have students consider what they know about the composition of the atom and atomic theory. Review the periodic table and how elements are organized by atomic number and the number of valence electrons.

You also may want to review the following concepts:
- Atoms are the smallest unit of an element that retains the properties of the element.
- Atoms are made up of protons, neutrons, and electrons.
- Protons and neutrons exist in a small space called the nucleus.
- Because protons are positively charged, the nucleus is positively charged.
- Electrons are located in the space around the nucleus and are small, lightweight particles.
- Interactions between atoms are governed by opposite-charge attraction and like-charge repulsion.
- Patterns in the number of valence electrons are apparent on the periodic table, and these patterns can be used to predict how atoms will combine.

Professional Development Go online to view **Professional Development videos** with strategies to integrate CCCs and SEPs, including the ones used in this lesson.

Content Background

Chemical reactions occur when atoms and molecules collide with one another. The collision must occur with enough energy and at the correct orientation for the reaction to occur. In a chemical reaction, bonds break in reactant molecules, and bonds form in product molecules. A chemical equation is a summary statement of what happens during a chemical reaction. Because a chemical equation is a summary, a reaction that has a very simple chemical equation may occur in several intermediate steps that are not shown in the chemical equation. Chemical equations must be balanced to accurately reflect the law of conservation of mass.

Classifying chemical reactions into different types, such as synthesis, decomposition, and displacement, can help students understand chemical reactions. Understanding the patterns in the periodic table that influence how atoms interact to form compounds provides a deeper understanding of how chemical reactions occur.

For example, one atom of the element sodium, Na, from the alkali metals joins with one atom of the element chlorine, Cl, from the halogens to form the compound sodium chloride, NaCl. Other alkali metals and halogens likewise form similar compounds. As another example, the element nickel, Ni, will replace the lead, Pb, in lead nitrate, $Pb(NO_3)_2$, because Ni is more reactive than Pb. Nickel will not replace iron, Fe, in iron(II) nitrate, $Fe(NO_3)_2$, because Ni is less reactive than Fe.

Differentiate Instruction

KEY WORDS
- chemical reaction
- law of conservation of mass
- chemical equation
- coefficient

ELL SUPPORT

Have students collect information about their own learning as they work through this lesson. Have them make a list of questions they have about the various types of reactions and the techniques that help in balancing chemical reactions. Students can work with partners to read materials more closely to answer their questions.

ENGAGE: Investigative Phenomenon

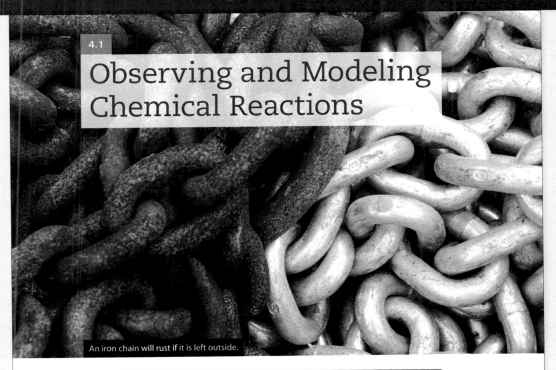

4.1

Observing and Modeling Chemical Reactions

An iron chain **will rust if** it is left outside.

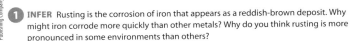

CAN YOU EXPLAIN THE PHENOMENON?

Some metal objects, such as this iron chain, will corrode within a few months if left outdoors. Other objects, such as something made of gold, probably will not. *Corrosion* is the reaction of metals with substances in their environment. Many metals are prone to corrosion. In humid or wet climates, the corrosion of metals is common. In dry climates, however, corrosion is much less prevalent, which explains why automobiles and metal structures in dry areas last longer. Not all corrosion is bad. The green hue on the Statue of Liberty is corrosion that protects the underlying copper from further damage.

1 **INFER** Rusting is the corrosion of iron that appears as a reddish-brown deposit. Why might iron corrode more quickly than other metals? Why do you think rusting is more pronounced in some environments than others?

_____

_____

_____

_____

2 **Evidence Notebook** As you explore the lesson, gather evidence to explain why rust forms and how it can be prevented.

Lesson 1 Observing and Modeling Chemical Reactions **231**

Lesson Objective

Students develop and use models, including balanced chemical equations, to describe the conservation of mass in chemical reactions.

Cultivating Student Questions

Have students look at the photo of chains. Prompt them to ask all questions that come to mind. Questions might involve how much time passed before the chain on the left became rusted, how the rust formed, and what rust is made of. Record the questions, and then sort them based on their focus. With students, narrow the questions down to the ones that directly relate to the learning objective. Have students reflect on this list throughout the lesson and check off questions as they are answered.

Can You Explain the Phenomenon?

The Investigative Phenomenon is the focus of the lesson. Students are asked to record their initial thoughts about the **everyday phenomenon** of rust formation. Have students write a simple word equation that describes what they think happens during rusting. Students will collect evidence related to this phenomenon throughout the lesson and revisit the question at the end of the lesson to use what they have learned to explain chemical reactions.

1 **Sample answer:** Iron might corrode more quickly if it is more reactive than other metals. Corrosion is worse in wet or humid climates. This might mean that water plays an important role in the formation of rust.

Evidence Notebook

2 The topic of the formation of rust will be revisited throughout this lesson.

Lesson 1 Observing and Modeling Chemical Reactions 231

EXPLORATION 1 Evaluating Systems in Chemical Reactions

3D Learning Objective

Students **plan and carry out an investigation** in which they describe and quantify changes in matter in chemical reactions and explore the conservation of matter in closed systems.

Everyday phenomena discussed throughout the Explorations of the lesson can often be used to connect the science content to students' personal experiences.

Hands-On Lab 👥 Small groups ⏱ 90 minutes

Evaluating Systems in Chemical Reactions

SEP **Constructing Explanations and Designing Solutions**

Students plan an investigation in which they record qualitative and quantitative observations of two chemical reactions. Students should consider how the type of system (open or closed) is related to their ability to accurately measure the total mass of the reactants and products. In Part I, the reaction is carried out in an open system. In Part II, students attempt to design a closed system that contains all the products of the reaction (including carbon dioxide gas).

Advance Preparation Before the investigation, organize the lab area so that all materials can be found near where they will be used. Place the weighing boats or weighing paper near the balance, along with spatulas, calcium chloride, and sodium bicarbonate. If possible, set up the required number of lab stations for the number of groups performing the lab, and include at each station the balloons and plastic bags, Bunsen burner, Erlenmeyer flask, graduated cylinder, tongs, water, and magnesium ribbon. The use of a crucible limits the loss of ash and the likelihood that students will stare at the bright white light.

For the reaction in Part I, magnesium also reacts with nitrogen in the air to form magnesium nitride, but this is a minor product. This product can be removed from the original ash by adding a few drops of water and reheating, which releases the nitrogen as ammonia gas.

Hands-On Lab

Evaluating Systems in Chemical Reactions

In your everyday life, you have seen many examples of chemical reactions. Chemical reactions involve the change of one or more substances—the reactants—into one or more different substances—the products. Burning wood is an example of a chemical reaction. The wood and oxygen from the air change into carbon dioxide, water, and ash.

Observable evidence that a chemical change has occurred includes a color change, the formation of a new solid or gas, and the release of energy in the form of light, sound, or heat. Chemical reactions may also absorb energy, leaving the reaction vessel feeling cold to the touch. But how do you quantify the amount of matter consumed and produced by a chemical reaction?

In this lab, you will perform two reactions, each occurring in a different type of system. For each reaction, you should record both qualitative and quantitative data, including evidence that a chemical reaction has occurred and the masses of the reactants and products.

RESEARCH QUESTION How does the flow of energy and matter in chemical reactions in open and closed systems differ? Develop a visual model to explain your findings.

POSSIBLE MATERIALS

- indirectly vented chemical splash goggles, nonlatex apron, nitrile gloves
- balance
- balloon, nonlatex
- Bunsen burner
- calcium chloride, $CaCl_2$, (5–10 g)
- crucible
- Erlenmeyer flask, 250 mL
- funnel
- graduated cylinder, 25 mL
- magnesium, Mg, ribbon, (5 cm)
- resealable plastic bag
- sodium bicarbonate, $NaHCO_3$, (5–10 g)
- spoons or spatulas (2)
- tongs
- water, 25 mL
- weighing boats or weighing paper (4)

SAFETY INFORMATION

- Wear indirectly vented chemical splash goggles, a nonlatex apron, and nitrile gloves during the setup, hands-on, and takedown segments of the activity.
- Use caution when working with Bunsen burners, because this heat source can seriously burn skin and clothing.
- Secure loose clothing, wear closed-toe shoes, and tie back long hair.
- Use tongs to handle magnesium. Never look directly at magnesium when it is burning.
- Never pour chemicals, either used or unused, back into their original container. Dispose of chemicals according to your teacher's instructions.
- Use caution when working with glassware, which can shatter and cut skin.
- Wash your hands with soap and water immediately after completing this activity.

indirectly vented chemical splash goggles

Student Lab Worksheet and complete Teacher Support are available online.

Part I: Burning Magnesium in an Open System

1 MAKE A CLAIM

In Part I, you will burn magnesium in a crucible. Magnesium emits a bright light when burning, as shown in Figure 1, so do not look directly at the burning magnesium. A crucible is an open system. How will the mass of the reactants compare to the mass of the products in an open system?

_____

_____

_____

2 PLAN THE INVESTIGATION

Describe the experimental setup for this investigation. What do you think will happen, and how will you collect and measure any products that form?

_____

_____

_____

In your Evidence Notebook, develop a procedure and a safety plan for your investigation. Have your teacher approve your plans before proceeding.

COLLECT DATA

Collect both quantitative and qualitative data before and after the reaction. Choose an appropriate level of accuracy, and record your data in a table.

ANALYZE

1. What evidence is there that a chemical reaction occurred in Part I?

_____

_____

2. Use your data to compare the reactants and products. Is this what you expected to observe? How would you explain any changes in mass between the reactants and the products?

_____

_____

_____

FIGURE 1: Magnesium is ignited in an open system.

Differentiate Instruction

ELL Support Students who have lived in other countries may use different names for important materials used in the investigation. Be sure students are familiar with the terms _weighing boat, sodium bicarbonate, balance, Bunsen burner, funnel_, and _graduated cylinder_. Encourage students to share the names they are familiar with, but be sure they also recognize and use the terms from the investigation.

Extension Have students determine the percentage of mass gained in Part I, which occurs in an open system. Have them write an equation in words and numbers using data from the experiment.

CCC Energy and Matter

Have students use mathematical concepts to demonstrate that matter can enter or leave an open system but is conserved when the system is closed.

1 Students may claim that a reaction completed in an open system will lose products to or gain reactants from the environment, resulting in products that differ in mass from the original reactants in the system.

2 **Sample answer:** We will burn the magnesium ribbon in the crucible, using the tongs to hold the ribbon and the burner to ignite the magnesium. We think the magnesium will be used up as it burns, and the products will have less mass than the reactants. We will find the mass of the crucible and the magnesium, separately, before the reaction and the mass of the products plus the crucible after the reaction. Subtracting the mass of the crucible will give us the mass of the products.

Analyze

1. Evidence that a chemical reaction occurred includes the production of heat, light, and a white solid.

2. **Sample answer:** The solid product has more mass than the original magnesium, and it looks different. We expected the product to look different, but we also expected the product to have less mass, not more, than the reactant. If it has more mass, that must mean something was added, possibly from the air.

CCC Energy and Matter

Students should recognize that the ability to collect all matter in a chemical reaction also involves the ability to trap any gases generated as the reaction occurs. Help students understand that it is important to correctly measure the mass of a gas that may otherwise have escaped the area.

Language Arts Connection

Have students research calcium chloride and sodium bicarbonate, two of the substances used in the experiment, to find out their common everyday uses in **everyday phenomena.** Calcium chloride is used for melting ice on slick roads at temperatures lower than sodium chloride can be used. Calcium chloride is also used in some single-use heat packs, as its ionization in water is very exothermic. Sodium bicarbonate is baking soda, which is used in baking, as a deodorizer, as a natural toothpaste and deodorant, as an antacid, and to relieve itching of insect bites. Have students write a short advertisement promoting the uses of one of the compounds. **(WHST.9-12.2)**

1 Performing the reaction in an open system caused the measurements of mass for the reactants to be inaccurate. The open system allowed oxygen gas to react with the magnesium to produce magnesium oxide. Evidence of this reaction includes light, heat, formation of a white solid, and the fact that the product had more mass than the reactant. Oxygen was not measured as a reactant. Therefore, the overall mass of the reactants was not measured accurately.

2 Students may claim that the masses of the reactants and products will be the same in a reaction completed in a closed system.

---

1 DRAW CONCLUSIONS

Write a conclusion that addresses each of the points below.

Claim When magnesium metal burns, it reacts with oxygen gas in the air to form a compound called magnesium oxide. How did performing this reaction in an open system affect measurements of mass for the reactants and products?

Evidence Describe evidence from your experiment to support your claim.

Reasoning Explain how the evidence you cited supports your claim. How does your evidence show the effects the open system had on your measurements?

_____

_____

_____

_____

_____

_____

_____

_____

_____

_____

_____

Part II: Capturing Carbon Dioxide Produced in a Closed System

2 MAKE A CLAIM

In Part II, you will design a closed system that will capture all of the products of the chemical reaction, including carbon dioxide gas. How will the mass of the reactants compare to the mass of the products in a closed system?

_____

_____

_____

_____

PLAN THE INVESTIGATION

To perform this experiment, you will combine water, calcium chloride, and sodium bicarbonate in a plastic bag. The closed system should include only these substances. The water you add is not a reactant, but it is necessary for the reaction to proceed because calcium chloride and sodium bicarbonate only react in solution. The products are calcium carbonate, sodium chloride, water, and carbon dioxide. The mass of water can be calculated indirectly by measuring its volume because the density of water is 1.00 g/mL. For example, 30.0 mL of water has a mass of 30.0 g.

© Houghton Mifflin Harcourt Publishing Company

1. Your task is to determine how the mass of the reactants compares to the mass of the products in a closed system. Describe what you think will happen and how you will collect and measure products that form.

_____

_____

_____

_____

2. Draw a diagram that shows your experimental setup to carry out the reaction in a closed system using a plastic bag.

In your Evidence Notebook, develop a procedure and a safety plan for your investigation. Ask your teacher to approve your plans before proceeding.

COLLECT DATA

Collect both quantitative and qualitative data before and after the reaction. Choose an appropriate level of accuracy, and record your data in a table. Consider how you will account for the mass of the container when analyzing your data.

ANALYZE

1. What evidence is there that a chemical reaction occurred in Part II of this lab?

_____

_____

2. Use your data to compare the reactants and products in Part II. Is this what you expected to observe?

_____

_____

_____

_____

_____

Students will collect their gaseous product in a plastic bag. Suggest that they keep their bags overnight to challenge the idea that a "solid" plastic bag is really impervious to the movement of gases. The volume of trapped gas will decrease over time as some of the CO_2 molecules escape through the molecular-size "holes" in the bag. However, in the short time of the lab procedure, very little CO_2 leaves the bag, so the system can be considered closed.

Plan the Investigation

1. **Sample answer:** We will perform the reaction within a sealed plastic bag to trap the carbon dioxide product. We think the bag will expand as the gas forms. We will measure the mass of the empty bag and dry reactants and calculate the mass of water before the experiment. We will also measure the mass of the bag plus the products after the reaction occurs.

2. Diagrams should model how a plastic bag can be used to form a closed system in which to carry out the reaction. Students should isolate the dry reactants in a corner of the bag and then twist the bag several times before adding the water. This will prevent the water from contacting the dry reactants before the bag is resealed. Remind students to keep the trapped air in the bag at a minimum when adding the water. Ensure each system is set up correctly before approving student procedures.

Analyze

1. A gas was produced, and the bag felt cold.

2. **Sample answer:** The mass of the products equaled the mass of the reactants. This is what we expected because only the reactants were placed in the bag, and the seal kept almost all of the gas in.

DCI PS1.B Chemical Reactions

Write the chemical equation for magnesium reacting with oxygen, and have students consider how the law of conservation of mass applies.

Analyze (continued)

3. Students should explain that with quality measurements of all reactants and products, the masses should be the same for a reaction that takes place in a closed system. Students should compare their experimental results from Part II with the results from Part I as evidence to support the claim that closed systems allow you to measure all inputs and outputs.

1 Performing the chemical reaction in a closed system led to accurate measurements of mass for the reactants and products. In Part II, the mass of the products equaled the mass of the reactants. This shows that all reactants and products were accurately measured. Also, no products escaped the system and no unmeasured reactants entered the system.

2 Oxygen gas is more reactive than nitrogen gas. Nitrogen forms a strong triple bond that is hard to break, and oxygen is more electronegative than nitrogen. In determining reactants and products in a chemical reaction, it must be considered whether other reactants react with nitrogen or oxygen in the air.

Evidence Notebook

3 **Sample answer:** Both rusting and the magnesium reaction take place in open systems where air is a factor and changes to the metals occur. One difference between the reactions is that the magnesium is burned to produce magnesium oxide, but the iron does not have to burn to rust. The iron might be interacting with oxygen in the air, just as the magnesium did to form magnesium oxide. Rust could be an iron oxide. I think the iron has more mass after rusting because the mass of the oxygen that reacted is added to the mass of the iron.

FORMATIVE ASSESSMENT

Quick Write Have students write a paragraph summarizing the results of the lab.

---

3. With precise and accurate measurements, do you think the measured mass of reactants will always equal the measured mass of products in a chemical reaction that occurs in a closed system? Use evidence to support your answer.

_____

_____

_____

_____

1 DRAW CONCLUSIONS

Write a conclusion that addresses each of the points below.

Claim How did performing this reaction in a closed system affect measurements of mass for the reactants and products?

Evidence Describe evidence from your experiment to support your claim.

Reasoning Explain how the evidence you cited supports your claim. How does your evidence show the effects the closed system had on your measurements?

_____

_____

_____

_____

_____

_____

_____

_____

_____

_____

_____

_____

_____

_____

2 EXTEND

Air is 78% nitrogen gas and 21% oxygen gas by volume. Which gas is more reactive, and what causes the difference in reactivity? Why must air be considered when determining reactants and products in a chemical reaction?

3 **Evidence Notebook** Compare rusting to your experiment burning magnesium. List similarities and differences between the two reactions, and predict what might be happening in the formation of rust. Do you think a rusty iron chain has more or less mass than the original chain?

EXPLORATION 2 Exploring the Conservation of Mass

EXPLORATION 2

Exploring the Conservation of Mass

Chemists have long observed patterns in the way matter changes when undergoing chemical reactions. In the late 1700s, Antoine Lavoisier, often called the first "modern chemist," hypothesized that matter was never created or destroyed during a chemical reaction. To test this hypothesis, Lavoisier needed to take accurate and precise measurements while performing experiments under controlled conditions. He designed apparatus for his experiments that would prevent gases from escaping. This allowed Lavoisier to carefully weigh the materials before and after his experiments.

Explore Online ▶

Hands-On Lab

The Composition of Hydrates
Analyze how much water is released when varying amounts of copper sulfate pentahydrate are heated.

 Collaborate As a class, discuss why it was important for Lavoisier to measure his experiments accurately and precisely. How might the production of gases have frustrated earlier attempts to understand conservation of mass?

Mass Is Conserved

Through further experimentation, scientists confirmed that when a chemical reaction occurs, the total amount of matter present in a system before the reaction always equals the total amount of matter present after the reaction. So, the total mass of the reactants, or starting materials, equals the total mass of the products, or ending materials. This is known as the law of conservation of mass, and it is illustrated in Figure 2.

FIGURE 2: Hydrogen and oxygen react to form water. Count the number of atoms of hydrogen and oxygen in the reactants and the product. Mass has been conserved.

    →

5 ANALYZE How does this representation of the formation of water, H_2O, from hydrogen gas, H_2, and oxygen gas, O_2, demonstrate the law of conservation of mass? What is the relationship between atoms and mass?

_____
_____
_____
_____
_____
_____

3D Learning Objective

Students use mathematical representations of chemical reactions to support the claim that atoms, and therefore mass, are conserved in chemical reactions. Students observe patterns at microscopic and macroscopic scales to gather evidence of the conservation of mass.

History of Science

Some historians give the label "first modern chemist" to English scientist Robert Boyle. Boyle worked on gas laws, and his 1669 book, _The Skeptical Chemist,_ offered the first modern definition of a chemical element. Have students research Robert Boyle and Antoine Lavoisier to see who they think deserves to be called the first modern chemist.

Explore Online ▶

Hands-On Lab 👥 Small Groups ⏱ 90 minutes

The Composition of Hydrates

SEP **Using Mathematics and Computational Thinking**

Students perform an experiment to calculate the amount of water released when copper sulfate pentahydrate is heated.

Student lab worksheet and teacher support available online.

4 To prove that matter is not created or destroyed in a reaction, you need to show that the mass of the reactants equals the mass of the products. Accurate and precise measurements provide the evidence to support this claim. Many gases that react or are produced in chemical reactions can easily escape detection. If chemists did not measure these gases, the measurements of mass before and after an experiment would be inaccurate.

5 The number of atoms of each element in both the reactants and the product is equal. Atoms of each element have a specific mass, whether those atoms are in a reactant or a product. If there is the same number of atoms of each element before and after a reaction, there is also the same mass before and after the reaction. Mass is conserved.

Lesson 1 Observing and Modeling Chemical Reactions   237

CCC Energy and Matter

Ask students to think about whether their work in this exploration verifies that the total amount of matter in a closed system is conserved. In a class discussion, have them explain why or why not.

Preconception Alert

Have students consider the reaction of water decomposing into hydrogen and oxygen. They may think that twice as much hydrogen by mass should be produced because there are two hydrogen atoms for every oxygen atom in water. Encourage students to think about how these two elements differ and how that difference might affect the mass of each product.

Exploring Visuals

Have students study **Figure 3.** Ask why sulfur appears on the right side in the second reaction and lead appears on the right side in the third reaction. Have students explain in terms of the conservation of mass.

1 In each experiment, the total mass of the reactants is equal to the total mass of the product plus the mass of any leftover reactant. Therefore, mass is conserved. A pattern emerges that shows that every 10.00 g of lead reacts with 1.56 g of sulfur to produce 11.56 g of lead sulfide. This pattern repeats no matter the quantity of reactants used. After lead and sulfur react in this proportion until all of one reactant is used up, any leftover reactant does not react. The pattern illustrates that atoms combine in specific ratios to form compounds.

2 Ecological pyramids show how mass and energy move between trophic levels in an ecosystem. Identified patterns will depend on the model being examined but may include lower biomass or overall energy at higher trophic levels. These decreases can be explained by considering loses to the environment as waste products between and within trophic levels.

You can also observe conservation of mass in the formation of lead sulfide from the elements lead and sulfur. Lead sulfide, also known as galena, forms black, metallic crystals and is an important naturally occurring compound of lead. Lead sulfide is used in infrared detectors and humidity sensors and as a semiconductor in solar cells. Figure 3 shows different amounts of lead and sulfur that react to form lead sulfide.

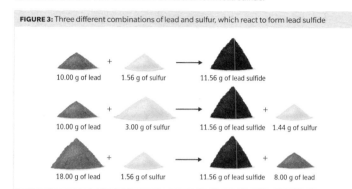

FIGURE 3: Three different combinations of lead and sulfur, which react to form lead sulfide

10.00 g of lead + 1.56 g of sulfur → 11.56 g of lead sulfide

10.00 g of lead + 3.00 g of sulfur → 11.56 g of lead sulfide + 1.44 g of sulfur

18.00 g of lead + 1.56 g of sulfur → 11.56 g of lead sulfide + 8.00 g of lead

1 **GATHER EVIDENCE** How do the data shown in Figure 3 support the law of conservation of mass? What other patterns do you notice in the data?

_____

_____

_____

_____

Patterns

FIGURE 4: Mass and energy are conserved as they cycle between Earth's systems.

Cycles in Nature

Mass and energy are conserved in the Earth system. Plants use light energy from the sun along with water and carbon dioxide to produce sugar and oxygen. When animals, such as the bison in Figure 4, eat plants they take in the matter that was in the plants. Animals use oxygen and these food sources to build DNA, proteins, and carbohydrates. When animals die, their tissues decompose and are cycled again.

2 **Language Arts Connection** Research different ecological pyramids. How can patterns at the macroscopic scale of a pyramid be explained by interactions at the atomic scale? Write a paper that explains how these pyramids demonstrate the conservation of mass and energy. Ask a classmate to review your paper. Then, revise your explanation based on the feedback.

Elements React in Predictable Proportions

You may have noticed patterns in the data for the formation of lead sulfide from lead and sulfur. The amount of lead sulfide produced was the same, even when a portion of one reactant remained. Observations such as this led scientists to conclude that when elements combine to form compounds, they do so in predictable proportions. The table shows the composition of water by mass as an example.

Composition of Water by Mass		
Mass of water (g)	Mass of oxygen (g)	Mass of hydrogen (g)
18	16	2
36	32	4
54	48	6
72	64	8

3 **EXPLAIN** Select the correct terms to complete the statement.

According to the data in the table, the simplest ratio by mass of hydrogen to oxygen in a water molecule is 1 | 2 | 8 | 16 to 1 | 2 | 8 | 16 . These data show this ratio to be true in every example given. This means that exactly 10 g | 80 g | 160 g of hydrogen would combine with 10 g | 80 g | 160 g of oxygen to form water with no reactant left over. The proportion of hydrogen to oxygen always remains the same.

Scientists also noticed that when metals were burned in air, the metals always combined with a proportional amount of oxygen. If potassium burned in oxygen, every 39.1 g of potassium combined with 8.00 g of oxygen. If calcium burned, every 40.1 g of calcium combined with 16.0 g of oxygen. These observations became known as the *law of definite proportions*. This law states that chemical compounds contain fixed, constant proportions of their constituent elements.

4 **MODEL** An unknown mass of hydrogen gas and oxygen gas react in a closed system, producing 108.0 g of water. An oxygen atom is 16 times more massive than a hydrogen atom. Using the space provided, develop a mathematical equation demonstrating that mass is conserved and that elements react in definite proportions. Use your equation to determine the mass of hydrogen and oxygen gas that reacted in the closed system. Recall that oxygen and hydrogen are both diatomic molecules.

© Houghton Mifflin Harcourt Publishing Company

Math Connection

Some students may be confused about the switch from a 1:8 ratio in the table to a 1:16 ratio in the modeling exercise. Make sure students realize that the 1:8 ratio compares the masses of the two atoms of hydrogen with the one atom of oxygen in a water molecule, and the 1:16 ratio compares the mass of one hydrogen atom with the mass of one oxygen atom in the reaction that forms water. **(MP.2)**

Collaborate

Take and Pass Tell students that nitrogen forms several oxides with oxygen. Give them the formulas NO, NO_2, and NO_5. Have students in groups write one thing they know about these three compounds based on the law of definite proportions. The ratio by mass of nitrogen and oxygen in each oxide will be constant. Have students pass their paper to the right and add their response to the next paper. Continue until students get their own paper back. Discuss responses.

DCI PS1.B Chemical Reactions

Emphasize that the conservation of mass and of atoms, in combination with the fact that compounds of chemical elements have unique emergent properties that are different from their constituent atoms, are key principles of chemistry. Have students give an example of an **everyday phenomenon** that shows this principle.

3 1, 8, 10 g, 80 g; According to the law of definite proportions, a given compound always contains the same proportions of elements by mass. In the case of hydrogen to oxygen in water, that proportion is 1 to 8, so 10 g of hydrogen would combine with 80 g of oxygen to form 90 g of water.

4 **Sample answer:** 2 parts diatomic H_2 and 1 part diatomic O_2 react to form 2 parts H_2O. Therefore, a water sample of 108.0 g = 2(2H) + 1(2O). If the unknown mass of 1 part of H in grams = x, and O is about 16 times more massive than H, then 108.0 g = 2(2x) + 1(2(16x)) = 2(2x) + 32x. This represents the formation of water because there are 2 molecules of diatomic H_2 [2(2x)] for every 1 molecule of diatomic O_2 (32x) in the reaction. $x = 3.0$ g; therefore, 12.0 g of hydrogen and 96.0 g of oxygen form 108.0 g of water.

Collaborate

Discussion Have student pairs discuss the laws of definite proportion and multiple proportion. Have them write a few sentences explaining in their own words the differences between the two laws.

① Row 2: 24, 64; Row 3: 36, 96

② **Sample answer:** This sample is hydrogen peroxide. The ratio by mass of oxygen and hydrogen in water is 8:1. Hydrogen peroxide has twice as much oxygen, so the ratio would be 16:1. The sample ratio is also 16:1, so it must be hydrogen peroxide.

 **Evidence Notebook**

③ Atoms are conserved when oxygen and iron react to form iron oxides because the atoms in the reactants rearrange to form the products. Atoms are not created or destroyed during the reaction. If atoms are conserved, it follows that mass will be conserved because the atoms of each element have a unique mass. Iron and oxygen combine in multiple proportions to form different types of rust. Each type will have a different iron-to-oxygen ratio and some different properties, including color. .

FORMATIVE ASSESSMENT

Have students look at a hydrogen peroxide molecule, which is made up of hydrogen and oxygen. The formula is H_2O_2. Explain that the law of multiple proportions states that two or more atoms can sometimes combine in multiple ways to form different molecules. ***Ask:*** *For a hydrogen peroxide molecule, what is the ratio of hydrogen atoms to oxygen atoms? How does this ratio tell you that hydrogen peroxide is not water?* Students should state that the ratio of hydrogen atoms to oxygen atoms in hydrogen peroxide is 2:2, which simplifies to 1:1. The molecule cannot be water, as only a 2:1 ratio of hydrogen atoms to oxygen atoms is water.

FIGURE 5: Models of carbon monoxide, CO, and carbon dioxide, CO_2, molecules

CO CO_2

As more chemical compounds were identified, chemists realized that while a specific compound always had the same proportions of elements, the same elements sometimes could form different compounds, each with its own specific proportions. In each compound, the ratio of elements reduced to small, whole-number ratios unique to the compound. This is known as the *law of multiple proportions*. For example, carbon monoxide contains a different proportion of carbon and oxygen atoms than does carbon dioxide, as shown in Figure 5. However, both compounds have ratios of carbon to oxygen that are reducible to small, whole-number ratios. Scientists concluded that in chemical reactions atoms do not break apart. Rather, combinations of atoms simply rearrange. This phenomenon is evident in the data tables below.

Composition of Carbon Monoxide by Mass		
Mass of carbon monoxide (g)	Mass of carbon (g)	Mass of oxygen (g)
28	12	16
56	24	32
84	36	48

① **EVALUATE** Complete the remaining rows of the table to show the pattern of composition of carbon dioxide.

Composition of Carbon Dioxide by Mass		
Mass of carbon dioxide (g)	Mass of carbon (g)	Mass of oxygen (g)
44	12	32
88	_____	_____
132	_____	_____

② **APPLY** Hydrogen and oxygen can form water, H_2O, or hydrogen peroxide, H_2O_2. A chemist determined that a sample contains 20 g of hydrogen and 320 g of oxygen. Is this sample water, or is it hydrogen peroxide? Include evidence to support your claim.

_____

_____

_____

_____

_____

_____

③ **Evidence Notebook** Iron reacts readily with oxygen in the presence of water to form iron oxides, also known as rust. Rust can be yellow, black, red, or brown, but each type of rust is made of the same elements. Explain how atoms and mass are conserved in these reactions and why iron and oxygen can combine to form differently colored compounds.

EXPLORATION 3 Modeling Chemical Reactions

© Houghton Mifflin Harcourt Publishing Company • Image Credits: ©Wicki58/Getty Images

EXPLORATION 3

Modeling Chemical Reactions

If you are able to use patterns to predict chemical reactions, you can perform a reaction more efficiently and minimize waste. Imagine you own a company that makes ready-to-eat foods. You want to buy exactly the right amounts of ingredients to make a certain number of turkey and cheese sandwiches. For the most efficient process, you would have to know the proportions in which the ingredients combine, and, to do this, you would need to model the recipe.

2 pieces of bread + 4 slices of turkey + 1 piece of cheese → 1 sandwich

 Collaborate If you needed to make 1350 sandwiches, how many slices of turkey would you need? Explain to a partner how you determined your answer.

Writing Chemical Equations

Chemical reactions can also be modeled in order to make predictions about how much product is expected to form. Consider the burning of magnesium. Magnesium is an element, so it can be represented by its chemical symbol from the periodic table, Mg. Oxygen is one of several diatomic elements. These elements exist in nature as molecules made up of two atoms of that element. Therefore, the chemical formula for a molecule of oxygen is O_2. Mg and O_2 combine to yield a product called magnesium oxide, MgO.

In a chemical equation, the reactants are separated with plus signs, as are the products. The production of a new substance is shown with an arrow. The ratio of magnesium atoms to oxygen atoms in magnesium oxide is 1:1 because a magnesium atom loses two electrons to form a 2+ charge, and an oxygen atom gains two electrons to form a 2− charge.

$$Mg + O_2 \rightarrow MgO$$

 MODEL Draw a model illustrating this reaction at the atomic level. Use labels to show whether the reaction, as shown in the equation, obeys the law of conservation of mass.

Chemical equations also may indicate the reactant's or product's physical state. This is shown as a lowercase letter in parentheses, such as (*g*) for gas, (*l*) for liquid, (*s*) for solid, and (*aq*) for aqueous. For this magnesium reaction, the physical states are indicated as

$$Mg(s) + O_2(g) \rightarrow MgO(s)$$

FIGURE 6: Making sandwiches with exact proportions of ingredients

Explore Online ▶

Hands-On Lab

Modeling the Conservation of Mass Model the relationships between the masses of reactants and products in a chemical reaction.

3D Learning Objective

Students **use balanced chemical equations to mathematically represent** the conservation of mass during a chemical reaction in a closed system. Students explore types of reactions and **predict the outcome of chemical reactions based on chemical properties and the fact that atoms are conserved.**

Differentiate Instruction

MTSS/RTI Make sure students realize that the analogy of a sandwich has some limitations. Actual sandwiches are mixtures, not pure chemical compounds that follow the law of definite proportions. Ask students to work in pairs to share their experiences and ideas. Guide them to listen respectfully to what their partner has to say without interrupting.

Explore Online ▶

Hands-On Lab 👥 Small Groups ⏱ 90 minutes

Modeling the Conservation of Mass

SEP **Constructing Explanations and Designing Solutions**

Students model the conservation of mass and relationships between reactants and products in a chemical reaction.

Student lab worksheet and teacher support available online.

④ Have students show their mathematical process on paper and share their answer with a partner. Have them write a brief summary of how their mathematical processes compare. 1350 sandwiches × 4 slices of turkey/sandwich = 5400 slices of turkey.

⑤ Diagrams should show one atom for Mg, two bonded atoms for O_2, and two bonded atoms for MgO. Labels should show that there are three total atoms on the left side of the equation and two on the right side. Therefore, the law of conservation of mass is not supported here, and this is not a correct, balanced equation.

Using Mathematics and Computational Thinking

Be sure students understand that an equation for a reaction is balanced when the number of each type of atom or ion is the same on the reactant and product sides of the equation. Provide the hint that they should leave hydrogen and oxygen atoms until the end of their balancing and deal first with the less common atoms or the atoms that appear in only one reactant and one product.

Math Connection
MP.2 Reason abstractly and quantitatively.

Have students discuss with a partner how chemical equations represent a chemical reaction, what operations are used to describe chemical reactions, and what the operations represent in the real world reactions.

CCC Scale, Proportion, and Quantity

A balanced chemical equation represents interactions at all scales. This includes reactions of single atoms at the molecular scale, reactions of small amounts of substances in a high school chemistry lab, and even reactions of large amounts of substances in large-scale industrial reactions. The relative proportions of atoms that react are the same at all scales.

Classroom Practice

Write the coefficients necessary to balance each chemical reaction.

1. $AgI + Na_2S \rightarrow Ag_2S + NaI$

   2, 1, 1, 2

2. $N_2 + H_2 \rightarrow NH_3$

   1, 3, 2

3. $SiO_2 + HF \rightarrow SiF_4 + H_2O$

   1, 4, 1, 2

 Problem Solving
Balancing Chemical Equations

SAMPLE PROBLEM The chemical equation you saw for the burning of magnesium is unbalanced. There are two oxygen atoms in the reactants and only one in the product. But, the law of conservation of mass states that matter cannot be destroyed. The equation must be balanced to show the true ratios in which the reactants combine. All chemical reactions are represented by balanced equations that follow the conservation of mass.

PLAN To balance a chemical equation, first list the number of atoms of each element on both sides of the equation. Figure 7 shows there are 1 Mg atom and 2 O atoms on the reactants side, and 1 Mg atom and 1 O atom on the products side.

FIGURE 7: Count the atoms in the equation.

$$Mg \quad + \quad O_2 \quad \rightarrow \quad MgO$$
Mg: 1   Mg: 1
O: 2   O: 1

ANALYZE Next, identify any element that does not have the same number of atoms on both sides of the equation. The number of atoms of each element needs to be the same for the reactants and the products for the equation to be balanced. Figure 8 shows that for this equation, the oxygen is not balanced because there are 2 O atoms on the left and only 1 O atom on the right.

FIGURE 8: Compare the number of atoms.

$$Mg \quad + \quad O_2 \quad \rightarrow \quad MgO$$
Mg: 1   Mg: 1
O: 2   O: 1

SOLVE Then, use coefficients to balance the equation. Coefficients are numbers that are placed in front of a reactant or product to indicate the number of units of the substance. When a coefficient is placed in front of a chemical formula with subscripts, you multiply each subscript by the coefficient to determine the number of atoms for each element in the chemical formula. Remember that subscripts represent the ratio of atoms in a chemical formula. You cannot change the subscripts in a chemical formula when balancing a chemical equation because this would change the identity of the substance. When no coefficient or subscript is shown, it is assumed to be 1.

FIGURE 9: Add coefficients.

$$Mg \quad + \quad O_2 \quad \rightarrow \quad 2MgO$$
Mg: 1   Mg: 1   2
O: 2   O: 1   2

As shown in Figure 9, a coefficient of 2 is added to MgO, bringing the product to 2 Mg atoms and 2 O atoms. This balances the number of O atoms, but it also disrupts the balance of the Mg atoms. Figure 10 shows that a coefficient of 2 is added to Mg, bringing the total number of atoms in the reactants to 2 atoms of Mg and 2 atoms of O. This matches the number of atoms on the products side. The equation is now balanced. The ratio of coefficients for this equation is 2:1:2. You can translate this as 2 parts magnesium react with 1 part oxygen to produce 2 parts magnesium oxide.

FIGURE 10: Balanced equation

$$2Mg \quad + \quad O_2 \quad \rightarrow \quad 2MgO$$
Mg: 1 2   Mg: 1 2
O: 2   O: 1 2

CHECK YOUR WORK Check your work by multiplying the coefficient by the subscript for each element or compound. The number and type of atoms or ions should be equal on both sides.

---

1. Sodium phosphate, Na_3PO_4, is a compound that makes cake batter thicken and baked goods rise. Sodium phosphate reacts with calcium chloride, $CaCl_2$, to form sodium chloride, $NaCl$, and calcium phosphate, $Ca_3(PO_4)_2$. Calcium phosphate is the main mineral in human bones and teeth. The unbalanced equation for this reaction is:

$$Na_3PO_4(aq) + CaCl_2(aq) \rightarrow NaCl(aq) + Ca_3(PO_4)_2(s)$$

PLAN List the number of atoms of each element or ions on each side of the equation. Polyatomic ions such as PO_4^{3-} can be treated as a single unit if they are found on both sides of the equation.

Reactants		Products
_____	Ca	_____
_____	Cl	_____
_____	Na	_____
_____	PO_4^{3-}	_____

ANALYZE In your list above, circle the elements and ions that are not balanced. Add coefficients to begin balancing the equation. Repeat the Plan and Analyze steps as needed until all elements are balanced.

SOLVE Use coefficients to write the balanced chemical equation. Verify that the number and type of atoms and ions on both sides of your equation are equal.

2. Aluminum oxide, Al_2O_3, is a major component of the mineral bauxite and is known as corundum. The hardness of aluminum oxide makes it useful as an abrasive in sandpaper and toothpaste. Rubies and sapphires are large crystals of Al_2O_3 that contain metal ion impurities, which give them their color. In a chemical reaction, aluminum oxide breaks apart into aluminum atoms and oxygen molecules.

SOLVE Follow the Plan and Analyze steps to write the balanced chemical equation. Verify that the number and type of atoms on both sides of your equation are equal.

CCC Energy and Matter

Explain that another way to show a chemical reaction, in addition to writing a balanced equation, is to illustrate reactants and products so that the numbers of atoms or ions of each type on the reactant side are equal to the numbers of atoms or ions of each type on the product side.

Practice Problem Answers

1. PLAN Left column: 1, 2, 3, 1; right column: 3, 1, 1, 2

   ANALYZE None of the elements are balanced, so all of the elements and ions should be circled. Students may take different paths to balance the chemical equation.

   SOLVE $2Na_3PO_4(aq) + 3CaCl_2(aq) \rightarrow 6NaCl(aq) + Ca_3(PO_4)_2(s)$

2. SOLVE $2Al_2O_3 \rightarrow 4Al + 3O_2$

For the complete solutions to the Practice Problems and Classroom Practice, see the online Problem Solutions.

Technology Connection

A simulation of balancing chemical equations can be found at the University of Colorado website. Some have found this simulation useful. It is not necessary for this program. HMH neither controls nor endorses this simulation.

DCI PS1.B Chemical Reactions

Ask students to explain how a balanced chemical reaction and the law of conservation of matter are the same concept. Atoms cannot be created or destroyed, so the same number of each type of atom on the reactant and product side reflects that no atoms are created or destroyed. Help students understand how to use knowledge of chemical properties of elements, based on such concepts as location on the periodic table and valence electrons, to describe and predict chemical reactions.

Differentiate Instruction

MTSS/RTI Explain to students that in the synthesis reaction described, a prerequisite for writing the balanced equation is knowing that elemental sodium, Na, is monatomic, elemental chlorine, Cl_2, is diatomic, and the ionically bonded sodium chloride, NaCl, is predicted by the law of definite proportions and the periodic table. Routinely encourage students to write in their Evidence Notebooks or share with a partner to reflect on what they have learned and what they are struggling with. Offer to help students with understanding as needed.

1 Examples of information students could determine include number of valence electrons, electronegativity, ionization energy, solubility, and bond type. Knowing how many electrons an atom may gain or lose during a reaction, how tightly the electrons are held, whether a compound is soluble in water or other solvents, and the type of bonds different elements may form makes it possible to predict the outcome of a chemical reaction.

2 1, 7, lose, gain, ionic, electronegativities

3 $2Na + Cl_2 \rightarrow 2NaCl$

Evidence Notebook

4 $4Fe + 3O_2 \rightarrow 2Fe_2O_3$; Iron loses 3 electrons, making Fe^{3+}. Oxygen has 6 valence electrons and readily gains 2 more to have a full and stable energy shell, making O^{2-}. When Fe^{3+} and O^{2-} combine, they form iron(III) oxide, Fe_2O_3.

5 $2H_2O_2 \rightarrow 2H_2O + O_2$

Patterns in Types of Reactions

There are millions of possible chemical reactions. Analyzing the reactants helps chemists predict the products. These predictions are used to classify reactions into recognizable patterns based on how the reactants break apart, combine, or rearrange.

1 **Collaborate** With a partner, list information you can determine about reactants and products in a chemical reaction. Consider how the arrangement of and patterns within the periodic table can help you determine characteristics of elements. How could this information be used to identify or predict the outcome of a chemical reaction?

Synthesis

In a synthesis reaction, two or more reactants combine to form one product. The reactants may be elements or compounds. The product is always a compound.

2 **EXPLAIN** Select the correct terms to describe the synthesis of sodium chloride.

Sodium, Na, has 1 | 2 | 7 valence electron(s), and the chlorine atoms in diatomic chlorine, Cl_2, have 5 | 7 | 8 valence electrons. In this reaction, Na atoms gain | lose one electron and Cl atoms gain | lose one electron, forming full and stable outer energy shells. When Na and Cl_2 combine, ionic | covalent | metallic bonds are formed because of the large difference in atomic sizes | electronegativities | ionization energies.

3 **APPLY** Write a balanced chemical equation for the synthesis of sodium chloride, NaCl.

4 **Evidence Notebook** Write a balanced chemical equation for rusting, a synthesis reaction between iron, Fe, and oxygen gas, O_2. Analyze valence electrons, chemical properties, and bond types to predict the outcome. Assume that iron loses 3 electrons in the reaction.

FIGURE 11: Hydrogen fuel pumps deliver compressed hydrogen gas to vehicles.

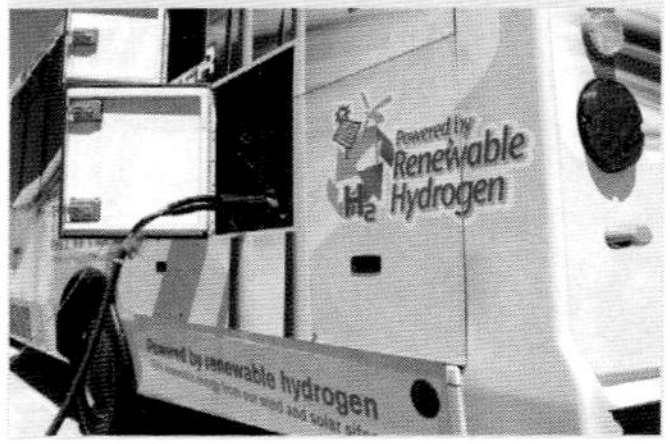

Decomposition

Due to its low density and chemical reactivity, hydrogen gas does not naturally occur on Earth; it must be produced by the decomposition of substances that contain hydrogen atoms, such as water molecules. In a decomposition reaction, one reactant breaks down to form two or more simpler products. The formation of hydrogen through the decomposition of water is still relatively expensive, which makes clean-burning hydrogen fuel expensive. However, scientists are working to optimize a reaction that would make hydrogen fuel cheaper to make and use in vehicles.

$$2H_2O(l) \rightarrow 2H_2(g) + O_2(g)$$

5 **APPLY** Write a balanced chemical equation for the decomposition of hydrogen peroxide, H_2O_2, into water and oxygen molecules.

Single Displacement

Copper, Cu, is a ductile, highly conductive metal that is used in electrical systems, as a building material, and in jewelry. Silver nitrate, $AgNO_3$, has antiseptic properties and is used to prepare silver compounds used in photographic film. When a copper wire is added to a solution of silver nitrate, a single displacement reaction occurs in which one element replaces another element or ion in a compound.

6 **APPLY** Write a balanced chemical equation for the single displacement reaction of copper with silver nitrate.

FIGURE 12: A copper wire is placed in a solution of silver nitrate. The products are solid silver and aqueous copper(II) nitrate.

In an aqueous solution, silver nitrate exists as a combination of Ag^+ ions and NO_3^- ions. When a copper wire is added to aqueous silver nitrate, the copper atoms lose electrons and become Cu^{2+} ions. The Ag^+ ions gain electrons and become solid, elemental silver, which is deposited on the copper wire, as shown in Figure 12. This reaction occurs because copper is more reactive than silver and so forms compounds more readily. If enough copper is used, all of the silver will come out of solution. The Cu^{2+} ions in the aqueous copper(II) nitrate give the solution a blue tint.

Double Displacement

In a double displacement reaction, ions of two compounds switch places. This type of reaction occurs when solutions of potassium iodide, KI, and lead(II) nitrate, $Pb(NO_3)_2$, both soluble ionic compounds, are mixed together. The lead and potassium ions essentially switch places.

7 **APPLY** Write a balanced chemical equation for the double displacement reaction of potassium iodide and lead(II) nitrate.

FIGURE 13: When solutions of lead(II) nitrate and potassium iodide are combined, solid lead(II) iodide and aqueous potassium nitrate are produced.

The Pb^{2+} ions bond with the I^- ions to form lead(II) iodide. Lead(II) iodide is insoluble in water at room temperature and precipitates as a yellow solid, shown in Figure 13. Lead(II) iodide was once used as a yellow pigment in lead paint, but this was discontinued due to the dangers of lead poisoning.

Potassium nitrate is the other product of this reaction. It is an ionic compound only moderately soluble in water and is often not seen due to the yellow lead(II) iodide precipitate. Potassium nitrate is used as a fertilizer, a food preservative, and a major component in gun powder and fireworks.

© Houghton Mifflin Harcourt Publishing Company • Image Credits: ©HMH

Patterns

Elicit from students the idea that synthesis and decomposition reactions are opposite processes. Point out that not all synthesis reactions can be reversed as decomposition reactions. Have students think about rust, a synthesis reaction involving one product (rust) and two reactants (iron and oxygen). Rust cannot simply decompose to form pure iron and release oxygen. Some synthesis reactions can be reversed through decomposition, but this is based on a concept of equilibrium, which is a balance between two processes, or the addition of energy, such as thermal energy.

SEP **Developing and Using Models**

An analogy of switching dance partners may be helpful for students to visualize displacement reactions. A single displacement reaction would be like a person "cutting in" on a dancing couple when one person leaves the dancing couple and is replaced by another. A double displacement reaction would be like two dancing couples who switch dancing partners, almost like two single displacements that occur simultaneously. Challenge students to think of other analogies.

Collaborate

Think-Pair-Share Have students look at the five main types of chemical reactions and decide which they suspect would be the easiest to balance and which would be the most difficult. Then, have students pair up and share their thoughts on their choices.

Conservation Connection

Hydrogen is clean burning but cannot be considered a primary fuel because it can be obtained only by expending energy to free it chemically from naturally occurring compounds such as H_2O or CH_4. Help students recognize the potential benefits of using hydrogen fuel in the transportation sector, such as allowing pollution controls to be centralized at a smaller number of hydrogen-generating plants versus needing pollution controls on a much larger number of cars and trucks that burn fossil fuels.

6 $Cu + 2AgNO_3 \longrightarrow 2Ag + Cu(NO_3)_2$

7 $Pb(NO_3)_2 + 2KI \longrightarrow PbI_2 + 2KNO_3$

Lesson 1 Observing and Modeling Chemical Reactions   245

Differentiate Instruction

Extension Discuss the improbability of having three students each throw a green tennis ball and four students each throw a red tennis ball—all toward the center of the classroom—and the balls all collide simultaneously. Stress that chemical reactions are simply the summary of what happens during a reaction; they do not indicate the steps needed to get there.

Preconception Alert

A common misconception is that all greenhouse gases are bad. Help students understand that without some amount of greenhouse gases in our atmosphere, Earth would be much cooler and would be incapable of supporting life as we know it. The problem is that human activities since the beginning of the Industrial Revolution have produced a 40% increase in the atmospheric concentration of carbon dioxide, CO_2, from 280 ppm in 1750 to 406 ppm in early 2017.

Earth Science Connection

With the exception of gold, and sometimes silver, nearly all metals are found in nature as oxides, sulfides, or carbonates. Single displacement reactions can be used to isolate a more valuable, less chemically reactive metal (such as silver) from a compound by using a less expensive but more reactive metal (copper) to displace it.

Explore Online ▶

Encourage students to go online to view the video of an exploding hydrogen-filled balloon.

1 chemical energy, thermal energy, an increase

Evidence Notebook

2 Equations should be balanced, which shows that individual components follow the law of definite proportions and the reaction follows the law of conservation of mass.

Energy and Matter

Combustion Reactions

Explore Online ▶

FIGURE 14: A balloon filled with hydrogen gas explodes when ignited.

Combustion reactions are often used to provide heat and light, as they do in fireplaces and bonfires. These reactions often release large amounts of energy. Figure 14 shows the results of this energy after a balloon filled with hydrogen gas is ignited and explodes.

Most automobiles, buses, and airplanes have internal combustion engines, in which a fuel containing hydrocarbons burns in oxygen to produce carbon dioxide, water, and energy. An internal combustion engine is an inefficient system because much of the energy it produces is lost to the environment.

1 **EXPLAIN** Select the correct terms to describe combustion reactions.

In a combustion reaction with carbon-based fuels, thermal energy | chemical energy in the reactants is converted to thermal energy | chemical energy when the fuel is ignited. Carbon dioxide is a greenhouse gas, so using combustion engines leads to a decrease | an increase in the amount of energy stored in Earth's atmosphere and hydrosphere.

As a result of these increased carbon dioxide emissions, scientists are looking for alternative energy sources that do not contain carbon. Hydrogen fuel might be an alternative because the end product of the combustion of hydrogen is water, not carbon dioxide. One of the challenges with hydrogen fuel is that elemental hydrogen is not found in nature as the hydrocarbons of petroleum and natural gas are.

 Evidence Notebook Identify the type of reaction you are modeling for your unit project and write a balanced chemical equation. Use your reaction equation to show how matter is conserved during the reaction.

Predicting the Outcomes of Chemical Reactions

The periodic table can be a useful tool for predicting the outcomes of chemical reactions or even whether or not a reaction will occur. For example, from an element's position on the periodic table, you can determine the number of outermost electrons it has. This tells how likely the element is to gain or lose electrons when forming bonds. In addition, periodic trends in electronegativity, ionization energy, and atomic size also influence the types of chemical bonds two elements will form. The relative significance of each trend also can be determined from an element's position on the periodic table. Examining a reaction will help show how this might work.

Thermite is a mixture of aluminum, Al, and iron(III) oxide, Fe_2O_3. When thermite is exposed to high temperatures, an exothermic reaction occurs, shown in Figure 15. The two metals in this reaction, aluminum and iron, can be ranked by their tendency to lose electrons and form cations.

3 **ANALYZE** Which metal in this reaction is more reactive? How might you determine this?

◯ **a**. Al is more reactive because it has a lower ionization energy than Fe.

◯ **b**. Al is more reactive because it has a higher ionization energy than Fe.

◯ **c**. Fe is more reactive because it has a lower ionization energy than Al.

◯ **d**. Fe is more reactive because it has a higher ionization energy than Al.

The difference in electronegativities between oxygen and iron is 1.7. This means the iron(III) oxide bond is slightly ionic. Oxygen holds the shared electrons more strongly than does iron, but the electrons are not fully transferred. The energy added to start the thermite reaction makes it easier to break the bonds in iron(III) oxide. If a more reactive metal is present, it will take the place of iron, producing a different oxide and different elemental metal.

4 **PREDICT** Write the balanced chemical equation for the thermite reaction. Think about how many valence electrons aluminum and oxygen have when writing the formulas for the products. What type of reaction is this?

A reaction of thermite releases a large amount of energy and reaches temperatures high enough to melt iron. This makes thermite useful for welding, or joining, large pieces of metal such as railroad rails. An outside energy source begins the reaction. Once started, the thermite reaction produces enough energy to continue. The molten iron produced fills the weld joint, and the energy produced from the exothermic reaction joins the ends to be welded together with the new joint.

In the thermite reaction, aluminum is more reactive than iron. Therefore, when the reaction begins, iron is displaced by aluminum. The products of this reaction are aluminum oxide and elemental iron. The iron is what is useful in welding applications. It is heavier and sinks to the bottom of the weld, and the aluminum oxide, called *slag* in this case, rises to the top.

5 **Evidence Notebook** Rust often flakes away, exposing more iron underneath. Explain why this makes rust particularly destructive for iron or iron alloys. Why is the prevention of rust an important problem to solve? Use your knowledge of rust to suggest a solution. As you consider solutions, think about the materials and conditions that are necessary for rust to form.

FIGURE 15: Thermite reaction

© Houghton Mifflin Harcourt Publishing Company • Image Credits: ©Albert Russ/Shutterstock

---

DCI **PS1.B Chemical Reactions**

Have students work together to recognize patterns in combustion reactions. In most combustion reactions, a hydrocarbon combines with diatomic oxygen to produce water, carbon dioxide, and energy. Ask students to think about why energy is released in some chemical reactions and absorbed by others. When energy is released during a reaction, more energy is stored in the chemical bonds of the reactants than in the chemical bonds of the products.

3 a

4 $2Al + Fe_2O_3 \rightarrow Al_2O_3 + 2Fe$; single displacement reaction

 Evidence Notebook

5 The fact that rust flakes away means that there is a net loss of material from the iron. The prevention and treatment of rust is a major societal challenge and economic cost. Chemical engineers look for ways to extend the life of cars, bridges, and buildings. Iron may rust when it is exposed to oxygen and water, two common components of many environments. Rusting weakens iron, making it unsuitable for many of its intended functions or even dangerous if the iron is part of a large structure such as a building or bridge. Because both oxygen and water are required for iron to corrode, keeping one or both away from iron will prevent rust. A coat of waterproof paint over iron that has not rusted will keep both oxygen and water from interacting with the iron.

FORMATIVE ASSESSMENT

Have students pause to think about how balanced chemical equations relate to the conservation of mass. Then have them respond to the following prompts: *I became more aware of . . ., I didn't realize that . . ., I still don't understand . . .* Have volunteers share their answers with the class.

Sample answer: I became more aware of how coefficients and superscripts are necessary to correctly show chemical reactions. I didn't realize that reactions could be categorized. I still don't understand combustion reactions.

Lesson 1 Observing and Modeling Chemical Reactions   247

TAKE IT FURTHER Hands-On Lab

Collaborate

You may choose to assign this activity or direct students to the Interactive Online Student Edition, where they can choose from all available paths.

Hands-On Lab Small groups ⏱ 90 minutes

Modeling the Conservation of Mass

SEP **Constructing Explanations and Designing Solutions**

Students develop a model of a chemical reaction and use their model to demonstrate the conservation of mass.

Advance Preparation To save time and manage classroom movement, group all materials together for each pair of students.

CCC **Energy and Matter**

Have students discuss how different types of models, such as physical or mathematical models, demonstrate the conservation of mass in different ways.

Claims, Evidence, and Reasoning

Have students clearly state a claim that explains how a model can demonstrate conservation of mass. They should provide evidence from the lab and state their reasoning.

1 Students may claim that any type of model will show the same number of atoms in the reactants and products of a chemical reaction. Because each atom has a set mass, showing that atoms are conserved also shows that mass is conserved. Students may also claim that a physical model will allow them to directly measure the mass of the reactants and products, and they will show with quantitative measurements that atoms and mass are conserved.

Plan the Investigation

1. $C_3H_8 + 5O_2 \rightarrow 3CO_2 + 4H_2O$

 Hands-On Lab

Modeling the Conservation of Mass

There are many types of models, including conceptual, physical, mathematical, and computer models. Some models are better at demonstrating certain characteristics of a system than others. Make a model to demonstrate conservation of mass in a chemical reaction. Then, use your model to determine how much product is made when different amounts of reactant are available.

RESEARCH QUESTION Explore different types of atomic models. Which model type would allow you to demonstrate a connection between number of atoms and mass in a chemical reaction?

1 **MAKE A CLAIM**

How can a model of a chemical reaction be used to demonstrate conservation of mass?

_____

_____

_____

POSSIBLE MATERIALS

- indirectly vented chemical splash goggles, nonlatex apron
- balance
- beads, assorted sizes and colors
- chemical modeling kit
- computer
- glue
- nuts and bolts
- paper clips, assorted sizes and colors
- paper, white and assorted colors
- polystyrene-foam balls, assorted sizes and colors
- scissors
- snap-together blocks
- string
- tape
- toothpicks
- trays, plastic (2)

SAFETY INFORMATION

- Wear indirectly vented chemical splash goggles and a nonlatex apron during the setup, hands-on, and takedown segments of the activity.
- Use caution when using sharp tools, which can cut or puncture skin.

indirectly vented chemical splash goggles

PLAN THE INVESTIGATION

1. Consider the reaction in which propane, C_3H_8, is burned in oxygen to produce carbon dioxide and water. Propane is a flammable gas at room temperature and pressure. It can easily change from a liquid to a gaseous state with changes in pressure. This property makes it a suitable fuel to heat homes that are not served by natural gas lines. Write a balanced chemical equation for the combustion of propane.

_____

 Student Lab Worksheet and complete Teacher Support are available online.

2. Write a procedure describing the type of model you will use to show the conservation of mass in this reaction. If you need additional materials, discuss these with your teacher. Write a safety plan for making and using your model. Have your teacher approve your balanced chemical equation and plans before you start.

3. How will your model demonstrate that atoms combine in definite proportions to form compounds and that subscripts in a chemical formula show these proportions?

_____

_____

CARRY OUT THE INVESTIGATION

Construct your model according to your plan. Then, use your model to investigate and record what happens when different amounts of reactants are available.

② DRAW CONCLUSIONS

Write a conclusion that addresses each of the points below.

Claim How did your model demonstrate conservation of mass?

Evidence Describe evidence from your experiment to support your claim.

Reasoning Explain how the evidence you cited supports your claim. How did different amounts of reactants affect your model?

_____

_____

_____

_____

_____

_____

_____

_____

_____

_____

COMMUNICATE

Present your model to your classmates. Explain how it demonstrates conservation of mass, and use it to show how changing the amount of available reactants affects the amount of carbon dioxide and water produced.

| MORE PRACTICE WITH BALANCING EQUATIONS | FLUORIDE AND YOUR TEETH | 🧪 THE COMPOSITION OF HYDRATES | Go online to choose one of these other paths. |

© Houghton Mifflin Harcourt Publishing Company

Ecology Connection

Have small groups of students research an example of an **everyday phenomenon** that uses a chemical reaction to protect the environment in some way. Examples might involve balancing the pH of acidic lakes and streams, soil chemistry, hazardous waste, air pollution, and water treatment.

Plan the Investigation (continued)

3. Student models should always show the correct number and type of atoms in the reactants and products. This corresponds to atoms combining in definite proportions, which is represented by subscripts in chemical formulas.

② **Sample answer:** We measured the mass of the blocks we used to model this reaction before and after each reaction we simulated. Each time, the mass of the reactants equaled the mass of the products plus any leftover reactant.

Explore Online ▶

More Practice with Balancing Equations

Students practice balancing chemical equations that have different levels of difficulty.

Fluoride and Your Teeth

Students explain and model how fluoride in toothpaste is used to prevent tooth decay.

The Composition of Hydrates

Students measure the percentage of water composition for several different masses of a hydrate and make a claim about whether the percentage of water varies by the amount of hydrate tested.

EVALUATE Lesson Self-Check

Can You Explain the Phenomenon?

Claims, Evidence, and Reasoning

Have students clearly state their claim—their explanation for the phenomenon they have been investigating throughout this lesson. They should present their reasoning for making this claim, along with evidence such as facts, examples, and statistics that support their claim. You may want to have students present their arguments orally, in writing, or as a debate.

Cultivating Student Questions

Assessing Student Growth Review the list of questions students generated at the beginning of the lesson. Have volunteers select any unanswered questions and suggest how they could be investigated. After approving student plans, have small groups conduct the investigations and report back to the class.

Environmental Science Connection

Road salt is a major factor contributing to rusting of cars in areas that have significant winter snowfalls. The use of road salt lowers the melting point of water, which makes roadways less icy. However, this also exposes cars on the road to salt and water at the same time. The resulting saltwater solution is an electrolyte that speeds up rusting by increasing the movement of electrons. Have students do research into the use of antirust products to counter this problem.

 Evidence Notebook

1 Students should claim that iron is a metal that reacts with oxygen in wet or humid environments to form iron oxide, or rust. Student solutions to preventing rust should include ways to paint or coat iron objects to prevent oxygen and water in the air from coming in contact with the iron. The fact that iron rusts faster in wet or humid environments is evidence that water is required for rusting to occur. Students should write the balanced equation for rusting, $4Fe + 3O_2 \rightarrow 2Fe_2O_3$, as evidence that oxygen and iron react to form rust and that mass is conserved during the reaction.

Lesson Self-Check

CAN YOU EXPLAIN THE PHENOMENON?

FIGURE 16: Rusting is a chemical reaction.

Rusting is the corrosion of iron. The reddish-brown signs of rust can be seen in everyday life, such as on a rusty can or rooftop. The rusting process tells you how iron interacts with its environment. When a chemical reaction such as rusting occurs, mass is conserved. You can use your knowledge of chemical properties and periodic trends to predict and describe the outcomes of chemical reactions, including the formation of rust.

 Evidence Notebook Refer to your notes in your Evidence Notebook to make a claim about why rust forms and how it can be prevented. Your explanation should include a discussion of the following points:

Claim Make a claim that explains how rust forms, why rusting occurs more readily in some climates, and how rust can be prevented.

Evidence Give specific evidence to support your claim. Include a balanced chemical equation for the formation of rust.

Reasoning Describe, in detail, the connections between the evidence you cited and the claim you are making.

 Formal Assessment Go online for student self-checks and other assessments.

Name _____   Date _____

Check Your Understanding

1. How is the law of conservation of mass met in a balanced chemical equation? Select all correct answers.

☐ **a.** The same number of atoms of each element appears on both sides of the equation.

☐ **b.** Subscripts are added to balance the number of atoms of each element.

☐ **c.** Formulas of reactants are changed to ensure that the mass of elements is conserved.

☐ **d.** Coefficients are added to balance the number of atoms of each element.

☐ **e.** Formulas of products are changed to ensure that the mass of elements is conserved.

2. Write the coefficients necessary to balance the equation for the reaction between aluminum and hydrochloric acid.

___ $Al(s)$ + ___ $HCl(aq)$ → ___ $AlCl_3(aq)$ + ___ $H_2(g)$

3. Match the description of the reaction type with the correct chemical reaction.

Simpler substances are made from a complex substance. ○	○ Magnesium and hydrochloric acid react to form magnesium chloride and hydrogen gas.
A new compound is the only product. ○	○ Iron(II) sulfide reacts with hydrochloric acid to form hydrogen sulfide and iron(II) chloride.
One element replaces another. ○	○ Calcium carbonate is heated until calcium oxide and carbon dioxide form.
Two elements are exchanged. ○	○ Aluminum and bromine react to form aluminum bromide.

4. The atmosphere is 21% oxygen gas. How would a combustion reaction change if it were carried out in a closed system with 80% oxygen instead of an open system with 21% oxygen? Assume all other variables remain the same.

○ **a.** The products of the reaction would change because more oxygen is present.

○ **b.** The reaction would proceed slower because there would not be enough fuel for the oxygen to react with.

○ **c.** The equation representing the combustion reaction would need to be rebalanced because more oxygen is present.

○ **d.** The reaction would proceed faster because more oxygen atoms would react with the fuel in a shorter amount of time.

5. Write the chemical equation for the complete combustion of methane, CH_4.

6. Ammonia, NH_3, has a nitrogen-to-hydrogen ratio by mass of 14:3. What is the mass of a sample of ammonia if there are 25.0 g of nitrogen?

○ **a.** 3.00 g

○ **b.** 5.36 g

○ **c.** 30.4 g

○ **d.** 75.0 g

7. Which of the following is an accurate description of the decomposition of water in a closed system?

○ **a.** 36 g of water decomposes to 2 g of hydrogen gas and 32 g of oxygen gas.

○ **b.** 36 g of water decomposes to 4 g of hydrogen gas and 32 g of oxygen gas.

○ **c.** 4 g of hydrogen gas and 32 g of oxygen decompose to 36 g of water.

○ **d.** 36 g of water decomposes to 36 g of oxygen gas.

© Houghton Mifflin Harcourt Publishing Company

Answers

1. a, d

2. 2, 6, 2, 3

3. Simpler substances are made from a complex substance: calcium carbonate reaction

A new compound is the only product: aluminum reaction

One element replaces another: magnesium reaction

Two elements are exchanged: iron(II) sulfide reaction

4. d

5. $CH_4 + 2O_2 \rightarrow CO_2 + 2H_2O$

6. c

7. b

Answers

8. The law of definite proportions states that a given chemical compound is always composed of the same proportion of atoms by mass. In each example, calcium makes up 40% of the $CaCO_3$ compound.

9. In an open system, the gaseous reactant can escape from the system. In a closed system, the gas is trapped within the system. In both systems, the reaction continues until one of the reactants is used up. At that point, less product is produced in an open system because of the decrease in the gaseous reactant.

10. In a double displacement reaction, components of two compounds are exchanged between each other. The two reactants must have been $Pb(NO_3)_2$ and K_2CrO_4. The chemical equation is $Pb(NO_3)_2 + K_2CrO_4 \rightarrow PbCrO_4 + 2KNO_3$.

Make Your Own Study Guide

Have students create a study guide that helps them organize and visualize the important information from this lesson. Their study guide should focus on the main ideas from the lesson and tie multiple ideas together. Students can make an outline, a concept map, a graphic organizer, or another representation.

EVALUATE

CHECKPOINTS (continued)

8. In one trial, scientists find that a 200-g sample of chalk, $CaCO_3$, contains 80 g of calcium. In a second trial, the scientists find that a 100-g sample of chalk contains 40 g of calcium. Explain how the data demonstrate the law of definite proportions.

_____

_____

_____

_____

9. How can the setup of a system—that is, whether matter can enter or leave the system—affect the outcome of a chemical reaction in which one of the two reactants is a gas?

_____

_____

_____

_____

10. A double displacement reaction between two reactants produces $PbCrO_4$ and KNO_3. What must have been the two reactants? Be sure to write the correct formulas and a balanced equation for the reaction, and explain how you determined the answer.

_____

_____

_____

_____

MAKE YOUR OWN STUDY GUIDE

 In your Evidence Notebook, design a study guide that supports the main ideas from this lesson:

The law of conservation of mass and the law of definite proportions are the basis for writing balanced equations and apply to all chemical reactions.

The outcome of a reaction can be predicted using patterns in chemical properties.

Remember to include the following information in your study guide:

• Use examples that model main ideas.
• Record explanations for the phenomena you investigated.
• Use evidence to support your explanations. Your support can include drawings, data, graphs, laboratory conclusions, and other evidence recorded throughout the lesson.

Consider how the methods you developed in this lesson can be used to model patterns in chemical reactions and show that the total mass in all closed systems is conserved.

Analyzing Chemical Reactions

Building to the Performance Expectations

The learning experiences in this lesson prepare students for mastery of

HS-PS1-7 Use mathematical representations to support the claim that atoms, and therefore mass, are conserved during a chemical reaction.

 Trace Tool to the NGSS

Go online to view the complete coverage of standards across lessons, units, and grade levels.

 **SEP** **Science & Engineering Practices**

Using Mathematics and Computational Thinking
Use mathematical representations of phenomena to support claims.

▶ **VIDEO** Using Data, Mathematical Thinking, and Computational Thinking

Scientific Investigations Use a Variety of Methods
New technologies advance scientific knowledge.

Scientific Knowledge is Open to Revision in Light of New Evidence
Most scientific knowledge is quite durable but is, in principle, subject to change based on new evidence and/or reinterpretation of existing evidence

 **DCI** **Disciplinary Core Ideas**

PS1.B Chemical Reactions
The fact that atoms are conserved, together with knowledge of the chemical properties of the elements involved, can be used to describe and predict chemical reactions. (HS-PS1-7)

ETS1.A Defining and Delimiting Engineering Problems
Humanity faces major global challenges today, such as the need for supplies of clean water and food or for energy sources that minimize pollution, which can be addressed through engineering. These global challenges also may have manifestations in local communities. (HS-ETS1-1)

ETS1.B Developing Possible Solutions
When evaluating solutions, it is important to take into account a range of constraints including cost, safety, reliability and aesthetics, and to consider social, cultural and environmental impacts. (HS-ETS1-3)

▶ **VIDEO** Engineering: Chemistry

 **CCC** **Crosscutting Concepts**

Energy and Matter
The total amount of energy and matter in closed systems is conserved.

Scientific Knowledge Assumes an Order and Consistency in Natural Systems
Science assumes the universe is a vast single system in which basic laws are consistent.

Scale, Proportion, and Quantity
The significance of a phenomenon is dependent on the scale, proportion, and quantity at which it occurs.

Science Addresses Questions About the Natural and Material World
Science knowledge indicates what can happen in natural systems—not what should happen. The latter involves ethics, values, and human decisions about the use of knowledge.

MATH STANDARDS

MP.2 Reason abstractly and quantitatively.

HSN-Q.A.1 Use units as a way to understand problems and to guide the solution of multi-step problems; choose and interpret units consistently in formulas; choose and interpret the scale and the origin in graphs and data displays.

ELA STANDARDS

RST.11-12.1 Cite specific textual evidence to support analysis of science and technical texts, attending to important distinctions the author makes and to any gaps or inconsistencies in the account.

Supporting All Students, All Standards

Integrating the Three Dimensions

In this lesson, students use mathematical representations (**SEP Using Mathematics and Computational Thinking**) to show that the total amount of matter existing as atoms is conserved and that the properties can be used to make predictions about chemical reactions (**DCI PS1.B, CCC Energy and Matter**). Students conduct an investigation to produce data that serve as evidence to demonstrate that atoms are conserved and, together with knowledge of the chemical properties of the elements involved, can be used to describe and predict chemical reactions. Students also use the data to find the amount of reactant from the amount of product formed (**DCI PS1.B**). Students explore greenhouse gas emissions on a global scale (**CCC Scale, Proportion, and Quantity**).

Preassessment

Have students complete the unit pretest or see the Assessment Guide.

Build on Prior Knowledge

Have students consider what they know about chemical reactions. Discuss with students the ideas of limiting reactants and excess reactants. Ask students what would happen in a chemical reaction if different amounts of reactants were mixed together and how it would affect the amount of product and the amount of reactants left after the reaction was completed. For an example or demonstration, ask what would happen if a few drops of vinegar were dropped onto a pile of baking soda. Ask what would happen if a tiny amount of baking soda was added to a beaker of vinegar. Students should understand that if only a small amount of one reactant was added, the other reactant would be left when the reaction was complete because one was used up and one was not.

Professional Development Go online to view **Professional Development videos** with strategies to integrate CCCs and SEPs, including the ones used in this lesson.

Content Background

The relationship between moles, numbers of particles, and mass in grams allows quantitative predictions about relative quantities of reactants and products. Chemical stoichiometry is the description of these relationships. For example, if the mass of available reactants is known for a given reaction, the amount of product that should be formed can be predicted by using stoichiometry.

Stoichiometry is essentially dimensional analysis. Conversion factors are used to cancel given units and convert to other units. A balanced chemical equation is required when solving stoichiometry problems. The coefficients in the balanced equation represent actual ratios.

While stoichiometric problems may solve for different quantities, all conversions involve molar relationships.

Stoichiometry is also used to determine the course of chemical reactions. The reaction will proceed only until the reactant that is present in a limited amount is used up. At that time, the reaction stops. Students may not understand that one of the reactants is limited because they may just assume that reactions simply occur. There are many ways to help students understand the concept of limited reactants, such as using parts to assemble an object. The total number of objects made is based on whichever part is limited.

Differentiated Instruction

KEY WORDS

- mole
- conversion factor
- molar mass
- limiting reactant
- excess reactant

ELL SUPPORT

Have students make a graphic organizer that shows how the amount of a product is calculated using stoichiometry. They should identify all of the key words in their graphic organizer. When students have completed the graphic organizers, pair them so they can explain their graphic organizer to a partner.

ENGAGE: Investigative Phenomenon

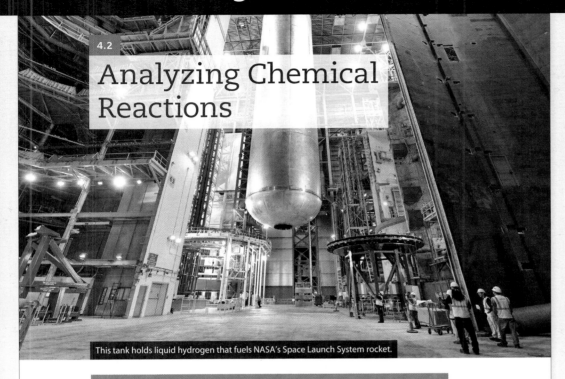

4.2
Analyzing Chemical Reactions

This tank holds liquid hydrogen that fuels NASA's Space Launch System rocket.

CAN YOU SOLVE THE PROBLEM?

Chemical reactions occur at all scales, from those that occur in living cells to those that occur in incredibly large rocket fuel tanks. Rockets, unlike most vehicles, use liquid hydrogen as fuel. Hydrogen is lightweight, burns at a very high temperature, and provides more thrust per unit of volume than other fuel. Liquid oxygen is required to make the hydrogen burn. When these two reactants combine explosively inside a rocket engine, water is formed. A water molecule, H_2O, contains twice as many hydrogen atoms as oxygen atoms. Scientists must consider the exact proportions of substances involved in this reaction to calculate the amount of fuel that is required for a mission.

1 ASK Suppose you wanted to optimize the fuel mixture used for a space flight in order to avoid the presence of excess fuel. What questions would you ask to get started?

_____

_____

_____

_____

2 **Evidence Notebook** As you explore the lesson, gather evidence to explain how, given a certain quantity of oxygen, you could determine the exact amount of hydrogen needed for a space flight.

Lesson 2 Analyzing Chemical Reactions   **253**

Build on Prior Lessons

In Lesson 1, students learned about the properties of materials. Lesson 2 builds on these concepts as students explore cycles of matter in chemical reactions.

Lesson Objective

Students analyze how matter in chemical reactions can be quantified.

Cultivating Student Questions

Have students look at the photo of a tank of liquid hydrogen used to fuel the rockets in NASA's Space Launch System. Prompt them to ask all questions that come to mind. Record the questions on chart paper, and then sort the questions based on their focus. With students, narrow the questions down to ones that directly relate to the learning objective. Have students reflect on this list throughout the lesson and check off questions as they are answered.

Can You Solve the Problem?

The Investigative Phenomenon is the focus of the lesson. Encourage students to think about how hydrogen is used as a rocket fuel and how much hydrogen would be needed to move a rocket into space. Students will collect evidence related to this phenomenon throughout the lesson and revisit the question at the end of the lesson to use what they have learned to explain how hydrogen is used as fuel.

1 Sample answer: What distance will be covered, and how much fuel is typically required for this distance? What is the balanced chemical equation for this reaction? How do the masses of the reactants and products compare?

Evidence Notebook

2 The topic of using stoichiometry to determine the amount of hydrogen needed for a space flight will be revisited throughout this lesson.

Lesson 2 Analyzing Chemical Reactions   253

EXPLORATION 1 Quantifying Matter in Chemical Reactions

3D Learning Objective

Students **use mathematical representations** of chemical reactions to support claims that **atoms are conserved** and to illustrate that **matter is conserved.**

Everyday phenomena discussed throughout the Explorations of the lesson can often be used to connect the science content to students' personal experiences.

CCC **Energy and Matter**

Elicit from students the idea that mole ratios come from balanced chemical reactions. Remind students that a mole ratio is a conversion factor, and all conversion factors are equal to 1. The masses of reactants and products can be accurately calculated only if the balanced chemical reaction is taken into account. Therefore, a mole ratio should be included in any stoichiometry problem.

Differentiate Instruction

ELL Support Have students work in pairs to show relationships between reactants and products in a chemical reaction. Have students pick a double displacement reaction and write as many mole ratios as possible for the reaction. Have student pairs share their ratios to ensure that all ratios have been written.

1 Students should notice that the number of particles in a mole does not change. The name for the types of particles can change.

2 226 sandwiches, 9.03×10^{24} atoms carbon

EXPLORATION 1

Quantifying Matter in Chemical Reactions

A balanced chemical equation demonstrates the conservation of matter. So, you can use an equation to make predictions about the amounts of matter a reaction should produce.

Quantifying Moles in Chemical Reactions

FIGURE 1: One mole of several substances

Atoms and molecules are too small to be measured individually, so chemists use a unit of measurement called the mole to quantify matter in chemical reactions. Figure 1 shows exactly one mole of five substances. From left to right, they are: sugar, salt, carbon, oxygen (in a balloon), and copper.

1 **Collaborate** The table below shows the number of particles in one mole of each substance in the photo. Discuss the patterns you see with a partner. Does the chemical formula affect the number of particles in one mole of each substance? What is similar about one mole of each substance, and what is different?

Substance	Table sugar $(C_{12}H_{22}O_{11})$	Salt (NaCl)	Carbon (C)	Oxygen (O_2)	Copper (Cu)
Particles in one mole	6.02×10^{23} molecules	6.02×10^{23} formula units	6.02×10^{23} atoms	6.02×10^{23} diatomic molecules	6.02×10^{23} atoms

The mole is referred to as "the chemist's dozen" because it can be used to compare different substances by count. But atoms and molecules are much, much smaller than everyday items, such as eggs, so the number of particles in one mole of a substance is incredibly large. This number, which is approximately 6.02×10^{23}, is also called Avogadro's number. It was originally defined as the number of atoms in 12 g of carbon-12.

In order to understand how moles are used to quantify matter in chemical reactions, think back to the ingredients needed to make sandwiches.

2 slices of bread + 4 slices of turkey + 1 piece of cheese → 1 sandwich

If you had 288 slices of turkey, how many sandwiches could you make? You could use a technique called dimensional analysis to find out. Start by writing the known amount, 288 slices of turkey. Then, multiply this amount by a fraction that compares sandwiches to slices of turkey. The unit "slices of turkey" cancels out, leaving 72 sandwiches.

$$288 \text{ slices of turkey} \times \frac{1 \text{ sandwich}}{4 \text{ slices of turkey}} = 72 \text{ sandwiches}$$

2 **APPLY** Use dimensional analysis to complete the problems.

How many sandwiches could you make with 452 slices of bread and plenty of other ingredients? _____ sandwiches

Using a fraction comparing Avogadro's number and 1 mole, determine how many atoms are in 15.0 moles of carbon. _____ atoms

---

You can also use dimensional analysis to predict how much matter a chemical reaction should produce. Consider the following reaction, in which magnesium burns in oxygen. This reaction produces a bright white light, so it is often used in fireworks and road flares.

$$2Mg + O_2 \rightarrow 2MgO$$

You can use the coefficients in this equation to make predictions about amounts of reactants and products. To do this, you must use a conversion factor that shows the coefficients as mole quantities. A conversion factor is a ratio between two quantities that is written as a fraction. By definition, a conversion factor always equals one, so either quantity can be written as the numerator. Below are some conversion factors that could be used to solve problems related to this chemical equation.

Comparing magnesium to magnesium oxide:

$$\frac{2 \text{ mol Mg}}{2 \text{ mol MgO}} \quad \text{or} \quad \frac{2 \text{ mol MgO}}{2 \text{ mol Mg}}$$

Comparing oxygen to magnesium oxide:

$$\frac{1 \text{ mol O}_2}{2 \text{ mol MgO}} \quad \text{or} \quad \frac{2 \text{ mol MgO}}{1 \text{ mol O}_2}$$

3 MODEL Use the balanced equation for the synthesis of magnesium oxide to write the conversion factors you could use to compare moles of oxygen to moles of magnesium.

	or	

Problem Solving

Calculating Molar Amounts

SAMPLE PROBLEM If 45.3 moles of magnesium burn in excess oxygen, how many moles of magnesium oxide should be produced?

$$2Mg + O_2 \rightarrow 2MgO$$

ANALYZE Start with the given amount. Then, set up a conversion factor that will allow you to cancel the given unit and convert to the requested unit.

$$45.3 \text{ mol Mg} \times \frac{\text{mol ?}}{\text{mol ?}} = \text{mol MgO}$$

SOLVE Use the balanced equation to complete the conversion factor and solve.

$$45.3 \text{ mol Mg} \times \frac{2 \text{ mol MgO}}{2 \text{ mol Mg}} = 45.3 \text{ mol MgO}$$

PRACTICE PROBLEMS SOLVE Use the balanced equation to complete these problems. Report your final answers using the correct number of significant figures.

1. How many moles of MgO are produced if 0.37 moles of O_2 react with excess Mg?

2. If 8.2 moles of Mg are burned, how many moles of O_2 are consumed?

<sidebar>
© Houghton Mifflin Harcourt Publishing Company
</sidebar>

SEP **Using Mathematics and Computational Thinking**

Be sure students understand that a mole ratio is a count of the particles in the material, not a weight of the material. A mole ratio of 1:2 does not mean that twice the mass will form; it means twice as many particles will be produced.

DCI **PS1.B Chemical Reactions**

Ask students to explain how the periodic table can be used to predict reactions. For example, if magnesium reacts with oxygen to form magnesium oxide, what would happen if calcium were to react with oxygen? Students should explain that elements in the same column of the periodic table show similar chemical reaction behaviors.

Math Connection
MP.2 Reason abstractly and quantitatively.

After students complete the Practice Problems, have them write some of their own problems using the chemical equation from the Practice Problems. Have students trade problems with a partner and solve each other's problems. Students can then write a brief summary of the process they used and describe any patterns they noticed.

Classroom Practice

Students should use the balanced equation
$$Pb(NO_3)_2 + 2KI \rightarrow PbI_2 + 2KNO_3$$ to complete these problems:

How many moles of PbI_2 are made if 0.56 moles of KI react with excess $Pb(NO_3)_2$? 0.28 moles of PbI_2 are made.

If it is found that 5.14 moles of PbI_2 formed in the reaction, how many moles of $Pb(NO_3)_2$ were used? 5.14 moles of $Pb(NO_3)_2$ were used.

Practice Problem Answers
1. 0.74 moles of MgO will be produced.
2. 4.1 moles of O_2 will be consumed.

For the complete solutions to the Practice Problems and Classroom Practice, see the online Problem Solutions.

3 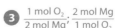 $\dfrac{1 \text{ mol O}_2}{2 \text{ mol Mg}}, \dfrac{2 \text{ mol Mg}}{1 \text{ mol O}_2}$

DCI PS1.B Chemical Reactions

Students should recognize that after a chemical reaction is balanced, not only can the number of particles of reactants and products be calculated, but—using the molar mass of the particles—the mass of a reactant needed or of a product produced can also be calculated.

Exploring Visuals

Remind students that the chemical formulas for specific substances, such as those in **Figure 2,** "obey" the law of definite proportions based on the bonding rules related to the number of valence electrons. Getting this right is a prerequisite step of doing any stoichiometry problems. In this case, the formula for sucrose has an exact number of carbon, hydrogen, and oxygen atoms. *Ask: According to the chemical formula for sucrose, how many carbon, hydrogen, and oxygen atoms are present in one molecule?* 12 carbon, 22 hydrogen, and 12 oxygen atoms are in one molecule of sucrose.

Collaborate

Discussion Hold a class discussion about chemical formulas. Encourage students to take their time when molecules become more complicated. Many organic molecules have formulas in which the same type of atom can be found in more than one place in the molecule. For example, C_6H_5COOH has carbon, hydrogen, and oxygen atoms in multiple places. The reason these molecular formulas are written this way is to help convey the structure of the molecule.

1 a different, depends, does not depend

2 The sucrose molecule contains many more atoms than the diatomic oxygen molecule does. When there are more atoms within the molecule, as there are in sucrose, the mass of one mole is likely to be higher than it will be when there are fewer atoms within the molecule, as there are in oxygen. However, the mass of one mole depends on both the mass of each atom and the number of atoms, not just the number of atoms in the molecule.

Quantifying Mass in Chemical Reactions

Using a balanced chemical equation to calculate quantities of matter, such as moles, volumes, or masses, is called *stoichiometry*. Stoichiometry allows you to convert from a quantity that is difficult to measure, such as the number of atoms in a substance, to a quantity that is easy to measure, such as the mass in grams. So how can you convert from moles to mass? Think back to the sandwich-making scenario. If you had to order sandwich supplies by mass, you would need to know the mass of the ingredient you were working with. For example, if you purchased 1000.0 grams of turkey and wanted to calculate how many sandwiches you could make, you would need to know the mass of one slice of turkey. If you knew that one slice of turkey had a mass of 15.0 grams, you could use dimensional analysis to determine how many sandwiches are possible.

$$1000.0 \text{ g turkey} \times \frac{1 \text{ slice of turkey}}{15.0 \text{ g turkey}} \times \frac{1 \text{ sandwich}}{4 \text{ slices of turkey}} = 16.7 \text{ sandwiches}$$

In the same way that you must know the mass of each item when ordering food by mass, you must consider the mass of different particles to make predictions about the mass of product made in a chemical reaction. You can measure mass by putting a substance on a balance, but how do you determine the mass of one mole?

The following table shows the mass in grams of one mole of each substance.

Substance	Table sugar $(C_{12}H_{22}O_{11})$	Salt (NaCl)	Carbon (C)	Oxygen (O_2)	Copper (Cu)
Mass of one mole in grams	342.3 g	58.44 g	12.01 g	32.00 g	63.55 g

 EXPLAIN Complete the statement based on the data shown in the table.

One mole of sugar has the same | a different mass than one mole of salt. This indicates that the mass of one mole of a substance depends | does not depend on the chemical makeup of the substance. However, the number of particles in one mole depends | does not depend on the identity of the substance.

FIGURE 2: Molecular models of oxygen and sucrose molecules show how the atomic composition of these substances differs.

oxygen, O_2 sucrose, $C_{12}H_{22}O_{11}$

Why does the mass of one mole differ from one substance to another, but the number of particles in one mole does not? Consider the atomic composition of each of the substances presented in the table. Figure 2 shows models of two of these substances—a diatomic oxygen molecule and a sucrose (sugar) molecule.

2 **PREDICT** What differences do you notice when looking at the models of an oxygen molecule and a sucrose molecule? How do you think the mass of one mole of these substances is related to their atomic composition?

_____

_____

_____

The mass in grams of one mole of an element or compound is called its molar mass. The molar mass of a single monatomic element, such as carbon, is equivalent to its atomic mass, as listed on the periodic table, expressed in grams. So, the mole is a unit that allows you to convert from grams, which you can measure on a balance, to individual molecules or atoms. The molar mass of a substance is expressed in grams per mole, or g/mol.

$$\text{molar mass in grams} = 1 \text{ mole} = 6.02 \times 10^{23} \text{ particles}$$

The molar mass of a compound depends on the atomic masses of the elements that make it up and how many atoms of each element are present. For example, a copper atom has a higher molar mass than an oxygen molecule, even though an oxygen molecule is made up of two atoms. This is because copper has a much higher atomic mass than oxygen. Large molecules, such as sucrose, have high molar masses because so many atoms are present in one particle. In the case of sucrose, one molecule contains 45 atoms!

To calculate molar mass, use the periodic table to find the atomic masses of the elements. (Unified atomic mass units, u, are equivalent to grams per mole.) Multiply each atomic mass by the number of atoms indicated by the subscripts, and add the values you obtain. For example, the molar mass of sucrose, $C_{12}H_{22}O_{11}$, is calculated as follows:

C: 12.01 u (g/mol) × 12 atoms

H: 1.008 u (g/mol) × 22 atoms

O: 15.999 u (g/mol) × 11 atoms

So, the molar mass is: $(12.01 \times 12) + (1.008 \times 22) + (15.999 \times 11) = 342.3$ g/mol

 SOLVE Use a periodic table to calculate the following molar masses.

1. The molar mass of $CaCl_2$ is _____ g/mol.

2. The molar mass of $Mg_3(PO_4)_2$ is _____ g/mol.

Suppose you wanted to obtain the molar mass of a substance to use in a chemical reaction. You would have to measure out that mass in grams on a balance. The precision of your balance can make a big difference in your final outcome.

 Scale, Proportion, and Quantity

Molar Mass at an Industrial Scale

Correctly calculating the molar mass of a substance and correctly measuring that mass on a balance are two requirements for large-scale industrial processes. Imagine, for example, a chemical process for manufacturing a product such as aspirin tablets on an industrial scale. If a chemical engineer either miscalculated the molar mass of the ingredients or they made an error in measuring their mass on a balance, the entire product batch would be affected. Too little reactant would produce a smaller product yield. Too much of a reactant might show up as an impurity in the finished product, with dangerous health effects.

FIGURE 3: Even on an industrial scale, precise measurement is crucial to obtaining the desired amount of product.

 Language Arts Connection Research the production of aspirin. Then write an explanation for how a small calculation or measurement error might affect the production of this medicine at an industrial scale. Explain how the error might occur and why it would affect the final product in the way you claimed.

Differentiate Instruction

MTSS/RTI Provide guidance and support for students as they work through the mole ratios and multiple fraction calculations in this lesson. Reinforce the concept that 3/2 times 2 equals 3. Relate this to **everyday phenomena** by reasoning that cars/trucks times trucks equals cars. This analogy will help students understand that numbers and words can cancel out in the fractions of the calculations.

Math Connection
MP.2 Reason abstractly and quantitatively.
Remind students that the subscripts in a chemical formula tell the number of atoms found in a unit of the substance. When they are calculating the molar mass, they must account for the mass of all atoms in a unit of the substance.

Solve
1. 110.98
2. 262.86

Language Arts Connection
WHST.9-12.2 Write informative/explanatory texts, including the narration of historical events, scientific procedures/experiments, or technical processes.
Remind students that when writing an explanation, they should provide an introduction that clearly states the topic and engages readers, organize their ideas to make important connections and distinctions, include details that support their ideas, and provide a conclusion that supports their explanation.

3 Students should find that, to produce aspirin tablets, cornstarch and water are combined with acetylsalicylic acid. Binding agents help hold the tablets together, and fillers give the tablets greater bulk. A small error could cause a large difference at the industrial scale. For example, if the molar mass of cornstarch was miscalculated, too much of this ingredient could be added. The result would likely be excess filler, which could make it more difficult to produce a pure product.

EXPLORATION 1   *Quantifying Matter in Chemical Reactions, continued*

Classroom Practice

Calculate how much oxygen is produced in grams, if 9.85 g of mercury oxide is heated, according to the reaction $2HgO \rightarrow 2Hg + O_2$. 0.728 g

Calculate how much water is produced in grams, when 5.38 g of sodium hydroxide decompose, according to the reaction $2NaOH \rightarrow Na_2O + H_2O$. 1.21 g

Practice Problem Answers

1 molar mass of aluminum: 26.98 g/mol; molar mass of aluminum oxide: 101.957 g/mol

2 100.4 g Al_2O_3 × 1 mol Al_2O_3/101.957 g Al_2O_3 × 4 mol Al/2 mol Al_2O_3 × 26.98 g Al/1 mol Al = 53.14 g Al

For the complete solutions to the Practice Problems and Classroom Practice, see the online Problem Solutions.

3 36.9 g Al × 1 mol Al/26.98 g Al × 3 mol O_2/4 mol Al × 6.02×10^{23} molecules O_2/1 mol O_2 = 6.18×10^{23} molecules O_2

Evidence Notebook

4 $2H_2 + O_2 \rightarrow 2H_2O$

3.45×10^8 g O_2 × 1 mol O_2/31.998 g O_2 × 2 mol H_2O/1 mol O_2 × 18.015 g H_2O/1 mol H_2O
= 3.88×10^8 g H_2O

3.45×10^8 g O_2 × 1 mol O_2/31.998 g O_2 × 2 mol H_2O/1 mol O_2 × 6.02×10^{23} molecules H_2O/1 mol H_2O
= 1.30×10^{31} molecules H_2O

FORMATIVE ASSESSMENT

Have students research and model the possible assembly of atoms for the molecules fructose, dextrose, and aspirin.

Ask: *How are these molecules similar? How are they different?*

Sample answer: All of them contain H, C, and O atoms. Aspirin contains 9 C atoms, 8 H atoms, and 4 O atoms. Fructose and dextrose both contain 6 C atoms, 12 H atoms, and 6 O atoms. All three molecules have a molar mass of 180.2. The difference in fructose and dextrose is the organization of the atoms. Fructose has a five-carbon ring structure, and the ring structure in dextrose has six carbon atoms, as does the ring structure in aspirin.

Problem Solving

Calculating Mass

SAMPLE PROBLEM   Consider again the reaction between magnesium and oxygen. Imagine you wanted to know how much MgO would be produced if you burned 3.06 g of Mg. You would again reference the balanced chemical equation, which demonstrates conservation of matter.

$$2Mg + O_2 \rightarrow 2MgO$$

ANALYZE   To convert from grams of magnesium to grams of magnesium oxide, you need to know the molar masses of both substances. Do not include the coefficients when calculating molar mass. They will be included in another step of the solving process.

Mg: 24.31 g/mol

MgO: (24.31 g/mol × 1) + (15.999 g/mol × 1) = 40.309 g/mol

SOLVE   Now, you start with the given quantity and set up conversion factors in a way that allows all the units to cancel except for the unit on your final answer.

$$3.06 \text{ g Mg} \times \frac{1 \text{ mol Mg}}{24.31 \text{ g Mg}} \times \frac{2 \text{ mol MgO}}{2 \text{ mol Mg}} \times \frac{40.309 \text{ g MgO}}{1 \text{ mol MgO}} = 5.07 \text{ g MgO}$$

Notice that the mole-to-mole ratio, shown in the middle of the three conversion factors, is always present in a stoichiometry problem. Other conversion factors can be placed before and after it, but the comparison of moles of one substance to moles of another based on the balanced chemical reaction is vital to any stoichiometry problem.

PRACTICE PROBLEM   How many grams of aluminum are produced in this reaction if 100.4 grams of aluminum oxide are supplied? Report your answer using the correct number of significant figures.

$$2Al_2O_3 \rightarrow 4Al + 3O_2$$

1 **ANALYZE** Calculate the molar masses of aluminum and aluminum oxide.

2 **SOLVE** Start with the given from the question, and set up the conversion factors in a way that will allow units to cancel out, leaving only the unit required for the final answer.

3 **Collaborate** With a partner, show how you could determine the number of oxygen molecules produced if 36.9 grams of aluminum are consumed in this reaction.

4 **Evidence Notebook** The unbalanced equation for the burning of hydrogen in a rocket engine is:
$$H_2 + O_2 \rightarrow H_2O$$
Balance this equation and calculate how many grams of water are produced if 3.45×10^8 grams of oxygen are burned in excess hydrogen. Then, calculate how many water molecules are produced by burning the same amount of oxygen. Last, write an explanation for how you solved these problems.

© Houghton Mifflin Harcourt Publishing Company

EXPLORATION 2 Limiting and Excess Matter

EXPLORATION 2

Limiting and Excess Matter

Consider again the reaction between magnesium and oxygen. Only now, imagine two different scenarios. In one, the reaction between the magnesium ribbon and oxygen takes place in the open air. In the second, the reaction occurs in a glass chamber that prevents the magnesium from reacting with any more oxygen than what is present in the chamber.

FIGURE 4: Magnesium is ignited in an open system and a closed system.

a Magnesium is ignited in the open air.

b Magnesium is ignited inside a glass chamber.

5 **PREDICT** The mass of magnesium oxide produced in the open system in Figure 4a differs from the mass produced in the closed system in Figure 4b. Why do you think this is? How might this relate to the amount of reactants available in each scenario?

_____

_____

_____

_____

Quantifying Limiting and Excess Matter

When following a recipe, it may be the case that you have more than enough of one ingredient or a limited amount of another. Think about making sandwiches using this recipe.

2 slices of bread + 4 slices of turkey + 1 piece of cheese → 1 sandwich

If you had 20 slices of bread, 10 pieces of cheese, and 39 slices of turkey, you would run out of turkey first and could only make 9 sandwiches. In chemistry, having too much or too little reactant also occurs. If there is too little of one reactant compared to another, the reactant that runs out first is called the limiting reactant. The reactant that has extra left over after the reaction ends is called the excess reactant.

6 **ANALYZE** Select the correct terms to complete the statement.

Imagine you had 75 slices of bread, 200 slices of turkey, and plenty of cheese to make sandwiches with. You would run out of turkey | bread first, so it is the limiting | excess ingredient. There would be cheese and turkey | bread left over when all the sandwiches are made, so these are the limiting | excess ingredients.

© Houghton Mifflin Harcourt Publishing Company • Image Credits: (l, cl, cr, r) ©HMH

Lesson 2 Analyzing Chemical Reactions   **259**

3D Learning Objective

Students use **mathematical representations** of **chemical reactions** to support claims while showing that **patterns** provide causality in explanations of phenomena in which **the total amount of matter is conserved.**

Differentiate Instruction

Extension Have students think about everyday situations in which a process must stop when one item is used up. Examples include assembling sandwiches for lunch, replacing batteries in electronic devices, and doing laundry. Have students share their examples of these **everyday phenomena** with a partner. Ask students to consider when it would and would not be advantageous for a material to run out during a chemical reaction. For example, in the combustion of wood, it would be advantageous to have the oxygen run out during a wildfire, but perhaps not for a campfire.

CCC **Patterns**

Elicit from students the idea that the natural world is predictable in many ways and that if the same conditions for a chemical reaction were repeated many times, the same outcome would be expected every time. However, it may not be possible to exactly replicate all conditions. Even a slight change to temperature or atmospheric pressure can affect gases that may be part of the reaction.

5 In an open system, enough oxygen is available to fully react all of the magnesium, thus maximizing the mass of magnesium oxide that can form. In a closed system, if there is not enough oxygen to react all of the magnesium, then some of the magnesium will be left unreacted, and a lower-than-maximum amount of magnesium oxide will form.

6 bread, limiting, turkey, excess

EXPLORATION 2 Limiting and Excess Matter, continued

 SEP Developing and Using Models

Be sure students understand how to identify limiting reactants and reactants in excess—and that a reaction will always stop when one of the reactants is used up. To help students understand the concept of limiting and excess reactants, give them a bag of bolts, nuts, and washers with the task of making as many fully assembled kits as possible. This activity provides a visual for the concept of limiting and excess reactants.

Math Connection
MP.2 Reason abstractly and quantitatively.

Explain to students that a mole ratio is always present in a stoichiometry problem and that conversion factors may appear on either side of the mole ratio, depending on what quantity is given and what quantity is requested.

Classroom Practice

For the reaction $8Fe + S_8 \rightarrow 8FeS$, if 42.0 g of each reactant is used, how many grams of FeS will form? 66.1 g FeS

For the reaction $AgNO_3 + NaCl \rightarrow AgCl + NaNO_3$, if 41.5 g of $AgNO_3$ reacts with 6.75 g of NaCl, how many grams of AgCl will form?
16.6 g AgCl

Practice Problem Answers

1 58.0 g

2 magnesium, oxygen

For the complete solutions to the Practice Problems and Classroom Practice, see the online Problem Solutions.

 Evidence Notebook

3 This Evidence Notebook question refers to the Unit Project. The mole ratio is responsible because 2 mol Mg reacts with 1 mol O_2 to form 2 mol MgO. Therefore, the mole ratio for the first calculation is 1:1, whereas the mole ratio for the second calculation is 2:1. Students should explain how understanding mole ratios relates to their unit project.

Problem Solving
Determining Limiting and Excess Reactants

SAMPLE PROBLEM To determine the limiting and excess reactant for a reaction, you must first know the quantity of each reactant that is available. Consider this problem:

If you burn 48.6 grams of magnesium in 39.0 grams of oxygen:

1. How much magnesium oxide is produced?

2. Which reactant is the limiting reactant?

3. Which is the excess reactant?

$$2Mg + O_2 \rightarrow 2MgO$$

ANALYZE To determine how much product will actually be made, we must determine how much product each amount of reactant would produce if the other reactant was in excess. This means we will calculate two quantities.

$$48.6 \text{ g Mg} \times \frac{1 \text{ mol Mg}}{24.31 \text{ g Mg}} \times \frac{2 \text{ mol MgO}}{2 \text{ mol Mg}} \times \frac{40.309 \text{ g MgO}}{1 \text{ mol MgO}} = \boxed{80.6 \text{ g MgO}}$$

$$39.0 \text{ g O}_2 \times \frac{1 \text{ mol O}_2}{31.998 \text{ g O}_2} \times \frac{2 \text{ mol MgO}}{1 \text{ mol O}_2} \times \frac{40.309 \text{ g MgO}}{1 \text{ mol MgO}} = 98.3 \text{ g MgO}$$

SOLVE The amount of product that can be made is equal to the lesser amount from the two calculations because the limiting reactant runs out when this amount is made. Therefore:

1. The amount of product made is equal to 80.6 g MgO.

2. Magnesium is the limiting reactant.

3. Oxygen is the excess reactant.

1 PRACTICE PROBLEM **ANALYZE** If a sample of magnesium with a mass of 35.0 grams reacts with 35.0 grams of oxygen, how much magnesium oxide will be produced? Show your work, and circle your final answer.

2 **SOLVE** In this reaction, the limiting reactant is _____ and the excess reactant is _____ .

3 **Evidence Notebook** In the sample problem, the reactant that was present in a greater amount was actually the limiting reactant. Explain why this is, citing evidence from the balanced chemical equation to support your claim. Last, explain how you could apply this concept to the chemical reaction you are modeling as part of your unit project.

© Houghton Mifflin Harcourt Publishing Company

Determining Percent Yield

In the real world, chemical reactions do not always produce the expected amount of a product. Often, unpredictable side reactions take place. For example, if you ignite 0.972 g of Mg metal in the open air, you may get only 0.988 g of MgO, not the expected 1.61 g. The possible reasons for this include the fact that some hot Mg metal will react with nitrogen in the air to produce magnesium nitride, Mg_3N_2. Also, the hot magnesium can react with any water vapor that might be present to yield magnesium hydroxide, $Mg(OH)_2$. The products of these side reactions are called byproducts and may be difficult to predict.

The amount of product that should be produced from given amounts of reactants is called the theoretical yield of a reaction. The amount of product that actually results from a reaction is called the actual yield. If the actual yield of a reaction is the same as the theoretical yield, the reaction is said to be 100% efficient. With some exceptions, reactions are not 100% efficient. The efficiency of a reaction is measured by calculating percent yield. The percent yield is the ratio of the actual yield to the theoretical yield, multiplied by 100.

$$\text{Percent yield} = \frac{\text{actual yield}}{\text{theoretical yield}} \times 100$$

4 **EXPLAIN** If the percent yield for a chemical reaction is below 100%, are atoms still conserved? Explain your thinking.

_____

_____

_____

_____

_____

_____

Percent yield is important when trying to determine how much product will actually be produced in a chemical reaction. When a chemist is considering a reaction, he or she needs to know whether the expectations about the amount of product formed is realistic.

5 **SOLVE** Suppose you burn magnesium in a limiting amount of oxygen in a closed system, expecting to get 1.61 g MgO. You measure only 0.988 g MgO after the reaction. Show how you would calculate the percent yield for this reaction.

The percent yield of this reaction is _____%

The theoretical yield of a reaction reflects an idealized situation. In real situations, however, there are a number of factors that reduce the actual yield of a chemical reaction, so the actual yield of a reaction is never quite equal to the theoretical yield. The factors that reduce actual yield include side reactions, reactions of a product with other substances in the surroundings, and impurities in the reactants. Even inaccurate measurements can affect the percent yield of a reaction. Although 100% yields are almost never possible, chemists and chemical engineers try to run reactions under conditions that will maximize the percent yield. This lowers the cost of chemical production and reduces waste.

Ask students to research percent yields for industrial processes. Have them focus on why the percent yield is not 100% in these processes. Focus students on two very important aspects of industrial chemistry: cost from materials and cost from time needed for the reaction to occur. Point out that because some reactions take too long to occur, companies will sacrifice yield for the cost of time needed for more product to form. Students might also find out how companies maximize their yield, including the use of catalysts.

Collaborate

Draw-Pair-Share Have students work in pairs to draw a diagram that illustrates their thinking while answering the Explain question. Have each partner draw their diagram and then explain to the other how their diagrams illustrate their thoughts about this question. For example, a student might draw objects with two different shapes to represent particles of two different reactants. The particles react to form a new product, but the particles of one reactant are completely used up and particles of the other product still remain. Therefore, the percent yield is lower than 100%, but no atoms were destroyed.

Math Connection
MP.2 Reason abstractly and quantitatively.

Encourage students to think about why a percent yield can be much lower than 100%. Focus students on such parameters as how often particles collide to form products, what happens to the frequency of the collisions as reactant concentrations start to decrease, and how particles collide.

4 **Sample answer:** Yes. Atoms that do not become part of a product either undergo different reactions to form other products or remain part of the reactants that did not react.

5 0.988 g MgO/1.61 g MgO $\times$ 100 = 61.4%

DCI ETS1.A Defining and Delimiting Engineering Problems

Review with students the differences between criteria and constraints. Criteria are things that the solution needs to be successful. Constraints are limitations on the solution. Examples of constraints include the cost of materials, the amount of time available, and other limitations. Criteria can be ranked in order of their importance. Encourage students to think about how they would rank the criteria they list.

1 **Sample answer:** The temperature of the reaction could be increased, and different enzymes or increased enzyme concentrations could be used. Engineers could use computer models to test new methods for maximizing the percent yield.

2 **Sample answer:** Although scientific discoveries often lead to the development of new technology, the technology may be too costly to be practical. Also, it might produce byproducts that could be harmful to the environment. Producing hydrogen could require a large amount of energy, which would need to be obtained from some other source.

Evidence Notebook

3 **Sample answer:** For a NASA space flight, it would be necessary to calculate exact proportions of fuel so that there is not an excess of one reactant. If, for example, oxygen were the limiting reactant, there would be excess hydrogen. Carrying excess of either hydrogen or oxygen would be counterproductive as it would take more energy to lift it without any benefit of its contributing to extra thrust. Laboratory experiments might allow scientists to calculate the typical percent yield for this reaction.

FORMATIVE ASSESSMENT

3-Minute Pause Have students pause to think of the concepts presented in the section. Have them respond to the following prompts.

I became aware of . . .
I didn't realize that . . .
I still don't understand . . .

Engineering
Maximizing Percent Yield

FIGURE 5: Hydrogen can be made from wood chips.

Hydrogen is a clean-burning fuel, producing only water vapor when it is burned. This fuel is used to power a small number of buses and automobiles as well as rocket engines. But it is not widely used at this time because hydrogen does not occur in any significant concentrations as a pure element on Earth. If hydrogen-fueled vehicles become more numerous, a large amount of hydrogen fuel will be needed.

Hydrogen can be chemically removed from a wide variety of abundant, naturally occurring hydrogen-containing compounds. One solution to producing low-cost hydrogen in quantity is to stockpile and distribute biomass, converting it to hydrogen as needed. The wood chips in Figure 5 are one such example of biomass.

Unlike fossil fuels, plant material such as wood, leaves, and stalks are renewable. Chemists and chemical engineers are collaborating to develop a process that produces hydrogen from sugars in wood. Enzymes convert the sugars to hydrogen gas with a yield of two hydrogen molecules per carbon atom, the maximum possible yield. The hydrogen can then be easily separated from aqueous substances in the reaction chamber. Wood that would have normally been discarded can be used for this process.

1 **PREDICT** Describe some of the solutions that engineers might propose for maximizing the percent yield of hydrogen from discarded wood.

_____

_____

_____

_____

2 **ANALYZE** What types of criteria and constraints might engineers consider when evaluating competing solutions for maximizing the percent yield for this process? Discuss issues related to technology, science, affordability, and environmental impacts.

_____

_____

_____

_____

_____

3 **Evidence Notebook** Explain how the concepts of limiting reactant, excess reactant, and percent yield apply to the question of how NASA calculates the necessary amount of hydrogen fuel for a space flight.

EXPLORATION 3 Case Study: Greenhouse Gas Emissions

EXPLORATION 3

Case Study: Greenhouse Gas Emissions

Many of our daily activities are possible because of combustion reactions. The thermal energy released by the combustion of fossil fuels, such as coal, petroleum, and natural gas, can be converted to electricity or used to power vehicles. When a carbon-based fuel reacts with oxygen in a combustion reaction, carbon dioxide and water are released. The amount of carbon in Earth's atmosphere has increased significantly since the Industrial Revolution due to human activities involving combustion reactions. Because carbon dioxide is a greenhouse gas, an increasing concentration of this gas in Earth's atmosphere has led to an increase in average global temperatures.

4 **ASK** Imagine you are a researcher calculating the amount of carbon dioxide emitted by your family, class, or other local group. Write some questions you would ask to get started.

_____

_____

_____

_____

Sources of Greenhouse Gases

Greenhouse gases are emitted as the result of many different types of human activities. While carbon dioxide makes up the great majority (over 80%) of the greenhouse gases emitted by human activities, other greenhouse gases such as methane, nitrous oxide, and fluorinated gases are also released.

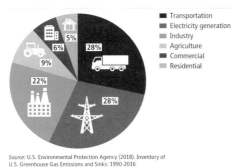

■ Transportation
■ Electricity generation
■ Industry
■ Agriculture
■ Commercial
■ Residential

FIGURE 6:
The greenhouse gas emissions produced in the United States in 2016 came from several different sectors. The percentages shown have been rounded.

5% 28%
6%
9%
22% 28%

Source: U.S. Environmental Protection Agency (2018). Inventory of U.S. Greenhouse Gas Emissions and Sinks: 1990-2016

5 **SOLVE** Use the graph in Figure 6 to answer the following question.

The total greenhouse gas emissions in the United States in 2016 was the equivalent of 6511 million metric tons (MMT) of CO_2. Use the graph to calculate how much of this total was emitted by the transportation sector. _____

Lesson 2 Analyzing Chemical Reactions **263**

3D Learning Objective

Students apply their knowledge of **chemical reactions** to analyze the effects of greenhouse gases in a **closed system.** They **use mathematical representations** to calculate amounts of carbon dioxide in greenhouse gas emissions and learn that that **science addresses questions about the natural and material world.**

Differentiate Instruction

Extension Carbon dioxide is only one of the greenhouse gases in the atmosphere. Ask students to select one of the others and research it. Have them make an infographic that describes the gas, its sources, and how scientists study its effect on the atmosphere.

Earth Science Connection

Help students understand that carbon dioxide is a greenhouse gas, which means it allows incoming solar energy to pass through it, but it traps much of the infrared radiation that Earth would normally radiate back into space. Scientists have shown that increasing concentrations of carbon dioxide correlate to an increase in global average temperatures. Data from computer simulations and lab tests with model systems demonstrate that this relationship is a causative one.

DCI **PS1.B Chemical Reactions**

Remind students that the products of combustion reactions occur as **everyday phenomena** when a substance containing carbon and hydrogen reacts with oxygen and burns. Invite students to think of specific examples, such as burning wood in a fireplace. The products of a combustion reaction are carbon dioxide and water. Because of the stoichiometry of chemical reactions, the more carbon contained in a reactant, the more carbon dioxide produced by the reaction.

4 **Sample answer:** How much energy does the average U.S. citizen use? Which fuels are used to provide this energy? How much carbon dioxide is produced by burning a given amount of each fuel?

5 6511 MMT × 0.28 = 1823 MMT

CCC Energy and Matter

The carbon cycle is an important biochemical cycle. Plants take CO_2 from the atmosphere and turn it into glucose during photosynthesis. The glucose is used to produce energy in plants and animals during cellular respiration. One of the products of cellular respiration is CO_2, which is returned to the atmosphere. Carbon in fossil fuels is stored on a much longer-term basis and is returned to the atmosphere when the fuel is burned.

Preconception Alert

Biology books can sometimes create the misconception that plants produce glucose and oxygen "just for us" and other animals. However, *all* cells, including plant cells, must use cellular respiration for their own growth.

1 2370.0 g C_8H_{18} × 1 mol C_8H_{18}/114.224 g C_8H_{18} × 16 mol CO_2/2 mol C_8H_{18} × 44.008 g CO_2/1 mol CO_2 = 7304.9 g CO_2;
7304.9 g CO_2 × 143 billion = $1.04 × 10^{15}$ g CO_2

2 Students should find that the amount of carbon dioxide absorbed by photosynthesis is not enough to fully offset the amount of carbon dioxide produced by humans each year. Therefore, this is not a viable solution for completely offsetting carbon dioxide emissions, and it should be combined with other solutions.

Evidence Notebook

3 Both are combustion reactions that use oxygen to burn a fuel. In a rocket engine, hydrogen combines with oxygen to produce water. No carbon dioxide is emitted. In the combustion of fossil fuels, carbon combines with oxygen to produce carbon dioxide, which is released into the air.

FORMATIVE ASSESSMENT

3-2-1 Have students write three things they found out in the lesson, two things they found interesting, and one question they still have about the concepts presented in the lesson.

Almost all of the fossil fuel that is burned by the transportation sector comes from the burning of petroleum—gasoline, jet fuel, and diesel—in internal combustion engines.

1 ANALYZE Use this information to calculate the answers to the following questions. Gasoline is the main fuel used for transportation. It is composed mainly of octane, C_8H_{18}. The balanced chemical equation for the combustion of octane is shown below.

$$2C_8H_{18} + 25O_2 \rightarrow 16CO_2 + 18H_2O$$

Assume a gallon of gasoline contains 2370.0 grams of octane. How many grams of carbon dioxide would be produced by the complete combustion of the octane in this gallon of gasoline? _____ g CO_2

In 2017, people in the United States used about 143 billion gallons of gasoline. How many grams of carbon dioxide were generated by the combustion of this gasoline, assuming the value you calculated in the first question was accurate?

_____ g CO_2

About 68% of the electricity generated in the United States in 2016 came from the combustion of coal and natural gas. The industry sector uses various fossil fuels both as an energy source and as reactants in the chemical reactions that make products such as plastics. The commercial and residential sectors also use various fossil fuels, mainly for heating, so the amount of emissions depends on weather conditions. Emissions from agriculture come from farming and livestock. Because each sector uses different fossil fuels with different chemical components, solutions for reducing greenhouse gas emissions will vary.

Absorbing Greenhouse Gases

Carbon dioxide can also be absorbed and stored. Anything that absorbs and stores carbon is called a *carbon sink*. One major carbon sink is photosynthetic organisms. Plants and algae take in carbon dioxide from the atmosphere and water from the soil. Using energy from sunlight, they make sugars during photosynthesis. Oxygen gas is given off as a byproduct.

$$6H_2O + 6CO_2 \rightarrow 6O_2 + C_6H_{12}O_6$$

Forests are a major natural carbon sink. The carbon dioxide forests absorb is used to make carbon compounds that are stored in wood. When trees and other organisms die, the carbon they contain moves into the soil. Thus, soil is another carbon sink. A third sink is water. Oceans and rivers absorb and store carbon dioxide from the atmosphere.

2 **Language Arts Connection** Conduct research about CO_2 emissions and CO_2 absorption via photosynthesis. Then prepare a report that answers the questions below. Cite specific text evidence to support your claims, and explain any gaps or inconsistencies you encountered.

- How much carbon dioxide is emitted by the global human population each year?
- How much carbon dioxide is absorbed by photosynthesis each year?
- Based on your findings, what conclusion can you make about using photosynthesis to completely offset human carbon emissions? Is this a viable solution? Why or why not?

3 **Evidence Notebook** Think back to the chemical reaction between hydrogen and oxygen in rocket engines. How is this reaction related to the chemical reaction that results in carbon dioxide emissions? How are the two reactions similar? How are they different?

EXPLORATION 4 Gravimetric Analysis

EXPLORATION 4

Hands-On Lab

Gravimetric Analysis

Hard water is water that has a high mineral content. Hard water causes problems because the minerals in the water can clog plumbing and make soaps less effective. One way to "soften" hard water is to use a water-softening agent, such as sodium chloride or potassium chloride, to help remove the ions that cause the water to be hard.

You are working for a company that makes water-softening agents for homes that have hard water. Recently, there was a mix-up on the factory floor. Sodium carbonate, Na_2CO_3, spilled into a 575-L tub of distilled water, and the company needs you to determine the amount of Na_2CO_3 in the tub.

When chemists are faced with problems that require them to determine the quantity of a substance by mass, they often use a technique called *gravimetric analysis*. In this technique, a small sample of the material undergoes a reaction with an excess of another reactant. For example, you can combine excess strontium chloride, $SrCl_2$, with the spilled sodium carbonate to form sodium chloride, $NaCl$, and solid strontium carbonate, $SrCO_3$. The unbalanced chemical equation for this reaction is shown below.

$$SrCl_2(aq) + Na_2CO_3(aq) \rightarrow NaCl(aq) + SrCO_3(s)$$

This double-displacement reaction produces a precipitate, which forms when one of the products is insoluble (does not dissolve) in water. The (s) in the chemical equation indicates that strontium carbonate, $SrCO_3$, is the precipitate in this reaction. Because the precipitate is not dissolved, it is easy to separate, dry, and weigh the solid. This provides the mass for one of the products.

RESEARCH QUESTION How can you use the results of a reaction that produces a precipitate to determine how much reactant was present in an aqueous solution?

4 MAKE A CLAIM

How do you think you can use the results of this chemical reaction to determine how much sodium carbonate was spilled into the tub of water?

_____

_____

_____

_____

MATERIALS

- indirectly vented chemical splash goggles, a nonlatex apron, and nitrile gloves
- beaker tongs
- beakers, 250 mL (3)
- distilled water
- drying oven
- electronic balance
- filter paper
- glass funnel or Büchner funnel
- glass stirring rod
- graduated cylinder, 100 mL
- paper towel
- ring and ring stand
- rubber policeman
- sodium carbonate, Na_2CO_3, solution
- spatula
- strontium chloride, $SrCl_2$, solution, 0.30 M
- wash bottle

Lesson 2 Analyzing Chemical Reactions   **265**

 Student Lab Worksheet and complete Teacher Support are available online.

3D Learning Objective

Students **carry out an investigation** and apply the idea that **the total amount of matter is conserved in closed systems** to determine how much reactant was consumed in a **chemical reaction.**

Hands-On Lab 👥 Small Groups   ⏱ Two 45-minute class periods

Gravimetric Analysis

SEP Planning and Carrying Out Investigations

Students use gravimetric methods to measure the mass of an insoluble precipitate formed in a double-displacement reaction. Students then use stoichiometry to relate the mass of precipitate formed to the mass of reactants and explain to a company how to use this technique in the future.

Advance Preparation Prepare the 0.3 M $SrCl_2$ solution and the unknown solution. Prepare the Na_2CO_3 solution as the unknown solution by dissolving about 50 g of Na_2CO_3 into 1.00 L of water. Record the exact mass to calculate the concentration. Show students how to properly filter and rinse a precipitate.

Materials Alert Calcium chloride ($CaCl_2$) may be substituted for $SrCl_2$ if it is not available.

Safety Information Remind all students that indirectly vented chemical splash goggles, a nonlatex apron, and nonlatex gloves are to be worn during the setup, hands-on, and takedown segments of the activity. Remind students not to pour chemicals, either used or unused, back into the original container. Instruct them how to dispose of chemicals. Have students use caution when working with glassware, which can shatter and cut skin. Have them wash their hands with soap and water immediately after completing this activity.

4 Students may suggest that they can find the mass of strontium carbonate produced and then use stoichiometry to calculate how much sodium carbonate must have reacted to make that much strontium carbonate.

DCI **PS1.B Chemical Reactions**

The reaction between strontium chloride ($SrCl_2$) and sodium carbonate (Na_2CO_3) is a double displacement reaction. Double displacement reactions have positive and negative ions from two different reactants in an aqueous solution. When they react, the positive and negative ions exchange places to form two new compounds as the products. In this reaction, one compound is insoluble in water and forms a precipitate.

CCC **Energy and Matter**

In this double displacement reaction, one of the products is insoluble in water and falls out of solution as a precipitate. Because chemical reactions follow the law of conservation of matter, knowing the amount of one of the products produced can be used to calculate the mass of the limiting reactant. Students collect the precipitate by filtering it and drying it, and then they weigh it. From the mass of the precipitate, students can determine the number of moles of the precipitate and perform the stoichiometric calculations to find the amount of sodium carbonate in the solution.

Collaborate

Discussion Encourage lab partners to take a few minutes and discuss the research question before beginning the investigation. Pairs should work together to clearly define the problem and how they propose to perform the investigation to give them a valid conclusion. Working as a team is one way scientists find solutions to **everyday phenomena.**

Differentiate Instruction

ELL Support Some students may have difficulty following the use of chemical formulas and names for the different products and reactants throughout the investigation. Pair an ELL student with a student who understands the chemical formulas and names to work collaboratively to complete the investigation.

indirectly vented
chemical splash
goggles

SAFETY INFORMATION

- Wear indirectly vented chemical splash goggles, a nonlatex apron, and nitrile gloves during the setup, hands-on, and takedown segments of the activity.
- The substances used in this lab are toxic and should only be disposed of in the chemical waste container provided by your teacher. Never place these substances in the trash or sink.
- Secure loose clothing, wear closed-toe shoes, and tie back long hair.
- Follow your teacher's instructions for disposing of waste materials.
- Use caution when working with glassware, which can shatter and cut skin if dropped.
- Wash your hands with soap and water when you are finished handling chemicals.

CARRY OUT THE INVESTIGATION

1. Wash all of the necessary lab equipment with soap and water. Rinse each piece of equipment with distilled water.

2. Measure the masses of the following to the nearest 0.01 g, and record each mass in a data table in your Evidence Notebook:
   - a piece of filter paper
   - a paper towel (labeled with your name and the date) inside a clean, dry beaker

3. Measure 15 mL of the Na_2CO_3 solution into the graduated cylinder. Record this volume in your data table. Pour the Na_2CO_3 solution into a clean, empty 250-mL beaker. Wash and rinse the graduated cylinder.

4. Measure 25 mL of the $SrCl_2$ solution into the graduated cylinder. Record this volume in your data table. Pour the $SrCl_2$ solution into the beaker with the Na_2CO_3 solution. Gently stir the solution with a glass rod.

5. Repeat Step 4 with 10 mL of $SrCl_2$. Repeat this step until no more precipitate (solid) forms. Record the volume of $SrCl_2$ each time you repeat Step 4.

6. Once the precipitate has settled, slowly pour the mixture into the funnel. Use the rubber policeman to transfer as much of the precipitate into the funnel as possible. Rinse the rubber policeman once into the beaker. Pour the rinse water into the funnel, then rinse the beaker several times, pouring the rinse water into the funnel each time.

7. After all of the solution and rinses have drained through the funnel, use the wash bottle to slowly rinse the precipitate on the filter paper in the funnel with distilled water to remove any soluble impurities.

8. Carefully remove the filter paper from the funnel, and place it on your paper towel. Unfold the filter paper, and place the paper towel and filter paper in the rinsed beaker. Then place the beaker in the drying oven, if available. For best results, allow the precipitate to dry overnight.

9. Using beaker tongs, remove your sample from the drying oven, and allow it to cool. Measure and record the mass of the beaker with paper towel, filter paper, and precipitate to the nearest 0.01 g.

10. Clean up the lab and all equipment after use, and dispose of substances according to your teacher's instructions. Wash your hands thoroughly after all lab work is finished and before you leave the lab.

CALCULATE

1. Write a balanced equation for the reaction between strontium chloride and sodium carbonate. Which product is the precipitate? Are atoms of each element conserved in this reaction?

2. Calculate the mass of the dry precipitate. Use this mass to calculate the moles of $SrCO_3$ produced in this reaction.

3. According to your results from Question 2 and the balanced chemical equation, how many moles of Na_2CO_3 were present in the starting sample of 15 mL?

4. According to your results from Question 3, how many grams of Na_2CO_3 were present in the starting sample?

5. How many grams of Na_2CO_3 were present in the factory's 575-L tub? (Hint: Use conversion factors to convert from the sample size to the tub size.)

ANALYZE

1. Why was the precipitate rinsed in Step 7? What soluble impurities could have been on the filter paper along with the precipitate? How would the calculated results vary if the precipitate had not been completely dry? Explain your answer.

Calculate

1. $SrCl_2(aq) + Na_2CO_3(aq) \rightarrow 2NaCl(aq) + SrCO_3(s)$. The precipitate is strontium carbonate, $SrCO_3$. Atoms are conserved because the same number of each kind of atom appears on both sides of the balanced equation.

2. **Sample answer:** The mass of the precipitate can be calculated by subtracting the initial mass of the beaker containing the paper towel and the initial mass of the filter paper from the final mass of beaker, paper towel, and filter paper with dry precipitate. According to the sample data given, the calculated mass of the $SrCO_3$ precipitate is 1.06 g. From this quantity, the moles of $SrCO_3$ can be calculated: 7.18×10^{-3} mol $SrCO_3$ was produced in the reaction.

3. **Sample answer:** The balanced chemical equation from Question 1 shows that one mole of $SrCO_3$ is formed from one mole of Na_2CO_3. Therefore, 7.18×10^{-3} mol Na_2CO_3 was in the starting sample.

4. **Sample answer:** Students should multiply moles of Na_2CO_3 by the molar mass of Na_2CO_3. Using the sample data, 0.761 g Na_2CO_3 were present in the starting sample.

5. **Sample answer:** Using the mass obtained from the sample data, 2.92×10^4 g Na_2CO_3 were present in the factory's tub.

Analyze

1. **Sample answer:** The precipitate was rinsed to remove any impurities that may have remained on the $SrCO_3$. These impurities may have included $SrCl_2$ or $NaCO_3$ that did not react. If the precipitate were not completely dry, the measured mass of the precipitate would have been erroneously high because it would have included the mass of a small amount of water. An accurate measurement of the mass of the $SrCO_3$ precipitate is necessary because it is the only quantity that is experimentally determined and is the basis for all calculations.

Analyze (continued)

2. **Sample answer:** According to the sample data, the percentage error is –4.28%.

3. **Sample answer:** The percentage error is negative, so a smaller amount of strontium carbonate was obtained than what was expected. Some strontium carbonate might have been lost when the precipitate was being filtered or transported from one location to another.

1 Sample answer: The method used involved reacting excess reactant ($SrCl_2$) with the reactant being analyzed (Na_2CO_3) to form a precipitate ($SrCO_3$) that can be filtered, dried, and measured. Through stoichiometry, the moles of precipitate are related to the moles of Na_2CO_3, which can be converted to grams in the original 15 mL sample. This amount can then be converted to the number of grams in the 575 L tub. The data showed that 1.06 g $SrCO_3$ precipitated from the solution. By converting mass to moles, it was determined that 7.18×10^{-3} mol $SrCO_3$ were produced. From the balanced equation, 1 mol $SrCO_3$ was produced from 1 mol Na_2CO_3. So this amount of moles was converted to 0.761 g Na_2CO_3 in the original 15 mL sample. This was then converted to the number of grams in a 575 L tub. The results showed that there were 2.92×10^4 g Na_2CO_3 in the tub. These same methods could be applied to a situation in which a chemical has been spilled into a tub of water, as long as the calculations take into account the balanced chemical equation for the reaction and the molar masses of the reactants and products.

Evidence Notebook

2 Sample answer: Gravimetric analysis probably could not be used because no precipitate forms in the reaction between hydrogen and oxygen. The only product is water, which is released in the explosive reaction. If the water could be trapped during the explosion and its mass determined, gravimetric analysis might be possible.

FORMATIVE ASSESSMENT

Quick Write Allow students some more time to consider the Evidence Notebook question more fully. Have them write a short essay to answer the question.

---

2. Based on the concentration of the Na_2CO_3 solution you used, the theoretical mass of Na_2CO_3 is 0.795 g for every 15 mL of sample. Calculate your percentage error.

$$\text{Percentage error} = \frac{\text{value}_{\text{experimental}} - \text{value}_{\text{accepted}}}{\text{value}_{\text{accepted}}} \times 100$$

3. Was your percentage error value positive or negative? What does this tell you about how your final value compares with the theoretical value? How might errors have contributed to this result?

_____

_____

_____

_____

_____

1 DRAW CONCLUSIONS

Write a conclusion that addresses each of the points below.

Claim To help this company address this problem in the future, summarize the method you used. How can you use the results of a reaction that produces a precipitate to determine how much reactant is present in an aqueous solution?

Evidence Give specific examples from your investigation that support your claim.

Reasoning Explain how the evidence you gave supports your claim. Describe, in detail, the connections between the evidence you cited and the arguments you are making.

_____

_____

_____

_____

_____

_____

_____

_____

_____

_____

_____

  Evidence Notebook Could rocket engineers use gravimetric analysis to determine how much liquid hydrogen was present in a fuel tank before the reaction with liquid oxygen took place? Explain your answer.

TAKE IT FURTHER Guided Research

TAKE IT FURTHER

Guided Research

Redefining the Mole

When is a kilogram not a kilogram? Are all kilograms equal? These riddles don't seem to make sense until you learn that the definitions of the kilogram, the mole, and some other units of measurement have recently changed.

Since 1889, the kilogram had been officially defined as the mass of a small metal cylinder that is kept inside three glass jars within an underground locked vault in France. But, scientists observed that whenever this prototype kilogram was weighed, its mass was a tiny bit less than the mass of its six official replicas. They hypothesized that a few atoms of the metal rubbed off when the prototype was handled. In addition, the prototype got dirty and had to be cleaned to remove tiny specks of dust and dirt. Cleaning rubbed off a few atoms, too. As a result, the prototype kilogram lost 50 micrograms of mass over its 129 years. But because the mass of the kilogram was defined as the mass of the prototype, this meant that when the prototype changed, the amount of mass in one kilogram also changed! By definition, the mass of the prototype could not be different from one kilogram. Instead, all of the replicas were now too massive by 50 micrograms.

Scientists from 58 countries decided to change the definitions of several SI units, including the kilogram, to give them more precision. They proposed to define these units in terms of calculations based on universal constants of nature rather than on physical objects. The scientists met in November 2018 and voted unanimously for the changes.

The definition of a mole was also changed. Previously, a mole was defined as the amount of a substance that contains as many elementary particles as there are atoms in 0.012 kilograms of carbon-12. These particles could be electrons, atoms, ions, or molecules. But this definition of a mole had drawbacks. It was tied to the old definition of a kilogram, which, as you have just read, had difficulties. The Avogadro's constant that defines the mole is now defined as precisely $6.022\,140\,76 \times 10^{23}$.

FIGURE 7: This silicon sphere in a measuring machine was used as part of the International Avogadro Project.

The silicon sphere shown in Figure 7 is a uniform crystal of silicon-28, which was carefully shaped into a sphere. Using the mass and dimensions of the sphere, the structure of silicon's crystal lattice, and the atomic mass of silicon, scientists can calculate the total number of atoms in the sphere. Scientists in many different countries worked together in this effort, titled the International Avogadro Project, and performed measurements on several different silicon spheres. The redefinition of these units will allow the work of scientists to be more precise in the future.

 Language Arts Connection Conduct research to learn more about the techniques scientists used to originally define and then redefine the mole and the kilogram. Then write a blog post that answers the following questions.

- How are the mole and the kilogram related?
- What specific techniques and experiments did scientists use to redefine the mole as part of the International Avogadro Project?
- How will this project affect future scientific work?

| MORE PRACTICE WITH STOICHIOMETRY | CAREER: ATMOSPHERIC SCIENTIST | EXPLAINING STOICHIOMETRY | Go online to choose one of these other paths. |

© Houghton Mifflin Harcourt Publishing Company • Image Credits: ©Andrew Brookes/National Physical Laboratory/Science Source

Collaborate

You may choose to assign this activity or direct students to the Interactive Online Student Edition, where they can choose from all available paths. These activities can be assigned individually, to pairs, or to small groups.

History of Science

The kilogram has had a long history of change. The loss in mass from cleaning the kilogram can be calculated as $(50 \times 10^{-6}\ \text{g})/(10^3\ \text{g}) \times 100 = 5 \times 10^{-6}\ \%$. While this seems extremely small, it is still measurable and not a desirable characteristic for a standard. Have students research the different ways the kilogram has been defined and create a timeline to include in their blog posts that show its history. Encourage students to research other standards that are used to define SI units and how they have changed over time.

 Language Arts Connection
WHST.9-12.2 Write informative/explanatory texts, including the narration of historical events, scientific procedures/experiments, or technical processes.

Students should summarize their findings and explain how scientists used specific techniques to redefine the kilogram and the mole.

Explore Online ▶

More Practice with Stoichiometry

Students practice calculating mass, particles, and moles using stoichiometry.

Career: Atmospheric Scientist

Students explore the career of an atmospheric scientist and research laws related to greenhouse gas emissions.

Explaining Stoichiometry

Students make a booklet to explain how to carry out stoichiometry calculations.

EVALUATE Lesson Self-Check

Can You Solve the Problem?

Claims, Evidence, and Reasoning

Have students clearly state their claim—their explanation for the phenomenon they have been investigating throughout this lesson. They should present their reasoning for making this claim, along with evidence such as facts, examples, and statistics that support their claim.

You may want to have students present their arguments orally, in writing, or as a debate. Refer students to the **English Language Arts Handbook** for more information on evaluating claims and presenting arguments.

Cultivating Student Questions

Assessing Student Growth Review the list of questions students generated at the beginning of the lesson. Have volunteers select any unanswered questions and suggest how they could be investigated. After approving student plans, have small groups conduct the investigations and report back to the class.

📝 Evidence Notebook

1 The chemical equation must first be balanced in order to satisfy the law of conservation of mass. The balanced chemical equation for this reaction is $2H_2 + O_2 \rightarrow 2H_2O$. The mass of oxygen should be converted to moles of oxygen. Then a mole ratio based on the balanced equation should be used to convert from moles of oxygen to moles of hydrogen. Moles of hydrogen can then be converted to grams of hydrogen using the molar mass of hydrogen. This process can be used to predict expected amounts of products for a chemical reaction as long as the calculations performed are based on a balanced chemical equation.

Lesson Self-Check

CAN YOU SOLVE THE PROBLEM?

FIGURE 8: Tanks aboard NASA's Space Launch System rocket hold liquid hydrogen fuel and liquid oxygen oxidizer.

How did engineers know how large to make the tanks that hold the liquid hydrogen and oxygen in the rocket, and how much fuel they would need? A thorough knowledge of the chemical reaction that will boost the rocket into space was needed. Carrying excess reactant would result in extra weight without extra thrust, decreasing efficiency and increasing cost. In this lesson, you learned that hydrogen burns in the presence of oxygen to produce water.

1 **Evidence Notebook** Refer to your notes in your Evidence Notebook to make a claim about how you could determine the amount of hydrogen needed for a space flight. Your explanation should include a discussion of the following points:

Claim Explain how, given a certain quantity of oxygen, you could determine the exact amount of hydrogen needed for a space flight.

Evidence Use evidence and examples to support your claim. Show the balanced equation for this reaction and include example calculations to illustrate your thinking.

Reasoning Explain how the evidence you cited supports your claim.

 Formal Assessment Go online for student self-checks and other assessments.

CHECKPOINTS

Check Your Understanding

1. A chemist wants to calculate the amount of product that will be formed in a chemical reaction. Which of the following steps ensures that the chemist's calculations are in alignment with the law of conservation of mass?

- ○ **a.** writing the states of matter for each reactant and product
- ○ **b.** looking up the atomic numbers for each element involved in the reaction
- ○ **c.** correctly balancing the chemical equation
- ○ **d.** determining whether one product is a precipitate or not

Silicon dioxide, or sand, reacts with finely ground carbon at high temperatures to produce silicon carbide and carbon monoxide gas. Use this chemical equation to answer Questions 2 and 3:

$$SiO_2(s) + 3C(s) \rightarrow SiC(s) + 2CO(g)$$

2. Select the correct terms to complete the statement.

When 50.0 grams of silicon dioxide reacts with excess carbon, carbon monoxide gas is formed. This amount of silicon dioxide is equal to 83.2 | 0.832 | 1.66 moles. As a result, 83.2 | 1.66 | 0.416 moles of carbon monoxide are formed. This amount of carbon monoxide is equal to 46.6 | 25.7 | 11.6 grams.

3. Suppose 50.0 grams of silicon dioxide reacts with excess carbon. How many grams of silicon carbide should be produced? _____

4. Select the correct terms to complete the statement.

A chemist has two bottles of gas. One bottle contains 2.6 moles of O_2, and the other bottle contains 2.6 moles of Cl_2. The two bottles contain equal | different numbers of particles and equal | different amounts of mass.

5. Which of the following are sources of carbon dioxide emissions? Select all correct answers.

- ☐ **a.** internal combustion engines
- ☐ **b.** generation of electricity in fossil-fueled power plants
- ☐ **c.** solar energy panels on roofs of homes
- ☐ **d.** photosynthesis by green plants and algae

Sodium and chlorine can be isolated from sodium chloride, which is a natural source of these two valuable elements. Use this chemical equation to answer Questions 6 and 7:

$$2NaCl(s) \rightarrow 2Na(s) + Cl_2(g)$$

6. What mass of sodium should be produced from 25.0 mol of sodium chloride?

- ○ **a.** 288 g Na
- ○ **b.** 575 g Na
- ○ **c.** 1150 g Na
- ○ **d.** 1460 g Na

7. What mass of chlorine should be made from 25.0 mol of sodium chloride?

- ○ **a.** 222 g Cl_2
- ○ **b.** 443 g Cl_2
- ○ **c.** 886 g Cl_2
- ○ **d.** 1772 g Cl_2

8. A chemist mixed sodium sulfide and cadmium nitrate solutions in a test tube. The equation is

$$Na_2S(aq) + Cd(NO_3)_2(aq) \rightarrow 2NaNO_3(aq) + CdS(s)$$

Sodium sulfide is the limiting reactant. Which substances are found in the test tube after the reaction has ended? Select all correct answers.

- ☐ **a.** Na_2S
- ☐ **b.** $Cd(NO_3)_2$
- ☐ **c.** $NaNO_3$
- ☐ **d.** CdS

Answers

1. c

2. 0.832, 1.66, 46.6

3. 33.4 grams

4. equal, different

5. a, b

6. b

7. c

8. b, c, d

Answers

9. The law of conservation of mass states that atoms cannot be created or destroyed in chemical reactions, so chemical equations must be balanced. Therefore, the ratio of reactants to products must be considered when performing stoichiometric calculations. The coefficients in the balanced equation can be used to determine mole ratios.

10. 824 g NH_3 × 1 mol NH_3/17.03 g NH_3 × 4 mol NO/4 mol NH_3 = 48.4 mol NO; 824 g NH_3 × 1 mol NH_3/17.03 g NH_3 × 6 mol H_2O/4 mol NH_3 = 72.6 mol H_2O

11. The mass is not truly lost; it is simply not in the form of a product. The missing mass may be in the form of a byproduct or unreacted (excess) reactant. The atoms are not destroyed; they simply did not recombine to form the product.

Make Your Own Study Guide

Have students create a study guide that helps them organize and visualize the important information from this lesson. Their study guide should focus on the main ideas from this lesson and tie multiple ideas together. Students can make an outline, a concept map, a graphic organizer, or another representation.

EVALUATE

CHECKPOINTS (continued)

9. Explain why, when performing stoichiometric calculations, it is important to use a balanced equation with correct chemical formulas and to consider the coefficients in the equation when converting from one quantity to another.

_____

_____

_____

_____

10. Nitric acid has a wide variety of industrial uses, including as an oxidizer in liquid-fueled rockets. The first step in the industrial manufacture of nitric acid is the catalytic oxidation of ammonia.

$$4NH_3(g) + 5O_2(g) \rightarrow 4NO(g) + 6H_2O(g)$$

The reaction is run using 824 g NH_3 and excess oxygen. Show how you could determine how many moles of NO and how many moles of H_2O are formed.

_____

_____

_____

11. Explain what happens to the mass that appears to be "lost" when the percent yield of a reaction is less than 100%. According to the law of conservation of mass, what happens to the atoms that did not become part of the product?

_____

_____

_____

_____

MAKE YOUR OWN STUDY GUIDE

In your Evidence Notebook, design a study guide that supports the main ideas from this lesson:

The mole is the basic unit for all calculations used to determine the expected amount of product or reactant for a chemical reaction.

Stoichiometric calculations must be based on a balanced chemical equation in order to be in alignment with the law of conservation of mass.

Reactants might be limiting or in excess.

Remember to include the following information in your study guide:
• Use examples that model main ideas.
• Record explanations for the phenomena you investigated.
• Use evidence to support your explanations. Your support can include drawings, data, graphs, laboratory conclusions, and other evidence recorded throughout the lesson.

Consider how the methods you have developed in this lesson can be used to show that the total amount of matter in all closed systems is conserved.

Investigating Energy in Chemical Reactions

Building to the Performance Expectations

The learning experiences in this lesson prepare students for mastery of

HS-PS1-4 Develop a model to illustrate that the release or absorption of energy from a chemical reaction system depends upon the changes in total bond energy.

HS-ETS1-4 Use a computer simulation to model the impact of proposed solutions to a complex real-world problem with numerous criteria and constraints on interactions within and between systems relevant to the problem.

 Trace Tool to the NGSS

Go online to view the complete coverage of standards across lessons, units, and grade levels.

 SEP ## Science & Engineering Practices

Developing and Using Models
Develop and use a model based on evidence to illustrate the relationships between systems or between components of a system.

 **VIDEO** Developing and Using Models

Using Mathematics and Computational Thinking
Use mathematical models and/or computer simulations to predict the effects of a design solution on systems and/or the interactions between systems.

Constructing Explanations and Designing Solutions
Evaluate a solution to a complex real-world problem, based on scientific knowledge, student-generated sources of evidence, prioritized criteria, and tradeoff considerations.

DCI ## Disciplinary Core Ideas

PS1.A Structure and Properties of Matter
A stable molecule has less energy than the same set of atoms separated; one must provide at least this energy in order to take the molecule apart. (HS-PS1-4)

PS1.B Chemical Reactions
Chemical processes, their rates, and whether or not energy is stored or released can be understood in terms of the collisions of molecules and the rearrangements of atoms into new molecules, with consequent changes in the sum of all bond energies in the set of molecules that are matched by changes in kinetic energy. (HS-PS1-4)

PS3.B Conservation of Energy and Energy Transfer
Uncontrolled systems always evolve toward more stable states—that is, toward more uniform energy distribution (e.g., water flows downhill, objects hotter than their surrounding environment cool down). (HS-PS3-4)

PS3.B Conservation of Energy and Energy Transfer
Energy cannot be created or destroyed, but it can be transported from one place to another and transferred between systems. (HS-PS3-4)

 **CCC** ## Crosscutting Concepts

Energy and Matter
Changes of energy and matter in a system can be described in terms of energy and matter flows into, out of, and within that system.

Systems and System Models
When investigating or describing a system, the boundaries and initial conditions of the system need to be defined and their inputs and outputs analyzed and described using models.

Systems and System Models
Models (e.g., physical, mathematical, computer models) can be used to simulate systems and interactions—including energy, matter, and information flows—within and between systems at different scales.

MATH STANDARDS

MP.2 Reason abstractly and quantitatively.

MP.4 Model with mathematics.

HSN-Q.A.1 Use units as a way to understand problems and to guide the solution of multi-step problems; choose and interpret units consistently in formulas.

ELA STANDARDS

RST.11-12.1 Cite specific textual evidence to support analysis of science and technical texts.

SL.11-12.5 Make strategic use of digital media (e.g., textual, graphical, audio, visual, and interactive elements) in presentations to enhance understanding of findings, reasoning, and evidence and to add interest.

Supporting All Students, All Standards

Integrating the Three Dimensions

In this lesson, students learn about the laws of thermodynamics and how to follow the transfer of energy as heat through systems (CCC Systems and System Models). Students use models in the form of chemical equations and graphs to explain changes of energy and matter that occur due to rearrangements of atoms during endothermic and exothermic reactions (SEP Developing and Using Models, DCI PS1.B, CCC Energy and Matter). Students consider how the sum of all bond energies relates to changes in energy and matter during endothermic and exothermic reactions (SEP Using Mathematical and Computational Thinking, DCI PS1.A). They identify criteria and constraints of various choices of combustion fuels and consider impacts on society and the environment from the use of fossil fuels (DCI ETS1.A). Students then develop and use models to design a solution to a complex real-world problem (SEP Developing and Using Models, SEP Constructing Explanations and Designing Solutions).

Preassessment

Have students complete the unit pretest or see the Assessment Guide.

Build on Prior Knowledge

Have students list what they know about energy in chemical bonds. After they have made a comprehensive list, ask them to share their list with a partner and discuss any differences. Compile a classroom list that can be added to over the course of this lesson.

You may want to review the following concepts:
- Energy cannot be created or destroyed. It can only change from one form to another.
- A chemical bond is an attractive force between particles.
- In a chemical reaction, one or more types of particles break apart, and the atoms reform to produce one or more new substances.
- All chemical reactions require an input of energy to start the reaction.
- A change in temperature indicates a chemical reaction.
- Some chemical reactions have a net decrease of energy, and some have a net increase of energy.

Professional Development Go online to view **Professional Development videos** with strategies to integrate CCCs and SEPs, including the ones used in this lesson.

Content Background

Understanding the energy changes that occur during chemical reactions is understanding the transfer of energy in systems. Thermodynamic laws dictate that energy can only change from one form into another. Therefore, the energy in a system is always constant. Accurately defining system boundaries is important to following these transformations.

The atoms that make up a compound have potential energy due to the forces that hold the atoms together. This potential energy is responsible for how stable the bonds that hold atoms together are. The bond is most stable when the potential energy is lowest.

During a chemical reaction, the bonds of reactants must first be broken. This requires energy The atoms then rearrange and form new bonds. This releases energy. The potential energy decreases if the bonds between the reactant atoms are stronger overall than the bonds between the product atoms, and the reaction is exothermic. The potential energy increases if the bonds between the reactant atoms are weaker overall than the bonds between the product atoms, and the reaction is endothermic.

Differentiate Instruction

KEY WORDS

- potential energy
- kinetic energy
- thermal energy
- law of conservation of energy
- specific heat capacity
- exothermic reaction
- endothermic reaction

ELL SUPPORT

Guide students in contrasting the terms *endothermic reaction* and *exothermic reaction*. Have them relate the word *exothermic* to the exit from a building. Have them relate the word part *therm* to a thermometer.

ENGAGE: Investigative Phenomenon

4.3

Investigating Energy in Chemical Reactions

A sparkler gives off energy in the form of light that can be seen and heat that can be felt.

CAN YOU EXPLAIN THE PHENOMENON?

The brilliant flashes of light produced by a sparkler make it popular in many different celebrations around the world. A sparkler is a small, handheld firework that consists of a thin metal rod coated at one end with a combustible paste. The paste contains a fuel source such as carbon or sulfur, and an oxidizing compound. When the sparkler is lit, chemical reactions occur that release energy in the form of light and heat. Bits of metal embedded in the paste, such as iron, aluminum, and titanium, make the sparks that you see when a sparkler burns. Other metals present in the sparkler may make sparks of different colors.

1 **INFER** What do you think is the source of the energy in a chemical reaction, such as the reaction that occurs when you light a sparkler?

_____

_____

_____

2 **Evidence Notebook** As you explore the lesson, gather evidence to explain how energy in the form of heat is transferred in processes such as the chemical reactions that light up a sparkler.

Build on Prior Lessons

In Lessons 1 and 2, students learned about modeling and analyzing chemical reactions. Lesson 3 builds on these concepts as students explore energy changes in chemical reactions.

Lesson Objective

Students analyze changes in energy during chemical reactions and use different types of models to describe the changes that occur.

Cultivating Student Questions

Prompt students to ask questions about the sparkler's energy source. Record questions on chart paper, and sort them based on their focus. With students, narrow the questions down to the ones that directly relate to the learning objective. Have students reflect on this list throughout the lesson and check off questions as they are answered.

Can You Explain the Phenomenon?

The Investigative Phenomenon is the focus of the lesson. Students are asked to record their initial thoughts about the source of energy for chemical reactions, such as the reaction that occurs when you light a sparkler. Students will revisit these predictions at the end of the lesson to explain the change in energy and to compare the bond energy and stability of the compounds in a sparkler.

1 The light and heat from a sparkler suggest that the reaction releases energy. Students may have correct or incorrect ideas about the source of the energy. For example, they may think reaction energy is the same energy that initiates the reaction. They will learn in this lesson that energy released is the difference between energy needed to break bonds and energy released when bonds form.

Evidence Notebook

2 The topic of energy absorbed and released by chemical reactions will be revisited throughout this lesson.

EXPLORATION 1 Investigating Thermal Energy and Heat

3D Learning Objective

Students investigate energy transformations and how energy cannot be created or destroyed. They **plan and conduct an investigation** to explore how systems evolve toward more uniform energy distribution when substances of different temperatures are combined.

Everyday phenomena discussed throughout the Explorations of the lesson can often be used to connect the science content to students' personal experiences.

CCC Energy and Matter

Have students brainstorm examples of **everyday phenomena** that involve energy transformations. For each example, have them describe what happens to the energy at each transfer or each transformation and how energy is conserved.

Collaborate

Accessing Prior Knowledge To activate what students already know about temperature and heat, demonstrate or describe two Bunsen burners that are heating two beakers containing different amounts of water, 100 mL and 1 L. *Ask: How will the temperatures of the two water samples change after 10 minutes of heating?* The 100 mL sample will increase in temperature far more than the 1 L sample. *How will the amount of energy in the form of heat added to the two water samples compare?* Both samples will receive the same amount of energy in the form of heat.

DCI PS3.D Energy in Chemical Processes

Emphasize to students that in addition to releasing energy in the form of heat, chemical reactions can also release energy in the form of light, sound, and electrical energy. *Ask: What are some examples of chemical reactions that release these forms of energy?* **Sample answer:** Light and sound energy are released from a burning building. Electrical energy is released from reactions in a battery.

 b, c

Investigating Thermal Energy and Heat

Energy comes in many different forms. It may take the form of stored energy, such as energy stored in a chemical bond, or it may take the form of movement, such as the energy associated with the movement of individual particles. Energy may also change form or be transferred from one place to another. Scientists and engineers study energy transformations so that they can control natural and designed systems.

FIGURE 1: Examples of materials that store chemical energy include foods, such as carbohydrates, and fuels, such as propane.

Energy Transformations

Potential energy is stored energy associated with the position, shape, or condition of an object. One form of potential energy is chemical energy, which is the energy stored in the bonds of chemical compounds, such as the examples shown in Figure 1. Energy stored in the chemical bonds of food is transformed into other forms that your body can use. Energy in the chemical bonds of a fuel such as propane is released as heat when the fuel is burned. Other forms of potential energy include gravitational potential energy, elastic potential energy, and nuclear energy. Recall that nuclear energy is released when the nucleus of an atom breaks apart or when the nuclei of two smaller atoms fuse.

Kinetic energy is the energy associated with the motion of an object. Many processes transform potential energy to kinetic energy, or vice versa. When you throw a baseball, you transfer potential energy from your muscles to the ball, which then has kinetic energy while it is moving. Molecules and atoms also have kinetic energy. Sound energy is a form of kinetic energy because it is caused by the vibration of molecules in a medium such as air.

Electromagnetic energy is a type of kinetic energy carried by electromagnetic waves, which are types of radiation that include visible light, x-rays, and microwaves. Electromagnetic energy can be transferred to an object, increasing the kinetic energy of its particles.

Any form of energy can transform into any other. In particular, when chemical reactions and other processes transfer energy as heat, there are always transformations between potential energy and kinetic energy.

1 EXPLAIN Which of the following are examples of kinetic energy? Select all correct answers.

☐ **a.** the energy in a sports drink

☐ **b.** the energy given off by the sun

☐ **c.** the energy of molecules in motion

☐ **d.** the energy of a book on a tall shelf

☐ **e.** the energy that holds together ions in a crystal

Temperature and Thermal Energy

Thermal energy is the total kinetic energy of the particles in a substance. Temperature is a measure of the average kinetic energy of the particles of a substance. When there is a temperature difference between two systems that are nearby or in contact with each other, thermal energy will transfer from the higher temperature system to the lower temperature system. This transfer of energy is the result of collisions between individual particles that make up the two substances. The mechanism by which thermal energy is transferred is called *heat transfer*.

When you feel hot, the temperature of your body has risen, either because thermal energy is transferring to your body, or because your body is generating too much thermal energy. When you feel cold, thermal energy is being transferred from your body to the surrounding system. If a system and its surroundings have the same temperature, they are in *thermal equilibrium*, and no net energy transfer occurs.

The pressure cooker in Figure 2 is an example of a closed system in which heat transfer is taking place. When the pressure cooker is sealed, thermal energy from the stovetop is transferred to the pressure cooker and is trapped there. This allows food within it to be cooked rapidly.

FIGURE 2: A pressure cooker is a rigid container designed to cook food at high temperatures and pressures.

2 APPLY Select the correct terms to complete the statement about the pressure cooker. Some terms may be used once or not at all.

kinetic energy   thermal energy   thermal equilibrium

Heat transfer from the stove increases the _____

of the particles of the pressure cooker system, which increases its

_____ . The pressure cooker's temperature reflects the

average _____ of the particles in it.

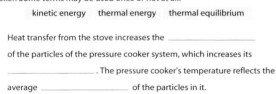

Temperature Scales

You are probably familiar with the Celsius and Fahrenheit temperature scales. The Fahrenheit scale was one of the earliest widely adopted temperature scales, and it is still commonly used in the United States. In this scale, water freezes at 32 °F and boils at 212 °F. In the Celsius scale, which is more commonly used worldwide, water freezes at 0 °C and boils at 100 °C. The degrees in the Celsius scale are 100 equal divisions between these two arbitrarily assigned values.

Having to carry out calculations with negative temperature values can complicate a scientist's work. So, they often use the Kelvin temperature scale, which has its zero point at *absolute zero*, a theoretical temperature at which all particle motion stops. Thus, a kelvin temperature will never be negative. Because the Kelvin scale is absolute, temperatures on it are measured in *kelvins* rather than degrees.

3 **Language Arts Connection** Research the types of analyses that are typically carried out using kelvins. Then make a claim for why the Kelvin scale is necessary for a certain type of analysis. Cite specific text evidence from scientific sources to support your claim.

 SEP **Constructing Explanations and Designing Solutions**

Ask students if they have ever used a hot pack to warm their hands on a cold night. Have them refer to the motion of particles to explain the transfer of heat that occurs when the hot pack is held against the skin. Ask students to describe what happens when the pack and the skin reach thermal equilibrium.

Math Connection

Students may have difficulty understanding the circumstances under which scientists use the Kelvin scale. Because temperatures are absolute on the Kelvin scale, there are no negative temperatures, and therefore the ratio between any two temperatures can easily be calculated. This scale is also convenient to use when scientists work with very low temperatures, as with liquid nitrogen. The lack of negative numbers makes it easier to calculate differences between such low temperatures. **(MP.2)**

Language Arts Connection
RST.11-12.1 Cite specific textual evidence to support analysis of science and technical texts, attending to important distinctions the author makes and to any gaps or inconsistencies in the account.

Remind students that they can find tips for conducting research, making claims, and citing evidence in the online **English Language Arts Handbook.**

2 kinetic energy, thermal energy, kinetic energy

3 Students should describe a type of analysis that would not work well with negative numbers or one based on proportional changes in temperature. Students should cite specific text evidence from reliable sources to support their claim. Some of these sources may simply be explanations of when the Kelvin scale is appropriate, but students should also include evidence from an actual investigation.

CCC Energy and Matter

The law of conservation of energy states that energy cannot be created or destroyed. One type of energy is thermal energy, which can move from one place to another. ***Ask****: What happens when ice is placed in a glass of water?* The water becomes cold. *What happens when the glass of water is allowed to sit for a long period of time?* The ice melts, and the water eventually warms up to room temperature. *Where did the energy to warm up the water come from?* The water absorbed energy from its environment.

Explore Online

Encourage students to go online to view the video about the transfer of thermal energy when hot metal is submerged in cool water.

Earth Science Connection

First Law of Thermodynamics Explain to students that although chemistry usually applies the first law of thermodynamics to small systems, such as substances in a beaker or a flask, the law also applies to large systems. Earth, for example, can be considered a closed system. Except for a relatively small amount of dust that enters the atmosphere, matter does not enter or leave the Earth system. Energy, however, constantly enters the Earth system in the form of radiation from the sun and other astronomical bodies. Energy also leaves as thermal energy and radiation that reflects off the surface and back into space. According to the first law of thermodynamics, however, the change in the energy of the Earth system is the difference in the energy that enters and the energy that leaves.

1 equal to, to, from, increases

Conservation of Energy

When a system loses energy, that energy does not simply disappear. Rather, it is transferred to the system's surroundings. Similarly, if a system gains energy, the energy it gains must come from the system's surroundings. The law of conservation of energy states that energy cannot be created or destroyed, which means the total amount of energy in the universe remains constant.

Figure 3 shows an example of how the law of conservation of energy applies to a system made up of water in a beaker. The initial temperature of the water is due to its average thermal energy at the start. After a hot piece of metal is added to the system, thermal energy from the piece of metal is transferred to the water. An increase in the water's temperature provides evidence for this transfer. The temperature of the metal continues to drop until the metal and water are at thermal equilibrium—that is, when they are at the same temperature. Systems always evolve toward more stable states. In other words, the distribution of thermal energy in the system becomes more uniform over time.

FIGURE 3: Thermal energy is transferred when a hot piece of metal is submerged in cool water.   **Explore Online**

a Before the hot metal piece is added, the temperature of the water is 22.6 °C.

b After the hot metal piece is added, and the water and the metal reach thermal equilibrium. The temperature of the water is 26.2 °C.

1 ANALYZE Select the correct terms to complete the statement.

In the system shown in Figure 3, the amount of energy gained by the water is greater than | less than | equal to the amount of energy lost by the metal. Energy is conserved because the energy gained by the water was transferred from | to the water from | to the metal. Over time, stability in the system decreases | increases as thermal equilibrium is reached.

The First Law of Thermodynamics

In thermodynamics, the conservation of energy is described by the *first law of thermodynamics*. If you apply the law of conservation of energy to a system in which energy does not leave or enter the system, it means that the energy of the system does not change. Energy can be transformed or transferred within the system, but the total amount of energy in the system remains constant.

In an open or closed system, the first law of thermodynamics implies that the change in energy in the system is equivalent to the energy that passes through the system's boundaries. For example, in Figure 3, the amount of energy gained by the water is equal to the amount of energy that is lost by the hot piece of metal. Energy was not created, but rather transferred from one location to another.

The Second Law of Thermodynamics

The second law of thermodynamics states that thermal energy spontaneously flows from a substance at a higher temperature to a substance at a lower temperature. Heating a pot of water on a stove provides a good example of the direction of energy transfer. Thermal energy is transferred from the burning fuel or hot surface of a stove to the cooler pot of water. Thermal energy never moves from the cooler water back toward the stove. Once the stove is turned off, energy from the hot pan is transferred to the air until thermal equilibrium is reached, and the pan is the same temperature as the air.

FIGURE 4: Thermal energy spontaneously transfers from the flame on the stove to the cooler pan.

 Collaborate With a partner, write an explanation of how the first and second laws of thermodynamics apply to the system shown in Figure 4. As part of your explanation, describe the system boundaries, the direction of energy transfer, and the conservation of energy. Include diagrams as needed.

Particle Behavior and Energy Transfer

Imagine what would happen if you placed a cold metal object in the hot water in the pan in Figure 4. As you have seen, the system would eventually reach thermal equilibrium. But how would interactions between the water molecules and metal atoms account for your observations at the larger scale? At the particle level, thermal energy takes the form of kinetic energy. The particles of a substance with a higher temperature move faster on average because they have a higher kinetic energy.

 MODEL Draw a model showing how interactions between water molecules and metal atoms could cause a closed system to reach thermal equilibrium when a cold metal object is placed in hot water. Illustrate at least two points in time. Include components that help show how kinetic energy and collisions between particles are related to this phenomenon.

DCI ## PS3.B Conservation of Energy and Energy Transfer

Provide an analogy to help students understand the second law of thermodynamics: Just as balls naturally roll downhill from a place of higher gravitational potential energy to a place of lower gravitational potential energy, so thermal energy naturally "flows downhill" from a region of higher temperature to a region of lower temperature. Have students work in small groups to develop their own analogy of the second law of thermodynamics from **everyday phenomena.**

SEP ## Developing and Using Models

The models that students draw should show the system boundaries. **Ask:** *Why is it important to show not only the parts of the model within the system but also the system boundaries?* The boundaries are important to show the limit of the model. In a simple model like a pan system, it is important to show that only what happens within the system is being considered.

2 Students should explain that the system boundaries are the outside surface of the water. Energy from the hot flame is transferred to the pan and then to the water. The energy increase in the system is due to energy being transferred to the system, as the first law of thermodynamics states. Energy flows from the hot metal to the cool water, as the second law of thermodynamics states.

3 Drawings should show that, initially, the molecules that make up the cooler metal have less kinetic energy (and therefore exhibit less movement) than the molecules in the warmer water. When the metal is placed in the hot water, collisions between particles will cause the particles in the metal to move more quickly. When thermal equilibrium is reached, all of the parts of the system have the same temperature, so the particles have the same kinetic energy.

Lesson 3 Investigating Energy in Chemical Reactions 277

Hands-On Lab Pairs ⏱ 30 minutes

Exploring Thermal Energy and Temperature

SEP **Planning and Carrying Out Investigations**

Students plan and carry out an investigation to explore the relationship between the thermal energy and temperature of two systems of water.

Materials Alert You can use hot tap water for this investigation.

Safety Information Remind all students that indirectly vented chemical splash goggles and a nonlatex apron are to be worn during the setup, hands-on, and takedown segments of the activity. Have students use caution when working with glassware, which can shatter and cut skin. Tell them to immediately wipe up any spilled water on the floor so it does not become a slip/fall hazard.

1 Accept all reasonable claims. Students may know that mixing two temperatures of water will result in water at a temperature approximately halfway between the two original temperatures. A change in temperature indicates a change in thermal energy.

2 Students should obtain equal volumes of water at different temperatures and record the temperature of both systems. Then they should mix both samples into a third, larger beaker and measure the temperature of the water every few seconds.

3 Students should explain whether or not their data support their claim. If students predicted that the resulting temperature would be approximately halfway between the two original temperatures, their data will most likely support this statement. If students did not make this prediction, they should explain how their results differ from their initial claim.

4 Students should predict that the final temperature of the combined system is higher when using insulated containers because less thermal energy was lost to the surroundings.

Hands-On Lab

 # Exploring Thermal Energy and Temperature

The amount of thermal energy in a substance is related to both the temperature and the amount of substance. In this lab, you will plan and carry out an investigation to explore how thermal energy changes when water of different temperatures is combined into a single system.

1 **MAKE A CLAIM**

How can you use temperature to measure the change in thermal energy of a system?

_____

_____

_____

MATERIALS

· indirectly vented chemical splash goggles, nonlatex apron
· beaker, 500 mL (3)
· thermometer (3)
· water

SAFETY INFORMATION

· Wear indirectly vented chemical splash goggles and a nonlatex apron during the setup, hands-on, and takedown segments of the activity.

· Immediately wipe up any spilled water on the floor so it does not become a slip/fall hazard.

indirectly vented
chemical splash
goggles

2 **CARRY OUT THE INVESTIGATION**

In your Evidence Notebook, write a procedure and safety plan to test your claim. What are the variables of your investigation, and what qualitative and quantitative data will you collect to determine the change in the thermal energy of the system?

3 **DRAW CONCLUSIONS**

In your Evidence Notebook, write a conclusion that addresses each of the points below.

Claim How did thermal energy change when water of different temperatures was combined into a single system?

Evidence What evidence from your investigation supports your claim?

Reasoning Explain how the evidence you gave supports your claim. Describe, in detail, the connections between the evidence you cited and the argument you are making.

4 **EXTEND**

How do you think the transfer of thermal energy and the final temperature of the system would change if you used insulated bowls with lids instead of glass beakers? In your Evidence Notebook, write a procedure to investigate this question. If time allows, have your teacher approve your plan, and carry out your procedure.

 Student Lab Worksheet and complete Teacher Support are available online.

Analyzing Specific Heat Capacity

The amount of thermal energy needed to change the temperature of a system by one degree is the system's *heat capacity*. The heat capacity of a system depends on the type of material from which it is made and its mass. Therefore, heat capacity is an extensive property.

5 **PREDICT** Select the correct terms to complete the statement.

To change the temperature of a large tub of water and a small glass of water by the same amount, less | more energy must be added to the large tub of water than to the small glass of water. This is because the water in the glass has a lower | higher mass than the water in the tub.

In order to compare the heat capacities of different materials, scientists compare heat capacity per unit of mass. This is known as the specific heat capacity of the material. Specific heat capacity (c_p) is an intensive property defined as the amount of energy (q) required to raise the temperature of one gram of a substance by one kelvin. (The subscript p refers to standard pressure.) Specific heat capacity relates heat to a substance's temperature change by the following equation.

 Engineering Lab

Experimenting with Calorimetry Build a calorimeter and test it to determine the specific heat capacity of a known sample.

$$q = mc_p\Delta T$$

The SI unit for energy is joules (J), and values of specific heat capacity are often expressed in units of joules per gram per kelvin (J/(g·K)).

Specific Heat Capacities of Some Common Substances (at 298.15 K and atmospheric pressure)			
Substance	Specific heat (J/(g·K))	Substance	Specific heat (J/(g·K))
Water (*l*)	4.18	Iron (*s*)	0.449
Water (*s*)	2.06	Copper (*s*)	0.385
Aluminum (*s*)	0.897	Gold (*s*)	0.129

Materials with a low specific heat capacity undergo a larger increase in temperature as thermal energy is transferred to them than materials with a high specific heat capacity. These differences make certain materials more appropriate for different purposes. For example, as shown in Figure 5, the relatively high specific heat capacity of liquid water makes it useful as a coolant in industrial processes.

FIGURE 5: Water is sprayed over newly made steel rods to cool them.

6 **INFER** Suppose you had three pans with the same mass, but made of different materials: iron, aluminum, and copper. Based on the values in the table above and the definition of specific heat capacity, which pan would cook food the fastest?

7 **Evidence Notebook** Explain how conservation of energy and the laws of thermodynamics apply to the sparkler system you saw at the beginning of this lesson. What forms of energy are present in this example? How does this system demonstrate the principles of energy conservation?

© Houghton Mifflin Harcourt Publishing Company • Image Credits: ©Patrick Landmann/Getty Images News/Getty Images

---

Differentiate Instruction

MTSS/RTI Have students work in small groups to create an outline of specific heat capacity that includes a definition in their own words, the units used, and a description of how specific heat capacity can be used to compare or select materials for a specific purpose. Have students share their outlines with the rest of the class.

Explore Online ▶

Engineering Lab 👥 Small Groups 🕐 60 minutes

Experimenting with Calorimetry

SEP **Planning and Carrying Out Investigations**

Students build a calorimeter and test it by using it to determine the specific heat capacity of a known sample. Students explain that successful designs use materials that minimize the amount of energy lost to the surroundings. *Student lab worksheet and teacher support available online.*

5 more, lower

6 The copper pan would cook the food the fastest because it has the lowest specific heat of the three metals. This means less energy is required to raise one gram of copper by one degree than is required to do the same for iron and aluminum.

Evidence Notebook

7 In the sparkler system, chemical energy, a form of potential energy, is converted to thermal energy and light energy, which are forms of kinetic energy. The energy transferred to the surroundings is equal to the amount of energy that leaves the sparkler system. As the sparkler releases heat, this heat will warm the air around it because thermal energy moves from warmer substances to cooler ones.

FORMATIVE ASSESSMENT

Exit Card Write the vocabulary terms from this Exploration on the board. Have each student write a sentence on an index card telling how two of the words are related.

EXPLORATION 2 Measuring the Energy in Food

3D Learning Objective

Students **plan and carry out an investigation** of the energy content of food that demonstrates how energy **can be transported from one place to another** as it **flows into, out of, and within that system.**

Hands-On Lab Small Groups ⏱ 90 minutes
Measuring the Energy in Food

SEP Planning and Carrying Out Investigations

Students plan an investigation to determine the amount of energy in a snack food by measuring the amount of thermal energy released during its combustion.

Safety Information Remind all students that indirectly vented chemical splash goggles, a nonlatex apron, and nonlatex gloves are to be worn during the setup, hands-on, and takedown segments of the activity. Remind students to secure loose clothing, tie back hair, and remove flammable materials from the lab area.

You may want to light the food samples for students. This gives you an opportunity to check each group's procedure before students begin testing their food samples.

Materials Alert The materials list includes an evaporating dish for burning food samples, but an open crucible will also work well. The materials list does not include nuts due to allergy concerns, but nuts burn very well for this lab. Popular brands of corn chips can be readily lit on fire because of their high content of corn oil.

1 Students may predict that the energy values they calculate using their measurements will be less than the values on food labels because some energy will be lost to the surroundings during the experiment. To collect precise and accurate data, students should try to reduce the amount of energy lost due to the measurement setup being an open system. The calorimeter should be designed with proper insulation to keep as much energy inside it as possible.

EXPLORATION 2

Hands-On Lab

Measuring the Energy in Food

We get the energy we need by eating food. The energy comes from the chemical energy stored in the food that gets released during digestion. This energy is described on food labels with the unit Calorie (always with a capital C). One Calorie is equivalent to 4.184 kJ. How do food makers determine how many Calories a food has? They burn the food in a device called a calorimeter. In this lab, you will build a calorimeter to measure the energy released when two different snack foods are burned.

RESEARCH QUESTION How can the specific heat capacity of water be used to determine the amount of energy stored in another substance?

1 MAKE A CLAIM

Predict how well your energy values will compare to those on the food labels. What must you consider when designing your calorimeter to ensure that it measures the energy released as precisely and accurately as possible? Explain your thinking.

_____

_____

_____

MATERIALS

- indirectly vented chemical splash goggles, nonlatex apron, nitrile gloves
- aluminum foil, 30 cm × 30 cm sheet
- balance
- beaker tongs
- evaporating dish
- graduated cylinder, 100 mL
- matches or propane lighter
- ring and clamp
- ring stand
- snack foods with nutrition labels, 2 types (cheese puff, marshmallow, dry cereal, etc.)
- soda can
- spatula
- thermometer
- thermometer clamp
- three-finger clamp
- water
- weighing boat or weighing paper (2)
- wire gauze

SAFETY INFORMATION

- Wear indirectly vented chemical splash goggles, a nonlatex apron, and nitrile gloves during the setup, hands-on, and takedown segments of the activity.
- Secure loose clothing, wear closed-toe shoes, and tie back long hair.
- Never eat any food items used in a lab activity.

indirectly vented chemical splash goggles

PLAN THE INVESTIGATION

Write a procedure and safety plan in your Evidence Notebook explaining how you will measure the amount of energy contained in the snack foods using the calorimeter. Use Figure 6 and the materials list to develop your plan. Decide what substances you will test, and how many trials you will need to conduct. Ask your teacher to approve your procedure and safety plan before you begin.

280 Unit 4 Chemical Reactions

 Student Lab Worksheet and complete Teacher Support are available online.

COLLECT DATA

Make a data table in your Evidence Notebook. Use the specific heat equation below to determine the data you should collect for each food sample. Consider your experimental setup when deciding how much data to collect and how to ensure the data are as accurate as possible.

- When measuring the temperature of water in a container, the thermometer should only contact the water, not the container.

- Because the density of water is 1.00 g/mL, the volume of water can be used to infer its mass. A 50.0 mL sample of water is 50.0 g.

FIGURE 6: Energy from the burning snack food sample warms the water in the soda can calorimeter.

ANALYZE

1. Use the following equation to calculate the number of Calories per gram for each food:

$$q = mc_p\Delta T$$

How do your values compare to the Calories per gram shown on the nutrition label?

2. Sketch your calorimeter. Label the system and the surroundings. Use arrows to show the flow of energy into and out of the system.

3. Discuss the limitations of the data you collected. How do these limitations correlate to the design of your calorimeter? Describe how you would redesign your calorimeter to minimize energy loss.

Math Connection

Unit Conversions Students calculate the change in thermal energy by multiplying the mass of water by the change in temperature and the specific heat of water, which is 0.001 Cal/(g × °C). Remind students that measurements in science always include units and that calculations involving measurements must include the units. Model for students how the units of g and °C "cancel out" on the right side of the equation. When the units come out correctly, it serves as a check to show that the calculation was set up correctly. **(HSN-Q.A.1)**

CCC **Energy and Matter**

Help students relate the lab to **everyday phenomena** by having them think about foods they eat that likely have high energy content. Point out, however, that factors other than energy content contribute to each food's nutritional value.

Analyze

1. Students should use the specific heat equation to calculate the Calorie values for each food. They may find that the Calories per gram values they found are much less than the Calories per gram indicated by the nutrition label. This is because of the amount of energy released that was not transferred to the water.

2. Students should sketch their calorimeter and identify it as the system and the environment outside of the calorimeter as the surroundings. Students should use arrows to show the energy being transferred from the food to the soda can and from the soda can to the water. Students should also show the energy that was lost to the surroundings and not transferred to the water. Encourage students to include the types of energy and whether each type is kinetic or potential energy.

3. Because this calorimeter is an open system, one limitation to the data collected is that some of the energy was lost to the surroundings rather than transferred to the water. Therefore, the data collected are not as precise and accurate as they should be. Students should describe how they could better insulate their calorimeter to minimize the amount of energy lost to the surroundings.

Claims, Evidence, and Reasoning

Collaborate Explain to students that their claim should be a comparison of their data and calculations. To explain differences, have groups make a list of each step in the experiment. Then, have them discuss how energy could be lost during each step.

Analyze (continued)

4. Students should sketch a system that is closed off from its surroundings so the system cannot exchange energy or matter with its surroundings and vice versa.

1 Students may claim that the energy values they calculated are lower than the actual values. They should describe differences in their data and the energy values on food labels as evidence to support this claim. Students should suggest reasons for the differences, such as energy lost to the surroundings or difference in accuracy of measurements.

2 Students should explain their reasoning based on differences in heat capacity. The heat capacity and temperature change will be different, but the amount of energy transferred is the same.

Evidence Notebook

3 Students should relate the low mass of the spark to a low amount of energy, which produces a small change in temperature when this energy is transferred to your skin.

FORMATIVE ASSESSMENT

Write on the board: *True or false: Energy is created from food as your body digests it.* Asks students to raise their hands if they agree with this statement. Then ask them to raise their hands if they disagree. Ask volunteers to explain their reasoning. Guide the discussion to help students understand that stored chemical energy in the food is converted to other forms after it is eaten.

---

4. The calorimeter you used is an open system. Sketch how you could determine the energy content of a snack food using a closed system. Label the system in your sketch.

1 **DRAW CONCLUSIONS**

Write a conclusion that addresses each of these points.

Claim How do your findings compare with the values shown on the food labels for these foods? How did the design of the calorimeter affect the data you collected?

Evidence Use evidence from your data and calculations to support your claim.

Reasoning Explain how the evidence you cited supports your claim. In addition, discuss possible reasons for differences between your measurements and the Calorie values shown on the nutrition label for each food.

2 **EXTEND**

How do you think the results of your investigation would have been different if you had used a liquid with a different heat capacity, such as salt water? If time allows, write a procedure in your Evidence Notebook describing how you could investigate this question. With your teacher's permission, carry out your procedure, and analyze your results.

3 **Evidence Notebook** Discuss why you do not get burned if a few sparks from a sparkler touch your skin. Consider how the mass of the spark and its thermal energy affect this phenomenon.

EXPLORATION 3 Exploring Reaction Energy

Exploring Reaction Energy

Some chemical reactions release thermal energy, while others absorb it. These phenomena are explained in terms of the chemical energy stored in the bonds between the atoms that make up a compound. During a chemical reaction, energy must be absorbed by a reactant in order to break these chemical bonds, and energy is released when the chemical bonds of the products form. The difference in energy stored in the reactant bonds and the product bonds determines whether there is an overall absorption or release of thermal energy by the reaction.

Analyzing Changes in Energy

Observe the transformations that result from the three chemical reactions shown in Figure 7. Along with new substances being produced in the reactions, a significant amount of thermal energy is either absorbed or released to the surroundings.

FIGURE 7: Energy changes can happen in different ways during chemical reactions.

Explore Online ▶

a   Reaction 1 Sugar is combined with sulfuric acid, producing black carbon and water vapor. The water is vaporized due to the increase in temperature.

b   Reaction 2 When barium hydroxide reacts with ammonium chloride, the temperature in the flask decreases, and the flask freezes to the wood.

c   Reaction 3 When glycerin is added to a sample of potassium permanganate, the energy released by the reaction ignites the glycerin.

4   MODEL Draw the system and surroundings for each of the reactions in Figure 7. Identify the system boundaries and use arrows to model the movement of energy.

3D Learning Objective

Students **use models** in the form of chemical equations and graphs to explain changes of energy and matter that occur because of **rearrangements of atoms** during endothermic and exothermic reactions.

CCC Energy and Matter

Review with students the three methods of thermal energy transfer. *Convection* is the transfer of thermal energy carried by particles of a fluid (liquid or gas) rising due to density differences. *Conduction* is the transfer of thermal energy within substances or from one substance to another due to temperatures differences. The energy is transferred by particles of the substances as they collide. *Radiation* is the transfer of thermal energy by electromagnetic waves. As students explore the absorption and release of energy that occur during chemical reactions, encourage them to look for clues as to how energy is transferred and the results of that transfer.

Collaborate

Discussion Have students talk with a partner and brainstorm examples of **everyday phenomena** in which a chemical reaction occurs. Have them analyze each reaction and describe the new substance that is produced as well as the type of energy transfers and energy transformations that take place during the reaction.

4 The arrows in Reactions 1 and 3 should point from the reaction to the surroundings to show that energy is released by the reaction. Arrows in Reaction 2 should point from the surroundings to the reaction to show that energy is absorbed by the reaction.

Preconception Alert

Students may have previously heard the words *exothermic* and *endothermic* used to describe any reaction that releases or absorbs energy. Emphasize that these terms apply only to energy released or absorbed in the form of heat. In more general terms, any reaction that releases energy of any form is *exergonic,* and any reaction that absorbs energy of any form is *endergonic*. Have students apply these terms by describing **everyday phenomena** that are exergonic but not exothermic and phenomena that are endergonic but not endothermic.

Explore Online ▶

Hands-On Lab 👥 Small Groups ⏱ 60 minutes
Investigating Energy in Chemical Processes

SEP **Planning and Carrying Out Investigations**

Students design an experiment to classify to classify a variety of salts as undergoing exothermic or endothermic processes when dissolved in water.

Student lab worksheet and teacher support available online.

CCC **Energy and Matter**

Draw students' attention to the chemical equation. Point out that, although energy is not explicitly shown in this equation, energy can be considered to be a product, which indicates that the reaction is exothermic. Note also that oxygen gas (O_2) is a reactant. Explain that most oxidation reactions are exothermic.

1 The release of heat is evidence that the reaction between iron and oxygen is exothermic. The reaction transforms chemical energy in the form of bonds of the reactants to thermal energy released to the surroundings. The chemical energy of the reactants is greater than the chemical energy of the products. This exothermic reaction is used to heat the MRE. The heat released by the reaction causes the water to boil, which heats the food.

Exothermic and Endothermic Reactions

Explore Online ▶
Hands-On Lab 🧪

Investigating Energy in Chemical Processes Carry out an investigation to explore which chemicals make the best hot and cold packs.

A reaction that releases thermal energy is called an exothermic reaction. Other than an increase in temperature, the formation of light or sound can also indicate the release of energy in a chemical reaction. In these reactions, bond energy changes into kinetic energy that leaves the reaction system and enters the surroundings. This transfer of energy increases the temperature of the surroundings. A reaction that absorbs thermal energy is called an endothermic reaction. In an endothermic reaction, the temperature of the surroundings decreases because kinetic energy leaves the surroundings and enters the system. When kinetic energy is absorbed in an endothermic reaction, that energy becomes chemical potential energy in the products of the reaction.

Energy and Matter

Using Reaction Energy

FIGURE 8: MREs rely on chemical reactions to warm food.

Chemical hand warmers are used to warm up your hands and feet. These warmers contain finely powdered iron in a porous envelope inside a sealed pouch. When the pouch is opened, the iron reacts with atmospheric oxygen to form iron(III) oxide, releasing energy in the form of heat.

$$4Fe + 3O_2 \rightarrow 2Fe_2O_3$$

A similar reaction can also be used to produce higher temperatures, such as in MREs ("meals-ready-to-eat") used by the military. MREs contain iron and magnesium, both of which react with oxygen. Water is added to the MRE, which reacts with the magnesium, releasing energy in the form of heat. This allows military personnel to have hot meals without requiring heating equipment such as stoves.

An exothermic reaction such as this can gently warm your hands, or potentially produce enough heat to burn your skin. Thus, it is important that the MRE be a closed system. Once water is added to the MRE, it is sealed to prevent heat transfer from inside the system to the surroundings.

1 **APPLY** Is the chemical reaction between iron and oxygen endothermic or exothermic? In your explanation, discuss how energy is transformed in the MRE.

_____

_____

_____

 Collaborate With a partner, make a model of a system that shows how the potential energy in the chemical bonds in the MRE is transformed into kinetic energy in the surroundings through molecular collisions. Your model should show how energy is conserved in the system.

We can infer information about the properties of the substances involved in a reaction from the energy changes in the reaction. Consider the combustion of carbon.

$$C(s) + O_2(g) \rightarrow CO_2(g)$$

In this reaction, carbon dioxide is more stable than carbon or diatomic oxygen molecules due to the reactants having more potential energy than the products. The reaction is exothermic because energy is released into the surroundings as thermal energy.

FIGURE 9: Some reactions give off energy, and others absorb energy.

a   Burning coal is an exothermic process.

b   Nitric oxide, which contributes to smog, forms in an endothermic process.

The synthesis of nitric oxide, NO, is endothermic, so it requires energy:

$$N_2(g) + O_2(g) \rightarrow 2NO(g)$$

This reaction does not occur spontaneously at typical air temperatures. When fossil fuels are burned, the nitrogen and oxygen in the surrounding air can react to form nitric oxide. Nitric oxide is a major contributor to acid rain, ozone depletion, and smog. In the atmosphere, NO undergoes an exothermic reaction to form another pollutant, nitrogen dioxide, NO_2, which is an irritant to the respiratory system. The formation of NO is endothermic because much more energy is needed to break the chemical bonds of NO_2 than is used to form the chemical bonds of NO.

2   **ANALYZE** Select the correct terms to complete the statement.

For a chemical reaction to occur, particles must collide. Chemical bonds contain potential | kinetic energy. During the combustion of carbon, the reactant molecules must have enough potential | kinetic energy that their bonds will break when they collide. When new bonds form, the surroundings absorb potential | kinetic energy, and the temperature of the surroundings will increase | decrease.

Modeling Changes in Energy

Modeling energy changes can help clarify interactions that occur during chemical reactions. Examples include diagrams, graphs, and chemical equations. Reactions can first be classified in terms of whether the overall reaction absorbs energy or releases energy. Then, a model can be used to represent the flow of energy over the course of the reaction.

3   **Collaborate** With a partner, brainstorm examples of temperature changes caused by chemical reactions. For each example, model the chemical system and show how matter flows within it. Using your model, explain why these chemical reactions are accompanied by a transfer of thermal energy. How does the energy in the system change?

Differentiate Instruction

ELL Support Write the words *exothermic* and *endothermic* on the board. Circle *exo* and *therm* in *exothermic,* and circle *endo* and *therm* in *endothermic.* Explain that *exo-* means "out," *endo-* means "in," and *therm-* means "heat." Have students describe how these meanings relate to exothermic and endothermic chemical reactions.

Extension Draw students' attention to the sentence on this page about how the synthesis of NO is endothermic. Have students conduct research to explain why so much energy is required for this reaction to proceed and to learn about examples in which this stability is important. **Sample answer:** The N_2 molecule is highly stable because a triple bond exists between the nitrogen atoms. A lot of energy is needed to break this bond. Most organisms breathe N_2 in and out without chemically changing it. N_2 is the stable product of nitrogen-containing explosives.

Nature of Science

Science is a Human Endeavor Use the photo of smog in **Figure 9** as an example of how science influences society and society influences science. Divide the class into small groups, and have each group list both causes and possible solutions to the smog shown in the photo. Then, come back together as a class, have students share what they have learned in their group, and debate possible solutions.

2   potential, kinetic, kinetic, increase

3   Examples include a temperature increase when wood burns and an instant ice pack feeling cold when you squeeze the package. A temperature increase occurs when energy is released by the reaction, and a temperature decrease occurs when energy is absorbed. Energy leaves and exothermic system and enters an endothermic system.

SEP **Constructing Explanations and Designing Solutions**

Ask students to explain why the graph of an exothermic reaction has the label "initial energy" near the top, and the graph of an endothermic reaction has the label "final energy" near the top. For an exothermic reaction, the energy of the reactants is greater than the energy of the products. For an endothermic reaction, the energy of the products is greater than the energy of the reactants. Reactants are shown to the left of the graph, and products are on the right.

Preconception Alert

Draw students' attention to the equations on the page representing exothermic and endothermic reactions. Students may assume that because energy is shown as a product in the exothermic equation and as a reactant in the endothermic equation, energy is required to initiate an endothermic reaction but not an exothermic reaction. Explain that *all* reactions require an initial input of energy to break the reactant bonds. The classification of endothermic and exothermic depends on the difference in the reactant and product potential energies, not on whether energy is required for the reaction.

Biology Connection

Anabolic Reactions Explain to students that most reactions in nature are exothermic because the products are more stable, but some important biological reactions are endothermic. Endothermic reactions in organisms, called *anabolic reactions,* produce larger molecules from smaller ones using energy-rich molecules called adenosine triphosphate (ATP). Have students research and report on some of these critical endothermic reactions in organisms.

1 Students should write an equation that shows energy as a reactant for an endothermic reaction and an equation that shows energy as a product for an exothermic reaction. They should explain that endothermic reactions absorb heat from the surroundings. Therefore, energy is required for the reaction to occur, making it a reactant in the chemical equation. Energy is a product of exothermic reactions because energy is released into the surroundings at the end of the reaction.

Energy Diagrams

Graphs are a useful way to model the difference in energy between the reactants and products of a reaction. Time is represented on the horizontal axis, indicating how the reaction proceeds from reactants to products. The relative energy of reactants and products is represented on the vertical axis. The shape of the graph shows whether the reaction involves an overall absorption or release of energy.

FIGURE 10: Energy diagrams represent changes in energy as chemical reactions proceed from reactants to products.

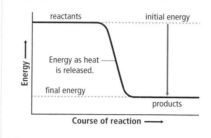
a Exothermic reaction

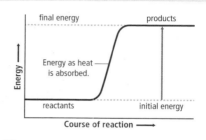
b Endothermic reaction

On the graph of an exothermic reaction, the potential energy of the reactants is higher than that of the products. On the graph of an endothermic reaction, the potential energy of the products is higher than that of the reactants. In both cases, the difference in energy between reactants and products represents the change in energy of the reaction.

 INFER Write generic chemical equations that include energy for the exothermic and endothermic reactions shown in Figure 10. Would energy be on the reactant or product side of the equations? Explain your reasoning.

Modeling Energy as a Reactant or a Product

The change in energy in a reaction can also be modeled as a reactant or a product. For example, because energy is released during the formation of CO_2, it can be represented as a product of the reaction, as shown below. This equation shows that 393.5 kJ of energy are released in the reaction per mole of CO_2 formed. Given the law of conservation of energy, this also means that 393.5 kJ of energy are needed to break down 1 mole of CO_2.

$$C(s) + O_2(g) \rightarrow CO_2(g) + 393.5 \text{ kJ}$$

For an endothermic reaction such as the formation of nitric oxide, energy from the surroundings is absorbed and becomes part of the chemical energy of the products. Therefore, energy can be represented as one of the reactants in the chemical equation.

$$\tfrac{1}{2}N_2(g) + \tfrac{1}{2}O_2(g) + 90.29 \text{ kJ} \rightarrow NO(g)$$

Normally, a balanced chemical equation for the formation of NO would have no coefficients for the reactants and a coefficient of 2 for the product. But to compare the amounts of energy released or absorbed, the chemical equations must each represent 1 mole of product formed, so the coefficients must all be divided by 2. The equation above does not indicate that half a molecule each of N_2 and O_2 can react to form NO.

In an exothermic reaction such as the one in which carbon dioxide is formed, energy is released from the system into the surroundings. Therefore, the final potential energy of the system is lower than the initial potential energy. In an endothermic reaction such as the one in which nitric oxide is formed, energy enters the system from the surroundings, so the system has higher potential energy after the reaction.

2 MODEL Draw two energy diagrams, one representing the reaction in which CO_2 is formed and another representing the reaction in which NO is formed. Label each graph with the amount of energy released or absorbed. Consider the origin and an appropriate scale when making your diagrams.

 Systems and System Models

Energy and Reaction Systems

When an energy diagram of an exothermic reaction shows the products having lower energy than the reactants, where does that energy go? The law of conservation of energy says that energy cannot be created or destroyed. So, to understand and control processes, scientists and engineers must keep track of energy. A useful way of doing this is to model thermodynamic changes in terms of a system and its surroundings. The compounds involved in a chemical reaction can be modeled as a system that absorbs energy from the surroundings or releases energy to the surroundings of the system.

3 Language Arts Connection Research changes in energy that occur during endothermic and exothermic reactions. Develop a presentation in which you describe a specific endothermic and exothermic reaction. Use various forms of digital media to model the energy changes that occur in each reaction.

 SEP **Developing and Using Models**

Suggest that students start their diagrams by drawing the axes and labeling them as in **Figure 10.** Have them use the chemical equations for the compounds on the previous page to decide which type of graph best represents each reaction. Students' graphs should reflect the fact that the change in energy in the NO reaction is about one-fourth the change in energy for the CO_2 reaction.

CCC **Systems and System Models**

Make sure students understand what is included in a chemical system and what is meant by the surroundings. A chemical system is only the particles and bonds that connect them. A beaker in which a reaction takes place, for example, is part of the surroundings, not part of the system. Energy moves into and out of the system as the bonds break and form. Call on students to explain how the graphs and the equations model these changes in the particles and the energy.

Language Arts Connection
SL.11-12.5 Make strategic use of digital media in presentations to enhance understanding.
Remind students that a successful multimedia presentation has a clear and consistent focus and an organization that is appropriate to its purpose and audience.

2 Student energy diagrams for CO_2 formation should show the initial energy higher than the final energy, with a slope downward from the initial condition to the final condition. For NO synthesis, the energy diagram should show the final energy higher than the initial energy, with a slope upward from the initial condition to the final condition. Students should write in the appropriate reactant molecules, product molecule, and energies for each reaction.

3 Students should select one endothermic and one exothermic reaction to include in their presentation. For each reaction, the system and surroundings should be defined, as should the flow of energy into and out of the system. The overall change of energy should also be discussed. Students should use various forms of digital media, such as text, visual aids, and graphs, to illustrate their findings.

Lesson 3 Investigating Energy in Chemical Reactions 287

Preconception Alert

Students may assume that because energy is stored in a chemical bond, breaking the bond must release that energy, which is an exothermic process. Remind them that breaking a chemical bond requires an input of energy, which is an endothermic process.

DCI PS1.A Structure and Properties of Matter

Preconception Alert Make sure students understand that a chemical bond is not a type of matter that connects two atoms. **Ask:** *What is a chemical bond?* A bond is the attractive force from the shared electrons between atoms that holds them together. **Ask:** *What does it mean to break a bond?* Breaking a bond means applying a force that separates the atoms enough that the bond force is no longer strong enough to keep the atoms together.

Explore Online ▶

Encourage students to go online to observe that nitrogen triiodide can be detonated with only the smallest of disturbances.

1 reactants, products, more

2 The bond energies of iodine and nitrogen molecules must be higher than those of nitrogen triiodide because they are more stable than nitrogen triiodide molecules.

Evidence Notebook

3 The light and energy emitted as heat by a sparkler are evidence that the reaction is exothermic. The energy diagram would therefore show the energy of the reactants as greater than the energy of the products. A chemical equation of the reaction would treat energy as a product.

FORMATIVE ASSESSMENT

3-2-1 Have students write three things they found out in the lesson, two things they found interesting, and one question they still have about the concepts presented in the lesson.

Reaction Energy and Bond Energy

FIGURE 11: These models show the formation of CO_2 and NO from their elements.

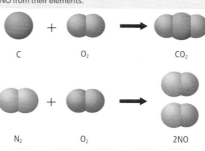

C + O_2 → CO_2

N_2 + O_2 → 2NO

All chemical reactions, even those that release energy, must first absorb enough energy for the reactant bonds to be broken. The energy required to break the bonds of a chemical compound is the bond energy. The difference in the energy required to break bonds in the reactants and the energy released when new bonds are formed in the products determines the overall reaction energy. Bond energies therefore determine the stability of the products of a reaction. Stable compounds have more bond energy than less stable compounds. CO_2 has a higher bond energy than O_2, so it is more stable, and its formation is exothermic. But NO has a lower bond energy than N_2 and O_2, so NO is less stable, and its formation is endothermic.

1 **APPLY** Select the correct terms to complete the statement.

In an exothermic reaction, the total bond energy of the products | reactants is greater than the total bond energy of the products | reactants, so the products are more | less stable than the reactants.

As chemical reactions occur, a change in the total bond energy is accompanied by changes in kinetic energy. Energy released during exothermic reactions is converted to kinetic energy, which increases the temperature of the surroundings. Endothermic reactions absorb energy from the surroundings, which decreases the kinetic energy and the temperature of the surroundings.

Explore Online ▶

FIGURE 12: The detonation of nitrogen triiodide

The solid compound nitrogen triiodide, NI_3, has high potential energy due to the low bond energy of its very weak chemical bonds. NI_3 easily undergoes a decomposition reaction forming nitrogen gas, N_2, and iodine gas, I_2. This reaction releases a great deal of energy, as can be seen in Figure 12.

2 **INFER** What can you conclude about the bond energies of nitrogen and iodine molecules compared to those of nitrogen triiodide?

Similarly to nitrogen triiodide, many commonly-used explosives are nitrogen-containing compounds that release stable, diatomic nitrogen as well as large amounts of energy. An example is nitroglycerine, $C_3H_5N_3O_9$, a component of dynamite. The decomposition of sodium azide, NaN_3, is used to inflate automobile air bags in as few as 40 milliseconds. Many fertilizers contain ammonium nitrate, NH_4NO_3. This compound is a cost-effective way to increase the amount of nitrogen in the fertilizer, but it is also extremely explosive. Manufacturers must use extreme care to keep any source of ignition away from ammonium nitrate.

3 **Evidence Notebook** What do you think an energy diagram would look like for the reaction that occurs when a sparkler is lit? Would energy be treated as a reactant or a product in the chemical equation of the reaction? What evidence supports your answer?

EXPLORATION 4 Case Study: Energy in Fuels

Case Study: Energy in Fuels

A combustion fuel is any substance that releases energy in the form of heat when it is burned. These fuels can be solids, liquids, or gases. Wood, for example, can be used as a fuel because it releases heat when it burns. The most common fuels for energy production are fossil fuels, including coal, petroleum, and natural gas. Fossil fuels are primarily hydrocarbons, which are compounds composed of only carbon and hydrogen atoms.

FIGURE 13: Gasoline is a mixture of liquid fossil fuels that releases energy in engines.

4 **PREDICT** If you were selecting a fuel for a new type of vehicle you were developing, what are three criteria and two constraints you might consider? Which would be most important to you?

_____

_____

_____

Combustion of Fuels

Hydrocarbon fuels release large amounts of energy during combustion because the carbon-hydrogen bond in the fuel has a lower bond energy than the carbon-oxygen double bond in carbon dioxide. The following chemical equations show the combustion reactions of methane, CH_4, and propane, C_3H_8.

$$CH_4(g) + 2O_2(g) \rightarrow CO_2(g) + 2H_2O(g) + 891 \text{ kJ}$$

$$C_3H_8(g) + 5O_2(g) \rightarrow 3CO_2(g) + 4H_2O(g) + 2200 \text{ kJ}$$

The table shows the amounts of energy released per mole by various hydrocarbon fuels.

Energy Released by Combustion of Carbon-Based Fuels		
Name	**Chemical formula**	**Energy released (kJ/mol fuel)**
Methane (natural gas)	CH_4	891
Ethane	C_2H_6	1561
Propane	C_3H_8	2200
Butane	C_4H_{10}	2878
Octane	C_8H_{18}	5430

5 **EXPLAIN** Select the correct terms to complete the statement.

When a fuel such as octane combusts, atoms are rearranged to form new molecules. This reaction is endothermic | exothermic, so the bond energy of the products is greater than | less than the bond energy of the reactants. In this reaction, chemical energy, a form of potential | kinetic energy, is transformed into thermal energy, which is related to the potential | kinetic energy of particles.

3D Learning Objective

Students identify the **criteria and constraints** of various choices of combustion fuels by considering their **impacts on society and the environment.** They use **mathematical and computational thinking** to engineer a solution to a complex real-world problem that can be solved with the use of alternative fuels.

Differentiate Instruction

MTSS/RTI Have students compare the equations for the reactions of methane and propane. **Ask:** *How can you tell from the equations that these are combustion reactions?* Both equations show a hydrocarbon reacting with oxygen to produce carbon dioxide and water. *How does the placement of energy in the equations show whether these are endothermic or exothermic reactions?* Energy is treated as a product, so the reactions are exothermic.

You may want to have students work in collaborative groups to answer the questions above. Encourage students to routinely evaluate how well they worked together in their group.

SEP **Using Mathematics and Computational Thinking**

Draw students' attention to differences in the energy released by the various carbon-based fuels in the table. Ask students to explain the differences. Help them understand that the compounds with greater numbers of hydrogen and carbon atoms release more energy. Have students conduct research to learn about the structures of the compounds. They will notice that each of them are straight-chain hydrocarbons. Challenge students to explain if the relative amounts of energy different fuels will release can be inferred based upon molecular structure.

4 Criteria include the energy output, the cost, and the amount of energy produced per volume of the fuel. Constraints to consider include availability of the fuel type and environmental impacts associated with it.

5 exothermic, less than, potential, kinetic

ETS1.A Defining and Delimiting Engineering Problems

Collaborate Have students work in small groups to carefully review the text on this page to identify benefits and drawbacks of using fossil fuels as an energy source. Explain that the benefits and drawbacks they include on their lists do not have to be explicitly listed on the page. Suggest that groups produce a two-column table to help organize their ideas. Benefits students identify might include the high energy content of the fuels and their availability in underground reserves. Drawbacks might include the release of toxic compounds into the atmosphere when the fuels are burned and the possibility that they are carcinogenic. Ask students to name an **everyday phenomenon** that depends on the use of fossil fuels.

Engineering Connection

Efficiency Caution students that while it might seem that the efficiency of gasoline engines could be significantly improved, in fact heat engines have theoretical as well as practical limits. Current generations of internal combustion engines (ICEs) have essentially reached these limits, even with the inclusion of hybrid engines and hydrogen fuel. Explain that ICEs need radiators that eject "waste heat" and friction of all internal parts, the ground, and air necessitate that 100% of the chemical potential energy in a fuel can never be transformed completely into the kinetic energy required to move a car in a desired direction and at the desired speed.

1 **Sample answer:** Petroleum refining produces pollutants that can cause human health problems, such as increased rates of asthma and developmental problems. A solution to this problem must still result in products that meet energy requirements and cannot cost too much money.

2 29%

3 Students might compare the average income, the regulatory laws, and the infrastructure of a country. For example, some countries encourage the use of electric vehicles by constructing charging stations and establishing tax refunds for the purchase of these types of vehicles.

FIGURE 14: An oil refinery breaks down crude oil to produce petroleum products in different forms for various uses.

Petroleum is a liquid fossil fuel extracted from underground rock formations. Unrefined petroleum is called crude oil. At oil refineries such as the one shown in Figure 14, crude oil is processed to produce a variety of petroleum products, such as kerosene, lubricants, and waxes. The main product of refineries is gasoline. Gasoline is a mixture of hydrocarbons, primarily octane (C_8H_{18}).

An environmental concern with petroleum refining is that refineries produce pollutants in areas where they are located. These include air pollutants such as benzene, nitrogen oxides, carbon monoxide, and sulfur dioxide. Benzene is a carcinogen, or cancer-causing agent. In addition, some of these pollutants cause developmental problems in children and exacerbate respiratory conditions such as asthma. Air pollution from refineries comes from a variety of sources. These include equipment leaks, the heating of steam and fluids, and high-temperature combustion processes.

1 **DEFINE** Write a problem statement that an engineer could use to develop a solution to an environmental problem associated with petroleum refining. Then write some criteria and constraints that might be associated with a successful solution.

_____

_____

_____

Efficiency

Some of the energy released in the combustion of gasoline is always lost as thermal energy that dissipates into the surroundings rather than powering an engine. Fuels and engines that maximize the amount of useful energy output are said to be more *efficient*, and thus reduce cost as well as pollution and carbon emissions.

The efficiency of a fuel can be expressed as the ratio of energy output to the energy released by the combustion reaction. The efficiency is often expressed as a percentage by multiplying this ratio by 100. The efficiency of gasoline engines is typically less than 50%.

$$\text{efficiency} = \frac{\text{power output}}{\text{power input}} \times 100$$

2 **SOLVE** Calculate the solution to the following question about efficiency.

A car engine produces 750 kJ of mechanical energy from a fuel capable of producing 2550 kJ of energy. Calculate the efficiency of this engine. _____

In an effort to increase fuel efficiency while decreasing pollution and carbon emissions, many governments around the world have set fuel efficiency and emissions standards for vehicles. Because these types of regulations vary from place to place, vehicle makers must consider a wide range of factors when developing new designs for international markets.

3 **Collaborate** With a partner, write a list of information you would gather to compare tradeoffs when developing a more fuel efficient vehicle for a certain country. What would you want to know about the country's laws, infrastructure, economy, and people?

© Houghton Mifflin Harcourt Publishing Company · Image Credits: ©Steve Allen/Allen Creative/Alamy

Criteria and Constraints

Fuels that have a higher efficiency can be designed, but the changes often require tradeoffs in other criteria for the fuel. Fuel dispensers at gas stations, for example, often have fuels with different octane levels available. Higher-octane fuels are more efficient, but they are also more expensive, and require engines that are specially designed to take advantage of them. So for the typical vehicle, higher-octane fuel does not offer enough benefit to make the added cost worthwhile.

Fuels that have a higher energy output may release more carbon dioxide or pollutants into the atmosphere, contributing to climate change and atmospheric pollution. Combustion fuel emissions include pollutants such as sulfur dioxide and nitrogen oxides, which can combine with water vapor and oxygen in the air to form smog and acid rain. Reducing these emissions is therefore also an important criterion in managing fuel use.

Designing combustion fuels that have low emissions of harmful gases can be difficult because of the associated costs. Reducing carbon dioxide emissions of liquid fuels decreases the energy output of the fuel, but other harmful emissions may be produced instead. Methods have been developed to reduce the sulfur dioxide output of coal, either before or after combustion, but the processes are expensive and have had limited success.

4 **EVALUATE** Consider the new type of fuel that you previously defined in terms of its criteria and constraints. How well does high-octane fuel meet the criteria and conform to the constraints that you specified?

_____

_____

_____

_____

_____

_____

Tradeoffs

Ethanol, C_2H_5OH, is commonly added to gasoline to reduce the amount of carbon monoxide produced when the fuel is burned. The combustion of ethanol releases 1337 kJ of energy per mole of ethanol burned. The chemical equation for this combustion is:

$$C_2H_5OH(g) + 3O_2(g) \rightarrow 2CO_2(g) + 3H_2O(g) + 1337 \text{ kJ}$$

While this more efficient combustion is better for the environment, the combustion of ethanol produces less energy per gram than the combustion of gasoline.

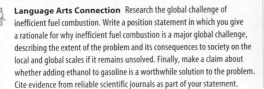

Language Arts Connection Research the global challenge of inefficient fuel combustion. Write a position statement in which you give a rationale for why inefficient fuel combustion is a major global challenge, describing the extent of the problem and its consequences to society on the local and global scales if it remains unsolved. Finally, make a claim about whether adding ethanol to gasoline is a worthwhile solution to the problem. Cite evidence from reliable scientific journals as part of your statement.

 Explore Online

FIGURE 15: This demonstration shows the rapid combustion of ethanol vapor, C_2H_5OH.

Agriculture Connection

Ethanol, also known as ethyl alcohol, is a type of biofuel produced primarily from corn. Its impact on agriculture is one of the controversial aspects of adding ethanol to gasoline. Using corn for the production of ethanol makes less corn available for food and animal feed. Land used to raise corn for ethanol may reduce the availability of farmland for other crops. Explain to students that about one-third of the corn grown in the United States is used for ethanol production. Have students debate the benefits and drawbacks of this use.

Explore Online

Encourage students to go online to watch a video about the combustion of ethanol vapor.

Language Arts Connection
WHST.9-12.9 Draw evidence from informational texts to support analysis, reflection, and research.
Remind students that they can find tips for conducting research, making claims, and citing evidence in the online **English Language Arts Handbook.**

Information Literacy Skills Have students ask themselves the following questions when obtaining information: _What upfront research should I do to finalize my research question or hypothesis? What is the best search engine or database for my research? How can I tell the difference between scholarly and popular publications?_ Remind students to scan resources to determine what they should read in depth. Use written or verbal responses as needed to assess students' information literacy skills.

4 **Sample answer:** High-octane fuel has a high energy output and has a lower emission of harmful chemicals, but it is more expensive and is best used in engines specially designed to burn it.

5 Students may find that adding ethanol to gasoline leads to positive changes in some criteria but negative changes in other criteria. They may report that the cost of ethanol fuel varies. It produces fewer pollutants, but it has a lower energy output.

EXPLORATION 4   *Case Study: Ene*

CCC **Influence of Engineering, Technology, and Science on Society and the Natural World**

Call on volunteers to describe the pattern in the carbon dioxide levels data presented on the graph in **Figure 16** and identify when the long historical trends appear to deviate. Have students discuss if they believe these consequences were anticipated as new technologies were developed at that time. Next, ask students to think of other technologies that have had unintended consequences, both positive and negative, and discuss how our understanding of the world is affected by this.

Differentiate Instruction

Extension Have students perform calculations to estimate the percentage rise above the historical high for the 2017 carbon dioxide level. Point out to students that the vertical axis starts at 140 parts per million, so they should be careful to use actual values. Students should estimate that the 2017 level was about a $(400 - 300)/300 = 33\%$ increase above the highest historical carbon dioxide level.

1 The concentration of carbon dioxide in Earth's atmosphere increased dramatically after 1950. The development of technologies powered by fossil fuels probably drove this increase.

2 Answers will vary. **Sample answer:** The consideration of these factors depends on what each member of the regulatory agency ranks as most important. Agencies probably ask for advice from experts in the related fields and also listen to representatives of business and individuals who will be affected by new regulations. They probably try to implement regulations that will be the least expensive and avoid harmful impacts on the environment while balancing the effects on society.

Carbon Emissions

A major concern with fossil fuels and other carbon-based combustion fuels is that they produce carbon dioxide. As the concentrations of carbon dioxide and other greenhouse gases increase in Earth's atmosphere, the flow of energy in Earth's atmosphere also changes. This leads to observable changes, such as increased average global temperatures, altered patterns of extreme weather events, and higher average ocean levels. In order to address the challenges associated with global climate change, scientists and engineers have begun working together to develop evidence-based solutions.

Figure 16 shows the carbon dioxide concentration in Earth's atmosphere over the last 400 000 years. The concentration of carbon dioxide is expressed in parts per million.

Historical Carbon Dioxide Levels

FIGURE 16: Atmospheric carbon dioxide levels fluctuated in the past, but have increased significantly in recent years.

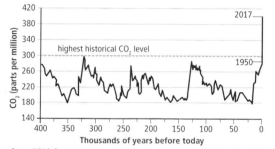

Source: NOAA, Reconstruction from ice cores data, as shown by NASA, Global Climate Change, Vital Signs of the Planet, Carbon Dioxide

1 **ANALYZE** Describe the patterns you see in the graph. How do you think carbon emissions from burning fuels have contributed to the increase in carbon dioxide concentration shown in Figure 16?

Because increased carbon emissions cause changes in Earth's climate, many countries have begun developing solutions that will minimize the use of fossil fuels and maximize the use of renewable energy sources. Some countries have put in place regulations that require all new vehicles purchased after a certain date to use electrical energy. Hydrogen fuel-cell vehicles are another solution that has been proposed. Each of these technologies has impacts on people and the environment. Some of these effects can be predicted, and some cannot. As a result, the impacts of a given solution must be carefully considered before it is implemented.

2 **PREDICT** How do you think regulatory agencies weigh important factors such as societal, economic, and environmental impacts when considering a new law or regulation related to fuel sources, fuel efficiency, or emissions levels for vehicles?

Engineering Lab

Fuel Alternatives

Increasing concerns about climate change have led to an urgency in the need to develop alternatives to fossil fuels used to power automobiles and produce electricity. The environmental impact of drilling for and refining fossil fuels is also a concern. In addition, fossil fuels are a nonrenewable resource, so over time supplies will become increasingly limited. Fuel mixtures have been developed that reduce harmful emissions, but clean-burning fuels are needed.

Most vehicles on the road today still use gasoline or diesel fuel, but alternatives are becoming common. Ethanol is an example of an alternative fuel that reduces the reliance on fossil fuels. Other examples of alternative fuels include biodiesel and hydrogen fuel.

FIGURE 17: Corn can be used as a biofuel, as ethanol can be produced from it.

DESIGN CHALLENGE Use a simulation to model large-scale societal reliance on different types of fuel for transportation, including alternative fuels. Your model should allow for comparison of tradeoffs and identify the criteria and constraints involved in fuel choices.

- -

CONDUCT RESEARCH

To learn more about the large-scale factors involved in fuel choices, research a range of sources and simulations. Based on your results, identify an appropriate computational model that will allow you to simulate your own system.

1. Describe the simulation you will use to investigate optimal fuel choices. What are the limitations of the simulation?

_____

_____

_____

_____

2. What factors involved in alternative fuel choices do you think can be modeled effectively through this simulation? Explain your answer.

_____

_____

_____

_____

3. How can you use the simulation to predict trends related to economic costs, societal considerations, and environmental impacts? Explain your answer.

_____

_____

_____

_____

 Engineering Lab 👥 Small Groups ⏱ 90 minutes

Fuel Alternatives

SEP Using Mathematics and Computational Thinking

Students develop a computational model to test design solutions for alternative ways of powering automobiles and producing electricity.

Safety Information Caution students about the need to be alert for webpages that are harmful or are not based on scientific facts.

DCI ETS1.B Developing Possible Solutions

Caution students that although some fuels may have high energy output, a more interesting value is each fuel's net energy output. This value better considers the entire system required to make the technology preferable to what is already in place. The net energy output subtracts all the energy required to produce the fuel and deliver it to market. Also, to realize any successful implementation of an alternative fuel vehicle, costs cannot be prohibitive and customers may require incentives to make the investment. These might also be considered part of the system.

A simulation allowing students to design and test policies to promote alternative fuel vehicles is available from the MIT Sloan School of Management. Some have found this simulation useful. It is not necessary for this program. HMH neither controls nor endorses this simulation.

Conduct Research

1. Students should explain characteristics of the simulation, how it would be used to model effects on the environment and society, and the limitations of the simulation.

2. Sample answer: Any simulation or other model will incorporate some factors but not others. It is therefore a simplified tool that may still be useful even if it cannot be used to predict results with complete accuracy.

3. Sample answer: Each factor should have some type of numerical way to monitor its use or effectiveness. Factors could include levels of harmful emissions, costs, the proportion of vehicles that use the fuels, energy output, and efficiency.

DCI ETS1.B Defining and Delimiting Engineering Problems

Decision Matrix Before students use their model to test solutions, provide them with examples of decision matrices to give them an idea of how to construct one and the types of information it should contain. Point out to students that they can use the solution criteria they have already identified as components for the decision matrix. They may add more criteria as well, but caution them against having a very long list. As a group, have students set up a rating scale (such as 1 to 10), and guide students as they discuss and assign the relative importance of each criterion. Students can then use their decision matrix to record their findings in the simulation.

1 **Sample answer:** The simulation could be used to predict which type of alternative fuel would be most sustainable over a long time period. The model should include a variety of fuel types and address effects on both society and the environment. It should not have so many factors that it becomes confusing, and the time scale should not be so long that assumptions become outdated.

2 Answers may vary based on students' use of their models to propose a solution.

3 Answers may vary based on students' results from using their models to test their solutions but should clearly use cause-and-effect reasoning to explain the results of different choices.

Evidence Notebook

4 Each fuel releases an amount of energy determined by the combustion reaction that occurs when the fuel is ignited. The energy that is released is the difference in the bond energies of the reactants and products of the reaction.

FORMATIVE ASSESSMENT

3-Minute Pause Have students pause to think about each heading in this Exploration. Have them respond to the following prompts: *I became more aware of … I didn't realize that … I still don't understand …* Have volunteers share their responses with the class.

---

1 **DEFINE THE PROBLEM**

Identify a long-term problem that you can solve in a sustainable way using the simulation you have chosen. Identify the criteria and constraints for a successful solution and rank them based on importance. Examples might include fuel cost, marketing considerations, emissions levels required by law, and tradeoffs measured as part of the simulation.

_____

_____

_____

_____

2 **DESIGN SOLUTIONS**

Brainstorm solutions that would help you fulfill the criteria and constraints of a successful solution. Your simulation should help you model the boundaries, inputs, and outputs of the system under study.

3 **TEST**

Use your model to simulate at least three solutions to your problem, and collect data on the consequences of the choices modeled in the system. Record your main findings here in the form of a decision matrix.

OPTIMIZE

Use your decision matrix to evaluate your criteria and constraints. Prioritize the criteria you outlined. Then adjust the inputs of your model and run your simulation again.

COMMUNICATE

Prepare a report for a specific client in which you synthesize and communicate the results of your research and tests. Explain your reasoning in the choices you made, and communicate clearly what you have concluded based on the results of your test using the model. Be prepared to defend your choices of tradeoffs, and use multiple forms of media in your presentation.

4 **Evidence Notebook** Explain how the type of fuel used in the paste part of a sparkler affects the amount of energy that is released when the sparkler is lit.

TAKE IT FURTHER Careers in Science

TAKE IT FURTHER

Careers in Science

Computational Chemist

Suppose scientists want to study the thermodynamics of a volcanic eruption. They might want to know how the sulfur, sulfur dioxide, and sulfur trioxide spewed into the atmosphere combine with water to form acid rain. A great many reactions involving sulfur and oxygen take place. These reactions cannot be duplicated in such a large scale in a lab, but they can be simulated in a computer model. The chemists must break down the overall reactions into subcomponents of the system to build their model.

Computational chemists use computer simulations to help solve chemical problems by building mathematical models. In 1995, three computational chemists won the Nobel Prize in chemistry for explaining how ozone forms and decomposes in the atmosphere. Their work involved little lab experimentation. Instead, they constructed models using known thermodynamic and chemical laws. The prize-winning chemists constructed their model by examining the relationships among chemical reactions involving chlorine and bromine atoms in the atmosphere. They used this model to study how these atoms interact with reactant concentrations, wind, air temperatures, and seasonal changes in sunlight.

Computational chemists may study atoms or molecules at a sub-microscopic level. Or, they may model the properties of larger systems, such as large volumes of gases, solutions, or solids. They may try to find a starting point for a new laboratory synthesis, such as to help develop new drugs. Computational chemists can also improve the productivity and efficiency of industrial processes using computer models to predict how reacting molecules combine under different conditions. Many chemical problems cannot be solved analytically or experimentally, so mathematical models are often necessary.

FIGURE 18: Computational chemists use computers to develop models and interpret data.

For example, much about ozone depletion in the atmosphere could not be studied experimentally. Computational chemists may use supercomputers and computing clusters that require massive amounts of data. Statistical analysis is often involved.

 Chemistry in Your Community Research a computational chemist whose contributions to the field were influenced by his or her community. How did his or her diverse background influence the decision to become a computational chemist? Imagine that you are such a chemist, and you have been asked to give a presentation using digital media for career night at your school. Make a presentation for your class that explains the following:

- the daily tasks of a computation chemist
- the research a computational chemist performs
- the educational background required for the position

| EXPLAINING ENDOTHERMIC AND EXOTHERMIC PROCESSES | PHOTOSYNTHESIS AND RESPIRATION | ALTERNATIVES IN FUEL SOURCES | Go online to choose one of these other paths. |

© Houghton Mifflin Harcourt Publishing Company • Image Credits: (tr) ©Ali Yazdani/Daniel J. Hornbaker/Science Source/©HMH

Collaborate

You may choose to assign this activity or direct students to the Interactive Online Student Edition, where they can choose from all available paths. These activities can be assigned individually, to pairs, or to small groups.

Differentiate Instruction

ELL Support Draw students' attention to the term *computational*. Point out that the root word is *compute,* which means "to add or count." Have students consider why this definition describes the work a computational chemist does.

Chemistry in Your Community

Students gather evidence from reliable sources about a computational chemist. You might want to have students locate a computational chemist who lives or works in your community and invite that person to speak to the class about what the career entails.

Explore Online ▶

Explaining Endothermic and Exothermic Processes

Students learn about endothermic and exothermic physical changes.

Photosynthesis and Respiration

Students explore the thermochemical properties of photosynthesis and cellular respiration reactions.

Alternatives in Fuel Sources

Students learn about fuel sources for vehicles that produce little or no pollutants.

EVALUATE Lesson Self-Check

Can You Explain the Phenomenon?

Claims, Evidence, and Reasoning

Have students clearly state their claim—their explanation for the phenomenon they have been investigating throughout this lesson. They should present their reasoning for making this claim, along with evidence such as facts, examples, and statistics that support their claim.

You may want to have students present their arguments orally, in writing, or as a debate. Refer students to the **English Language Arts Handbook** for more information on evaluating claims and presenting arguments.

Cultivating Student Questions

Assessing Student Growth Review the list of questions students generated at the beginning of the lesson. Have volunteers select any unanswered questions and suggest how they could be investigated. After approving student plans, have small groups conduct the investigations and report back to the class.

 Evidence Notebook

1 **Sample answer:** The source of the energy is the difference in the bond energies of the reactants and the bond energies of the products of the chemical reaction that occurs in the sparkler. The light and energy released by the reaction show that it is an exothermic reaction. Energy is released by an exothermic reaction, which indicates that the bond energies of the reactants are greater than the bond energies of the products.

EVALUATE

Lesson Self-Check

CAN YOU EXPLAIN THE PHENOMENON?

FIGURE 19: Chemical reactions produce the bright flashes of light from a sparkler.

Lighting a sparkler provides a small input of energy that starts a chemical reaction. The chemical system then emits intense flashes of light and burns at a temperature of about 650 °C, although it may burn at temperatures as high as 1000 °C. According to the second law of thermodynamics, energy moves from a warmer area to a cooler area. The release of light and heat energy from the sparkler system therefore shows that the sparkler is warmer than its surroundings. An energy diagram used to describe this reaction would show the chemical components of the sparkler having a high energy level, and the various gases that are products of the combustion reaction at a much lower energy.

1 **Evidence Notebook** Refer to your notes in your Evidence Notebook to make a claim about how energy is transferred in the form of heat in processes such as chemical reactions. Your explanation should include a discussion of the following points:

Claim What do you think is the source of the energy in a chemical reaction, such as the reaction that occurs when you light a sparkler?

Evidence Give specific evidence to support your claim.

Reasoning Describe, in detail, the connections between the evidence you cited and the claim you are making.

 Formal Assessment Go online for student self-checks and other assessments.

Name _____ Date _____

CHECKPOINTS

Check Your Understanding

1. You have two flasks of water. You place a thermometer in the first flask and leave it until the temperature no longer changes. The temperature reads 25 °C. When you move the thermometer to the second flask and again leave it, it also reads 25 °C. Select all correct answers for this scenario.

☐ **a.** The thermometer begins at thermal equilibrium with the first flask of water.

☐ **b.** The thermometer ends up at thermal equilibrium with the second flask of water.

☐ **c.** The two flasks of water are in thermal equilibrium with each other.

☐ **d.** The thermometer can be in thermal equilibrium only with the first flask.

2. Select the correct terms to complete the statement about energy transfer.

When a hot piece of metal is placed in cool water, thermal energy is transferred from the metal to the water | water to the metal.

The average kinetic energy of the particles in the metal increases | decreases | stays the same, while the average kinetic energy of the water molecules increases | decreases | stays the same. This results in an increase | a decrease | no change in the temperature of the metal.

3. Determine whether each description is characteristic of an endothermic reaction or an exothermic reaction.

Reaction Description	Reaction Type
absorbs heat	endothermic	exothermic
releases heat	endothermic	exothermic
warms the surroundings	endothermic	exothermic
cools the surroundings	endothermic	exothermic
product energy > reactant energy	endothermic	exothermic
product energy < reactant energy	endothermic	exothermic

4. In which reactions are the products more stable than the reactants? Select all correct answers.

☐ **a.** a reaction in which energy is absorbed

☐ **b.** a reaction in which energy is released

☐ **c.** a reaction in which energy is represented as a product

☐ **d.** a reaction in which the products have less bond energy than the reactants.

5. A scientist mixes two substances in a beaker and then notices that the outside of the beaker feels colder. Which of the following can the scientist infer about this reaction? Select all correct answers.

☐ **a.** The reaction absorbs thermal energy.

☐ **b.** The reaction releases thermal energy.

☐ **c.** The products are more stable than the reactants.

☐ **d.** Energy can be represented as a product of the reaction.

☐ **e.** Energy can be represented as a reactant of the reaction.

☐ **f.** The products have more potential energy than the reactants.

6. Select the correct terms to complete the statement about bond energy.

In an exothermic | endothermic reaction, the bond energy of the reactants is greater than that of the products of the reaction. Therefore, energy must be absorbed from | released into the surroundings. This decreases the potential | kinetic energy of the surroundings, which increases | decreases the temperature.

7. Which of these are among the tradeoffs that should be considered when attempting to increase fuel efficiency? Select all correct answers.

☐ **a.** environmental impacts

☐ **b.** economic impacts

☐ **c.** local regulations

☐ **d.** the chemical formula of the fuel

© Houghton Mifflin Harcourt Publishing Company

Lesson 3 Investigating Energy in Chemical Reactions **297**

Answers

1. b, c
2. metal to the water, decreases, increases, a decrease
3. absorbs heat: endothermic, releases heat: exothermic, warms the surroundings: exothermic, cools the surroundings: endothermic, product energy > reactant energy: endothermic, product energy < reactant energy: exothermic
4. b, c, d
5. a, e
6. endothermic, absorbed from, kinetic, decreases
7. a, b

Lesson 3 Investigating Energy in Chemical Reactions   **297**

Answers

8. Diagrams should illustrate how chemical potential energy is transformed into thermal kinetic energy and light energy when a sparkler is lit. Energy moves from the higher-temperature sparkler to the air that surrounds it.

9. **Sample answer:** Fuels that release more energy may release more carbon dioxide and other harmful emissions. High-octane fuels release more energy but are expensive and should be used in specialized engines.

Make Your Own Study Guide

Have students create a study guide that helps them organize and visualize the important information from this lesson. Their study guide should focus on the main ideas from the lesson and tie multiple ideas together. Students can make an outline, a concept map, a graphic organizer, or another representation.

EVALUATE

CHECKPOINTS (continued)

8. Sketch a diagram of a lit sparkler and illustrate how energy flows from one location to another and how energy changes form in this system.

9. Describe some of the tradeoffs in efficiency and emissions that must be considered when choosing fuels for automobiles.

_____

_____

_____

_____

_____

_____

_____

MAKE YOUR OWN STUDY GUIDE

 In your Evidence Notebook, design a study guide that supports the main ideas from this lesson:

Thermal energy moves from warmer areas to cooler areas.

A reaction releases thermal energy in an exothermic reaction and absorbs thermal energy in an endothermic reaction.

The energy absorbed or released during a reaction is the difference in bond energy between the reactants and the products.

Hydrocarbons are used as fuels because they release energy during combustion reactions.

Remember to include the following information in your study guide:
- Use examples that model main ideas.
- Record explanations for the phenomena you investigated.
- Use evidence to support your explanations. Your support can include drawings, data, graphs, laboratory conclusions, and other evidence recorded throughout the lesson.

Consider how changes in energy and matter during an exothermic or endothermic reaction affect the stability of the products of the reaction.

UNIT 4 Connections

Earth Science Connection

Cycling Matter The law of conservation of mass implies that atoms on Earth are continually recycled. Carbon, nitrogen, and other elements and compounds cycle through Earth's biosphere, geosphere, atmosphere, and hydrosphere. Because chemical changes are involved in the cycling of matter, an element can be transferred between different compounds throughout a cycle.

> Develop a model describing the cycling of one type of matter, such as carbon, through Earth's systems. Use your model to describe the chemical reactions that are involved in the cycle and explain whether the total amount of matter in the system is conserved. Research the ways large-scale chemical manufacturing and consumer habits can negatively impact the natural recycling systems and efforts to restore this balance.

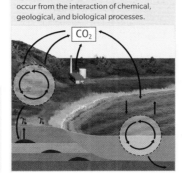

FIGURE 1: Changes in the carbon cycle occur from the interaction of chemical, geological, and biological processes.

Art Connection

Restoration Physical and chemical changes can degrade the original quality of artwork. A person trained in preserving and restoring paintings is called a conservator. Conservators evaluate paints and the surfaces on which they are applied. They must understand how paints age and how exposure to various chemicals and light affect them. Conservators must ensure that materials used in preserving and restoring paintings do not cause unintended reactions with the original artwork.

> Use multiple authoritative sources to make a brochure explaining how conservators use chemistry to restore and preserve paintings. Evaluate the strengths and limitations of each source and cite each one.

FIGURE 2: A conservator examines a painting for restoration.

Technology Connection

Smelting Most metals exist in nature as ores, which are rocks containing compounds of the metal mixed with other elements, such as oxygen. The smelting process extracts the metal from the ore. During smelting, ores are heated to provide energy for the chemical reactions that separate the metal from oxygen. The amount of energy needed to separate metal atoms varies with the metal and the type of ore. The most important advances in ancient metallurgy involved ways to make hotter fires to refine metals.

> Write a short report about the history of smelting in ancient cultures as well as modern smelting processes. When did different metals come into production? How has the necessary temperature for smelting been achieved, both historically and in modern industry?

FIGURE 3: The process of making pure metals, such as iron, from ores is an important industrial process.

Unit 4 Chemical Reactions **299**

Support for Unit Connections

Earth Science Connection

The cycling of carbon through Earth's systems is an example of a biogeochemical cycle. Various physical and chemical processes are essential parts of the cycle because they enable the transfer of carbon. Photosynthesis, for example, transfers carbon from carbon dioxide in the atmosphere and stores it as carbon-based sugars. Cellular respiration in plants and animals reverses this transfer as cells use oxygen to break down sugar molecules and produce carbon dioxide. Students' models should describe these types of transfers and explain how matter is conserved while flowing into and out of systems.

Art Connection

A conservator is trained in the restoration and conservation of art. Many conservators specialize in paintings, but others deal with sculptures and other art objects. Through the centuries, paintings have been produced using a wide variety of paints, each with different chemicals and formulations. Likewise, paintings have been created on a wide variety of surfaces, such as paper, canvas, and wood. Conservators must understand all of these factors as well as the interactions between the paints and surfaces. Paintings can deteriorate over time through exposure to air, water, or pollutants, and conservators work to repair such damage without altering the original art. Students' brochures should describe the job of a conservator and methods of restoring and preserving paintings.

Technology Connection

The earliest metal to be smelted, dating back to 4200 BCE, was most likely copper. Copper required furnaces that burned much hotter than open fires. Iron smelting uses furnaces at temperatures as high as 1600 °C, a level that was very difficult for ancient smelters to achieve. Modern blast furnaces often use pure oxygen to reach the very high temperatures needed to produce steel from iron ore. Cultures that were able to create stronger weapons and tools typically dominated those with inferior metal processing techniques. Student reports should describe the history of smelting metals, especially iron, lead, and copper. Reports should also describe ancient uses of these metals.

A BOOK EXPLAINING COMPLEX IDEAS USING ONLY THE 1,000 MOST COMMON WORDS

RANDALL MUNROE
XKCD.COM

ENERGY
How much is stored in things and how much it takes to do stuff

It is a fundamental law of science that the total amount of energy remains the same before and after a change. Energy cannot be destroyed or created. Take a look at some ways of measuring all that energy.

THE STORY OF HOW ENERGY HELPS US KEEP TRACK OF THINGS

ENERGY ISN'T A REAL THING. THAT IS, IT'S NOT A THING YOU CAN HOLD OR TOUCH. IT'S MORE LIKE A WAY OF KEEPING TRACK OF THINGS. IT'S KIND OF LIKE MONEY.

YOU CAN CHANGE YOUR MONEY FROM PAPER TO PIECES OF METAL TO NUMBERS ON A COMPUTER, BUT IT DOESN'T CHANGE HOW MUCH YOU HAVE.

EVEN THOUGH YOU DON'T HOLD ON TO ANY OF THE SAME STUFF, HOW MUCH YOU HAVE STAYS THE SAME.

...AS LONG AS I COUNTED RIGHT!

ENERGY IS LIKE THAT. IT'S NOTHING BUT A NUMBER THAT HELPS US KEEP TRACK OF THINGS. IT ALWAYS STAYS THE SAME — IT JUST MOVES FROM ONE THING TO ANOTHER. AND KNOWING HOW MUCH ENERGY SOMETHING HAS TELLS US ABOUT HOW MUCH IT CAN DO.

KEEPING TRACK OF ENERGY HELPS US KNOW HOW FAR WE CAN DRIVE A CAR, HOW HIGH WE CAN LIFT SOMETHING, AND HOW LONG YOUR PHONE WILL LAST BEFORE IT TURNS OFF.

KEEPING TRACK OF ENERGY CAN ALSO HELP US LEARN NEW THINGS. IF WE COUNT HOW MUCH ENERGY IS GOING INTO SOMETHING, AND HOW MUCH IS COMING OUT, SOMETIMES THOSE NUMBERS DON'T MATCH UP. THAT TELLS US THAT WE'RE MISSING SOMETHING, AND WE SHOULD LOOK AT EVERYTHING MORE CAREFULLY. THERE MIGHT BE SOMETHING BIG TO DISCOVER.

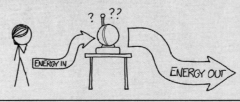

© Houghton Mifflin Harcourt Publishing Company

HOW MUCH ENERGY THINGS TAKE

These pictures show how much energy is stored in things and how much energy it takes to do things.

1 PIECE OF ENERGY

You can use different kinds of numbers to talk about how much energy is stored in something, just like how you can use different kinds of numbers to say how tall you are. Lots of countries got together and agreed to use one size of number for energy to make things less confusing. Each of these squares is "1" using that size.

CLIMBING A TREE

This is how much energy a small animal uses to climb a tree.

WHITE FOOD

This is how much energy is in one tiny piece of white food.

WATCH

This is how much energy is held in those silver circles that make small things like old watches run.

BIGGER BOXES

To show things with more stored energy, let's add a new kind of box that's as big as ten hundred of the old ones.

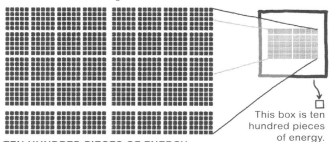

TEN HUNDRED PIECES OF ENERGY

This box is ten hundred pieces of energy.

GOING UP A FEW STAIRS

One of these bigger boxes is as much energy as it takes for a person to climb a short set of stairs.

GOING UP A FLOOR

Climbing enough stairs to go up one floor in a building takes about two of these boxes. (That's only six of those pieces of white food!)

1 FOOD-ENERGY

On the sides of food boxes in the US, they tell you how much energy is in the food. "1" using their numbers is the same as three of these boxes.

"AA" POWER BOX

A PHONE

The energy stored in a small phone or hand computer

THE ENERGY STORED IN A SMALL COMPUTER

These hold about as much energy as those things people throw at each other during wars.

THE ENERGY STORED IN THESE THINGS YOU STAND ON AND RIDE AROUND

These things have a name that makes it sound like they can fly, but they can't.

They're fun to ride around on, but they need so much energy that sometimes, if their power boxes aren't very well made, they catch fire.

Teacher Notes

_____

_____

_____

_____

_____

_____

_____

_____

_____

_____

_____

_____

_____

_____

_____

_____

Teacher Notes

_____

_____

_____

_____

_____

_____

_____

_____

_____

_____

_____

_____

MORE ENERGY

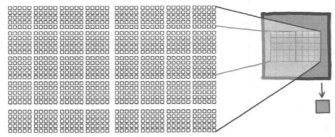

Here's how you write this much energy: 10^6J.

HAIR DRYER (10 MINUTES)
The energy used by a hair dryer in ten minutes

CAR STARTER
The energy in the power box that starts a car

OLD LIGHT (1 DAY)
The energy used by an old light in one day

NEW LIGHT (1 DAY)
The energy used by a new light in one day

FOOD (NORMAL PERSON)
The energy in the food a normal person eats in one day

FOOD (THE ROCK)
The energy in the food The Rock eats in a day. ("The Rock" is the name of a very strong man who acts in movies.)

$1 OF POWER
The energy you would get from your wall if you paid $1 to the power company

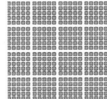
CAR THAT USES WALL POWER
This is how much energy is stored in the power box used by the kind of new car that doesn't burn anything.

EVEN BIGGER BOXES
To show things that carry more energy, each of the boxes in this part of the page hold as much energy as ten hundred of the boxes on the page before this one.

STORM FLASH HITTING SAND
The energy that goes into the ground and turns sand to rock and air when the ground is hit by a flash of light from a big storm

ONE LARGE BOOK
If you burned a big book for its heat, this is how much energy you'd get.

A HOUSE FOR A DAY
The energy used by a normal house in the US in one day

A CAR FOR A DAY
The energy used by a normal car in the US in one day

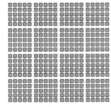

THE ENERGY USED TO MAKE A PAIR OF BLUE PANTS
This is how much energy is used by one pair of blue pants during its life. This counts the sun's light needed to grow the stuff the pants are made of and the energy to run the machines that keep the pants clean.

WAY MORE ENERGY

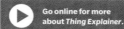 Go online for more about *Thing Explainer*.

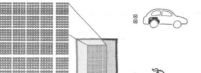

(Written: 10^9J)

 ENERGY IN A CAR
The energy in a normal car when you fill it up before a long drive

 **GOING TO SPACE**
This is how much energy it takes to lift a person to space (if you don't throw away energy on extra stuff along the way like a rocket does).

THE ENERGY IT WOULD TAKE TO DRIVE A CAR AROUND THE WORLD
(if there were a road running around the middle of the Earth)

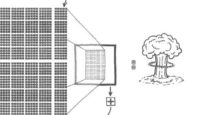

(Written: 10^{12}J)

BOX OF HEAVY METAL
The energy in a box of heavy metal powering a space car.

SKY BOAT
The energy in a sky boat that carries people across the sea

MOON BOAT
The energy in one of the space boats we flew in to visit the moon

A BIG OCEAN-CROSSING BOAT
The energy a big boat uses when carrying stuff across our biggest body of water

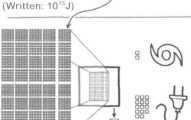

(Written: 10^{15}J)

CITY-BURNING MACHINE
The energy that would come out if we set off one of our war machines—the kind that flies around the world, blows up, and burns a city

ONE SECOND OF SUN
The energy from all the sun's light that hits the Earth in one second

(Written: 10^{18}J)

A BIG CIRCLE STORM
The energy from all the winds, from start to end, in the kind of big circle storm that forms over warm seas

US WALL POWER
The energy all the people in the US use in a year (only counting the kind of power carried by power lines)

US ENERGY USE (ALL KINDS)
The energy used by the US in a year, adding together all the stuff we get power from

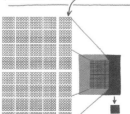

(Written: 10^{21}J)

 ONE DAY OF SUN
The energy in the sun's light that hits Earth every day

 ENERGY IN THE GROUND
The energy we could get if we dug up all the stuff in the ground we can burn for power

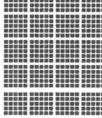 **SPACE ROCK OF DEATH**
Long ago, one of these hit Earth and killed most of the animals in the family birds are from. This is how much energy it let out when it hit.

Teacher Notes

_____

_____

_____

_____

_____

_____

_____

_____

_____

_____

_____

_____

_____

_____

_____

_____

UNIT 4 Performance Task

 Small Groups ⏱ Three 45-minute class periods

Optimizing Heat Packs

SEP **Constructing Explanations and Designing Solutions**

Students build a heat pack and optimize it by increasing the temperature or making it last longer.

Answers

1. Student answers should either increase the temperature or make the heat pack last longer. A criterion could be increasing the maximum temperature. A constraint might be the product size.

2. Heat packs produce energy from chemical reactions, physical changes, or electrical energy from a battery. Chemical reactions in heat packs might include the combustion of iron powder, lighter fluid, or charcoal. To compare hand warmers in their decision matrices, students should identify criteria such as the average temperature, the amount of energy released by the chemical reaction, how long the device lasts, and whether it is reusable.

3. Students develop a testing procedure for a homemade heat pack.

4. Based on the results of the original heat pack tests, students should optimize the heat pack to meet the criteria and constraints identified in their problem statement.

5. Students should explain how they decided if their design met criteria and constraints and if the data support their conclusions.

6. Posters should highlight each stage of the design process, show the chemical reaction in the heat pack and the amount of energy it releases, state whether the design was successful, and show the process and criteria used to evaluate and optimize the design.

Performance Task Scoring Rubric

Points	Criteria
	Problem statement is focused and addressed in presentation.
	Data on initial and final designs are clearly presented.
	Presentation includes evaluation of the effectiveness of the design solution process.

Hands-On Lab: Student lab worksheet and teacher support available online.

Optimizing Heat Packs

There are many different types of heat packs available, but what are the differences between them? Research heat packs and the different ways they release energy in the form of heat. Your engineering challenge is to build a heat pack and optimize it by increasing the temperature or making it last longer.

1. DEFINE THE PROBLEM

Decide which engineering challenge to investigate. What criteria and constraints need to be considered in your final design? Are there any tradeoffs to consider when developing a solution to this problem?

2. CONDUCT RESEARCH

Investigate three to four different kinds of heat packs that use a chemical reaction to release energy in the form of heat, and develop a decision matrix to help you weigh the pros and cons of each. Determine the type of chemical reaction that occurs in each heat pack and the amount of energy released by each reaction. Consider what situations or environments each kind of heat pack is designed to work within. How did these considerations influence each design?

3. CARRY OUT AN INVESTIGATION

With a small group, build a homemade heat pack.

Explore Online ▶

 Engineering Lab

Design a Heat Pack Many heat packs rely on simple chemical reactions to produce heat. Develop a homemade heat pack, then optimize your design.

4. PLAN AN INVESTIGATION

With your team, optimize your heat pack to either produce more heat or to last longer. Consider which materials in the heat pack are most important. Then, write a plan about how you will adjust your heat pack to build a successful solution. Consider what data you will collect and how you will measure success.

FIGURE 4: Heat packs can use physical or chemical changes to release energy in the form of heat.

a A reversible physical change releases energy when the disc in this heat pack is pressed.

b An irreversible chemical reaction releases energy when this heat pack is exposed to air.

5. EVALUATE DATA

Evaluate the data you collected for your heat pack. Was your design successful? How can you tell?

6. COMMUNICATE

Make a research poster that outlines your team's findings on heat packs and the design challenge you investigated. Your poster should display data on your initial heat pack, including the chemical reaction and the amount of energy it releases. Explain how you optimized the design and the data that shows whether your solution was effective. Finally, explain how you evaluated your design process.

✓ **CHECK YOUR WORK**

Once you have completed this task, you should have the following:

- a problem statement that was addressed in the final presentation
- data on the performance of the initial design
- a presentation explaining how the heat pack works and the process used to optimize it
- data on the performance of the final design
- an evaluation of the effectiveness of the design solution process

UNIT 4 Practice and Review

Name _____ Date _____

SYNTHESIZE THE UNIT

In your Evidence Notebook, make a concept map, other graphic organizer, or outline using the Study Guides you made for each lesson in this unit. Be sure to use evidence to support your claims.

When synthesizing individual information, remember to follow these general steps:
- Find the central idea of each piece of information.
- Think about the relationships among the central ideas.
- Combine the ideas to come up with a new understanding.

DRIVING QUESTIONS

Look back to the Driving Questions from the opening section of this unit. In your Evidence Notebook, review and revise your previous answers to those questions. Use the evidence you gathered and other observations you made throughout the unit to support your claims.

PRACTICE AND REVIEW

1. Consider the following unbalanced chemical equation:

$$Al + C \rightarrow Al_4C_3$$

What mass of aluminum is required to produce 125 g Al_4C_3?

- a. 12.6 g
- b. 23.4 g
- c. 46.9 g
- d. 93.7 g

2. Complete the statement.

When predicting the outcome of a chemical reaction, the periodic table is useful because it shows elements with similar chemical properties in the same column | row. The number of protons | valence electrons that elements have indicates how many bonds they can form. The number of moles of particles can | cannot change during a chemical reaction.

3. Using the unbalanced equation below, predict what happens if 1.5 moles of Na react with excess Cl_2.

$$Na + Cl_2 \rightarrow NaCl$$

If 1.5 moles of Na reacts with excess Cl_2, then

_____ moles of NaCl are produced, which

equals _____ grams of NaCl.

4. Which statements describe the reactants and products of an endothermic reaction? Select all correct answers.
- a. The products are more stable.
- b. The reactants are more stable.
- c. The products have greater bond energy.
- d. The reactants have greater bond energy.
- e. The reactants must have energy input to start reacting.

5. Complete the statement.

The first law of thermodynamics describes conservation of energy in a system. Energy is transferred within | removed from a system as faster | slower particles collide with faster | slower particles within that system.

6. Which statement describes the atoms and mass in a chemical reaction?
- a. The mass and the number of each type of atom can change.
- b. The mass and the number of each type of atom cannot change.
- c. The mass can change, but the number of each type of atom cannot.
- d. The mass cannot change, but the number of each type of atom can.

Synthesize the Unit

Suggest that students begin by writing the titles of the lessons and the explorations in each unit as well as any associated vocabulary. Encourage students to recognize relationships between concepts introduced in different lessons.

Driving Questions

Student may wish to use pens with different ink colors to extend their previous understanding of each question and visualize how it has changed since the start of the unit.

Practice and Review

SUMMATIVE ASSESSMENT

Answers

1. DOK 2 d
2. DOK 1 column, valence electrons, can
3. DOK 2 1.5, 88
4. DOK 1 b, d, e
5. DOK 1 transferred within, faster, slower
6. DOK 1 b

3D Item Analysis	1	2	3	4	5	6
SEP Using Mathematics and Computational Thinking	•		•			•
SEP Constructing Explanations and Designing Solutions				•	•	•
DCI PS1.A Structure and Properties of Matter		•		•		
DCI PS1.B Chemical Reactions	•	•	•	•		•
DCI PS3.B Conservation of Energy Transfer					•	
DCI PS3.D Energy in Chemical Processes					•	
CCC Patterns	•	•		•		•
CCC Energy and Matter		•		•	•	•

Answers

7. **DOK 3 Sample answer:** Substances that are present at the start of a chemical reaction react according to specific ratios of the reactants. If the number of moles of a reactant exceeds this ratio, then the excess amount of the reactant will not be consumed. Having stoichiometrically unbalanced amounts of reactants would cost money both at the input end and to remove excess, unreacted reactants from the final desired products.

8. **DOK 3 Sample answer:** In a balanced equation, there are equal numbers of each type of atom on both sides of the equation. Atoms in reactants are rearranged in a chemical reaction to form the products, but no matter is created or destroyed. Therefore, the same number of each type of atom must be present both in the reactant and products.

9. **DOK 3 Sample answer:** Fuels that release greater amounts of energy may release greater amounts of carbon dioxide. If the fuels have high octane levels, they can be used in engines that reduce the carbon dioxide emissions, but these systems are expensive.

3D Item Analysis	7	8	9
SEP Asking Questions and Defining Problems			•
SEP Using Mathematics and Computational Thinking	•	•	
SEP Constructing Explanations and Designing Solutions	•	•	•
DCI PS1.B Chemical Reactions	•	•	•
DCI.PS3.D Energy in Chemical Processes			•
DCI.HS-ETS1.B Developing Possible Solutions			•
CCC Patterns	•		
CCC Energy and Matter		•	•

---

7. Use the concept of a mole to explain why a chemical reaction may not consume all of the reactants. Why is this idea so important in chemical manufacturing?

8. Explain why chemical equations must be balanced and how this relates to the law of conservation of mass.

9. Fuels used in automobiles release different amounts of energy when burned. Explain some tradeoffs that must be considered when deciding whether to use fuels that release greater amounts of energy.

UNIT PROJECT

Return to your unit project. Prepare your research and materials into a presentation to share with the class. In your final presentation, evaluate the strength of your hypothesis, data, analysis, and conclusions.

Remember these tips while evaluating:

- How well did your model convey the energy released in a combustion reaction?

- In the United States, what percentage of greenhouse emissions are from heating buildings?

- How does your model demonstrate how heat is transferred through a building?

- Explain how tradeoffs between different fuel types and the energy they release add to gas emissions.

- What are some "green energy" alternatives to the combustion of fossil fuels for heating buildings?

Integrating the NGSS* Three Dimensions of Learning

Building to the Performance Expectations

The learning experiences in this unit prepare students for mastery of

Matter and Its Interactions

HS-PS1-5 Apply scientific principles and evidence to provide an explanation about the effects of changing the temperature or concentration of the reacting particles on the rate at which a reaction occurs.

HS-PS1-6 Refine the design of a chemical system by specifying a change in conditions that would produce increased amounts of products at equilibrium.

Engineering Design

HS-ETS1-3 Evaluate a solution to a complex real-world problem based on prioritized criteria and trade-offs that account for a range of constraints, including cost, safety, reliability, and aesthetics, as well as possible social, cultural, and environmental impacts.

HS-ETS1-4 Use a computer simulation to model the impact of proposed solutions to a complex real-world problem with numerous criteria and constraints on interactions within and between systems relevant to the problem.

Assessing Student Progress

Students practice aspects of the Performance Expectations by completing the **Unit Project: Investigating the Solvay Process.** After completing the lessons, students practice or can be assessed on aspects of the Performance Expectations by completing the **Unit Performance Task: Modeling Chemical Equilibrium.**

Unit Storyline In this unit, students explore rates of chemical reactions. They describe the dynamic equilibrium of chemical systems and apply these concepts to the design of a battery and other real-world chemical systems.

Lesson 1
Investigating Reaction Rates

In Lesson 1, students make observations and construct explanations of how various factors affect reaction rate **(SEP Constructing Explanations and Designing Solutions).** They identify cause-and-effect relationships between the rate of a chemical reaction and collisions of molecules that are involved **(DCI PS1.B, CCC Patterns).** Students use graphs as system models to show how energy is stored or released during reactions **(CCC Systems and System Models).** Using the rate law, students describe how patterns in concentration changes affect the rate of a chemical reaction **(SEP Constructing Explanations and Designing Solutions, DCI PS1.B, CCC Patterns).**

Lesson 2
Exploring Chemical Equilibrium

In Lesson 2, students investigate the dynamic and condition-dependent balance between a chemical reaction and the reverse reaction **(DCI PS1.B).** They use Le Châtelier's principle to describe patterns in how the stability of a system changes in response to stresses, such as changes in concentration, pressure, and temperature **(CCC Patterns, CCC Stability and Change).** They construct explanations for these phenomena in terms of collisions of molecules and the rearrangements of atoms into new molecules **(SEP Constructing Explanations and Designing Solutions, DCI PS1.B).** Students then plan and carry out an investigation to explore equilibrium in acid-base systems and learn how acids and bases are used in household products **(SEP Planning and Carrying Out Investigations, CCC Patterns).**

Lesson 3
Analyzing Chemical Systems

In Lesson 3, students explore patterns in natural and designed chemical systems at different scales, and they learn about the chemical reactions in a battery **(DCI ETS1.B, CCC Systems and System Models).** Students then apply what they have learned to construct explanations of real-world problems **(SEP Constructing Explanations and Designing Solutions).** Students learn how the green revolution offers possible solutions to adverse effects of industry on the environment **(DCI PS1.B, DCI ETS1.B, CCC Influence of Engineering, Technology, and Science on Society and the Natural World).** They explore how increasing carbon dioxide levels and ocean acidification are disrupting the stability of chemical systems in the environment **(DCI PS1.B, CCC Stability and Change).**

 You Solve It Go online to access two interactive simulations.

Integrating the NGSS, continued

NGSS across This Unit

▶ Explore Online

Next Generation Science Standards	Unit Project	Lesson 1	Lesson 2	Lesson 3	Unit Performance Task	You Solve It
SEP Asking Questions and Defining Problems	•					•
SEP Constructing Explanations and Designing Solutions	•	•	•	•	•	•
DCI PS1.B Chemical Reactions	•	•	•	•	•	•
DCI ETS1.A Defining and Delimiting Engineering Problems		•		•		•
DCI ETS1.B Developing Possible Solutions	•	•	•	•		• •
DCI ETS1.C Optimizing The Design Solution	•					•
CCC Patterns		•	•			
CCC Systems and System Models	•	•			•	
CCC Stability and Change	•		•	•	•	•
CCC Influence of Engineering, Technology, and Science on Society and the Natural World	•		•	•		•

NGSS across the Grades

Middle School

MS-PS1-4 Develop a model that predicts and describes changes in particle motion, temperature, and state of a pure substance when thermal energy is added or removed.

MS-ETS1-3 Analyze data from tests to determine similarities and differences among several design solutions to identify the best characteristics of each that can be combined into a new solution to better meet the criteria for success.

MS-ETS1-4 Develop a model to generate data for iterative testing and modification of a proposed object, tool, or process such that an optimal design can be achieved.

Grades 9–12

HS-PS1-5
HS-PS1-6
HS-ETS1-3
HS-ETS1-4

 Trace Tool to the NGSS Go online to view the complete coverage of standards across lessons and units.

Differentiate Instruction

Differentiate with Technology

Light Probe
A light probe is useful for monitoring the reaction rate of some reactions, enabling students to obtain data and graph the results. Demonstrate reaction rate by placing about 3 mL of sodium thiosulfate in a test tube with a light probe (connected to a data logger) directed toward the tube. Add 1 mL of hydrochloric acid to the test tube, and take readings of the cloudiness about every 15 seconds as a measure of reaction rate. Repeat with varying concentrations of sodium thiosulfate.

Reaction Videos
Have students produce their own videos of chemical reactions that have visual differences as the reaction progresses, varying factors such as temperature or concentration to change the reaction rate. Then have students use time stamps on the videos to analyze differences in reaction rates.

Video Lectures
While most of chemistry class should be interactive experiences between the teacher and students, consider videotaping your introductory presentations of topics so that students can replay them later.

Key Word Support

Key Words
collision theory
Lesson 1

reaction rate *Lesson 1*

activation energy
Lesson 1

catalyst *Lesson 1*

rate law *Lesson 1*

reversible reaction
Lesson 2

chemical equilibrium
Lesson 2

Le Châtelier's principle
Lesson 2

acid *Lesson 2*

base *Lesson 2*

pH *Lesson 2*

ocean acidification
Lesson 3

Reinforcing Key Words
Have students work in pairs to write cloze sentences for each key word on one side of an index card as they encounter it in the unit. Instruct them to leave blanks for either the key words or other important words in the sentences. Then have them write the answers on the back of the card. At various times throughout the unit, have students exchange cards with other students and complete them as a review of the terms.

Academic Vocabulary
Preview academic words that some students may find difficult in each lesson. Write each word on the board, and discuss its meaning. For Lesson 1, you might discuss the words *optimize, application, constant, phenomenon,* and *primarily*. For Lesson 2, you might discuss the words *proceed, industrial, stress,* and *manipulated*. For Lesson 3, you might discuss the words *components, extracting, procedure, variable, metabolize,* and *efficient*.

English Language Learners
Before starting on each lesson, have students write each key word and its definition in their notebook. Then, as students encounter each of the words in their reading, write the term on the board, and guide students in pronouncing the word and understanding its meaning. As much as possible, use simple words to describe the key terms and use pictures to aid understanding. Encourage students to use each term in a sentence.

ELL
ELL teaching strategies in this unit include

Lesson 1 p. 321
Lesson 2 pp. 344, 352
Lesson 3 p. 360

MTSS/RTI
Strategies for students who need extra support in this unit include

Lesson 1 pp. 321, 325
Lesson 2 pp. 332, 337, 347
Lesson 3 pp. 362, 366

Extension
Strategies for students who have mastered core content in this unit include

Lesson 1 p. 321
Lesson 2 p. 349
Lesson 3 pp. 362, 371

Making Connections

Connections to Community

Use these opportunities for informal science learning to provide local context and to extend and enhance unit concepts.

At Home

HOME CHEMICAL REACTIONS Have students work with a family member to make a list of chemical reactions they observe in their home over an entire weekend. Examples may include various types of cooking or a burning candle. For each reaction, have students predict how they could increase or decrease the rate of the reaction. *Use with Lesson 1.*

ACIDS AND BASES AT HOME Provide each student with several acid-base indicator strips. Have them use the strips to test some liquids in their home, such as foods or personal care products. Then have them make a list describing their results. *Use with Lesson 2.*

In the Community

ACIDITY MONITORING Arrange for a representative from a local water-management plant to speak to the class about techniques used to measure and monitor the acidity levels of water systems in the area and problems associated with managing these levels. If you live in a coastal community, ask the representative to discuss measuring and monitoring of ocean acidity levels. *Use with Lesson 2.*

FERTILIZER RUNOFF Have students make a list of locations in the community where fertilizer runoff from yards or farms might affect local water supplies. Also have them note signs, such as algae growth, that a water supply might be experiencing harm. Contact a local water system expert who can describe to the class procedures the community is implementing to protect local water systems. *Use with Lesson 3.*

Culture

EFFECT OF ACIDITY LEVELS ON FISHING Some cultures depend strongly on local fishing as a primary source of food. If water sources become highly acidic because of people's actions, their food source can be endangered. Invite students who have lived in this type of community, in the United States or elsewhere, to share their experiences. *Use with Lesson 2.*

Home Letters Use these letters to engage family members with unit concepts.

Collaborate

Opportunities for students to work collaboratively in this unit:

Think-Pair-Share pp. 325, 375

Discussion pp. 333, 369, 371, 372

Graffiti p. 346

Inside-Outside Circle p. 315

Jigsaw p. 363

One Moves p. 338

Connections to Other Disciplines

Opportunities to connect to other content areas in this unit:

Biology Connection pp. 316, 374

Engineering Design Connection p. 318

History Connection p. 315

Language Arts Connection pp. 320, 354, 368, 376, 377

Math Connection pp. 320, 325, 326, 334, 348, 374

3D Unit Planning

Lesson 1 Investigating Reaction Rates pp. 311–330

Overview

Objective Students gather evidence about reaction processes and the rate of reactions.

SEP Constructing Explanations and Designing Solutions
DCI **PS1.B** Chemical Reactions
DCI **ETS1.A** Defining and Delimiting Engineering Problems
DCI **ETS1.B** Developing Possible Solutions
CCC Patterns
CCC Systems and System Models

Math and **English Language Arts** standards and features are detailed on lesson planning pages.

Print and Online Student Editions

Explore Online

ENGAGE	**Investigative Phenomenon** p. 311 **Can You Explain the Phenomenon?** Why do you think the light stick in warm water glows more brightly than the light stick in cold water does?	**ELA Handbook**
EXPLORE/ EXPLAIN	**Observing Reaction Rates** p. 312 **Collision Theory** p. 315 **Energy Flow in Chemical Reactions** p. 319 **Problem Solving** Calculating Energy Requirements 🖳 Catalyzing Changes **The Rate Law** p. 324 **Math Connection** Identifying Rate Relationships **Problem Solving** Determining the Rate Law	**Hands-On Lab Worksheet** **Hands-on Lab Teacher Support** **Lab Safety Handbook** **Math Handbook** **Video** Decomposition of Hydrogen Peroxide
ELABORATE	**Take It Further** p. 327 🖳 Chemical Kinetics	**Take It Further** Reaction Mechanisms 🖳 Controlling Reaction Rates **Engineering Lab Worksheet** 🧪 Clock Reactions **Hands-On Lab Worksheet** **Hands-on Lab Teacher Support**
EVALUATE	**Lesson Self-Check** p. 328	**Lesson Quiz**

Hands-On Lab Planning

Observing Reaction Rates

🕐 90 minutes
👥 Small Groups

Objective Students plan and carry out an investigation to explore factors that affect the rate of chemical reactions. They construct explanations to describe how changing various reaction conditions affects the interactions between particles in a reaction system.

Materials
- beaker, 250 mL (3)
- Bunsen burner
- copper foil strip
- effervescent antacid tablet (3)
- graduated cylinder, 10 mL
- HCl solution, 0.1 M
- hot plate
- ice
- magnesium ribbon
- matches
- sandpaper
- steel wool
- test tube 16 × 150 mm (6)
- tongs
- vinegar
- water
- zinc strip

Additional Downloadable Lab Options
Controlling Reaction Rates

🕐 Three 45-minute class periods
👥 Pairs

Objective Students use a computer simulation to test a possible solution for controlling the rate of a reaction.

Clock Reactions

🕐 45 minutes
👥 Small Groups

Objective Students determine how changes in reactant concentrations affect the reaction outcome, how much time elapses for each reaction, and a rate law for the reaction that will allow them to predict the results with other combinations of concentrations.

Lesson 2 Exploring Chemical Equilibrium pp. 331–358

Overview

Objective Students identify how a change in conditions, such as concentration, temperature, or pressure, may affect the amounts of products and reactants in a system at chemical equilibrium and explore acid-base equilibrium systems.

SEP Planning and Carrying Out Investigations
SEP Constructing Explanations and Designing Solutions
DCI **PS1.B** Chemical Reactions
DCI **ETS1.B** Developing Possible Solutions
CCC Patterns
CCC Stability and Change
CCC Influence of Engineering, Technology, and Science on Society and the Natural World

Math and **English Language Arts** standards and features are detailed on lesson planning pages.

Print and **Online** Student Editions		**Explore Online** ▶
ENGAGE	**Investigative Phenomenon** p. 331 **Can You Explain the Phenomenon?** Could you use the same solution for both larger debris and microscopic organisms? Which type of contaminant is more dangerous to swimmers?	**ELA Handbook**

EXPLORE/ EXPLAIN	**Explaining Equilibrium** p. 332
	     Data Analysis Analyzing Concentrations of Reactants and Products
	 Concentration Influences Equilibrium p. 336
	 Pressure and Temperature Influence Equilibrium p. 339
	 Exploring Acids and Bases p. 346
	     The pH Scale
	     Analyzing Acids and Bases
	 Analyzing Acid-Base Equilibrium Systems p. 351
		Math Handbook
		   Modeling Chemical Equilibrium
		 Hands-On Lab Worksheets
		 Hands-On Lab Teacher Support
		 Lab Safety Handbook
		 Video Concentration
		 Video Pressure
		 Video Temperature

ELABORATE	**Take It Further** p. 354
	   Carbon Monoxide Poisoning
		Take It Further
		   Shifting Equilibrium
		 Hands-On Lab Worksheets
		 Hands-On Lab Teacher Support
		 Equilibrium in the Human Body
		 Practice with the Equilibrium Constant

EVALUATE	**Lesson Self-Check** p. 356	**Lesson Quiz**

Hands-On Lab Planning

Analyzing Acids and Bases

🕐 45 minutes
👥 Pairs

Objective Students plan and carry out an investigation to determine if different household substances are acidic or basic. They then combine acids and bases to observe and explain changes in the pH of the final solution.

Materials
- chalk (contains calcium carbonate, $CaCO_3$)
- conductivity probe
- deionized water in wash bottle
- droppers
- HCl solution, 0.1 M, in a dropper bottle
- NaOH solution, 0.1 M, in a dropper bottle
- pH paper and pH probe
- well plate
- household substances in solution: baking soda, coffee, glass cleaner, lemon juice, milk of magnesia, seltzer water, soapy water, vinegar

Additional Downloadable Lab Options

Modeling Chemical Equilibrium

🕐 45 minutes
👥 Small Groups

Objective Students use a physical model to demonstrate chemical equilibrium and identify weaknesses and improvements for the model.

Shifting Equilibrium

🕐 45 minutes
👥 Small Groups

Objective Students apply Le Châtelier's principle while carrying out an investigation to predict changes based on equilibrium shifts.

Lesson 3 Analyzing Chemical Systems pp. 359–380

Overview

Objective Students revisit systems and explore real-world chemical reactions and processes in designed and natural systems.

SEP Constructing Explanations and Designing Solutions
DCI **PS1.B** Chemical Reactions
DCI **ETS1.A** Defining and Delimiting Engineering Problems
DCI **ETS1.B** Developing Possible Solutions
CCC Patterns
CCC Systems and System Models
CCC Stabililty and Change
CCC Influence of Engineering, Technology, and Science on Society and the Natural World

Math and **English Language Arts** standards and features are detailed on lesson planning pages.

Print and Online Student Editions

Explore Online

ENGAGE
Investigative Phenomenon p. 359
Can You Explain the Phenomenon? How might equilibrium reactions and Le Châtelier's principle be involved in the degradation of calcium carbonate structures in marine animals?

ELA Handbook

EXPLORE/ EXPLAIN
Defining Chemical Systems p. 360
 Storing a Charge p. 363
Case Study: Optimizing an Industrial Reaction p. 366
Exploring the Effects of Carbon Dioxide and pH p. 370
Case Study: Ocean Acidification p. 373

Math Handbook
Engineering Lab Worksheet
Hands-On Lab Worksheet
Hands-On Lab Teacher Support
Lab Safety Handbook
Animation Model of Oceanic pH Levels

ELABORATE
Take It Further p. 377
Careers in Science Environmental Chemist

Take It Further
Carbon Reservoirs
Using Shells to Treat Water
Measuring Ocean pH

EVALUATE
Lesson Self-Check p. 378

Lesson Quiz

Hands-On Lab Planning

Storing a Charge

⏱ 90 minutes
👥 Small groups

Objective Students combine household items to design a battery and power a small LED. They gather data about different combinations, then draw conclusions about which arrangement results in the best battery..

Materials
- aluminum foil
- copper strip, 1 mm × 1 cm × 5 cm
- copper wire
- LED bulb
- lemon
- magnesium strip, 1 mm × 1 cm × 5 cm
- multimeter
- potato
- scalpel
- zinc strip, 1 mm × 1 cm × 5 cm

Exploring the Effects of Carbon Dioxide and pH

⏱ 90 minutes
👥 Pairs or Small Groups

Objective Students show experimentally that increased amounts of CO_2 result in decreased seawater pH. Then they plan an investigation to determine the effect of decreased pH levels on calcium carbonate, the main component of the shells and skeletons of marine organisms. Students should recognize that equilibrium among carbon dioxide, carbonate ions, and bicarbonate ions is sensitive to changes in concentration.

Materials Part I
- beaker, 200 mL
- bromothymol blue indicator solution (100 mL)
- drinking straw

Materials Part II
- indirectly vented chemical splash goggles, nonlatex apron, nitrile gloves
- beaker, 250 mL (2)
- chalk
- distilled vinegar
- hand lens
- pH indicator or probe
- seashells
- water

3D Unit Planning, continued

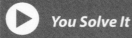

You Solve It   Go online for an additional
                      interactive activity and teacher support.

How Can You Increase Ammonia Production?

This interactive activity offers practice in
support of **HS-PS1-6** and **HS-ETS1-2.**

SEP Constructing Explanations and Designing
         Solutions
DCI **PS1.B** Chemical Reactions
DCI **ETS1.C** Optimizing the Design Solution
CCC Stability and Change

Learning Objective

Students refine the design of a model chemical system by changing conditions to produce
increased amounts of ammonia at equilibrium.

Activity Problem

The Haber process is a method used in industry for producing ammonia by the reaction of
nitrogen gas and hydrogen gas. In this activity, students assume the role of chemists tasked with
increasing plant production of ammonia by 15% using the Haber process.

At the beginning of the activity, students are provided with design requirements. They then
experiment with variable settings and analyze the change in ammonia output as well as the
effect on cost of production.

Interaction Summary

This You Solve It offers students the opportunity to make and support a claim about a
real-world process. They make a claim about how to increase ammonia production by at least
15% while meeting the cost criterion. Students support their claim with evidence from their
simulations, including the data collected from graphs. Students then explain their reasoning
about how the evidence supports their claims.

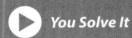

You Solve It   Go online for an additional interactive activity and teacher support.

How Can You Design a Battery?

This interactive activity offers practice in support of **HS-ETS1-1** and **HS-ETS1-4**.

SEP Asking Questions and Defining Problems
DCI ETS1.A Defining and Delimiting Engineering Problems
DCI ETS1.B Developing Possible Solutions
CCC Influence of Engineering, Technology, and Science on Society and the Natural World

Learning Objective

Students use models to combine materials in electrochemical cells to design a new battery that meets given qualitative and quantitative constraints.

Activity Problem

Students are given a scenario in which the Department of Energy has tasked them with designing a new battery for an electric vehicle. Students investigate three types of batteries and then experiment with positive electrodes and negative electrodes to determine which are the most efficient based on overall cell voltage and energy storage. Students use a data table to determine which element meets the given constraints. They make a claim, recommending materials for a new battery that has the best overall cell voltage and energy density and that meets costs and availability constraints. Students support their claims with evidence from the data they collect from the battery model and the data table. They explain their reasoning about how the evidence supports their claims.

Interaction Summary

This You Solve It offers students the opportunity to toggle between three battery types: lead-acid, lithium-ion, and lithium-air, along with a diagram and other information for each battery shown. Students select materials for the negative electrode and for the positive electrode from drop-down menus. Students see the overall cell voltage and the energy-storage results. Finally, they use a table to evaluate each battery combination.

Assessment Planning

Preassessment
Assessment Guide, Unit Pretest

Formative Assessment
Interactive Worktext: Explorations, Lesson Self-Check

Summative Assessment
Assessment Guide, Lesson Quiz

Interactive Worktext: Unit Performance Task, p. 386

Interactive Worktext: Unit Practice and Review, p. 387

Assessment Guide, Unit Test and Modified Unit Test

HMH Field Trips
powered by
Google Expeditions

Go to **HMH Google Expeditions** in the Resources tab on Ed: Your Friend in Learning for 3D, 360-degree experiences to share with your students and a Teacher Guide for you.

Unit Project

Overview and Planning

Investigating the Solvay Process

3D Learning Objective

Students evaluate a solution to a complex real-world problem.

Students research the Solvay process, which uses multistep chemical reactions to produce sodium carbonate, an important industrial chemical. They use diagrams of the system and equations of chemical reactions as models to recognize the factors that control the equilibrium. Students identify the effects of industrial processes on the environment and how they can be reduced.

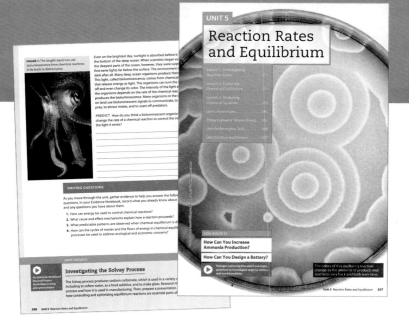

NGSS Focus

This project supports building student mastery of **Performance Expectations HS-PS1-6, HS-ETS1-2, and HS-ETS1-3.** Students will design, refine, and evaluate a solution to a complex real-world problem based on prioritized criteria and tradeoffs that account for a range of constraints, including cost, safety, and reliability.

Science and Engineering Practices

- Asking Questions and Defining Problems
- Developing and Using Models
- Constructing Explanations and Designing Solutions

Disciplinary Core Ideas

- **PS1.B** Chemical Reactions
- **ETS1.B** Developing Possible Solutions
- **ETS1.C** Optimizing the Design Solution

Crosscutting Concepts

- Cause and Effect
- Systems and System Models
- Stability and Change
- Influence of Engineering, Technology, and Science on Society and the Natural World

Classroom Management

👥 Small Groups

🕐 Three 45-minute class periods

Suggested Materials

- See the procedure for detailed materials list for the lab.

- Encourage students to be creative in designing their presentation. Discuss with them the different types of multimedia software that are available. Remind students to maintain the focus on conveying the scientific information and avoid an overly complicated presentation.

Safety

Remind students that they should use good judgment when visiting unfamiliar webpages. Caution them that the most reliable information can be found at governmental and educational webpages. Manufacturers of scientific materials may also have relevant information.

Suggested Resources

- **USGS Minerals Information: Soda Ash:** provides yearly data sheets describing the production and use of soda ash (sodium carbonate) in the United States

- **Soda Ash, Solvay Style—American Chemical Society:** includes a history and description of the Solvay process

▶ Go Online

Go online to download the teacher version of the student worksheet for this unit project, which includes additional questions, sample answers, and additional scaffolding to help students use evidence and reasoning to support their claims.

Introducing the Project

Prepare students for their investigation by asking the following questions:

- **What is a catalyst? What happens to a catalyst during a reaction?**
- **What is Le Châtelier's principle?**
- **Why is it useful to write the equation for an equilibrium reaction?**
- **How can you learn about the different steps in the Solvay process?**

Student Deliverables

A **student worksheet** is available to help students in planning and completing the project. Students can turn in their worksheets, or they can be assessed on a final lab report, their models, and/or final presentation explaining their project. Evidence Notebook prompts throughout the unit refer to the Unit Project to help keep its connection to the investigative phenomenon present in students' minds.

In addition to the worksheet, students should produce a poster or multimedia presentation illustrating the multiple steps in the Solvay process and explaining how equilibrium reactions at various points in the process are controlled to obtain the desired products.

Scoring Rubric for Unit Project	
	Presentation states a claim supported with detailed evidence about factors that affect chemical equilibrium in the Solvay process.
	Presentation presents work in a well-organized format that is logical, easy to understand, and informative.
	Presentation uses a model or flow chart, as well as chemical formulas and equations to explain claims.
	Presentation uses evidence to explain how various factors affect the chemical equilibrium in the Solvay process.

Guiding Students on Project Planning

Once students understand the project goals, the next step is for groups to discuss the four chemical reactions of the process, the reactants and products of each reaction, and how they work together. Understanding the complete process is necessary before students can decide how to focus their research. To help students think about the steps they will take, consider asking questions such as these:

- **What is the overall chemical reaction of the Solvay Process? Why is the overall reaction modeled and not the actual steps?**
  The overall reaction is $2NaCl(aq) + CaCO_3(s) \rightarrow Na_2CO_3(aq) + CaCl_2(aq)$. There are many intermediate steps in this reaction. By modeling the overall reaction, scientists can review the main reactants and products.

- **What is the purpose of the Solvay tower?**
  The tower slows down the reaction, allowing time for the carbon dioxide to be absorbed. It can then react with the ammonia, allowing the sodium hydrogen carbonate to precipitate out of the solution.

- **What is sodium carbonate used for?**
  Sodium carbonate (Na_2CO_3) is used for a variety of applications including as a water softener, in the manufacture of glass, and as an additive in swimming pool water to raise the pH.

Be sure to review and approve project plans before students begin. The Unit Project Worksheet can be used for formal approval.

Differentiate Instruction

MTSS/RTI Give students a list of webpages that have a simple explanation of the Solvay process and the chemical reactions involved in it. Students may have difficulty understanding complex descriptions provided in scientific websites, but they may be hesitant to reveal their difficulties. Depending on the situation, you may wish to preview the content with students or provide handouts that present the information at a lower reading level.

Extension Have students use computer software to make a presentation of the steps of the Solvay process. Encourage students to include descriptions of each step and to show molecular models that make the information understandable.

Teacher Notes

Reaction Rates and Equilibrium

YOU SOLVE IT

**How Can You Increase
Ammonia Production?**

How Can You Design a Battery?

 To begin exploring this unit's concepts,
go online to investigate ways to solve a
real-world problem.

The colors of this oscillating reaction
change as the amounts of products and
reactants vary back and forth over time.

The learning experiences in this unit prepare students for mastery of

Performance Expectations

HS-PS1-5 Apply scientific principles and evidence to provide an
explanation about the effects of changing the temperature or
concentration of the reacting particles on the rate at which a reaction
occurs.

HS-PS1-6 Refine the design of a chemical system by specifying
a change in conditions that would produce increased amounts of
products at equilibrium.

ETS1-2 Design a solution to a complex real-world problem by
breaking it down into smaller, more manageable problems that can
be solved through engineering.

HS-ETS1-3 Evaluate a solution to a complex real-world problem
based on prioritized criteria and trade-offs that account for a range of
constraints, including cost, safety, reliability, and aesthetics, as well as
possible social, cultural, and environmental impacts.

HS-ETS1-4 Use a computer simulation to model the impact of
proposed solutions to a complex real-world problem with numerous
criteria and constraints on interactions within and between systems
relevant to the problem.

Explore Online ▶

In addition to the print resources, the following resources are
available online to support this unit:

Lesson 1 Investigating Reaction Rates
- Online Student Edition
- Lesson Quiz

Lesson 2 Exploring Chemical Equilibrium
- Online Student Edition
- Lesson Quiz

Lesson 3 Analyzing Chemical Systems
- Online Student Edition
- Lesson Quiz

You Solve It How Can You Increase Ammonia Production?

You Solve It How Can You Design a Battery?

Unit Performance Task

Unit Test

Unit Prerequisite Knowledge

Students should understand these concepts before starting the unit:

- The rate of a chemical reaction can be understood in terms of the collisions of molecules and the rearrangements of atoms.
- Rates of chemical reactions can be controlled by varying factors such as temperature and concentration.
- Many chemical systems involve a dynamic balance between a reaction and the reverse reaction.

Collaborate

Driving Questions You may wish to have partners discuss their initial thoughts about the Driving Questions for this unit before you discuss the questions as a class. Encourage students to record the questions and their initial responses in their Evidence Notebook, where they can revise and add to their answers as they work through the unit.

Anchoring Phenomenon

Project Based Learning

Investigating the Solvay Process

SEP Constructing Explanations and Designing Solutions

An anchoring phenomenon connects student learning across the lessons in a unit. The Unit Project serves as an anchoring phenomenon as students use what they learn in the lessons about reaction rates and equilibrium in chemical systems to solve a complex real-world problem.

Tips on Cultivating Questions Have students divide into small groups and read the introductory text about the Solvay process. Then have them make a list of initial questions they have about the process, the type of research they might conduct to learn about the process, and the type of information they might look for.

1 Students may speculate that reaction rate depends on whether certain products form. Bioluminescence is the result of oxidation of luciferin. Some organisms also have the enzyme luciferase. Concentrations of these compounds affect the rate of reaction.

FIGURE 1: The longfin squid can use bioluminescence from chemical reactions in its body to distract prey.

Even on the brightest day, sunlight is absorbed before it reaches the bottom of the deep ocean. When scientists began exploring the deepest parts of the ocean, however, they were surprised to find eerie lights far below the surface. The environment is not all dark after all. Many deep ocean organisms produce their own light. This light, called bioluminescence, comes from chemical reactions that release energy as light. The organisms can turn the light on or off and even change its color. The intensity of the light emitted by the organisms depends on the rate of the chemical reaction that produces the bioluminescence. Many organisms in the ocean and on land use bioluminescent signals to communicate, to hunt for prey, to attract mates, and to scare off predators.

1 PREDICT How do you think a bioluminescent organism is able to change the rate of a chemical reaction to control the intensity of the light it emits?

_____

_____

_____

_____

_____

_____

DRIVING QUESTIONS

As you move through the unit, gather evidence to help you answer the following questions. In your Evidence Notebook, record what you already know about these topics and any questions you have about them.

1. How can energy be used to control chemical reactions?
2. What cause and effect mechanisms explain how a reaction proceeds?
3. What predictable patterns are observed when chemical equilibrium is disturbed?
4. How can the cycles of matter and the flows of energy in chemical equilibrium processes be used to address ecological and economic concerns?

UNIT PROJECT

Go online to download the Unit Project Worksheet to help plan your project.

Investigating the Solvay Process

The Solvay process produces sodium carbonate, which is used in a variety of applications, including to soften water, as a food additive, and to make glass. Research the Solvay process and how it is used in manufacturing. Then, prepare a presentation that explains how controlling and optimizing equilibrium reactions are essential parts of this process.

UNIT 5 Language Development

📖 Language Development

Use the lessons in this unit to complete the chart and expand your understanding of the science concepts.

TERM: collision theory

Definition	Example
Similar Term	Phrase

TERM: activation energy, E_a

Definition	Example
Similar Term	Phrase

TERM: reaction rate

Definition	Example
Similar Term	Phrase

TERM: chemical equilibrium

Definition	Example
Similar Term	Phrase

📖 Language Development

The summary chart graphic organizer allows students to practice using unit vocabulary to convey meaning and to communicate clearly. The chart shown, which is continued on the next page, may not include every unit vocabulary term.

Using the Chart As you encounter a highlighted vocabulary term within the unit, direct students to fill in the corresponding boxes in the summary chart. Students should always fill in the Definition column, but they need not fill in all others. Students can write a cognate from their home language in the Similar Term box. Students whose home language is English can fill in a synonym or word with the same root (such as *atomic* for the word *atom*). Accept all reasonable answers.

SAMPLE ANSWERS

collision theory: the number of new compounds formed in a chemical reaction is equal to the number of molecules that collide, multiplied by a factor that corrects for low-energy collisions; heating a system to speed up a chemical reaction; teoría de las colisiones; According to collision theory, lowering the temperature should reduce rates of reaction.

activation energy, E_a: the minimum amount of energy required to start a chemical reaction; sparklers require a match to start; energía de activación; Adding a catalyst lowers the activation energy, so a reaction can happen at a lower temperature.

reaction rate: the rate at which a chemical reaction takes place, measured by the rate of formation of the product or the rate of disappearance of the reactants; the decomposition of hydrogen peroxide is very slow; velocidad de reacción; Increasing the concentration of reactants increases the reaction rate.

chemical equilibrium: a state of balance in which the rate of a forward reaction equals the rate of the reverse reaction and the concentrations of products and reactants remain unchanged; when heated, mercury(II) oxide decomposes into mercury and oxygen at the same rate that they reform mercury(II) oxide; equilibrio químico; For the reaction in which nitrogen gas and hydrogen gas form ammonia, the rate of formation of ammonia equals the rate of dissociation of ammonia at chemical equilibrium.

Unit 5 Reaction Rates and Equilibrium 309

SAMPLE ANSWERS

Le Châtelier's principle: the principle that states that a system in equilibrium will oppose a change in a way that helps eliminate the change; increasing the concentration of a reactant increases the forward reaction rate; el principio de Le Châtelier; According to Le Châtelier's principle, a greater amount of product can be produced by removing product from the system.

acid: any compound that increases the number of hydronium ions when dissolved in water; hydrochloric acid, HCl; ácido; An acid has a pH below 7.

base: any compound that increases the number of hydroxide ions when dissolved in water; sodium hydroxide, NaOH; base; A base has a pH above 7.

pH: a value that is used to express the acidity or basicity (alkalinity) of a system, each whole number on the scale indicates a tenfold change in acidity, a pH of 7 is neutral, a pH of less than 7 is acidic, and a pH of greater than 7 is basic; the pH of cranberry juice is about 2.4; pH; Hydrochloric acid has a low pH and sodium hydroxide has a high pH.

TERM: Le Châtelier's principle

Definition	Example

Similar Term	Phrase

TERM: acid

Definition	Example

Similar Term	Phrase

TERM: base

Definition	Example

Similar Term	Phrase

TERM: pH

Definition	Example

Similar Term	Phrase

Investigating Reaction Rates

Building to the Performance Expectations

The learning experiences in this lesson prepare students for mastery of

HS-PS1-5 Apply scientific principles and evidence to provide an explanation about the effects of changing the temperature or concentration of the reacting particles on the rate at which a reaction occurs.

HS-ETS1-4 Use a computer simulation to model the impact of proposed solutions to a complex real-world problem with numerous criteria and constraints on interactions within and between systems relevant to the problem.

 Trace Tool to the NGSS

Go online to view the complete coverage of standards across lessons, units, and grade levels.

 SEP Science & Engineering Practices

Constructing Explanations and Designing Solutions
Apply scientific principles and evidence to provide an explanation of phenomena and solve design problems, taking into account possible unanticipated effects.

 **VIDEO** Constructing Scientific Explanations

DCI Disciplinary Core Ideas

PS1.B Chemical Reactions
Chemical process, their rates, and whether or not energy is stored or released can be understood in terms of the collisions of molecules and the rearrangements of atoms into new molecules, with consequent changes in the sum of all bond energies in the set of molecules that are matched by changes in kinetic energy. (HS-PS1-5)

ETS1.A Defining and Delimiting Engineering Problems
Humanity faces major global challenges today, such as the need for supplies of clean water and food or for energy sources that minimize pollution, which can be addressed through engineering. These global challenges also may have manifestations in local communities. (ETS1-1)

ETS1.B Developing Possible Solutions
Both physical models and computers can be used in various ways to aid in the engineering design process. Computers are useful for a variety of purposes, such as running simulations to test different ways of solving a problem or to see which one is most efficient or economical; and in making a persuasive presentation to a client about how a given design will meet his or her needs. (ETS1-4)

CCC Crosscutting Concepts

Patterns
Different patterns may be observed at each of the scales at which a system is studied and can provide evidence for causality in explanations of phenomena.

Systems and System Models
Models (e.g., physical, mathematical, computer models) can be used to simulate systems and interactions—including energy, matter, and information flows—within and between systems at different scales.

 **VIDEO** Models

---

MATH STANDARDS

HSN-Q-A.1 Use units as a way to understand problems and to guide the solution of multi-step problems; choose and interpret units consistently in formulas; choose and interpret the scale and the origin in graphs and data displays.

HSN-Q.A.3 Choose a level of accuracy appropriate to limitations on measurement when reporting quantities.

ELA STANDARDS

RST.11-12.1 Cite specific textual evidence to support analysis of science and technical texts, attending to important distinctions the author makes and to any gaps or inconsistencies in the account.

WHST.9-12.2 Write informative/explanatory texts, including narration of historical events, scientific procedures/experiments, or technical processes.

Supporting All Students, All Standards

Integrating the Three Dimensions

In this lesson, students plan and carry out an investigation to observe how changing reactant type, concentration, surface area, and temperature influence the rate of reaction (DCI PS1.B). They construct explanations relating to reaction processes and reaction rates using collision theory and the kinetic energy of particles (SEP Constructing Explanations and Designing Solutions, DCI PS1.B). Students use a computer simulation to test a prediction about how changing a variable affects reaction rate (CCC Systems and System Models). They use graphs to model energy changes during a chemical reaction and analyze these graphs to determine the activation energy required to initiate a chemical reaction and the energy absorbed or released in the process (DCI PS1.B). Students learn how catalysts increase the rate of a reaction and apply their knowledge to an engineering problem related to the global challenge of plastic waste (DCI ETS1.A). Using concentration and reaction rate data, students determine the rate law equation for various reactions and compare patterns of change in reactions (CCC Patterns).

Preassessment

Have students complete the unit pretest or see the Assessment Guide.

Build on Prior Knowledge

Ask students to list what they know about reaction rates. After they have made a comprehensive list, have them share their list with a partner and discuss any differences. Make a classroom list that can be added to over the course of this lesson.

You may want to review the following concepts:
- Temperature is a measure of the average kinetic energy of particles in a sample of matter.
- Molarity is a measure of solution concentration, calculated by dividing the moles of solute by the liters of solution.
- Chemical reactions may be represented by balanced chemical equations. Some are reversible, and some go to completion.

 **Professional Development** Go online to view **Professional Development videos** with strategies to integrate CCCs and SEPs, including the ones used in this lesson.

Content Background

The reaction rate for a chemical reaction is measured by the rate of formation of the products or the rate of disappearance of the reactants. In this lesson, students will gather mostly qualitative data about reactions they observe in the lab. How do chemists gather quantitative data to accurately measure changes in the concentrations of reactants or products?

There are a number of ways chemists can determine the change in concentration of a reactant or product per unit time. If one of the products of a reaction that happens in a solution is a gas, the gas can be collected and the volume measured. Then calculations can be done to determine how fast the gas was forming. If a reaction is slow enough, samples of a reaction mixture can be taken over time and analyzed to determine the concentration of a reactant or product. The analysis can be done using a variety of techniques, such as titration and spectroscopy. Whatever the technique, it must measure a property that changes as a product increases in concentration or a reactant decreases in concentration. For example, in a reaction that produces an electrolyte, conductivity could be measured as a proxy for concentration. Some techniques, such as measuring conductivity or using spectroscopy to determine concentration, can be done continuously as a reaction proceeds.

Differentiate Instruction

KEY WORDS
- collision theory
- reaction rate
- activation energy
- catalyst
- rate law

ELL SUPPORT

Have students work with a partner to write a short paragraph that shows the relationships among the vocabulary terms for this lesson. Have pairs exchange paragraphs to provide feedback, and then give students time to revise their work.

ENGAGE: Investigative Phenomenon

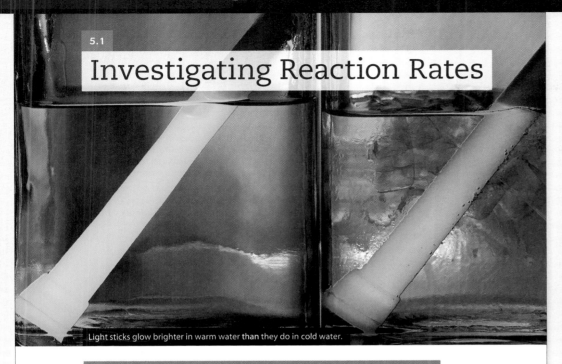

5.1

Investigating Reaction Rates

Light sticks glow brighter in warm water **than** they do in cold water.

© Houghton Mifflin Harcourt Publishing Company • Image Credits: ©Richard Megna/Fundamental Photographs

CAN YOU EXPLAIN THE PHENOMENON?

When you bend and then shake a light stick, it begins to emit light. The light is evidence that a chemical reaction is occurring inside the tube. This reaction is similar to the reaction that occurs in fireflies and other bioluminescent organisms. Light sticks are common decorations often used in festive settings. They can also serve as emergency light sources or distress signals in both military and civilian settings. Notice the difference in the light intensity emitted by the light sticks in the photograph. The light stick in the beaker of warm water on the left shines more brightly than the light stick in the beaker of ice water on the right does.

① **PREDICT** Why do you think the light stick in the warm water glows more brightly than the light stick in the cold water does?

② **Evidence Notebook** As you explore the lesson, gather evidence to explain at the particle level why changing the temperature of a light stick affects the intensity of the light it emits.

Lesson 1 Investigating Reaction Rates **311**

Lesson Objective

Students gather evidence about reaction processes and the rate of reactions.

Cultivating Student Questions

Have students look at the photo of glowing light sticks. Prompt them to ask questions about how the conditions surrounding a chemical reaction affect the rate of the reaction. Record the questions on chart paper, and then sort the questions based on their focus. With students, narrow the questions down to the ones that directly relate to the learning objective. Have students reflect on this list throughout the lesson and check off questions as they are answered.

Can You Explain the Phenomenon?

The Investigative Phenomenon is the focus of the lesson. Students observe in the photo that the light emitted from each glow stick is evidence of a chemical reaction. Then they are asked to observe the conditions present in each reaction system and relate them to how much each light stick glows. Students will collect evidence related to this phenomenon throughout the lesson and revisit the question at the end of the lesson to use what they have learned to explain reaction processes and the rate of reaction.

① Students may speculate that the materials mix together better at a higher temperature. Encourage them to think about how chemical reactions and interactions at the particle level might be related to this phenomenon.

Evidence Notebook

② Students should gather evidence about the way different factors, such as concentration and temperature, affect chemical reaction rates. They should relate patterns in reaction rates to collisions between particles and be able to explain the connections between the two. Students will revisit the topic of temperature and reaction rate throughout the lesson.

EXPLORATION 1 Observing Reaction Rates

3D Learning Objective

Students plan and carry out an investigation to explore factors that affect the rate of chemical reactions. They construct explanations to describe how changing various reaction conditions provides evidence for causality in explanations of the interactions between particles in a reaction system.

Hands-On Lab 👥 Small Groups ⏱ 90 minutes

Observing Reaction Rates

SEP **Planning and Carrying Out Investigations**

Students explore factors that affect the rates of chemical reactions. They describe how varying reaction conditions affects the particle interactions in a system.

Advance Preparation This lab works best using two 45-minute periods: one period to plan the lab and a second to conduct the lab and draw conclusions. Organize groups of four so different parts of the lab can be assigned to different group members.

Materials Alert For the concentration test in Part 3, different concentrations of HCl can be used in place of vinegar, if necessary.

Safety Information Students should wear indirectly vented chemical splash goggles, a nonlatex apron, and nitrile gloves during the setup, hands-on, and takedown segments of the activity. Instruct students how to dispose of waste materials as well as how to use the eyewash station, fire extinguisher, and emergency shower. Remind students to alert you immediately if there are spills or broken glass.

1 Students should make predictions based on their previous knowledge and experience. **Sample predictions:** Part 1: Different metals will react with a given amount of HCl at different rates depending on the reactivity of the metals. Part 2: The loosely balled steel wool will react faster than the tightly balled sample. Part 3: Increasing the vinegar concentration will increase the reaction rate. Part 4: Increasing the temperature will increase the reaction rate.

Hands-On Lab

Observing Reaction Rates

Some reactions occur very rapidly, and others occur much more slowly. When oxygen and hydrogen are mixed in a rocket engine, they explode instantaneously. But when you leave your bike outside in the rain, it rusts very slowly. The rates of the two reactions are quite different. A rate is a measure of change over time. There are several factors that can affect the rate of a reaction. Temperature, the surface area of the reactants, concentration, and the nature of the reacting substances can all have an effect.

The usefulness of a chemical reaction often depends on controlling the reaction so that it is not too fast or too slow for a particular application. Chemists often speed up or slow down reactions to optimize each reaction for a variety of safety, economic, and environmental reasons.

RESEARCH QUESTION How can scientists use knowledge of patterns in reaction rates to control the reactions that make useful products?

- -

 MAKE A CLAIM

Review the experiments you will be conducting. How do you think the factor being tested in each part will affect the reaction rate?

_____

_____

_____

_____

- -

MATERIALS

- indirectly vented chemical splash goggles, nonlatex apron, nitrile gloves
- beaker, 250 mL (3)
- Bunsen burner
- copper foil strip
- effervescent antacid tablet (3)

- graduated cylinder, 10 mL
- HCl solution, 0.1 M
- hot plate
- ice
- magnesium ribbon
- matches
- sandpaper

- steel wool
- test tube, 16 × 150 mm (6)
- tongs
- vinegar
- water
- zinc strip

SAFETY INFORMATION

- Wear indirectly vented chemical splash goggles, a nonlatex apron, and nitrile gloves during the setup, hands-on, and takedown segments of the activity.

- Use caution when working with Bunsen burners because this heat source can seriously burn skin and clothing. Secure loose clothing, wear closed-toe shoes, and tie back hair.

- Use caution when working with hot plates, which can cause skin burns or electric shock.

- Use caution when working with glassware, which can shatter and cut skin.

- Never pour chemicals, either used or unused, back into their original containers. Dispose of chemicals according to your teacher's instructions.

indirectly vented chemical splash goggles

Student Lab Worksheet and complete Teacher Support are available online.

2 PLAN THE INVESTIGATION

In your Evidence Notebook, develop procedures for the following four experiments. Identify the independent and dependent variables for each experiment. In addition, consider which variables should be held constant to ensure reliable results. Have your teacher approve your procedures and safety plans before proceeding.

Part 1 Test how magnesium, zinc, and copper react when each is placed in 0.1 M HCl. In these reactions, the metal combines with acid to produce hydrogen gas and an aqueous solution of the metal chloride. Compare the reaction rates for these reactions by observing hydrogen gas production. This indicates the rate of the reaction.

Part 2 Test how fast a small, tightly balled sample of steel wool burns in a flame compared to a loosely balled sample of steel wool. The amount and size of the flame indicate the rate of the reaction.

Part 3 Test how a strip of magnesium reacts in different concentrations of vinegar. Vinegar contains acetic acid. You can make different concentrations of vinegar by adding water to the vinegar solution. Compare the reaction rates for these reactions by observing hydrogen gas production.

Part 4 Test how water temperature affects the rate at which an effervescent antacid tablet reacts with water. The time it takes for the reaction to go to completion (when the tablet completely disappears) indicates the rate of the reaction.

3 COLLECT DATA

Develop a plan for collecting and organizing data. The data you record should provide evidence to support claims about how different factors affect reaction rate. Consider limitations such as time and the availability of materials when developing your plan. Draw data tables in your Evidence Notebook before carrying out your procedures.

ANALYZE

1. What factor that affected the reaction rate did you test in each of the four experiments?

_____

_____

_____

_____

2. In this investigation, there were limitations on the precision of the data you could obtain. How could the procedures you used be revised to obtain more precise data?

_____

_____

_____

_____

_____

_____

_____

2 **Independent and dependent variables: Part 1** IV: type of metal, DV: reaction rate; **Part 2** IV: compactness of steel wool, DV: reaction rate; **Part 3** IV: concentration of vinegar, DV: reaction rate; **Part 4** IV: water temperature, DV: reaction rate.
Sample procedure 1: Add 10 mL of 0.1 M HCl to each of three test tubes. To one test tube, add a 3 cm piece of magnesium ribbon; to a second, add a 3 cm zinc strip; and to a third, add a 3 cm copper strip. All metals should be the same width. If necessary, polish the metals with sandpaper until they are shiny. **SP 2:** Use tongs to hold a tightly balled, pea-sized piece of steel wool above the hottest part of the burner flame for 30 seconds. Repeat using the same mass of steel wool but with the strands teased apart. **SP 3:** To one test tube, add 10 mL of undiluted vinegar solution; to a second, add 5 mL of vinegar plus 5 mL of water; and to a third, add 2.5 mL of vinegar plus 7.5 mL of water. To each of the three test tubes, add a 3 cm piece of magnesium ribbon. **SP 4:** Add 100 mL of water to each of three beakers labeled A, B, and C. In A, use ice water; in B, use lukewarm tap water; in C, use hot water. Add one effervescent antacid tablet to each beaker. Record the amount of time for the reaction to go to completion.

3 **Sample results 1:** Magnesium reacts with vigorous bubbling, zinc with slower bubbling, and copper shows no observable reaction with HCl. **SR 2:** The small, tightly balled sample of steel wool glows red and has a small flame, while the loosely balled sample of steel wool burns in the flame. **SR 3:** A vigorous bubbling reaction occurs in 10 mL of undiluted vinegar solution, the reaction in 5 mL of vinegar and 5 mL of water is less vigorous, and the reaction in 2.5 mL of vinegar and 7.5 mL of water is even less vigorous. **SR 4:** The reaction in the hot water in Beaker C was completed first, then the reaction in the lukewarm tap water in Beaker B, and finally the reaction in the ice water in Beaker A.

Analyze

1. **Part 1:** the chemical nature of the reactant, **Part 2:** surface area or particle size, **Part 3:** concentration, **Part 4:** temperature
2. **Sample answer:** Conducting each experiment on a larger scale might have given better results for each factor. The volume of gas produced or the mass of other products produced could also be measured.

CCC **Cause and Effect**

Have small groups of students write a cause-and-effect chain to describe how altering reaction conditions might affect one of the chemical reactions conducted in the lab. In class discussion, ask groups to share and discuss their cause-and-effect chains.

1 Students should provide evidence from their data and explain their reasoning in terms of how the data support their claims. Different kinds of atoms react at different rates. More exposed surface area caused the reaction to proceed faster. Increasing the concentration or increasing the temperature caused the reaction to proceed faster.

Extend

1. **Sample answer for nature of reactant:** Show different atoms reacting at different rates in the same conditions. **Sample answer for surface area:** Show particles on a surface. A larger surface area has more exposed particles, increasing the reaction rate. **Sample answer for concentration:** Show particles in solution and relate an increase in concentration to an increase in the number of particles that are able to react. **Sample answer for temperature:** Show particles moving slowly at low temperature and faster at higher temperature.

2. **Sample answer:** Chemical reactions occur in three dimensions between moving and colliding particles. A two-dimensional model cannot represent this accurately. A computer model would have the benefit of being able to simulate particle interactions in a three-dimensional space and at the scale of individual particles.

Evidence Notebook

2 Students should recognize that temperature is the factor that is causing the difference in the intensity of the light sticks.

FORMATIVE ASSESSMENT

3-2-1 Have students write three things they learned during the lab, two ways they might slow down a chemical reaction, and one question they still have about factors that affect reaction rates.

---

1 **DRAW CONCLUSIONS**

Write a conclusion that addresses each of these points.

Claim For each experiment, explain how the factor you tested affected the reaction rate.

Evidence Give specific examples from your data to support your claim.

Reasoning Explain how the evidence you gave supports your claim. Describe, in detail, the connections between the evidence you cited and the argument you are making.

_____

_____

_____

_____

_____

_____

_____

_____

_____

_____

_____

EXTEND

1. Choose one factor you tested. Make a drawing to show how you think changing that factor affected the reaction rate at the scale of atoms, ions, or molecules.

2. What are the limitations of a two-dimensional model? What benefits would a computer simulation have when modeling the effect of a certain factor on reaction rate?

_____

_____

2 **Evidence Notebook** In the light stick example, what factor was changed to cause the light sticks to glow with different intensities?

EXPLORATION 2 Collision Theory

EXPLORATION 2

Collision Theory

When you burn charcoal in a grill, it burns slowly, often without a noticeable flame, as shown in the charcoal sample in Figure 1a. As it burns, the charcoal reacts with oxygen in the air in the cylinder. Air also contains other gases, such as nitrogen, argon, and carbon dioxide. The cylinder in Figure 1b shows charcoal burning in pure oxygen. In pure oxygen, the reaction is much faster and burns with a bright glow.

FIGURE 1: Charcoal burns differently in air than it does in pure oxygen.

a Charcoal in air b Charcoal in pure oxygen

 PREDICT Why do you think charcoal burns more slowly in air than it does in pure oxygen? How might this be related to interactions between the particles that make up the charcoal samples and those that make up the gas particles around them?

_____

_____

_____

_____

_____

If cylinders containing pure oxygen are exposed to a flame or other heat source, they can explode and cause serious bodily harm. As a result, the use, storage, and transportation of pure oxygen must be closely monitored. So, why does air, which is about 21% oxygen, not react in the same way? The answer has to do with collisions between particles.

Chemical Reactions and Collisions

Chemical reactions involve the breaking of bonds in the reactants, which absorbs energy, and the forming of new bonds in the products, which releases energy. How does this happen at the level of individual particles? During a chemical reaction, reactant particles are constantly colliding. In some of these collisions, products are formed, and in some collisions, the reactant particles remain unchanged. When a collision has sufficient energy and proper orientation, a reaction is likely to occur between the colliding particles. These requirements are explained in collision theory.

Lesson 1 Investigating Reaction Rates **315**

3D Learning Objective

Students construct explanations for how the number of effective collisions of particles affects the rates of chemical reactions. They use patterns they have learned about to predict how changing a variable will affect the rate of a reaction and use a computer simulation to model the effect on the reaction system of changing the variable.

Collaborate

Inside-Outside Circle Arrange the class into two concentric circles so each person is looking at a partner. Each student in the inner circle should think of a change to a reaction system that might affect its rate, such as "Decrease the concentration of a reactant." Students in the outer circle respond with how the change affects collisions and the reaction rate, such as "The number of collisions decreases, and the rate slows." Partners switch roles and identify a different cause-effect relationship involving reaction rates. The inner circle rotates clockwise to create new partners.

History Connection

On January 27, 1967, a fire in the Apollo I spaceship cabin spread quickly in the pure oxygen atmosphere, resulting in the deaths of all three U.S. astronauts. Ask students how the results of the fire might have been different if the cabin atmosphere were air.

DCI **PS1.B Chemical Reactions**

Ask: *Suppose a person blows on smoldering twigs when trying to start a campfire. How does collision theory explain why blowing on a smoldering ember encourages the fire to grow or spread?* When a person blows on the smoldering twigs, more air particles are directed at the twigs than would be present if the air were still. The moving air particles also have more energy, causing more effective collisions between the air and the twigs. More molecules will have an opportunity to react, and the reaction rate will probably increase.

 Students may state that in pure oxygen, the charcoal particles can come into contact with more oxygen particles than they do in air.

Biology Connection

Ask students to think about how human activities can change conditions in Earth's waters, which can, in turn, affect the rate of chemical reactions in natural cycles. Discuss how warming water causes dissolved oxygen levels to decrease. As the oxygen level decreases, less oxygen is available for cellular respiration, which releases stored energy from food molecules. Write the equation for respiration on the board: $C_6H_{12}O_6 + 6O_2 \rightarrow 6CO_2 + 6H_2O + energy$. Have students explain connections among factors that affect reaction rates, increasing water temperatures, and the health of fish in a lake.

Exploring Visuals

Have students look at **Figure 3. *Ask:** How does the diagram model the way increasing reactant concentration affects the number of effective collisions during a chemical reaction?* The colored balls in the diagram represent particles of reactants. The lines that connect them represent possible collisions. As the number of balls increases, the number of lines also increases. In this way, the figure models how the number of possible collisions increases when more particles are present.

CCC Systems and System Models

Remind students that, in any sample at any given temperature, molecules are moving at variable velocities but that temperature is a macro-measure of their average kinetic energy.

1 Figure 2a will result in the formation of a new product because the orientation of the particles is favorable and there is sufficient energy for an effective collision. Figure 2b will not produce a new product because there is not enough energy for an effective collision. Figure 2c will not produce a new product because the particles are not colliding with the correct orientation.

2 lower, pure oxygen, all, effective

Collision theory states that in order for a chemical reaction to occur, particles must collide with sufficient energy and in the correct orientation for bonds in the reactants to be broken and new bonds to form in the products. If a collision does not have enough energy, or if the colliding particles are not correctly oriented to cause a change, a collision will not result in a chemical reaction.

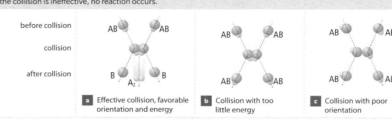

FIGURE 2: When two AB particles collide effectively, they react to form one A_2 and two B particles. If the collision is ineffective, no reaction occurs.

before collision

collision

after collision

a Effective collision, favorable orientation and energy

b Collision with too little energy

c Collision with poor orientation

1 **ANALYZE** Review the diagrams in Figure 2. Which of these collisions will result in a new product, and which will not? Explain your thinking.

_____

_____

_____

Reaction Rate Factors

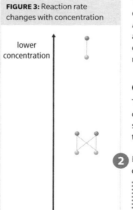

FIGURE 3: Reaction rate changes with concentration

lower concentration

higher concentration

The reaction rate of a chemical reaction is measured as the change in concentration of reactants per unit of time as the reaction proceeds. As the number of effective collisions per unit of time increases, reaction rate also increases. Changing a variable such as temperature, surface area, or concentration affects the rate of effective collisions and therefore changes the rate of the reaction.

Concentration

Though there are exceptions, almost all reactions increase in rate when the concentrations of the reactants are increased. Figure 3 is a simple model showing that, as the concentrations of the reactants increase, the number of total collisions between particles, represented by gray lines, also increases.

2 **EXPLAIN** Select the correct terms to complete the statement about why charcoal burns more quickly in pure oxygen than it does in air.

The concentration of oxygen in a cylinder filled with air is higher | lower than that in a cylinder filled with pure oxygen. So, the rate of collisions between reactant particles is higher in the cylinder of pure oxygen | air. Higher concentration causes an increase in effective | ineffective | all collisions between reactants, but an increase in effective | ineffective | all collisions is what leads to an increase in the rate of reaction.

You can observe patterns in reaction rates when cleaning with vinegar. Because vinegar contains acetic acid, it can remove hard water stains caused by the buildup of minerals. The type of vinegar used for cleaning is often more concentrated than the type used in foods. The higher the concentration of acetic acid, the more particles there are to collide with stain-causing particles.

3 **MODEL** Draw a diagram illustrating why, in the hands-on lab, the most concentrated vinegar solution reacted most vigorously with magnesium metal. In your diagram, include components that describe the connections among concentration, total collisions, effective collisions, and reaction rate.

Temperature

Temperature is a measure of the average kinetic energy of the particles in a substance. As temperature increases, particles move faster and have more energy. In the hands-on lab, you tested the effect of temperature on reaction rate by placing effervescent tablets in warm and cold water. This test is also shown in Figure 4.

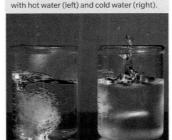
FIGURE 4: Effervescent antacid tablets react with hot water (left) and cold water (right).

4 **INFER** Use data from the hands-on lab to complete the statement. In the reactions between the antacid tablet and water, the molecules in the warmer water have less | more kinetic energy than those in the cooler water have. This energy difference leads to a higher frequency of collisions between molecules. Also, a greater percentage of the collisions have the energy | orientation to be effective. So, the reaction rate is greater when the tablets are placed in the cooler | warmer water.

Think about how you could control the temperature of an oven to manipulate the rates of reactions that occur when baking bread. As the temperature inside the oven increases, the kinetic energy of the particles in the ingredients increases, and they collide more frequently. This leads to an increase in reaction rates. To decrease the rates of these reactions, you could set the oven to a lower temperature, thereby decreasing the kinetic energy of the reactant particles and the rate of collisions between particles.

5 **Evidence Notebook** In your Evidence Notebook, write two claims for how changes in temperature and concentration lead to changes in reaction rate. For each claim, provide evidence from the reactions you observed in this lesson and explain how chemical bonds, particle collisions, and kinetic energy are related to your observations. Last, explain how the concepts you described are related to the solutions you are evaluating as part of your unit project on the Solvay Process.

 SEP **Using Mathematics and Computational Thinking**

Preconception Alert Students may think that larger objects have larger surface areas than smaller objects, so increasing surface area means making particles larger. Use math to expose this misconception. Have students sketch two cubes, A and B, on a piece of paper. Cube A should have sides that are 3 cm long, while Cube B should have sides that are 1 cm long.

Ask: *What is the total surface area of each cube?* Cube A = area of 1 side × 6 sides = $(3 \text{ cm})^2 \times 6 = 54 \text{ cm}^2$. Cube B = $(1 \text{ cm})^2 \times 6 = 6 \text{ cm}^2$. *What is the total volume of each cube?* Cube A = length × width × height = $(3 \text{ cm})^3 = 27 \text{ cm}^3$. Cube B = $(1 \text{ cm})^3 = 1 \text{ cm}^3$. *Which cube has more surface area compared with its volume? Use ratios to help you answer.* For Cube A, the surface area-to-volume ratio is 54 cm^2 to 27 cm^3, which reduces to 2:1. For Cube B, the ratio is 6 cm^2 to 1 cm^3, or 6:1. Cube B has more surface area compared with its volume. *How could you increase the surface area of a solid reactant?* **Sample answer:** I could grind up the particles to make them smaller.

3 Diagrams should show that concentrated vinegar has more particles of acetic acid per unit of volume, and therefore more collisions occur. Not all of these collisions are effective, though. Only effective collisions result in a chemical reaction. If there are more overall collisions, there will also be more effective collisions.

4 more, energy, warmer

Evidence Notebook

5 **Sample answer:** As temperature increases, reaction rate increases. This is evidenced when antacid tablets react with cold and hot water. Temperature is a measure of average kinetic energy. As temperature increases, the kinetic energy of the reactant particles increases. Greater energy and greater frequency of collisions between particles increase the likelihood that collisions will be effective. As concentration increases, reaction rate increases. This is evidenced by the results of reacting magnesium metal with different concentrations of acetic acid and the results of charcoal burning in pure oxygen and air. At higher concentrations, there are more particles per unit of volume, so more collisions occur per unit of time. This leads to a higher reaction rate.

Engineering Design Connection

Catalytic Converters Have students conduct research to learn how engineers maximize surface area in catalytic converters. These **everyday phenomena** remove pollutants from car exhaust. You may need to explain the role catalysts play in increasing reaction rates. After their research, check students' understanding. **Ask:** *In addition to using catalysts, how does the design of a catalytic converter attempt to maximize the breakdown rate of gaseous pollutants in car exhaust?* Catalytic converters run exhaust gases through a honeycomb grid coated with catalysts. The honeycomb structure provides many small surfaces. The total surface area of the honeycomb is larger, so it increases the likelihood of effective collisions between exhaust molecules and catalyst molecules.

1 The loosely balled steel wool had a greater surface area, so the reaction between the steel wool and oxygen in the air occurred at a higher rate. This was evidenced by the larger flame that was observed in the lab. The loosely balled steel wool had more metal particles exposed to the air than the tightly balled steel wool did. Therefore, there were more particle collisions per unit of time.

2 a

3 Students should use the results of their simulation tests to explain whether their predictions were correct and to make revisions to their predictions. Students should provide evidence from graphs, data tables, or other quantitative results and explain how the evidence supports their predictions.

Evidence Notebook

4 The temperature of the reaction in the two light sticks is different because one of the light sticks is at a higher temperature. In the light stick at higher temperature, the reactant particles have greater kinetic energy so they collide more frequently and with more energy. Therefore, the reaction takes place at a faster rate and produces more light.

FORMATIVE ASSESSMENT

Quick Write Give students a few minutes to write a description of how each of the four factors they studied affects reaction rate.

Surface Area

In chemical reactions involving two phases, such as a liquid and a solid reactant, collisions can only occur where the phases come together. In this type of reaction, known as a heterogeneous reaction, the reaction rate partly depends on surface area—the area of contact between the two phases. In Figure 5, equal masses of crushed marble and solid marble react with hydrochloric acid. The crushed marble has a greater surface area, so more particle collisions occur per unit of time. In the solid marble piece, only the particles on the outside surface are available to collide.

FIGURE 5: Crushed marble (left) reacts more vigorously in hydrochloric acid than a solid piece of marble (right) does.

1 **EXPLAIN** Explain why, in the hands-on lab, the loosely balled steel wool reacted at a higher rate than the tightly balled steel wool did. Use evidence from your data to support your claim, and relate your observations to interactions at the particle level.

_____

_____

_____

_____

Nature of Reactants

Different substances can vary greatly in their tendencies to react. As you observed in the lab, different metals react differently with the same acid. In this case, the reaction rate is determined by the metal's reactivity. Reactivity in this example is the ease with which the metal atoms give up their valence electrons to hydrogen ions in acid to form metal ions.

2 **ANALYZE** Based on the results you obtained in the hands-on lab, which type of metal most easily lost valence electrons?

○ **a.** magnesium   ○ **b.** zinc   ○ **c.** copper

Patterns

Simulating Reaction Rate

Computer models can simulate the effects of different factors on particle collisions and reaction rates. Many simulations report inputs and outputs in the form of data tables and graphs that show proportions of reactants and products. They may also allow the user to examine the effectiveness of collisions between individual particles.

3 **Language Arts Connection** Find a simulation that will allow you to alter one of the factors that affects particle collisions and reaction rate. Using the patterns you have learned about, predict how changing a certain variable will affect the rate of a reaction. Then use the simulation to gather data related to your claim. Last, write an explanation that tells whether your prediction was correct and how you might revise your prediction based on the results you obtained.

4 **Evidence Notebook** What is happening at the particle level that causes the difference in the amount of light produced when light sticks are submerged in cold and in warm water?

EXPLORATION 3 Energy Flow in Chemical Reactions

EXPLORATION 3

Energy Flow in Chemical Reactions

For a chemical reaction to occur, particles must collide with enough energy to break the bonds in the reactants. Breaking bonds always requires energy, and forming bonds always releases it. Why, then, do some reactions release energy while others absorb it?

5 **Collaborate** Describe to a partner why you think only some reactions give off energy.

Investigating Reaction Energy

Many chemical reactions do not occur spontaneously. The magnesium in Figure 6, for example, is quite stable when exposed to air. Adding thermal energy from a lighted match, however, causes it to burn rapidly, releasing heat and bright light. For a chemical reaction to occur, the kinetic energy of the reactant particles must be great enough to break the bonds of reactants. In Figure 6, the heat from the match provides that energy. The minimum kinetic energy required for the collision of reactant particles to result in a reaction, or the "hill" in Figure 7, is called the activation energy, E_a. For a collision to be effective, two particles must collide with adequate kinetic energy to get "over the hill." Once started, the reaction proceeds spontaneously.

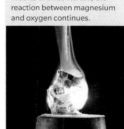

FIGURE 6: Once started, the reaction between magnesium and oxygen continues.

Exothermic Reactions

In an exothermic reaction, as shown in Figures 6 and 7, chemical potential energy in the reactants is converted to kinetic energy. This energy may be released in the form of heat, light, or sound. The potential energy of the products is lower than that of the reactants, so the energy change for the reaction, or ΔE, is negative. ΔE is equal to the energy of the products minus the energy of the reactants and represents the energy released.

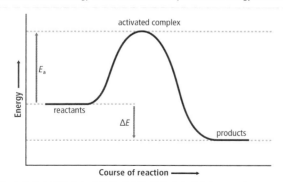

FIGURE 7: In an exothermic reaction, the reactants have more potential energy than the products, and energy is released into the surrounding system. The overall change in energy between the reactants and products is calculated as the energy of the products minus the energy of the reactants, so the change in energy, ΔE, is negative.

6 **Evidence Notebook** In your Evidence Notebook, explain how energy changes form in the light stick reaction. Cite evidence to support your claim, and explain your reasoning.

3D Learning Objective

Students **construct explanations** for how **energy is stored or released** during chemical reactions. They describe the **patterns** that exist in bond energy and in the kinetic energy of molecules. Students explore an **engeering problem** related to the global challenge of plastic waste.

Nature of Science

Scientific Knowledge Assumes an Order and Consistency in Natural Systems Scientists observe the rates of chemical reactions by performing the reactions in a lab. They trust that the observed rate changes due to changes in various conditions will also be observed outside the laboratory. Discuss examples of the consistency of rate patterns. For example, when scientists test how increasing temperatures affect the behavior of a particular medicine in a lab, they trust that they can predict how the medicine might behave in people both at normal body temperature and when temperature increases due to fever. ***Ask:*** *In what **everyday phenomena** might scientists use experimental measurements of reaction rates to make predictions?* List responses on the board and encourage students to identify examples that affect their daily lives.

Preconception Alert

Students may think the light stick reaction is exothermic, but it does not release thermal energy. It is, however, an *exorgonic* (energy-releasing) reaction. The energy that is released excites electrons in dye molecules, and then light is emitted as the electrons lose energy.

5 Students' discussions will reveal their thinking about endothermic and exothermic reactions. Ask them to consider how potential and kinetic energy are related to this phenomenon.

 Evidence Notebook

6 **Sample answer:** The chemical potential energy in the reactants is converted into kinetic energy as light. Thus, the potential energy of the products is lower than that of the reactants.

Language Arts Connection

Have students write analogies that relate to energy changes. The analogies should follow the same pattern as rolling a ball up a hill. For example, a child must use energy to climb a slide's ladder. When the child slides down, energy is released. The child must use energy again to climb back up the ladder. (WHST.9-12.2)

CCC Systems and System Models

Remind students that all representations of chemical reactions are models and that scientists use models to explain or investigate natural phenomena that are difficult to observe directly. **Ask:** *What do rate curves model?* They model what happens to energy during a reaction. *What do reaction equations model?* They model what happens to the arrangement of atoms during a chemical reaction. They might also show whether energy is absorbed or released.

Math Connection
MP.2 Reason abstractly and quantitatively.

In the Problem Solving activity on the next page, students label and interpret rate curves. Before students begin, have them describe differences between the rate curves presented in the activity. They will notice that one shows an overall "uphill" reaction, and the other shows an overall "downhill" reaction. Emphasize that each reaction requires and releases energy.

1 Increasing the concentration increases the number of collisions and so would increase the chances of an activated complex forming.

2 potential, kinetic, kinetic, potential

3 Diagrams should show that energy flows from the system to the surroundings. Graphs should follow the general pattern of an exothermic reaction, showing that the potential energy of the products is lower than that of the reactants.

At the peak of the graph in Figure 7, a transitional structure called the *activated complex* forms as the reactant bonds are broken and the product bonds are formed. The activated complex may go on to form products, or it may return to the original reactants. Increasing the temperature of the reaction causes more particles to have sufficient energy to form the activated complex on collision. This is why reaction rate increases as temperature increases. Increasing temperature increases the opportunities for products to form.

1 **APPLY** According to what you have learned about concentration, how does increasing the concentration of one or more reactants affect the formation of the activated complex?

_____

_____

_____

Endothermic Reactions

In an endothermic reaction, kinetic energy is converted to chemical potential energy. As shown in Figure 8, the products of an endothermic reaction have more chemical potential energy than the reactants do. So, ΔE is positive for endothermic reactions and represents the energy that endothermic reactions absorb from the environment. These reactions typically feel cold to the touch because thermal energy is converted to chemical potential energy in the form of chemical bonds in the products.

FIGURE 8: In an endothermic reaction, the products have more chemical potential energy than the reactants.

activated complex

E_a

ΔE

products

reactants

Energy →

Course of reaction →

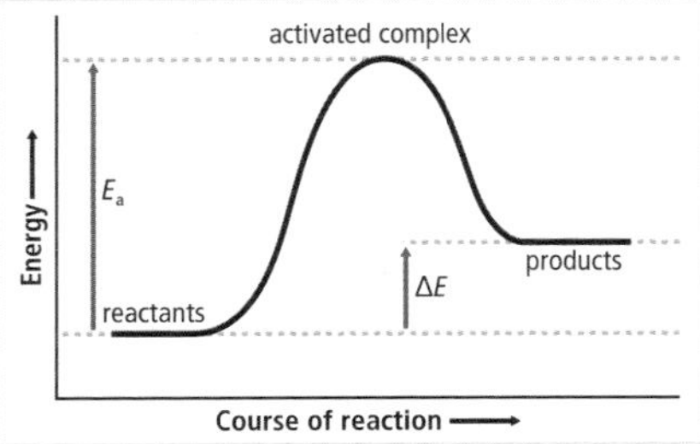

2 **EXPLAIN** Select the correct terms to compare the way energy flows in exothermic and endothermic reactions.

In exothermic reactions, potential | kinetic energy is converted to potential | kinetic energy, so the products have less potential energy than the reactants, and ΔE is negative. The energy released may take the form of heat, light, or sound. In endothermic reactions, potential | kinetic energy is converted to potential | kinetic energy in the form of bonds, so the products have more potential energy than the reactants, and ΔE is positive.

Systems and System Models

Analyzing Reaction Energy

When you light a Bunsen burner or a gas stove, methane in natural gas reacts with oxygen in the air to produce carbon dioxide and water. This is an exothermic reaction in which energy in the form of heat and light is released.

3 **Collaborate** With a partner, illustrate how energy changes in the system described in this scenario. First, draw a diagram that defines the boundaries of the system you would like to use and show the general direction of energy flow. Next, draw a graph showing the relationship between energy in the reactants and energy in the products.

Problem Solving
Calculating Energy Requirements

SAMPLE PROBLEM

Figure 9 shows an energy diagram for a hypothetical chemical reaction. The energy level of the reactants is shown to the left, and that of the products is shown to the right. The total energy change, ΔE, is the difference between these two levels. Activation energy, E_a, is the minimum energy for an effective collision. E_a is the difference between the reactant energy level and the peak.

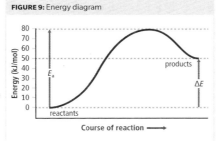

FIGURE 9: Energy diagram

Course of reaction ⟶

Use the graph to calculate the value of ΔE and E_a. Then, use your calculations to determine whether this reaction is endothermic or exothermic.

SOLVE

1. To calculate ΔE, subtract the energy of the reactants from that of the products.

$\Delta E =$ energy of products − energy of reactants
$\Delta E = 50 \text{ kJ/mol} - 0 \text{ kJ/mol} = 50 \text{ kJ/mol}$

2. To calculate E_a, subtract the energy of the reactants from that of the activated complex.

$E_a =$ energy of activated complex − energy of reactants
$E_a = 80 \text{ kJ/mol} - 0 \text{ kJ/mol} = 80 \text{ kJ/mol}$

3. To determine whether the reaction is endothermic or exothermic, analyze the relationship between the energy of the products and the energy of the reactants. In this case, the energy of the products is higher than the energy of the reactants, so energy was absorbed, and the reaction is endothermic.

PRACTICE PROBLEM

SOLVE Use the energy diagram in Figure 10 to calculate each of the following values:

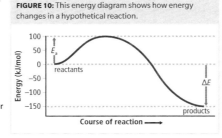

FIGURE 10: This energy diagram shows how energy changes in a hypothetical reaction.

Course of reaction ⟶

1. ΔE _____

2. E_a _____

3. Is this reaction endothermic or exothermic? Use evidence to support your claim.

_____
_____
_____
_____

Differentiate Instruction

MTSS/RTI Have struggling students work in pairs. Partners can take turns explaining how to find ΔE on a reaction rate curve. Encourage partners to work collaboratively through the sample problem step by step before they attempt the practice problems.

ELL Support Ask students if all rate curves have an "uphill" portion. Have them explain their answers. If necessary, point out an "uphill" portion of a curve. Yes, all reactions require some activation energy to start because breaking the bonds of reactants requires energy.

Extension Give students a table of bond energies (in units of kJ/mol) and structural diagrams for hydrogen peroxide, hydrogen gas, and oxygen gas. Have them write the balanced chemical equation for the decomposition of hydrogen peroxide and then use the bond energies to calculate all values needed to draw an accurate reaction rate curve for the process. Remind students that they will need to account for the number of moles of each reactant and product as they calculate E_a. Have partners compare and correct their calculations and graphs using an answer key.

Classroom Practice

Choose the response that correctly completes this statement.

When ΔE is a positive value,

a. the reaction is exothermic.

b. the products have more energy than the reactants.

c. the rate curve will look like a "downhill" reaction.

d. the activation energy is a negative value.

Answer: b

Practice Problem Answers

1. −150 kJ/mol

2. 100 kJ/mol

3. This reaction is exothermic because the reactants have a higher energy level than the products, as shown by the negative value of ΔE.

For the complete solutions to the Practice Problems and Classroom Practice, see the online Problem Solutions.

CCC Stability and Change

Explain to students that many reactions happen slowly because the reactant molecules are very stable. Catalysts introduce a mechanism to help stable molecules collide effectively, which reduces the energy needed to help the molecules form an activated complex. Catalysts are "change agents."

Explore Online ▶

Collaborate Have students go online to watch the video of the decomposition of hydrogen peroxide using a catalyst, and then have them list questions they might ask about the reaction. Assign partners, and direct them to construct an explanation of how the catalyst speeds up the reaction. Tell students that their explanation could be in the form of a diagram, a graph, or written sentences.

DCI PS1.B Chemical Reactions

Explain to students that many catalysts speed up reactions by changing the series of steps needed for a reaction to take place. The new steps require less energy to proceed than the energy required for the reaction without catalysis. Refer students to the Engineering feature on the next page. Ask students to apply their understanding of catalysis to what they learn about the breakdown of polyethylene. Students should explain that catalysts add two new steps to the reaction, one that removes hydrogen atoms and another that breaks apart the carbon double bonds that form when the hydrogen atoms are removed.

1 Students may ask questions related to the change in reaction rate that causes the foam to form. **Sample answer:** Why does adding the sodium iodide change the rate at which hydrogen peroxide breaks down?

2 Students should write H_2O_2 on the left side of the curve and H_2 and O_2 on the right side. The graphs will have the same start and end points, but the curve for the catalyzed reaction will have a lower peak.

Lowering Activation Energy

Hydrogen peroxide decomposes to form water and oxygen gas in a very slow chemical reaction. When soap is added, the reaction causes bubbles to form. In Figure 11, a small amount of sodium iodide, NaI, is added to the mixture, and bubbles form rapidly.

FIGURE 11: When sodium iodide is added to a hydrogen peroxide and dish soap solution, the reaction occurs very quickly.   **Explore Online** ▶

1 **ASK** What questions do you have about the role of sodium iodide in this reaction?

_____

_____

_____

In this reaction, the sodium iodide acted as a catalyst. A **catalyst** is a substance that increases the rate of a chemical reaction without being consumed during the reaction. As a result, catalysts are written above the arrow in a chemical equation.

$$2H_2O_2 \xrightarrow{\text{NaI}} O_2 + 2H_2O$$

Catalysts help lower the activation energy required to form the activated complex in a chemical reaction. So, a lower activation energy is required to start the reaction. Many reactions inside living things are catalyzed by proteins called enzymes so they can proceed rapidly at relatively low temperatures.

2 **ANALYZE** The energy diagram for the decomposition of hydrogen peroxide is shown. Label the graph with the chemical formulas of the reactants and products. Then, draw a line representing the energy of this reaction when the sodium iodide catalyst is added.

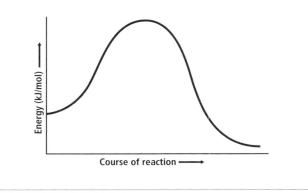

Engineering

Catalyzing Changes

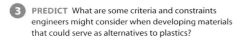

Think about all of the things you use that are made of plastic: shopping bags, packaging materials, bottles, plastic wrap, and many others. Plastic is convenient, but it can also be a big problem. Plastic materials, such as polyethylene bottles, do not break down in the environment for a very long time. As a result, plastic accumulates in landfills.

FIGURE 12: Mountains of plastic waste have accumulated around the world.

3 **PREDICT** What are some criteria and constraints engineers might consider when developing materials that could serve as alternatives to plastics?

_____

_____

_____

Scientists are now studying a process that uses two catalysts to convert waste plastic into diesel fuel. The conversion is a two-step process using polyethylene, the most common plastic material in use. Polyethylene, $(C_2H_4)_n$, is commonly produced from the catalytic polymerization of ethylene, which comes from crude oil. Polyethylene is made up of a long chain of carbon atoms, each attached to two hydrogen atoms. The first catalyst speeds up a reaction that removes the hydrogen atoms from these long chains. As the hydrogen is removed, double bonds form between carbon atoms of the giant polyethylene molecules. This reaction is useful because carbon chains with double bonds react much more readily with other compounds than do chains with only single bonds.

Although the double bonds provide sites for reactions that break apart the chain, those reactions are not fast enough to be practical for handling large volumes of plastic. This is where a second catalyst comes into play. This catalyst reduces the activation energy and helps break apart the plastic at the double bonds. The result is a mixture of hydrocarbon chains of various lengths. The reactions that are sped up by the catalysts continue to break apart the long hydrocarbon chains until they are short enough to be recycled for other purposes, such as fuel.

The catalyst molecules for this process are expensive to produce. They contain expensive metals, such as iridium and rhenium. To make the process cost-effective, the catalysts are recovered and reused. Each molecule of catalyst can promote the conversion of polyethylene molecules over and over again.

4 **Language Arts Connection** Research this method of converting plastic into fuel, and write a news article explaining its benefits and drawbacks. Cite specific text evidence to support your analysis, and discuss possible unanticipated effects of using this method.

5 **Evidence Notebook** Draw an energy diagram for the light stick reaction, and label the reactants, products, and the activation energy of the reaction. Then explain your reasoning for drawing the energy diagram the way you did.

© Houghton Mifflin Harcourt Publishing Company • Image Credits: ©microgen/E+/Getty Images

---

DCI **ETS1.A Defining and Delimiting Engineering Problems**

Tell students that breaking down polyethylene to produce diesel fuel helps the environment in multiple ways. **Ask**: *In addition to reducing the number of plastics that contribute to pollution, how else does the **everyday phenomenon** of catalytic breakdown of plastics into diesel fuel help the environment?* Students may say it might reduce the need to obtain fossil fuels from abiotic reservoirs, a limited resource.

3 Criteria might be that materials be durable in the short term but break down in the environment over the long term. Other criteria could be that the production of the material is not excessively costly and does not produce pollution. Constraints might include limits on the availability of technology or raw materials.

4 Student news articles should cite specific evidence from the text and discuss possible benefits and drawbacks.

Evidence Notebook

5 **Sample answer:** The light sticks were placed in beakers of water at different temperatures, which affected the rate of the chemical reaction that produced light. The energy diagram should show an exothermic reaction and indicate the activation energy.

FORMATIVE ASSESSMENT

Have students respond to one of the following questions.

A chemist dissolves two chemicals in water so that they will react with each other. She must stir the solution vigorously. As the reaction takes place, the solution grows colder. Describe the rate curve for this reaction. The rate curve for this reaction would show an endothermic process. The energy level of the reactants would be lower than the energy level of the products. *A student argues that adding a catalyst to an exothermic reaction will increase the amount of energy the reaction releases to the surroundings. Is he correct?* No. While the catalyst will reduce the activation energy for the process, it does not change the energy stored in the reactant and product molecules. The ΔE of the reaction is the difference between the energy stored in the products and the energy stored in the reactants.

EXPLORATION 4 The Rate Law

3D Learning Objective

Students observe patterns in how changes in concentration affect reaction rate and construct explanations for how those patterns can be represented in the rate law expressions for chemical reactions.

Preconception Alert

Collaborate Students may think that reaction rates determine whether or not a reaction will reach completion. They might assume that slow reactions rarely reach completion. Have student pairs make a T table to compare reaction rate and reaction completion. Point out that few, if any, of the descriptors for one column *must* also be included in the other column.

DCI PS1.B Chemical Reactions

Explain that in some reactions, the reaction rate does not depend on the concentration of the reactants. These reactions usually involve a catalyst, and the available surface area of the catalyst determines the rate. Remind students that catalysts are not consumed in the reaction, and they do not appear in the reaction equation. **Ask:** *How could you increase the rate of a catalyzed reaction?* increase the amount of catalyst to increase the surface area available for reactions

CCC Patterns

Use the data in the Experimental Reaction Rates Data table to compare linear relationships with exponential relationships. There is a linear relationship between [H₂] and reaction rate, whereas there is an exponential relationship between [NO] and reaction rate. Have students brainstorm other linear and exponential relationships they have observed in **everyday phenomena** in the natural world or in formulas. For example, they may know that gravity weakens exponentially with distance.

1 Reaction rates are determined by measuring the amount of product formed in a given time. To measure the reaction rate of an explosion, the reaction is carried out on a small scale so that the products can be contained and measured.

The Rate Law

FIGURE 13: A series of controlled explosions breaks apart rock at a quarry.

An explosion at a quarry is an impressive example of a chemical reaction. Explosive materials such as nitroglycerin, trinitrotoluene (TNT), and dynamite are primarily organic substances. They contain mostly carbon, hydrogen, oxygen, and nitrogen atoms held together by relatively weak bonds.

These materials undergo rapid decomposition. The released elements immediately react to form gaseous N_2, CO, CO_2, and NO_2. These molecules are much more stable than those in the original explosive material, so an enormous amount of energy is released. In addition, the sudden formation of gaseous material causes a tremendous increase in pressure that provides the force to demolish an unwanted building or break apart rock for building roads.

1 PREDICT How do you think scientists determine the reaction rate of an explosive reaction?

_____

_____

_____

_____

Relating Concentration and Reaction Rate

We can experimentally determine the rate of a reaction by measuring the rate at which reactants are consumed or products are formed. It is often important to know and control the rate of a chemical reaction. For example, in an industrial process, equipment must be designed to handle a certain rate of production. If the reaction rate is too slow, then more time is required to make a product, and the product may cost too much as a result. If the reaction rate is too fast, gaseous products and energy may be produced too rapidly. This can damage equipment or even cause a dangerous explosion.

The relationship between reaction rate and concentration is determined by keeping the temperature of the system constant and varying the concentration of a single reactant at a time. By running a series of such experiments, changing the concentration of one reactant at a time, a chemist can determine how the concentration of each reactant affects the reaction rate.

For example, nitrogen monoxide gas reacts with hydrogen gas to produce nitrogen gas and water vapor as shown in the equation:

$$2NO(g) + 2H_2(g) \rightarrow N_2(g) + 2H_2O(g)$$

A series of experiments was performed to measure the rate of this reaction. First, scientists measured how changing the H_2 concentration affected the reaction rate when the NO concentration was held constant. Then, the scientists ran another series of experiments to measure the effect of the NO concentration while the H_2 concentration was held constant. When determining the rate of a reaction, it is important to change the concentration of only one reactant at a time. Otherwise, scientists would not be able to determine the effect of each reactant on the rate.

Experimental Reaction Rates Data		
Concentration of NO	Concentration of H_2	Rate
Initial	Initial	R
Initial	Doubled	2R
Initial	Tripled	3R
Doubled	Initial	4R
Tripled	Initial	9R

 Math Connection

Identifying Rate Relationships

To calculate the relationship of rate to concentration for a reaction, you can analyze patterns in data. For example, the Experimental Reaction Rates Data table shows how the rate of this reaction changes as the concentration of each reactant changes.

 ANALYZE Select the correct terms to complete the statement.

According to the data in the table, doubling the concentration of H_2 causes the reaction rate to double | triple | quadruple . So, the reaction rate is inversely | directly proportional to the concentration of H_2. Doubling the concentration of NO causes the reaction rate to double | triple | quadruple . Thus, the reaction rate is directly proportional to the square | cube of the concentration of NO.

A rate law is an equation that expresses the dependence of reaction rate on the concentrations of the reactants. The general form of a rate law is

$$R = k[A]^n[B]^m$$

where R represents the reaction rate, k is the specific rate constant, and [A] and [B] represent the molar concentrations of reactants A and B. The powers to which the concentrations are raised in calculating the rate law are represented by n and m. The rate law is applicable for a specific reaction at a given set of conditions. The value of k must be determined experimentally after the exponents have been determined experimentally.

In the example of the hydrogen gas and nitrogen monoxide gas reaction, we can use patterns in the concentration and reaction rate data to determine the rate law. Based on the experiment, you can determine that the rate is directly proportional to the concentration of hydrogen gas. So, the n in this rate law is 1, which is not written. The rate is also directly proportional to the square of the nitrogen monoxide concentration. So, the m in this rate law is 2. Thus, the concentration of NO is squared in the rate law equation.

$$R = k[H_2][NO]^2$$

The specific rate constant does not change over the course of the reaction if conditions other than concentration of reactants and products are constant. A change in the temperature of the reaction mixture, however, does change the value of k.

Differentiate Instruction

MTSS/RTI Have student pairs collaborate to review symbols in the rate law equation. Have pairs label the different components of the rate law for the reaction described on this page. They should label R as the reaction rate (at a specific temperature and pressure), k as a constant determined experimentally, $[H_2]$ as the concentration of H_2, and [NO] as the concentration of NO. The subscripts on each reactant represent the relationship between the concentration of the reactant and the rate of the reaction.

Collaborate

Think-Pair-Share On the board, write a general reaction: A + B → C. Explain that as the concentration of A doubles, the concentration of C quadruples. As the concentration of B doubles, the concentration of C doubles. Have students write the rate law for this reaction and then compare their answers with a partner. Repeat with different scenarios.

SEP **Using Mathematics and Computational Thinking**

Display the rate law equation for the reaction between hydrogen gas and nitrogen monoxide: $(R = k[H_2][NO]^2)$. Remind students that each value presented on the right side of the equation has a direct effect on the rate. That is, if k or the concentration of H_2 increases, so does the rate. Changing the concentration of NO affects the rate exponentially.

 Math Connection
MP.4 Model with mathematics.

Remind students that linear relationships show a one-to-one correspondence between two dependent values. Exponential relationships will show an x-to-x^n correspondence. For example, if $n = 2$, and x increases by a factor of 3, x^n increases by a factor of 9. **Ask**: *Suppose you decrease* [A] *by half, and the rate decreases by one-fourth. What is the relationship between rate and* [A]? R is proportional to $[A]^2$

 double, directly, quadruple, square

Math Connection

MP.2 Reason abstractly and quantitatively.

Students can work in groups to solve the Classroom Practice problem. You might assign the Practice Problem as homework to confirm that each student can explain the rate order for each reactant in a reaction.

Classroom Practice

Scientists tested to find the rate law for the equation $2NO(g) + 2H_2(g) \rightarrow N_2(g) + 2H_2O(g)$. Write the rate law using these data:

Experiment	[NO]	[H₂]	Rate (mol/L·s)
1	0.1 M	0.1 M	1.5×10^{-4}
2	0.1 M	0.2 M	3.0×10^{-4}
3	0.2 M	0.2 M	1.2×10^{-3}

$R = k[NO]^2[H_2]$

Practice Problem Answer

1 The rate doubles when the concentration of O_2 doubles, so the rate is directly proportional to the concentration of O_2. The rate quadruples when the concentration of NO doubles, so the rate is proportional to the square of the concentration of NO. The rate law is $R = k[O_2][NO]^2$.

For the complete solutions to the Practice Problems and Classroom Practice, see the online Problem Solutions.

 Evidence Notebook

2 You would need to consider the identity and concentrations of all of the reactants in the reaction, the solvent in which they are dissolved, and a procedure to measure the reaction rate when the concentrations are changed.

FORMATIVE ASSESSMENT

Have students make a conceptual data table that shows [A], [B], and the reaction rate for a reaction with this rate law: $R = k[A]^2[B]$. The data table should show that as the concentration of A doubles, the reaction rate quadruples. As the concentration of B doubles, the reaction rate also doubles.

 Problem Solving

Determining the Rate Law

SAMPLE PROBLEM   Fluorine gas reacts with chlorine dioxide gas according to the following equation:

$$F_2(g) + 2ClO_2(g) \rightarrow 2FClO_2(g)$$

Use the following experimental data to write a rate law for this reaction.

Experiment	Concentration of F₂	Concentration of ClO₂	Rate (mol/L·s)
1	0.10 M	0.10 M	1.1×10^{-3}
2	0.20 M	0.10 M	2.2×10^{-3}
3	0.10 M	0.20 M	2.2×10^{-3}
4	0.20 M	0.20 M	4.4×10^{-3}

ANALYZE   To write the rate law, first examine the data to see how the rate of reaction changes as the concentrations of the reactants change.

When [F₂] doubles and [ClO₂] remains constant, the rate of reaction doubles. So, the reaction rate is directly proportional to [F₂].

When [ClO₂] doubles and [F₂] remains constant, the rate of reaction also doubles. So, the rate is directly proportional to [ClO₂].

SOLVE   Because the reaction rate is proportional to both [F₂] and [ClO₂], you can write the rate law $R = k[F_2][ClO_2]$. The data from Trial 4 help confirm the rate law because when both [F₂] and [ClO₂] double, the rate increases by a factor of four, from 1.1×10^{-3} mol/L·s to 4.4×10^{-3} mol/L·s.

1 **PRACTICE PROBLEM**   **SOLVE** Nitrogen monoxide forms in combustion engines and can subsequently react with oxygen in the air to produce nitrogen dioxide, which is an air pollutant:

$$O_2(g) + 2NO(g) \rightarrow 2NO_2(g)$$

Experiment	Concentration of O₂	Concentration of NO	Rate (mol/L·s)
1	1.20×10^{-2} M	1.40×10^{-2} M	3.30×10^{-3}
2	2.40×10^{-2} M	1.40×10^{-2} M	6.60×10^{-3}
3	1.20×10^{-2} M	2.80×10^{-2} M	1.32×10^{-2}

Use this data to briefly explain how the rate changes as the concentration of each reactant changes. Then use your explanation to write the rate law for this reaction.

_____

_____

_____

2 **Evidence Notebook** Consider the rate law for the reaction occurring in a light stick. What information would you need in order to set up an experiment to determine the rate law?

TAKE IT FURTHER Engineering

Engineering

Chemical Kinetics

Industrial explosives are used to break apart rock, clear paths for new roads, and even demolish buildings. During the explosion of these materials, matter moves very rapidly—several kilometers per second—and with a lot of force. In order to design explosives that are both safe and effective, chemists must apply their knowledge of reaction rates, also called chemical kinetics. Because these reactions occur at such high rates and give off so much energy, it can be difficult to study exactly how these chemical changes occur.

There are many forms of explosives used in mining, each with unique properties and reactions. Mining explosives are designed to be stable and safe to handle for long periods of time, but they also need to provide as much energy as possible when they are used. Because they provide so much energy, engineers must understand how they will react in order to prevent accidental explosions.

Scientists and engineers process data from test explosions to model exactly what is occurring during the reaction. By calculating the rate of reaction under different conditions and the amount of energy released, they can determine the best design for an explosive system that performs the task safely.

Understanding chemical kinetics also helps in the design of safer materials. For example, a simple mechanical impact on an explosive device can result in localized heating. This effect can cause mechanical deformation and possibly fracturing or fragmenting of the material. One section may ignite, and as the ignition spreads, the energy released could lead to anything from slow combustion of the material to violent detonation of the whole explosive device. Chemists, materials scientists, and engineers work together to predict explosive sensitivity and design new materials that do not accidentally detonate.

FIGURE 14: A detonation test for a mining explosive

The behavior of explosives is a challenging topic because the reactions themselves are very complex, and they occur extremely rapidly. Modern technology allows engineers to determine reaction rates with more precision than in the past. This advancement allows them to design explosive materials and direct forces in a way that maximizes productivity and safety.

 Language Arts Connection   Conduct research to learn more about how engineers use knowledge of chemical kinetics to optimize processes in another field, such as pharmaceutical production or food storage. Then, write a blog post that explains your findings and addresses the following questions. Focus on the most important aspects of the information, and explain any inconsistencies you find.

- How do engineers use knowledge of chemical kinetics to optimize this process?
- How are the data and results from chemical kinetics experiments and tests used in this field?
- Why is an understanding of reaction rates important when optimizing this process?

 **CONTROLLING REACTION RATES**   **REACTION MECHANISMS**   **CLOCK REACTIONS**   Go online to choose one of these other paths.

© Houghton Mifflin Harcourt Publishing Company • Image Credits: ©Crown Copyright/Health & Safety Laboratory/Science Source

Lesson 1 Investigating Reaction Rates   **327**

Collaborate

You may choose to assign this activity or direct students to the Interactive Online Student Edition, where they can choose from all available paths. These activities can be assigned individually, to pairs, or to small groups.

3 Students should use reliable scientific sources to write blog posts explaining how engineers use knowledge of chemical kinetics to optimize a process. Students' blog posts should focus on the most important aspects of their findings and explain conflicting information as necessary. Examples of processes engineers have optimized might include the Haber process, various pharmaceutical production processes, or the slowing of reaction rates in the field of food storage.

Explore Online ▶

Controlling Reaction Rates

Students use a computer simulation to model the impact of proposed solutions to a real-world engineering problem.

Reaction Mechanisms

Students learn about multistep reactions and how the rates of different steps affect the overall reaction rate.

Clock Reactions

Students investigate how changes in reactant concentrations affect the reaction outcome of a multistep reaction.

EVALUATE Lesson Self-Check

Can You Explain the Phenomenon?

Claims, Evidence, and Reasoning

Have students clearly state their claim—their explanation for the phenomenon they have been investigating throughout this lesson. They should present their reasoning for making this claim, along with evidence such as facts, examples, and statistics that support their claim. You may want to have students present their arguments orally, in writing, or as a debate.

Cultivating Student Questions

Assessing Student Growth Review the list of questions students generated at the beginning of the lesson. Have volunteers select any unanswered questions and suggest how they could be investigated. After approving student plans, have small groups conduct the investigations and report back to the class.

Nature of Science

Scientific Knowledge is Based on Empirical Evidence If each light stick is placed in the opposite beaker, their relative light output per unit time will reverse. At the extreme, if a glowing light stick from the warm bath is put into a freezer, the rate of the reaction will slow enough that if hours later it is warmed, it will emit light again. You may want to perform this demonstration to provide strong data for the Evidence Notebook answer as well as additional support for science concepts in this lesson.

 Evidence Notebook

1 **Sample answer:** A warm temperature will cause the light stick to glow brighter than a colder temperature. In the lab, the effervescent tablet reacted faster in the warm water than it did in the cold water. When a substance is at a higher temperature, its particles have more kinetic energy. They travel faster, so they can have more collisions with more energy in the same amount of time. Because the number of effective collisions increases, the reaction rate increases.

Lesson Self-Check

CAN YOU EXPLAIN THE PHENOMENON?

FIGURE 15: Temperature affects the rate of the reaction in the light sticks.

Light sticks consist of two nested tubes. The tough, plastic, outer tube is filled with a solution of a reactant and a dissolved dye. A thin, inner tube made of glass or brittle plastic holds a solution of a second reactant. When the tube inside a light stick is broken, the two reactants mix and start reacting. The reaction releases energy that is absorbed by the dye. Energy released by the reaction causes the dye to glow. As the reactants are used up and their concentration decreases, the light stick gradually becomes dimmer.

 1 **Evidence Notebook** Refer to your notes in your Evidence Notebook to make a claim about this phenomenon. Your explanation should include a discussion of the following points:

Claim Make a claim to explain at the particle level why changing the temperature of a light stick affects the intensity of the light it emits.

Evidence Provide specific evidence to support your claim.

Reasoning How does the evidence support your claim? Explain how the breaking of bonds, particle collisions, and kinetic energy are related to this phenomenon.

 Formal Assessment Go online for student self-checks and other assessments.

Name _____   Date _____

CHECKPOINTS

Check Your Understanding

1. Select the correct terms to complete the statement about reaction rates.

The rate of a chemical reaction depends on a number of different factors. At a higher concentration of reactants, the frequency of collisions decreases | increases | is not affected, so the reaction rate decreases | increases | remains the same. When temperature decreases, the kinetic energy of the particles decreases | increases | is not affected. As a result, particles collide less frequently and with less energy, so reaction rate decreases | increases | is not affected.

2. According to collision theory, which variables affect the rate of a chemical reaction? Select all correct answers.

- [ ] **a.** concentrations of dissolved reactants
- [ ] **b.** chemical properties of reactants
- [ ] **c.** size of crystals of solid reactants
- [ ] **d.** shape of the container holding reactants

3. Select the correct terms to complete the statement about particle collisions.

In order to form a new product, reactant particles must collide with sufficient kinetic | potential energy to break | form bonds in the reactant particles. This is why increasing temperature increases the rate of a chemical reaction.

4. Which of these are reasons that a collision between particles might not lead to the formation of a new product? Select all correct answers.

- [ ] **a.** The particles did not collide with sufficient energy to break bonds in the reactants.
- [ ] **b.** The particles had a very high mass, which prevents effective collisions.
- [ ] **c.** The particles do not have the correct shape to form new products.
- [ ] **d.** The orientation of the particles was not correct.

Use the table to answer Question 5.

Energy Values of a Chemical Reaction	
Chemical Species	**Energy (kJ/mol)**
Reactants	0
Products	−110
Activated complex	45

5. Complete the statement.

During the reaction described in the table, the overall energy of the reaction is −110 kJ/mol | 110 kJ/mol, indicating that the reaction is endothermic | exothermic. The energy required to cause effective collisions between particles is 45 kJ/mol | 110 kJ/mol.

Use the table to answer Questions 6 and 7.

Reaction Rates for A(aq) + B(aq) ⟶ C(aq)			
Experiment	**[A]**	**[B]**	**Rate (M/s)**
1	0.150 M	0.300 M	0.013
2	0.150 M	0.600 M	0.052
3	0.300 M	0.300 M	0.026

6. Complete the statement. Some terms may not be used or may be used more than once.

doubles   quadruples   remains unchanged

Based on the data in the table, when the concentration of reactant A doubles, the reaction rate _____, and when the concentration of reactant B doubles, the reaction rate _____.

7. What is the rate law for the reaction between A and B?

- ○ **a.** $R = k[A][B]$
- ○ **b.** $R = k[A]^2[B]$
- ○ **c.** $R = k[A][B]^2$
- ○ **d.** $R = k[A]^2[B]^2$

Answers

1. increases, increases, decreases, decreases

2. a, b, c

3. kinetic, break

4. a, d

5. −110 kJ/mol, exothermic, 45 kJ/mol

6. doubles, quadruples

7. c

Answers

8. The answer should include two of the following:

   - Increasing temperature increases the reaction rate by increasing the energy and frequency of collisions among reacting particles, leading to an increase in the number of effective collisions.

   - Increasing concentration increases the total number of collisions, so there are a greater number of effective collisions.

   - Increasing the surface area increases the number of particles exposed to collisions, leading to a greater number of effective collisions.

   - Adding a catalyst decreases the activation energy, which increases the number of effective collisions.

9. **Sample answer:** A chemical reaction between molecules occurs only when the reactants collide with enough energy and in the correct orientation to react. A candle cannot start burning until its molecules have enough energy for effective collisions. This activation energy must be supplied to the reaction. After the candle starts burning, the reaction continues to release enough energy to keep causing effective collisions.

10. **Sample answer:** The reaction is endothermic, so it has to have energy to continue reacting. The energy comes from the solution as it loses energy and becomes colder during the reaction. The activation energy must be relatively low because the solvent, which is initially at room temperature, can provide enough energy to start the reaction.

Make Your Own Study Guide

Have students create a study guide that helps them organize and visualize the important information from this lesson. Their study guide should focus on the main ideas from this lesson and tie multiple ideas together. Students can create an outline, a concept map, a graphic organizer, or another representation.

CHECKPOINTS (continued)

8. Describe two ways to make a chemical reaction proceed faster, and explain at the particle level why the rate increases.

   _____

   _____

   _____

   _____

9. Explain why a candle cannot start burning until a flame is brought to the wick, but it continues burning once started.

   _____

   _____

   _____

10. When vinegar and baking soda are mixed together in an aqueous solution, the solution becomes colder as the reaction proceeds. How does an endothermic reaction continue without the addition of energy from outside the solution system? What can you conclude about the activation energy of the reaction?

    _____

    _____

    _____

    _____

MAKE YOUR OWN STUDY GUIDE

 In your Evidence Notebook, design a study guide that supports the main ideas from this lesson:
  The rate of a chemical reaction can be measured, and it can vary depending on the nature of the reactants, surface area, temperature, concentration, and the presence of a catalyst.

According to collision theory, a reaction can occur when particles collide with sufficient energy and in a favorable orientation.

The rate law of a reaction describes the correlation between the concentration of each reactant and the reaction rate.

Remember to include the following information in your study guide:
- Use examples that model main ideas.
- Record explanations for the phenomena you investigated.
- Use evidence to support your explanations. Your support can include drawings, data, graphs, laboratory conclusions, and other evidence recorded throughout the lesson.

Consider how patterns in data obtained from experiments and simulations can be used to support explanations for how interactions at the particle level are related to changes in reaction rates.

Exploring Chemical Equilibrium

Building to the Performance Expectations

The learning experiences in this lesson prepare students for mastery of

HS-PS1-5 Apply scientific principles and evidence to provide an explanation about the effects of changing the temperature or concentration of the reacting particles on the rate at which a reaction occurs.

HS-PS1-6 Refine the design of a chemical system by specifying a change in conditions that would produce increased amounts of products at equilibrium.

 Trace Tool to the NGSS

Go online to view the complete coverage of standards across lessons, units, and grade levels.

 SEP ## Science & Engineering Practices

Constructing Explanations and Designing Solutions
Apply scientific principles and evidence to provide an explanation of phenomena and solve design problems, taking into account possible unanticipated effects.

Constructing Explanations and Designing Solutions
Refine a solution to a complex real-world problem, based on scientific knowledge, student-generated sources of evidence, prioritized criteria, and tradeoff considerations.

 **VIDEO** Constructing Scientific Explanations

DCI ## Disciplinary Core Ideas

PS1.B Chemical Reactions
Chemical processes, their rates, and whether or not energy is stored or released can be understood in terms of the collisions of molecules and the rearrangements of atoms into new molecules, with consequent changes in the sum of all bond energies in the set of molecules that are matched by changes in kinetic energy. (HS-PS1-5)

PS1.B Chemical Reactions
In many situations, a dynamic and condition-dependent balance between a reaction and the reverse reaction determines the numbers of all types of molecules present. (HS-PS1-6)

PS1.B Chemical Reactions
The fact that atoms are conserved, together with knowledge of the chemical properties of the elements involved, can be used to describe and predict chemical reactions. (HS-PS1-2) (HS-PS1-7)

ETS1.B Developing Possible Solutions
When evaluating solutions, it is important to take into account a range of constraints including cost, safety, reliability and aesthetics and to consider social, cultural and environmental impacts. (ETS1-3)

CCC ## Crosscutting Concepts

Patterns
Different patterns may be observed at each of the scales at which a system is studied and can provide evidence for causality in explanations of phenomena.

Stability and Change
Much of science deals with constructing explanations of how things change and how they remain stable.

Influence of Engineering, Technology, and Science on Society and the Natural World
New technologies can have deep impacts on society and the environment, including some that were not anticipated. Analysis of costs and benefits is a critical aspect of decisions about technology.

MATH STANDARDS

MP.2 Reason abstractly and quantitatively.

MP.4 Model with mathematics.

HSN-Q.A.1 Use units as a way to understand problems and to guide the solution of multi-step problems; choose and interpret units consistently in formulas; choose and interpret the scale and the origin in graphs and data displays.

ELA STANDARDS

WHST.9-12.7 Conduct short as well as more sustained research projects to answer a question or solve a problem; synthesize multiple sources on the subject, demonstrating understanding of the subject under investigation.

WHST.9-12.2 Write informative/explanatory texts, including the narration of historical events, scientific procedures/experiments, or technical processes.

Supporting All Students, All Standards

Integrating the Three Dimensions

In this lesson, students explain (**SEP Constructing Explanations and Designing Solutions**) how chemical equilibrium systems change and stabilize (**CCC Stability and Change**) as a dynamic equilibrium shifts due to changing conditions (**DCI PS1.B**). Students investigate (**SEP Planning and Carrying Out Investigations**) the differences between acids and bases and identify constraints that guide the treatment of pool water (**DCI ETS1.B**). Finally, students identify patterns (**CCC Patterns**) in acid-base equilibrium systems and explain the reactions between strong and weak acids and bases.

Preassessment

Have students complete the unit pretest or see the Assessment Guide.

Build on Prior Knowledge

Have students list what they know about chemical reactions and how the progress of a chemical reaction on a molecular level can be monitored by observable properties of the reaction. Review concepts such as reactants and products as well as the factors that cause a chemical reaction to occur.

You may want to review the following concepts:

- Reactant molecules must collide with enough energy and in the correct orientation in order to form the activated complex.
- The energy needed to reach the activated complex is called the activation energy, which is different for each reaction.
- Not all chemical reactions that can be written as an equation will occur in the real world. For example, in a single displacement reaction of copper in a silver nitrate solution, the solution turns a blue color. This indicates that copper(II) ions are present in solution. In addition, solid silver can be seen forming on the copper. However, if a piece of silver is placed into a copper(II) nitrate solution, no reaction will occur, even though the chemical equation for this reaction can be written.

 **Professional Development** Go online to view **Professional Development videos** with strategies to integrate CCCs and SEPs, including the ones used in this lesson.

Content Background

Homeostasis is the process by which a living organism maintains a stable internal environment. Maintaining body fluids within specific pH ranges is one type of homeostasis. A buffer system that helps maintain the pH of fluids within human cells is the dihydrogen phosphate, $H_2PO_4^{2-}$, and hydrogen phosphate, HPO_4^{3-}, equilibrium.

Dihydrogen phosphate is a weak acid, and hydrogen phosphate is its conjugate base. If a base is added to this system, the dihydrogen phosphate reacts with the base to form water and hydrogen phosphate, with little or no change to the pH of the cellular fluid. If an acid is added, it reacts with the hydrogen phosphate to form dihydrogen phosphate. Again, the pH of the system is relatively unchanged.

A buffer system important for homeostasis in human blood is the carbonic acid, H_2CO_3, and bicarbonate ion, HCO_3^-, equilibrium. This system involves two equilibrium reactions:

$$CO_2(aq) + H_2O(l) \rightleftharpoons H_2CO_3(aq) \rightleftharpoons H^+(aq) + HCO_3^-(aq)$$

It also involves the solution equilibrium between CO_2 in the air in the lungs and CO_2 dissolved in the blood. Some of the regulation of the pH of blood happens because CO_2 can be removed from the body in the respiratory system and HCO_3^- can be removed from the body by the kidneys. These processes affect equilibrium by removing a reactant or a product from the system. Additional pH control happens because this system can neutralize added acids and bases. If a base is added, it reacts with the carbonic acid and is neutralized, and if an acid is added, it reacts with the bicarbonate ion and is neutralized.

Differentiate Instruction

KEY WORDS

- reversible reaction
- chemical equilibrium
- Le Châtelier's principle
- acid
- base
- pH

ELL SUPPORT

Before students encounter each new key term in their reading, pause to pronounce and explain each term. Help students connect the term to words and concepts they have already learned and to cognates in their home language, as appropriate.

ENGAGE: Investigative Phenomenon

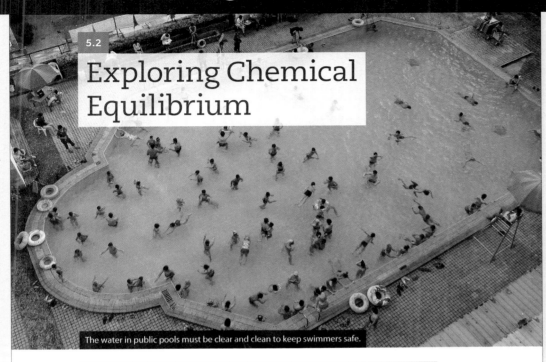

5.2

Exploring Chemical Equilibrium

The water in public pools must be clear and clean to keep swimmers safe.

CAN YOU EXPLAIN THE PHENOMENON?

Public swimming pools are a great place to cool off on a hot day. Clean water in a pool makes swimming safer and more enjoyable. Depending on the size of the pool, there could be anywhere from thousands to millions of liters of water to keep clean. Larger materials, such as leaves, dirt, and hair, need to be removed from the pool. There also may be unseen microscopic contaminants, such as bacteria and algae, present in harmful concentrations in water that appears to be clean.

1 **PLAN** Brainstorm ideas for how to treat contaminants in pool water. Could you use the same solution for both larger debris and microscopic organisms? Which type of contaminant do you think is more dangerous to swimmers?

_____

_____

_____

_____

2 **Evidence Notebook** As you explore the lesson, gather evidence to explain how a chemical equilibrium system in swimming pools can be managed to provide safe water for swimmers.

© Houghton Mifflin Harcourt Publishing Company • Image Credits: ©Photography by Jesse Warren/Moment/Getty Images

Lesson 2 Exploring Chemical Equilibrium   **331**

Build on Prior Lessons

In Lesson 1, students learned about reaction processes and the rate of reactions. Lesson 2 builds on these concepts as students explore reaction processes and rates related to chemical equilibrium.

Lesson Objective

Students identify how a change in conditions, such as concentration, temperature, or pressure, may affect the amounts of products and reactants in a system at chemical equilibrium. They also explore acid-base equilibrium systems.

Cultivating Student Questions

Have students look at the photo of a crowded swimming pool. Prompt them to ask all questions that come to mind about how the water in a swimming pool is kept clean enough to swim in. Record the questions on chart paper, and then sort the questions based on their focus. With students, narrow the questions down to ones that directly relate to the learning objective. Have students reflect on this list throughout the lesson and check off questions as they are answered.

Can You Explain the Phenomenon?

The Investigative Phenomenon is the focus of the lesson. Students are asked to record their initial thoughts about swimming pool water. They will collect evidence related to this phenomenon throughout the lesson and revisit the question at the end of the lesson to use what they have learned to trace the connection between equilibrium conditions of chemical reactions and water quality.

1 Students may brainstorm many ideas, including a filter to remove the large debris and chemicals to remove the organisms. They may be familiar with chlorine as a pool treatment but may not understand the reaction. Students will likely identify smaller bacteria as the most dangerous contaminants.

Evidence Notebook

2 The topic of pool water treatment using a chemical reaction at equilibrium will be revisited throughout this lesson.

Lesson 2 Exploring Chemical Equilibrium   331

EXPLORATION 1 Explaining Equilibrium

3D Learning Objective

Students use **scientific principles and evidence to construct an explanation** for how concentrations and reaction rates change and stabilize as a **dynamic and condition-dependent equilibrium is established between a forward and reverse reaction.**

Everyday phenomena discussed throughout the Explorations of the lesson can often be used to connect the science content to students' personal experiences.

SEP Developing and Using Models

Ask students to model the boundaries, inputs, and outputs of a reversible system such as a rechargeable battery. Students should identify the conditions that cause the system to function in opposite directions. For example, rechargeable batteries are drained as they convert chemical energy to electrical energy to run electrical devices. When the batteries are plugged into a charger, the process is reversed and electrical energy drives chemical reactions that increase the amount of chemical energy stored in the battery. At the end of the lesson, students can determine how the systems they modeled compare with chemical equilibrium systems.

Differentiate Instruction

MTSS/RTI Have students work in pairs to compare the copper sulfate pentahydrate reaction and the ammonium chloride reaction. Lead a class discussion on the similarities and differences between these two reactions. Have students decide whether this information can be used as evidence that the ammonium chloride reaction is reversible.

 b

Explaining Equilibrium

When wood burns in a fire, atoms in molecules such as cellulose are rearranged to form new products, such as carbon dioxide, water vapor, and ash. Burning wood is not a reversible process because wood cannot be remade from ash. However, some reactions are reversible and can proceed in both forward and reverse directions.

Reversible Reactions

A chemical reaction in which the products can react to reform the reactants is called a reversible reaction. An example of a reversible reaction is shown in Figure 1 and involves copper sulfate pentahydrate, a common fungicide and herbicide. The *hydrate* means water molecules are present in the copper sulfate crystal, and its formula is $CuSO_4 \cdot 5H_2O$.

FIGURE 1: Forward and reverse reactions involving copper sulfate pentahydrate

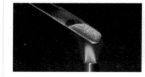  

a Blue crystals of copper sulfate pentahydrate are placed over a hot flame.

b Water is released from the compound, leaving white crystals of copper sulfate.

c Water is added back to the copper sulfate, and the crystals turn blue.

Stability and Change

FIGURE 2: The combustion of candle wax is effectively a one-way reaction.

Reversible and Irreversible Reactions

It was once believed that all chemical reactions were irreversible, and once products formed they could not change back to reactants. For example, when a candle burns, wax cannot be rebuilt out of compounds in the air.

But some reactions are different. Solid ammonium chloride forms small white crystals. When ammonium chloride is placed in a test tube and held over a flame, the gases ammonia and hydrogen chloride are produced. As the reaction proceeds, some solid white crystals form on the cooler sides at the top of the glass test tube.

1 GATHER EVIDENCE What evidence is there that the reverse reaction is occurring in the ammonium chloride reaction?

○ **a.** The reactants are burned over a flame.

○ **b.** Crystals appear at the top of the test tube.

○ **c.** All reactants are consumed in the reaction.

○ **d.** Two different gases are released as products.

© Houghton Mifflin Harcourt Publishing Company • Image Credits: (l, c) ©Turtle Rock Scientific/Science Source; (r) ©Richard Megna/Fundamental Photographs; (b) ©Jon Sparks/Alamy

Data Analysis

Analyzing Concentrations of Reactants and Products

What evidence might indicate that a reaction can proceed in both directions? And, does this type of reaction ever come to a stop?

Consider nitrogen dioxide, NO_2, an orange-brown gas that is a common component of polluted air. Nitrogen dioxide interacts with oxygen, water, and other pollutants in the atmosphere and forms acid rain. It can also cause haze or smog that is yellowish-brown in color. Two molecules of NO_2 react to form dinitrogen tetroxide, N_2O_4. Dinitrogen tetroxide is a colorless gas that can be used as a rocket propellant because it is highly reactive. The molecular structures of NO_2 and N_2O_4 are shown in Figure 3.

The table shows the concentration of each compound over time as NO_2 reacts to form N_2O_4 in a closed system.

2 **MODEL** Graph the data shown in the table as the concentration of each compound over time.

You can see based on the table data and your graph that the concentrations of nitrogen dioxide and dinitrogen tetroxide reach a steady state in which the concentrations do not change. A double arrow is used to show the reaction at a steady state, or equilibrium.

$$2NO_2(g) \rightleftharpoons N_2O_4(g)$$

3 **ANALYZE** Select the correct terms to complete the statement.

In this reaction, NO_2 molecules combine | break apart to form N_2O_4, and N_2O_4 molecules combine | break apart to form NO_2. The reaction reaches a stable state when the ratio of the two gases is 0.0100 | 0.0200 | 0.0500 mol/L NO_2 to 0.0000 | 0.0100 | 0.0200 mol/L N_2O_4. At this point, the gases are still | have stopped reacting. At a stable state, the rates of both reactions must be equal | unequal for the concentration of both compounds to remain steady.

FIGURE 3: Molecular structures of NO_2 and N_2O_4

a Nitrogen dioxide, NO_2

b Dinitrogen tetroxide, N_2O_4

Concentration of NO_2 and N_2O_4 as Reaction Proceeds	
NO_2 (mol/L)	N_2O_4 (mol/L)
0.0500	0.0000
0.0428	0.0036
0.0320	0.0090
0.0220	0.0140
0.0154	0.0173
0.0120	0.0190
0.0106	0.0197
0.0102	0.0199
0.0100	0.0200
0.0100	0.0200
0.0100	0.0200

DCI **PS1.B Chemical Reactions**

Demonstrate the $NO_2(g) \rightleftharpoons N_2O_4(g)$ equilibrium system in a sealed tube that is responsive to temperature changes. Prepared tubes can be ordered from science supply companies. Guide a class discussion about what may be occurring at the molecular level inside the tube. The demonstration can be revisited later in the lesson during the section exploring the effect of temperature changes on an equilibrium system. Have students revise their explanations of what is occurring inside the sealed tube.

CCC **Cause and Effect**

Students may need to be reminded that chemical reactions require collisions between reactant molecules. However, a collision between reactant molecules does not necessarily produce a reaction. The two molecules must collide with proper orientation for the reaction to occur. Conditions of enough energy and correct orientation will allow a collision to cause a reaction.

Collaborate

Discussion Have student pairs study how two NO_2 molecules react to form N_2O_4 by creating molecular diagrams for the two molecules. Then discuss the orientation at which NO_2 molecules must collide to form the product molecule. Given that the reverse reaction also occurs, have students explain how N_2O_4 might decompose to form NO_2.

2 Student graphs should have time on the x-axis and concentration on the y-axis. The two substances can be graphed as two different lines. Graphs should look similar to **Figure 4.**

3 combine, break apart, 0.0100, 0.0200, are still, equal

Math Connection

Figure 4 is a graph of the concentrations of nitrogen dioxide and dinitrogen tetroxide over time. **Ask:** *What is the reactant and what is the product for the forward reaction, based on the graph?* Nitrogen dioxide is the reactant, and dinitrogen tetroxide is the product.

Ask: *How did you arrive at your answer?* The starting concentration of nitrogen dioxide is higher than zero, while the starting concentration of dinitrogen tetroxide is zero, so nitrogen dioxide was the original reactant.

Ask: *What evidence from the graph indicates that the reaction reaches an equilibrium?* When both lines level off and form straight line segments parallel to the *x*-axis, this indicates the concentrations are no longer changing and the reaction has reached a steady state. **(MP.2)**

Preconception Alert

Students may erroneously associate the term *dynamic* with the terms *static*, *balance*, and *unchanging* because dynamic is used to describe the steady state, or equilibrium, of a reversible reaction. Have students use synonyms and antonyms of these terms to explain what changes in a system at equilibrium (forward and reverse reactions are still occurring) and what remains the same (reaction rates are stable and equal and concentrations are stable).

1 a, d, e

2 **Sample answer:** A graph like the one shown in **Figure 4** does not show that the forward and reverse chemical reactions are still occurring when the system reaches equilibrium. A dynamic model such as a molecular simulation could be used to represent this.

3 Reaction rates are determined by the number of effective reactant particle collisions per unit time. When there is a higher concentration of reactant particles, more collisions occur, and therefore effective collisions also occur more frequently. Chemical equilibrium occurs when the forward reaction rate equals the reverse reaction rate—and therefore depends upon particle collisions and concentrations in the system.

Chemical Equilibrium

The NO_2/N_2O_4 system is an example of an equilibrium. As the reaction progresses, the concentrations of NO_2 and N_2O_4 present at specific conditions stabilize. At this point, called **chemical equilibrium**, the forward and reverse reactions occur at the same rate. In contrast, the concentrations of the reactants and products are often different.

Figure 4 shows changes in the concentrations of NO_2 and N_2O_4 as the reaction progresses.

$$2NO_2(g) \rightleftharpoons N_2O_4(g)$$

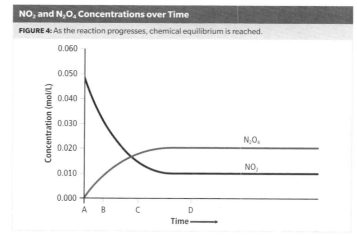

NO₂ and N₂O₄ Concentrations over Time

FIGURE 4: As the reaction progresses, chemical equilibrium is reached.

1 ANALYZE Which of the following statements about this reaction are true? Select all correct answers.

☐ **a**. At Time B, the reaction has not yet reached chemical equilibrium.

☐ **b**. Chemical equilibrium for this reaction occurs at Time C.

☐ **c**. At equilibrium, the concentrations of NO_2 and N_2O_4 are equal.

☐ **d**. At Time D, the reaction has reached chemical equilibrium.

☐ **e**. The concentrations of NO_2 and N_2O_4 differ when chemical equilibrium is reached.

2 **Collaborate** With a partner, discuss the limitations of models such as the Figure 4 graph in representing what occurs at chemical equilibrium. What kind of model could be used to represent the process more completely?

3 EVALUATE What is the relationship among reaction rate, effective particle collisions, and reactant concentration? How do these factors affect chemical equilibrium?

_____

_____

_____

Consider this generalized reaction at equilibrium:

$$A + B \rightleftharpoons C + D$$

4 **PREDICT** If you start with only A and B, when will C and D be produced the fastest? How does this relate to concentration?

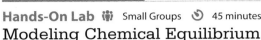

Explore Online ▶

🧪 **Hands-On Lab**

Modeling Chemical Equilibrium Develop a model of equilibrium using water and measuring cups.

_____

_____

_____

_____

The graph in Figure 5 shows the reaction rates as the system reaches equilibrium.

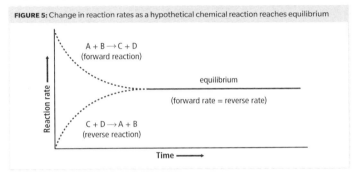

FIGURE 5: Change in reaction rates as a hypothetical chemical reaction reaches equilibrium

A + B → C + D
(forward reaction)

equilibrium

(forward rate = reverse rate)

C + D → A + B
(reverse reaction)

Reaction rate

Time

5 **EXPLAIN** Select the correct terms to complete the statement.

As the reaction proceeds, the rate of the forward reaction increases | decreases while the rate of the reverse reaction increases | decreases. This occurs because, as the concentrations of A and B increase | decrease, the concentrations of C and D increase | decrease. When the chemical reaction reaches equilibrium, the rate of the forward reaction is greater than | equal to | less than the rate of the reverse reaction.

This type of equilibrium is called a dynamic equilibrium because the system is in a constant, but balanced, state of change. Forward and reverse reactions continue, but no noticeable change in concentrations occurs because the reaction rates are the same.

6 **Language Arts Connection** Write an analogy that describes chemical equilibrium, including the relationship between the reaction at the molecular scale and the concentrations of the products and reactants measured at the macroscopic scale. Explain your analogy to a partner. How did different sources of information help you build your understanding?

7 **Evidence Notebook** Hypochlorous acid, HOCl, is used to treat pools. When HOCl is added to water, it breaks apart to form hydrogen ions, H⁺, and hypochlorite ions, OCl⁻. An equilibrium is established. Write the chemical equation for this equilibrium system. Describe how the concentration of each ion and HOCl changes when HOCl is added to water as a pool treatment.

© Houghton Mifflin Harcourt Publishing Company

Lesson 2 Exploring Chemical Equilibrium **335**

Hands-On Lab 👥 Small Groups 🕐 45 minutes
Modeling Chemical Equilibrium

SEP **Constructing Explanations and Designing Solutions**

Students use a physical model to demonstrate chemical equilibrium and identify weaknesses and improvements for the model. _Student lab worksheet and teacher support available online._

4 **Sample answer:** Starting with A and B, C and D will be produced the fastest when the reaction begins because the concentrations of A and B are the greatest at that point.

5 decreases, increases, decrease, increase, equal to

6 Answers may vary, but any analogy must include the fact that, on the macroscopic level, there does not seem to be a change in a measurable property. But when one looks more closely, changes can be seen. An example is a football game in which 22 players are on the field at any given time, but on a player level, the players are constantly changing between each play.

📝 **Evidence Notebook**

7 HOCl(aq) $\rightleftharpoons$ H⁺(aq) + OCl⁻(aq); When HOCl is added to water, it dissociates into hydrogen and hypochlorite ions. The reverse reaction occurs at the same time, so an equilibrium will be established. When the HOCl is first added, the concentration of HOCl is high, and the concentration of hydrogen and hypochlorite ions is very low. As the HOCl dissociates into ions, the concentration of HOCl decreases, and the concentration of the ions increases. An equilibrium will be established when the HOCl breaks down into ions at the same rate that the ions come together to form HOCl.

FORMATIVE ASSESSMENT

Quick Write _Ask: Can a given chemical reaction ever come to completion and stop on its own?_ Give students five minutes to write a short response based on this Exploration.

EXPLORATION 2 Concentration Influences Equilibrium

3D Learning Objective

Students identify patterns in an equilibrium system at different scales to help **construct an explanation** for how changing the concentration of reactants or products affects the number and types of molecules present at equilibrium.

Explore Online ▶

Encourage students to go online to view the video showing what happens when hydrochloric acid or water is added to a cobalt(II) chloride solution.

DCI PS1.B Chemical Reactions

Explain that many factors control whether a chemical equilibrium is established for any reversible reaction, including whether the reaction occurs in an open or closed system. **Ask:** *Why might a reversible reaction in an open system go to completion instead of establishing an equilibrium?* If the reaction produces a gas that leaves the system, the product will no longer be available to re-form the reactants. In a chemical equilibrium, the products of the forward reaction must remain in the system in order for the reverse reaction to take place.

1 Students should include a method for deciding when molecules interact. When products are added, the concentration of the products increases, there are more effective collisions between product particles, and the reverse reaction rate increases. When reactants are added, the concentration of the reactants increases, there are more effective collisions between reactant particles, and the forward reaction rate increases. The reverse relationships would be true for removing products or reactants.

2 Students should observe that the system turned blue when hydrochloric acid was added, suggesting that the concentration of $[CoCl_4]^{2-}$ increased. The system began to turn pink again when water was added, suggesting that the concentration of $[Co(H_2O)_6]^{2+}$ increased.

Concentration Influences Equilibrium

As in the example of nitrogen dioxide and dinitrogen tetroxide, many chemical systems in nature and industrial chemistry involve chemical reactions in equilibrium. The equilibrium states can be shifted to form an increased or decreased amount of the products.

 1 **Collaborate** With a group, develop a physical model for the reaction: $A + BC \rightleftharpoons BA + C$. One person should control the forward reaction and one person the reverse reaction. What happens when a classmate adds products or reactants? What happens when products or reactants are removed? Explain the changes in your model in terms of concentrations, collisions between particles, and reaction rates.

Adding Reactants or Products

Now consider another equilibrium system as a model for the principles of chemical equilibrium. The cobalt(II) chloride equilibrium system is modeled by the equation:

$$[Co(H_2O)_6]^{2+}(aq) + 4Cl^-(aq) \rightleftharpoons [CoCl_4]^{2-}(aq) + 6H_2O(l)$$
$$\text{Pink} \qquad\qquad\qquad\qquad \text{Blue}$$

When the solution has a higher concentration of $[Co(H_2O)_6]^{2+}$ ions, it appears pink. When the solution has a higher concentration of $[CoCl_4]^{2-}$ ions, it appears blue. As with all chemical equilibria, the ions and molecules in solution are constantly reacting in forward and reverse reactions. Figure 6 shows the color changes when hydrochloric acid, HCl, and then water, H_2O, are added to the cobalt(II) chloride solution.

FIGURE 6: The cobalt(II) chloride solution changes color as the chemical equilibrium shifts.

a Initially, the solution is pinkish-orange.

b After HCl is added, the solution turns blue.

c After water is added, the solution begins to turn pink again.

 2 **GATHER EVIDENCE** Using evidence from Figure 6, explain what happens to the product and reactant concentrations when hydrochloric acid or water is added to the system.

_____

_____

_____

Adding HCl to the cobalt(II) chloride system effectively adds chloride ions, a reactant when the chemical equation is read from left to right. Adding water to the cobalt(II) chloride system adds more product. Either of these changes disrupts the equilibrium and causes it to shift.

3 **EXPLAIN** Select the correct terms to complete the statement.

Adding more reactant increases the frequency of collisions between product | reactant particles, which shifts the reaction to the left | right in favor of the products | reactants . Adding more product increases the frequency of collisions between product | reactant particles, which shifts the reaction to the left | right in favor of the products | reactants .

Figure 7 shows the cobalt(II) chloride system before and after the addition of Cl⁻ ions. The sharp increase in the Cl⁻ line indicates when HCl was added. Water is not shown on the graph because the concentration of water remains approximately constant.

$$[Co(H_2O)_6]^{2+} (aq) + 4Cl^- (aq) \rightleftharpoons [CoCl_4]^{2-} (aq) + 6H_2O(l)$$

Addition of HCl to the CoCl₂ System

FIGURE 7: The concentrations in the cobalt(II) chloride equilibrium system change with the addition of hydrochloric acid.

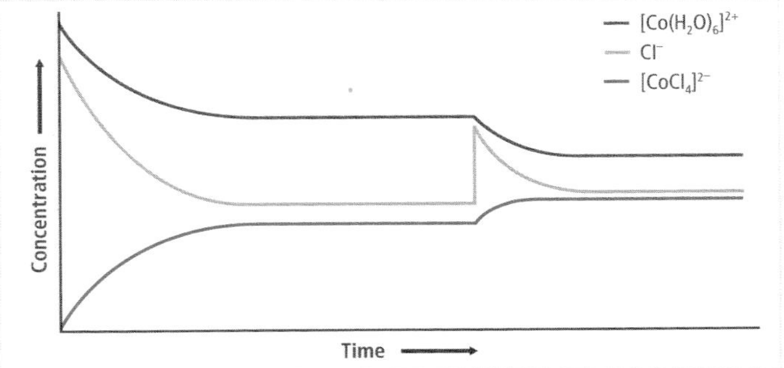

Legend:
— $[Co(H_2O)_6]^{2+}$
— Cl^-
— $[CoCl_4]^{2-}$

(y-axis: Concentration; x-axis: Time)

4 **ANALYZE** What keeps the concentrations in this reaction from reaching zero? Use evidence from the graph and reaction rates to support your claims.

_____

_____

_____

_____

_____

During an equilibrium reaction, adding reactants disrupts the dynamic equilibrium. As more reactants are converted to products, the forward reaction will slow because there are fewer reactant particles colliding. At the same time, because the concentration of product particles increases, the rate of the reverse reaction will increase. Eventually, the rates will equalize at a new equilibrium position. The opposite shift occurs with the addition of a product.

Differentiate Instruction

MTSS/RTI Have student pairs collaborate to describe how adding more reactant would affect a reaction that is not reversible and a reaction that is reversible. Have students also consider how adding more product would affect these reactions. Then have them work together to predict how removing a reactant would affect both reactions. Follow up by having students reflect on their ideas through a class discussion.

SEP **Constructing Explanations and Designing Solutions**

Ask students to explain how they know that the graph in **Figure 7** shows relative concentrations rather than exact concentrations. Then have them explain the reaction over time using key points from the graph as support. For example, the graph shows that only one species is present to begin with, but as the forward reaction begins, the reverse reaction also begins. Eventually, the concentrations of all species stabilize, but at different concentrations.

3 reactant, right, products, product, left, reactants

4 On the **Figure 7** graph, the only time a substance is at a concentration of zero is when the reaction first begins and no $[CoCl_4]^{2-}$ has been produced. After the reaction begins, both the forward and reverse reactions occur, eventually at the same rate. At equilibrium, the fact that both reactions occur at the same rate keeps the concentrations of the reactants and products stable and prevents any reactant or product from reaching a concentration of zero.

Collaborate

One Moves Have groups predict and list the factors that may affect a chemical system at equilibrium. Their lists should include pressure (for gases), temperature, and concentration of reactants and products. When groups have completed their lists, have one member from each group move to another group to share and compare information.

CCC Stability and Change

Ask students to come up with their own analogies that describe an equilibrium that changes in response to stress. Encourage students to think of **everyday phenomena** that may have these characteristics. Have students share their analogies with classmates and discuss any weaknesses or misconceptions related to each analogy. Students can revise their analogies throughout the lesson.

① The concentration of chloride ions should decrease sharply. The concentration of $[CoCl_4]^{2-}$ decreases and the concentration of $[Co(H_2O)_6]^{2+}$ increases. Then, both concentrations level out into two parallel lines when a new equilibrium is reached.

② Losing HOCl as it destroys contaminants is the same as removing a reactant from the system. It places a stress on the system that causes a shift in equilibrium. The forward reaction, which changes HOCl to H^+ and OCl^-, slows when a reactant is removed. The reverse reaction, which combines H^+ and OCl^- into HOCl, initially occurs at the same rate and continues to produce more HOCl. This shifts the reaction in favor of the reactant, HOCl, until a new equilibrium is reached. The new equilibrium, reaction rates, and concentrations depend on how much HOCl is removed.

Evidence Notebook

③ Because HOCl is removed from the system as it reacts with microscopic organisms, the levels need to be monitored to ensure that enough HOCl remains to disinfect the pool.

FORMATIVE ASSESSMENT

One-Sentence Summary Ask students to write a sentence answering this question: *How will the direction of a chemical reaction tend to change if some of the product is removed?*

Removing Reactants or Products

We saw that adding reactants or products can shift the equilibrium of a system. Now, what would happen if we removed a reactant or product from the cobalt(II) chloride system?

① **ANALYZE** Complete the graph to illustrate the changes in reactant and product concentrations when chloride ions are removed from the system.

$$[Co(H_2O)_6]^{2+}(aq) + 4Cl^-(aq) \rightleftharpoons [CoCl_4]^{2-}(aq) + 6H_2O(l)$$

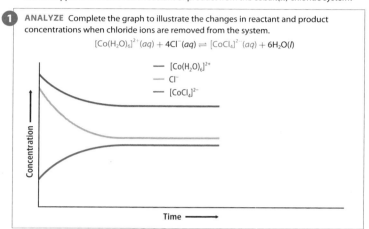

— $[Co(H_2O)_6]^{2+}$
— Cl^-
— $[CoCl_4]^{2-}$

When a reactant is removed from the system, the forward reaction slows but the reverse reaction occurs at the same rate. This results in more reactants being formed. For example, adding silver nitrate, $AgNO_3$, to the cobalt(II) chloride solution forms silver chloride, AgCl, as a precipitate. This removes Cl^- from the system, which slows the forward reaction and reduces the amount of products produced. The opposite effect is observed when a product is removed.

The disruption of an equilibrium system places stress on the system. Le Châtelier's principle states that when an equilibrium system is stressed, the equilibrium will shift in a way that reduces the stress. For example, the chemical equilibrium shifted when the concentration of a reactant or product was changed in the cobalt(II) chloride system.

② **APPLY** When HOCl is added to water, it dissociates to form hydrogen ions, H^+, and hypochlorite ions, OCl^-. HOCl is an effective pool treatment because the oxygen in the HOCl molecule destroys bacteria, algae, and other substances. This uses up the HOCl. Describe this stress at the molecular level, and explain the effect the stress has on the HOCl equilibrium in terms of Le Châtelier's principle.

_____

_____

_____

_____

_____

③ 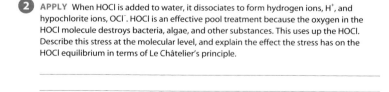 **Evidence Notebook** Why does the concentration of HOCl in the water of public pools have to be regularly monitored?

EXPLORATION 3 Pressure and Temperature Influence Equilibrium

Pressure and Temperature Influence Equilibrium

According to Le Châtelier's principle, an equilibrium system will change to reduce stress. Changing the concentration of reactants or products can add stress and shift an equilibrium system. Pressure can also influence equilibrium.

The pressure exerted by a gas on a surface depends on the frequency with which particles hit the surface. Increasing the pressure of a gas increases the number of collisions particles have with the surface and with each other. The gas molecules are in constant, random motion. The same number of moles of any gas occupies the same volume at a given pressure and temperature. Because volume and pressure are inversely related, decreasing the volume of a gas or gas mixture at constant temperature increases the pressure of the system.

Explore Online ▶

Hands-On Lab

Shifting Equilibrium Use Le Châtelier's principle to predict changes in products and reactants as a chemical equilibrium system changes.

 4 **Collaborate** With a partner, discuss why pressure and volume affect a gaseous equilibrium system but do not affect liquid or solid equilibrium systems. Use real-world examples to support your claim.

Consider the differences between these two equilibria:

$$2NO_2(g) \rightleftharpoons N_2O_4(g) \qquad H_2(g) + Cl_2(g) \rightleftharpoons 2HCl(g)$$

5 **EVALUATE** Which chemical equilibrium system has an equal number of moles of reactants compared to products and which has an unequal number? How might this affect equilibrium if pressure increases?

_____

_____

_____

_____

_____

Pressure and Equilibrium in a Gaseous System

When a molecule of NO_2 collides with another NO_2 molecule, a molecule of N_2O_4 may form. In the equilibrium system, N_2O_4 continuously decomposes into two molecules of NO_2. The number of effective collisions between reactant molecules determines the reaction rate. Increasing or decreasing the pressure on the system puts a stress on the system. Le Châtelier's principle predicts that the equilibrium will shift in a way that counteracts this stress.

Equilibrium shifts can be observed on the macroscopic scale when the reactants and products are different colors. For example, both tubes in Figure 8 contain a solution of NO_2/N_2O_4 at equilibrium. NO_2 is an orange-brown gas, and N_2O_4 is a colorless gas. Different concentrations of NO_2 give the tubes different colors. The tube on the left is a darker orange-brown color because it has a higher concentration of NO_2. The tube on the right is much lighter in color because it has a lower concentration of NO_2.

FIGURE 8: Two different NO_2/N_2O_4 equilibria

3D Learning Objective

Students **construct an explanation** for how equilibrium systems change and stabilize due to changes in pressure and temperature. They describe how these changes affect the number and type of molecules present in an equilibrium system.

Explore Online ▶

Hands-On Lab 👥 Small Groups ⏱ 45 minutes

Shifting Equilibrium

SEP **Developing and Using Models**

Students apply Le Châtelier's principle while carrying out an investigation to predict changes based on equilibrium shifts. _Student lab worksheet and teacher support available online._

Preconception Alert

Students generally master the concept that increases in pressure affect equilibrium, but they often misapply it to all pressure changes. Have students discuss whether or not the only gaseous systems affected by pressure changes are those in which the total numbers of reactant molecules and product molecules differ.

4 Students should find examples in which pressure affects volume in a gaseous system, such as a syringe filled with air, but does not have a similar effect on the volume of a liquid or solid system, such as liquids or solids in a syringe. When the volume of a gaseous system changes, the concentrations of products and reactants also change, and that affects equilibrium.

5 Students should identify 2 moles of reactant and 1 mole of product, an unequal amount, in the first equilibrium and 2 moles of reactants and 2 moles of product, an equal amount, in the second. Predictions about the effect of pressure on equilibrium will vary. Some students may recognize that increasing pressure will affect the equilibrium when there are unequal numbers of moles of reactant and product and will not affect the equilibrium when there are equal numbers of moles on each side.

Explore Online

Encourage students to go online and view the video showing what happens in a NO_2/N_2O_4 gaseous equilibrium system when pressure is changed.

Exploring Visuals

Figure 9 may be difficult for some students to follow because the color of the solution changes for two reasons. First, when the volume decreases within the syringe, the concentrations of reactants and products both increase and so the color becomes darker instantaneously. Second, the concentration changes cause an equilibrium shift in the system. This causes the color of the solution to change as the ratio of NO_2 molecules to N_2O_4 molecules shifts.

1 Drawings: **a** shows a mixture of NO_2 and N_2O_4; **b** shows the same ratio with particles closer together; **c** shows an increased ratio of N_2O_4; and **d** matches **a.** Initially, the reaction rates were equal. Increasing the pressure decreased the volume within the syringe and moved the particles closer together. NO_2 molecules collided more often, increasing the forward reaction rate. The reverse reaction sped up as more N_2O_4 became available to break apart. A new equilibrium was reached. At the original pressure, the space between the particles increased and the rate of the forward reaction decreased because NO_2 molecules collided less often. The rate of the reverse reaction also decreased.

2 Students should give and accept feedback in a constructive manner. Interactions at the microscale can be linked to the color of the gas in the syringe, which can be observed on a macroscale.

NO_2 and N_2O_4 form an equilibrium system that contains both gases. Figure 9a shows the system sealed in a syringe at room temperature and atmospheric pressure. The color of the gaseous solution in the syringe changes at each stage as stresses are applied to the system and the equilibrium shifts and is then reestablished at a different point.

FIGURE 9: The color of the NO_2/N_2O_4 gaseous equilibrium system changes as pressure changes.   Explore Online

a Initial pressure   **b** Compressed—initial   **c** Compressed—final   **d** Return to initial pressure

1 **MODEL** Make a diagram that shows what is happening inside the syringe on a molecular scale. For each stage, show the relative rates for the forward and reverse reactions and whether the densities, volumes, and concentrations of the gases are increasing or decreasing from one stage to the next.

2 **Collaborate** Present your model of the NO_2/N_2O_4 system to a partner. Incorporate any feedback and discuss how changes at the molecular scale in this system affect what is observed at the macroscopic scale.

Pressure Affects Concentration

At the instant the pressure increased in the syringe, the concentrations of the gases also increased. The equilibrium shifted to reduce the stress by favoring the side with fewer particles. This decreased the particle collisions with the surfaces of the syringe, which decreased the pressure. Changing pressure affects the reactant and product concentrations. However, there must be a difference in moles between reactants and products for a pressure change to cause an equilibrium shift. The graph below shows the change in concentrations after a pressure increase.

$$2NO_2(g) \rightleftharpoons N_2O_4(g)$$

3 **ANALYZE** Label the point on the graph at which the pressure change occurs.

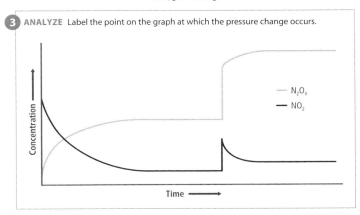

Legend: — N_2O_4 — NO_2

Concentration (y-axis), Time (x-axis)

4 **APPLY** What can you conclude about the changes that occur in the nitrogen dioxide/dinitrogen tetroxide equilibrium system when the pressure on the system changes?

○ **a.** An increase in pressure results in a shift toward NO_2 because the reverse reaction increases the number of NO_2 particles in the container.

○ **b.** An increase in pressure does not change the ratio of NO_2 and N_2O_4 because the system remains in equilibrium when the number of particles is constant.

○ **c.** An increase in pressure results in a shift toward N_2O_4 because the product side of the forward reaction has fewer molecules and reduces the pressure.

○ **d.** An increase in pressure changes the ratio of NO_2 and N_2O_4 because the rate of both the forward and reverse reactions slowed down.

Nitrogen oxides, including nitrogen dioxide, are formed during any high temperature combustion reaction in internal combustion engines and are key components of photochemical smog. Nitrogen dioxide is responsible for the characteristic brown color of smog. Like many systems in nature, there are dynamic equilibria in smog systems.

5 **Language Arts Connection** With a partner, use multiple sources to research photochemical smog, a type of air pollution. Write an essay that analyzes how different conditions, such as air pressure and temperature, affect smog and how smog affects human health. Be sure to identify any gaps or inconsistencies in the data.

Food Science Connection

There are several equilibria involved in bottled carbonated soft drinks that keep the drinks fizzy until the bottle is opened. One is the equilibrium between gaseous carbon dioxide in the air above the soft drink and aqueous carbon dioxide in the soft drink: $CO_2(g) \rightleftharpoons CO_2(aq)$. Another is the production of carbonic acid from water and aqueous carbon dioxide: $H_2O(l) + CO_2(aq) \rightleftharpoons H_2CO_3(aq)$. The beverages are bottled under increased pressure. When the bottle is opened, the pressure is reduced.

Collaborate

Numbered Heads Together Divide the class into groups, and assign a number to each group member. Ask groups to discuss the relationship between the two equilibria related to bottled carbonated soft drinks.

Ask: *What is the relationship between the two equilibria? How will the increase of pressure during the bottling of soft drinks affect each equilibrium? How will decreasing the pressure when the bottle is opened affect each equilibrium?*

Have students discuss the questions in their groups and arrive at answers and an explanation. Then call a number, and that student in each group will be responsible for sharing the group's response.

3 The label should be shown at the point where there is a sudden change in both species' concentration, as indicated by a vertical spike in the curve.

4 c

5 **Sample answer:** Temperature inversions occur when a warm air mass higher in the atmosphere traps cooler air below. This concentrates pollution, including photochemical smog, at the ground level. High-pressure air systems are characterized by light or no wind and few clouds. Without strong winds or rain to clear the air, photochemical smog can build up in areas with heavy emissions. Hot weather and sunshine increase ground-level ozone, which contributes to photochemical smog. Smog can severely affect people with respiratory illnesses such as asthma.

Earth Science Connection

Have students research ways in which scientists learn about the concentrations of atmospheric gases throughout Earth's history. For example, direct measurements of atmospheric carbon dioxide levels have been taken at the Mauna Loa Observatory in Hawaii since 1958. Analysis of air bubbles trapped in layers of ice hundreds of meters deep near the poles provides information on the composition of the atmosphere thousands of years ago. Clues to the atmosphere's composition millions of years ago can be found in ancient rock layers.

DCI ## ETS1.A Defining and Delimiting Engineering Problems

Ask interested students to research and report on how ice cores are sampled and how they are interpreted. Where are cores taken from? To what depth are the cores drilled? How do polar scientists measure the gases trapped in the ice? Students can make posters showing how ice cores are sampled.

CCC ## Stability and Change

Have students write a short paragraph in which they explain how carbon dioxide levels in Earth's atmosphere have changed and remained stable over time.

1 If the significant increase in carbon dioxide levels in recent years was part of a long-term cycle, then a similar increase should be seen at multiple points in long-term data, creating a cyclical pattern. If the recent carbon dioxide increase is not part of a long-term cycle, then a similar increase would not be part of the cyclical pattern in the historical data.

2 CO_2 in the soda bottle moves between the air and the liquid, similar to the way CO_2 in the Earth system moves between the atmosphere and water, such as the oceans. However, in the Earth system, CO_2 also cycles through the biosphere, geosphere, and cryosphere, in addition to the hydrosphere.

Stability and Change

Equilibrium in the Earth System

Historical Carbon Dioxide Levels

FIGURE 10: Atmospheric carbon dioxide levels fluctuated in the past, but they increased significantly in recent years.

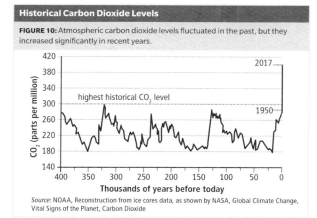

Source: NOAA, Reconstruction from ice cores data, as shown by NASA, Global Climate Change, Vital Signs of the Planet, Carbon Dioxide

Earth is a closed system. Although the total amount of matter on Earth does not change, it does cycle between various systems. Scientists are able to measure past levels of carbon dioxide in the atmosphere by determining the concentration of carbon dioxide, CO_2, in bubbles trapped in ice cores. Figure 10 shows that, over the past 400 000 years, CO_2 levels in Earth's atmosphere fluctuated within a relatively stable range. However, the amount of CO_2 in the atmosphere has increased significantly in recent years, outside of the historical pattern.

1 ARGUE Imagine the graph data went back an additional million years. What would you expect to see if the recent CO_2 increase is part of a longer CO_2 cycle over time in the Earth system? What would you expect to see if the recent CO_2 increase is not part of a longer CO_2 cycle over time?

_____

_____

_____

_____

Some CO_2 fluctuations over long periods of time could be the result of CO_2 levels in the ocean and atmosphere cycling as temperatures vary on the planet, changes in the biosphere, or massive volcanic eruptions. In the last century, however, CO_2 in the atmosphere increased significantly. The recent increase outside the historical range is due to human activities, including deforestation and burning fossil fuels.

2 EVALUATE A state of solution equilibrium exists in a closed soda bottle. Carbon dioxide gas is dissolved in both the liquid, making the drink fizzy, and in the gas above the liquid. CO_2 constantly moves between the liquid and the gas. Compare this small-scale system to how CO_2 moves on larger scales in the Earth system.

_____

_____

_____

_____

Endothermic and Exothermic Reactions

Adding or removing energy is another stress that can cause an equilibrium to shift. For example, the temperature on one side of the U-tube filled with cobalt(II) chloride solution in Figure 11 was increased using a Bunsen burner. The addition of energy caused the solution on that side to turn blue.

FIGURE 11: Energy in the form of heat is applied to the cobalt(II) chloride solution.

Explore Online

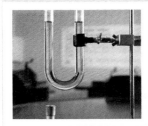  

 Collaborate With a partner, discuss what is happening on a molecular scale to cause the color on one side of the U-tube to change when the temperature increased.

4 **ANALYZE** Using the information in Figure 12, add the word *energy* to each equation as a product or reactant.

$$[Co(H_2O)_6]^{2+}(aq) + 4Cl^-(aq) \rightleftharpoons [CoCl_4]^{2-}(aq) + 6H_2O(l)$$

$$2NO_2(g) \rightleftharpoons N_2O_4(g)$$

5 **APPLY** Select the correct terms to describe how equilibrium shifts when energy is added.

For an endothermic reaction, adding energy in the form of heat shifts the reaction toward the products | reactants . In the cobalt(II) chloride system, adding energy formed more $[CoCl_4]^{2-}$ | $[Co(H_2O)_6]^{2+}$, causing the solution to turn blue. For an exothermic reaction, adding energy shifts the reaction toward the products | reactants . In the NO_2/N_2O_4 system, adding energy formed more NO_2 | N_2O_4 .

The effect of adding or removing energy as heat from an equilibrium system can be predicted by considering energy as a product or reactant. For an endothermic reaction, energy can be modeled as a reactant. Adding energy has the same effect as increasing the concentration of a reactant, which shifts the equilibrium in favor of the products. Removing energy, like removing a reactant, shifts the reaction in favor of the reactants.

FIGURE 12: Equilibrium systems in an ice bath on the left and a warm temperature on the right

a Cobalt(II) chloride system—pink on the left and blue on the right

b Nitrogen dioxide/dinitrogen tetroxide system—light brown on the left and dark brown on the right

---

Explore Online ▶

Encourage students to go online to view the video of what happens when a cobalt(II) chloride solution is heated.

SEP ## Constructing Explanations and Designing Solutions

Making a table may help students explain how various factors can shift an equilibrium. Write the following equation on the board.

$$2SO_2(g) + O_2(g) \rightleftharpoons 2SO_3(g)$$

Assign students to groups, and have each group make a chart with the left column labeled *Change* and the right column labeled *Effect on Equilibrium*. Have students write the following items under the *Change* head.

concentration of SO_2 increased
concentration of O_2 decreased
concentration of SO_3 decreased
pressure increased
temperature increased

Have groups complete the table using Le Châtelier's principle to predict how the equilibrium will shift. Then ask for volunteers to explain how each change would affect the equilibrium.

3 Adding energy in the form of heat to the reaction causes a shift that is similar to increasing the chloride concentration. In both cases, the change results in more effective collisions among the reactants. In turn, this increases the concentration of the products, leading to the change in color from pink to blue.

4 The first equation should have energy on the left side, and the second equation should have energy on the right side.

5 products, $[CoCl_4]^{2-}$, reactants, NO_2

Differentiate Instruction

ELL Support Remind students that the term *endothermic* contains the root *endo*, meaning "inside" or "within." An endothermic reaction must have energy added to the reaction system. The term *exothermic* contains the root *exo*, meaning "outside." An exothermic reaction gives off energy that is released by the reaction system. Have students construct sentences using the terms correctly.

 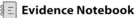 **PS1.B Chemical Reactions**

Emphasize to students that when determining the effect of a temperature change on a chemical reaction at equilibrium, energy in the form of heat can be considered as if it is a reactant (in the endothermic direction) or a product (in the exothermic direction). Connect to **everyday phenomena** by having students think about reactions that occur only when energy in the form of heat is transferred, such as those that take place during baking.

Exploring Visuals

Draw students' attention to the **Figure 13** graph. Be sure they recognize that the lines representing concentration change abruptly when heat is applied. When heat is no longer applied, the concentrations change gradually until the original equilibrium is reestablished.

1 a, b, c

📋 **Evidence Notebook**

2 This Evidence Notebook question refers to the Unit Project. Temperature and the concentration of sodium ions in the brine are used to control the portion of the reaction that occurs in the Solvay tower.

For an exothermic reaction, energy can be modeled as a product. Adding energy has the same effect as increasing the concentration of a product. The equilibrium shifts in favor of the reactants. Removing energy shifts the equilibrium in favor of the products.

Temperature and Equilibrium

Modifying the temperature of a system changes the average kinetic energy of the particles, which changes the number of effective collisions between molecules. For example, adding energy to the cobalt(II) chloride system increase the average kinetic energy of the particles and results in more effective collisions between reactants. This has the same effect as increasing the concentration of a reactant. The equilibrium will shift toward the products to relieve the stress. The reverse happens if energy is removed from the system. The equilibrium will shift toward the reactants.

$$\text{energy} + [Co(H_2O)_6]^{2+}(aq) + 4Cl^-(aq) \rightleftharpoons [CoCl_4]^{2-}(aq) + 6H_2O(l)$$

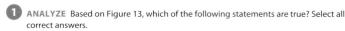
Changing the Temperature of a CoCl₂ Solution

FIGURE 13: The cobalt(II) chloride solution is initially at room temperature. Changing the temperature of the solution causes a change in the equilibrium concentrations.

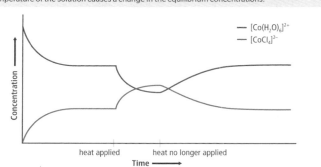

1 **ANALYZE** Based on Figure 13, which of the following statements are true? Select all correct answers.

☐ **a.** While heat is applied, a new equilibrium position is established.

☐ **b.** Increasing the temperature shifts the equilibrium toward $[CoCl_4]^{2-}$.

☐ **c.** When heat is no longer applied, the equilibrium returns to its original state.

Adding energy increases the concentration of $[CoCl_4]^{2-}$ in the solution, which changes the solution from pink to blue. This new equilibrium position can be maintained only as long as energy is added to the solution. When the solution is no longer heated, it changes from blue back to pink as the added energy dissipates and the equilibrium system shifts back to its original position.

 📋 **Evidence Notebook** What factors are used to control equilibrium in the Solvay process you are researching for your unit project?

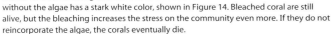

Influence of Engineering, Technology, and Science on Society and the Natural World

Temperature and Changing Oceans

Corals are marine invertebrates that mostly live in colonies consisting of many individual polyps. Coral reefs are formed from calcium carbonate, $CaCO_3$, that corals secrete in the process of forming their hard skeletons. Most corals display a range of colors, including brown, orange, red, yellow, and occasionally blue or green. The color comes not from the coral polyps, but from algae that live in the reef community. The corals provide habitat for the algae and, in exchange, corals receive food from the algae.

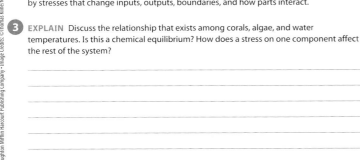

FIGURE 14: Bleached coral

Water temperatures in coral habitats are increasing due to climate change caused by human actions, most significantly the production of CO_2 through the burning of fossil fuels. As water temperatures increase, the corals become stressed and expel the algae. This is known as *coral bleaching* because the coral structure without the algae has a stark white color, shown in Figure 14. Bleached coral are still alive, but the bleaching increases the stress on the community even more. If they do not reincorporate the algae, the corals eventually die.

In 2005, the United States lost half of its coral reefs in the Caribbean in one year due to a massive bleaching event. And, coral bleaching is not the only consequence of rising ocean temperatures. Increasing temperatures also affect the amount of carbon dioxide that dissolves in the oceans. Concentration, pressure, and temperature have been discussed as stresses in a chemical system that can shift equilibria. In reality, all systems can be affected by stresses that change inputs, outputs, boundaries, and how parts interact.

3 EXPLAIN Discuss the relationship that exists among corals, algae, and water temperatures. Is this a chemical equilibrium? How does a stress on one component affect the rest of the system?

_____

_____

_____

_____

_____

_____

_____

4 **Evidence Notebook** Warm temperatures allow bacteria in water to multiply quickly. Direct sunlight, which is common in warm climates, speeds up the release of chlorine gas from the water into the air because the OCl^- ions break down rapidly in sunlight. How would chlorine pool treatment need to change in a warmer climate?

© Houghton Mifflin Harcourt Publishing Company • Image Credits: ©Thomas Kline/NewsCom

Lesson 2 Exploring Chemical Equilibrium **345**

 Influence of Engineering, Technology, and Science on Society and the Natural World

Have students perform group research to identify a solution or technology that has been proposed to help corals survive changes such as rising sea levels, increased water temperatures, and increased carbon dioxide levels. Students should collaborate on an infographic that explains the solution, including an analysis of costs and benefits.

3 Corals coexist with algae. The corals provide the algae with shelter and nutrients to use in photosynthesis. The algae remove waste, produce oxygen, and provide food for the corals. The corals and algae are adapted to a certain range of water temperatures. The state of ecological balance depends on dynamic equilibria between all species in the food web and homeostasis within individual organisms. A stress on any one component can upset the balance and cause changes to other components in the ecosystem.

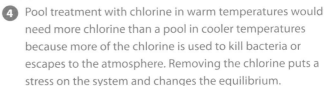 **Evidence Notebook**

4 Pool treatment with chlorine in warm temperatures would need more chlorine than a pool in cooler temperatures because more of the chlorine is used to kill bacteria or escapes to the atmosphere. Removing the chlorine puts a stress on the system and changes the equilibrium.

FORMATIVE ASSESSMENT
3-2-1 Have students write the following:

- three things they learned about how collision theory influences reaction rate
- two things they found interesting about the motion of particles and reaction rate
- one question they still have about the concepts presented in the lesson

EXPLORATION 4 Exploring Acids and Bases

3D Learning Objective

Students observe patterns in the behaviors of acids and bases at multiple scales and **plan and carry out an investigation** to identify acids and bases among household products. Students explore the pH scale and identify constraints that guide the treatment of water.

Collaborate

Graffiti Arrange students into groups. Give each group a large piece of drawing paper and several felt pens of different colors. Have students generate ideas about acids and bases drawn from their experiences and learning. They might write comparison statements, name substances that are acidic or basic, describe any properties they associate with acids and bases, or list societal uses of acids and bases. Consider posting the graffiti papers around the classroom so students can identify if what they learn throughout the lesson confirms or refutes their preconceptions.

SEP **Obtaining, Evaluating, and Communicating Information**

Have student pairs skim the text to choose an acid or base to research. Tell partners that they will be the "experts" about the chemical they choose and that they can provide useful information to their classmates when their chemical is part of a class discussion or activity. Point students to useful resources about acids and bases, such as Safety Data Sheets (SDSs), that are available online.

Questions students might answer about the acid or base:

- Does the chemical occur naturally? If so, where?
- How does the chemical compare with other acids and bases? Is it considered weak or strong?
- Does this chemical play a role in any environmental problems, either as a cause or as a possible solution?

1 Students will brainstorm questions, such as *Who works with acids and bases? What are acids and bases? Where might you find acids and bases? How are acids and bases produced?*

Exploring Acids and Bases

Many substances can be classified as an acid or a base. When scientists first started using these terms, acids were described as things that tasted sour, such as vinegar or lime juice, and bases were things that tasted bitter or felt slippery, such as soap. As scientists learned more about the properties of acids and bases, they developed more exact definitions. Scientists now use these terms to describe substances based on how they chemically react with water and with other substances.

 Collaborate Work with a partner or group to brainstorm questions you would like to investigate about acids and bases using the questions journalists ask: *Who? What? Where? When? Why? How?* Then share your questions with the class.

Properties of Acids and Bases

FIGURE 15: Many items that you use every day are acidic or basic.

a acidic   **b** basic

Citric acid in limes and grapefruits gives these fruits their sour taste. Milk, yogurt, and sour cream contain lactic acid. Vinegar is dilute acetic acid. Acids react with bases and with some metals. Acid molecules generally contain one or more hydrogen atoms. When they are added to water, most acids form ions. If a substance does not exist as ions but forms ions in solution, the substance is said to *ionize*. If a substance exists as ions and these ions separate in solution, the substance is said to *dissociate*. The ionization of most acids leads to the release of hydrogen ions, H^+, into a solution. For example, nitric acid, HNO_3, forms the following ions in water:

$$HNO_3(l) \xrightarrow{H_2O} H^+(aq) + NO_3^-(aq)$$

When acids ionize, the solution has the capacity to conduct electric current. Therefore, an acid such as HNO_3 is an electrolyte. Strong acids ionize or dissociate completely in solution and are therefore strong electrolytes. Weak acids do not ionize or dissociate completely in solution and are therefore weak electrolytes. The strength of an acid is not related to its concentration. A strong acid can be dilute, and a weak acid can be concentrated. The strength of an acid is a measure of the degree to which it ionizes or dissociates.

Common bases include baking soda and sodium hydroxide, which is used in drain cleaner. Bases taste bitter and feel slick—the slick feel of some soaps is the result of the presence of a base. Bases react with acids, but usually not with metals. Some bases contain a hydroxide ion, OH^-. When added to water, these bases dissociate, releasing hydroxide ions into the solution. For example, sodium hydroxide, NaOH, dissociates in water to form sodium ions and hydroxide ions:

$$NaOH(s) \xrightarrow{H_2O} Na^+(aq) + OH^-(aq)$$

Similar to acids, bases can conduct electric current and may be described as strong or weak based on the degree to which they dissociate or ionize. The strength of an aqueous base depends on the number of hydroxide ions it produces in solution, not on the number of hydroxide ions in the base.

Acids Donate Protons

Hydrogen chloride, HCl, is a corrosive gas at room temperature. HCl is used for cleaning, pickling, and tanning, among other industrial applications. HCl initially ionizes in water to form H^+ and Cl^- ions in an aqueous solution. Almost immediately, the hydrogen ions released from the ionization of the HCl are attracted to negatively charged areas on water molecules, and form hydronium ions, H_3O^+.

$$H^+(aq) + Cl^-(aq) + H_2O(l) \rightarrow H_3O^+(aq) + Cl^-(aq)$$

Because a hydrogen atom is made up of one electron and one proton, a positive hydrogen ion is simply a proton. When HCl is in water, we say that a proton is transferred from the acid to the water, as shown in Figure 17. Thus, one way to define an acid is a substance that donates protons in solution.

FIGURE 16: Hydrochloric acid, sometimes called muriatic acid, is used to treat the water in swimming pools.

FIGURE 17: This molecular model shows that when hydrochloric acid is added to water, hydronium ions and chloride ions are formed.

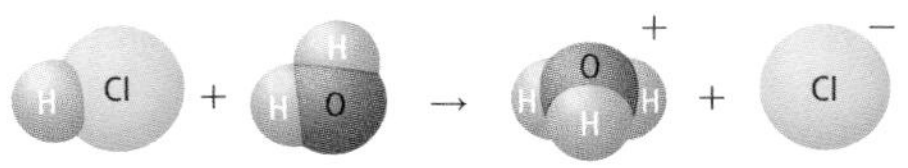

2 **EXPLAIN** Select the correct terms to complete the statement.

Sulfuric acid has the chemical formula H_2SO_4. When sulfuric acid interacts with water, protons are transferred to | from sulfuric acid to | from water, which produces hydroxide | hydronium ions.

Bases Accept Protons

The base ammonia, NH_3, is often found in household cleaners and is used in the production of fertilizer. Ammonia interacts with water to form ammonium ions and hydroxide ions:

$$NH_3(g) + H_2O(l) \rightarrow NH_4^+(aq) + OH^-(aq)$$

A base can be described as a substance that produces hydroxide ions in solution and accepts protons. Many bases, therefore, are metal hydroxides, such as sodium hydroxide, potassium hydroxide, and aluminum hydroxide. Ammonia is an example of a base that is a proton acceptor, as shown in Figure 18.

FIGURE 18: This molecular model shows that when ammonia is added to water, ammonium ions and hydroxide ions are formed.

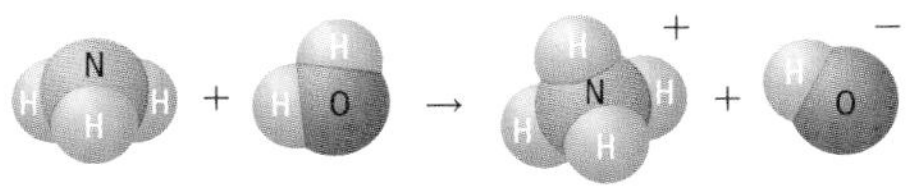

3 **EXPLAIN** Select the correct terms to complete the statement.

When ammonia is mixed with water, a proton is transferred to | from ammonia to | from water, which produces hydroxide | hydronium ions.

CCC **Patterns**

Conduct a class discussion to summarize the properties of acids and bases. Start a list for acids and bases on the board, and call on volunteers to a add characteristic property of each. Students will likely bring up the slippery feel of bases or the distinct tastes of either. When they do, emphasize that these characteristics tend to be true for acids and bases, but that for safety reasons, they should never use touch or taste to identify an unknown substance.

Differentiate Instruction

MTSS/RTI Help students decode the reaction equations that show the ionization or dissociation of an acid or base. Write the chemical equation for the dissociation of sodium hydroxide, NaOH, in water. Guide students' attention to the state symbols in the equation and how they change from reactants to products. Ask students to draw a diagram representing the dissociation of NaOH.

Art Connection

Acid Etching Display photographs of art or artifacts that have been etched using acids, such as the Renaissance works housed at the Victoria and Albert Museum in London. Explain that etching uses the corrosive properties of acids. The process begins when the artist covers a piece of metal with wax, which does not react with acids, and carves a pattern in the wax. Then the acid is applied and corrodes only the metal exposed in the carved pattern.

2 from, to, hydronium

3 to, from, hydroxide

DCI ETS1.B Developing Possible Solutions

The ideal pH for many commonly grown plants in vegetable gardens is slightly acidic, around 6.5. Have students work in groups to research and recommend products for remediating garden soil that is too acidic and soil that is too basic. Students should consider constraints such as cost, safety, reliability, and social and environmental impacts when they are making their selections. Each group can develop a pamphlet that explains their recommendations to gardeners.

Math Connection

Have students look at **Figure 19.** Point out that for every whole number decrease in pH, the concentration of H_3O^+ in solution increases by a factor of 10. **Ask**: *If the pH of a solution decreases from 4 to 1, by how much does the concentration of* H_3O^+ *change?* 10 × 10 × 10 = 1000; The concentration of hydronium ions increases by 1000 times. *If the pH of pool water increases from 7 to 8, by how much does the concentration of* H_3O^+ *change?* The concentration of hydronium ions decreases by a factor of 10. **(HSN-Q.A.1)**

CCC Scale, Proportion, and Quantity

To help students further understand the scale of quantities expressed using the pH scale, direct students to explore pH using online simulations. The University of Colorado at Boulder hosts helpful online simulations on this topic. Some have found these simulations useful, but they are not necessary for this program. HMH neither controls nor endorses these simulations.

1 Safety is the most important constraint. The chemical treatment must keep enough HOCl in the water to effectively destroy microscopic organisms—but not too much HOCl, which can be harmful to swimmers and allow algae blooms. Cost is also an important constraint. Adding more chemicals to the pool can increase the HOCl concentration, but adding more chemicals also costs more money. It would be ideal to find the best treatment for the pool for the least amount of money. Environmental impacts should be considered if the pool water is released to natural systems after use.

Engineering

The pH Scale

Acids form aqueous solutions with extra hydronium ions, and bases form solutions with extra hydroxide ions. A *neutral* solution contains equal amounts of both ions. Scientists can determine how acidic or basic a solution is by measuring the concentration of hydronium ions. Scientists use the pH scale for this measurement. The letters pH stand for the French *pouvoir hydrogène*, meaning "hydrogen power." **pH** is defined by the equation:

$$pH = -\log[H_3O^+]$$

The equation for pH is an example of a logarithmic function. The common logarithm, log, of a number is the power to which 10 must be raised to equal the number. When calculating pH, you take the negative of the log. So, if the hydronium ion concentration of a solution is 10^{-4} M, the log is −4. The pH is then −(−4), or 4. The pH scale allows scientists to model these large changes in concentration without the need for scientific notation.

FIGURE 19: The logarithmic pH scale

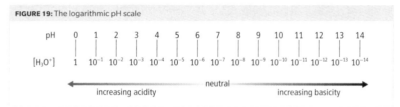

In treated pool water, an equilibrium exists between HOCl and H^+ and OCl^- ions. The pH scale is particularly useful for pool managers who have to decide how to adjust the chemicals in the pool water. The ideal pH of a swimming pool is 7.5. Above a pH of 7.8, the concentration of OCl^- ions in the water is too high. The OCl^- ions break down rapidly in sunlight and the chlorine is released as gas into the atmosphere. Therefore, having a high concentration of OCl^- ions at any given time can lead to losing too much chlorine from the system. Below a pH of 7.2, the concentration of HOCl becomes irritating to swimmers. Algae also flourish in this pH range. Pool managers test pool water using an acid-base indicator that changes color depending on the solution pH and the indicator being used.

1 IDENTIFY CONSTRAINTS What constraints guide the chemical treatment of a pool that an entire community uses? Think about the number one necessity for public pools, then consider other common constraints that may limit solutions. What happens to the water if the pool has to be drained?

_____

_____

_____

_____

_____

_____

Hands-On Lab

Analyzing Acids and Bases

Have you ever heard the term *acid* referenced in a movie or television show? If so, the acid was probably very strong and highly corrosive. It could have been powerful enough to eat through metal or dissolve evidence of a crime. Although these extreme applications of acids may be common storylines for entertainment, acids and bases are actually used in everyday household items. In this lab, you will design a procedure to determine whether several household substances are acidic or basic in solution based on the pH scale. Then, you will analyze what happens when you combine a strong acid and a strong base.

RESEARCH QUESTION Are there patterns to the way we use acids and bases in household products? Are acids better suited to certain tasks, and bases to other tasks?

② MAKE A CLAIM

Predict whether each household substance will be acidic or basic. What do you think will happen when you combine a strong acid and a strong base?

_____

_____

_____

_____

MATERIALS

- indirectly vented chemical splash goggles, nonlatex apron, nitrile gloves
- chalk (contains calcium carbonate, $CaCO_3$)
- conductivity probe
- deionized water in wash bottle
- droppers
- HCl solution, 0.1 M, in dropper bottle
- NaOH solution, 0.1 M, in dropper bottle
- pH paper and pH probe
- well plate
- household substances in solution: baking soda, coffee, glass cleaner, lemon juice, milk of magnesia, seltzer water, soapy water, vinegar

SAFETY INFORMATION

- Wear indirectly vented chemical splash goggles, a nonlatex apron, and nitrile gloves during the setup, hands-on, and takedown segments of the activity.

- Never taste any substance or chemical in the lab. Tell your teacher immediately if you spill chemicals on yourself, the work surface, or floor.

indirectly vented chemical splash goggles

PLAN THE INVESTIGATION

In your Evidence Notebook, develop procedures and safety plans for the following experiments. Have your teacher approve your plans before proceeding. If you need additional materials, discuss these with your teacher.

Part 1 Determine whether each household substance is acidic or basic. Consider properties such as pH, reactivity, and electrolytic behavior. Discuss the order in which you should make observations and how to best conserve time and materials. For example, if you placed 10 drops of lemon juice in a well plate, how could you most effectively perform multiple tests on the same 10 drops of this solution?

Lesson 2 Exploring Chemical Equilibrium **349**

 Student Lab Worksheet and complete Teacher Support are avaiable online.

Differentiate Instruction

Extension Ask students to research hydroxides of the alkali metals and the alkaline earth metals and explain why they are bases. Be sure to point out that not all bases are hydroxide bases. Challenge students to connect to **everyday phenomena** by researching bases that are commonly found in households and identifying examples that are not hydroxide bases.

Hands-On Lab Pairs ⏱ 45 minutes
Analyzing Acids and Bases

SEP **Planning and Carrying Out Investigations**

Students plan and carry out an investigation to determine if different household substances are acidic or basic. They combine an acid and base to observe and explain changes in the pH of the final solution.

Advance Preparation For one class, prepare 100 mL of each of the solutions of household substances and place them in labeled 250 mL beakers. Have one student from each pair bring a well plate to the common set of beakers and place a few drops of each solution into the well plate. For the baking soda and soapy water, mix roughly 2 tablespoons of substance with 100 mL deionized, DI, water. For glass cleaner, use a solution of diluted ammonia (10 mL ammonia and 90 mL DI water). A simple conductivity meter that uses a battery and has a low-voltage LED light can be used for the conductivity probe.

Safety Information Remind students to wear indirectly vented chemical splash goggles, a nonlatex apron, and nonlatex gloves during the setup, hands-on, and takedown segments of the activity. You should also remind students never to taste any substance in the lab and to notify you immediately if there are spilled chemicals on skin, clothing, the table, or the floor. Remind students that the two wires they place into the solutions must not touch, or they will obtain a false-positive test. Also, students should rinse and dry probes with DI water between tests to avoid cross-contamination. They should wash their hands thoroughly after they have completed their tests.

② Students may predict that coffee, lemon juice, vinegar, and seltzer water are acidic; glass cleaner, baking soda, soapy water, and milk of magnesia are basic; and combining an acid and a base will form a neutral solution.

Lesson 2 Exploring Chemical Equilibrium 349

Construct an Explanation

1. The pH indicates the concentration of hydronium ions. Conductivity indicates the strength of an acid or base. The reactivity test indicates which substances are acids because they are more reactive with calcium carbonate than bases are.

2. **Sample answer:** The pH of this solution is neutral. Maybe the H^+ from the HCl reacted with the OH^- from NaOH to make water, leaving sodium and chloride ions in solution.

3. Students may list the small sample size for each experimental group as a limitation. Testing more than one sample in each group and using the conductivity meter and pH probe consistently could increase the accuracy and precision of the data.

1 Students should explain that lemon juice, coffee, seltzer water, and vinegar are acids, and soaps, baking soda, cleaners, and milk of magnesia are bases. The acids had pH values lower than 7, reacted with carbonate, and conducted electric current. The bases had pH values higher than 7, did not react with carbonate, and conducted electric current. When the acidic and basic solutions are mixed, the OH^- ions accept an H^+ ion from the hydronium ions. This forms water and leaves Na^+ and Cl^- ions in solution, which form the ionic compound, NaCl.

2 **Sample answer:** If you combined a strong acid with a weak base, the solution would be acidic. If you combined a weak acid with a strong base, the solution would be basic.

Evidence Notebook

3 If the pH of the pool is decreased, more H^+ ions would be present. The extra H^+ ions would react with the OCl^- ions to produce more HOCl, increasing the HOCl concentration. If the pH of the pool is increased by adding a base, the extra OH^- ions would combine with some of the H^+ ions to produce water. More HOCl would break apart to form H^+, and OCl^- and the HOCl concentration would decrease.

FORMATIVE ASSESSMENT

Card Responses Have students write *acid* on one side of a notecard and *base* on the other. Then give a series of examples, such as *donates protons in solution, feels slick, tastes sour, have pH less than 7*. Have students raise their cards to show their understanding of the properties of acids and bases.

Part 2 Determine the pH of HCl, NaOH, and the solution produced when they are combined in equal parts. With your group, discuss appropriate procedures for safely making a solution composed of equal parts 0.1 M hydrochloric acid and 0.1 M sodium hydroxide. How will you make the solution, and how will you safely measure its pH?

COLLECT DATA

Make a data table in your Evidence Notebook in which to record your observations for both experiments. Decide on what you will measure, how many times you will take measurements, and the accuracy of measurements needed to produce quality data.

CONSTRUCT AN EXPLANATION

Answer the following questions in your Evidence Notebook.

1. What does the pH value tell you about each solution? What do the conductivity and reactivity tests tell you about each solution?

2. What did you notice about the pH of the solution made up of equal parts acid and base? What types of molecular-scale interactions might account for your observations?

3. What are the limitations of the data you collected during this lab? Describe how you could refine your procedure to improve the accuracy and precision of your data.

1 DRAW CONCLUSIONS

Claim Which solutions that you tested are acidic and which are basic? What happened when you combined a strong acid and a strong base?

Evidence Cite evidence from your data to support your claim. Include a chemical equation for the reaction in Part 2.

Reasoning Explain how the data you cited support your claim. What is the connection between the properties you observed and the acid-base reaction?

_____

2 EXTEND

In Part 2, you combined a strong acid and a strong base. What would happen if HCl was instead combined with a weak base and NaOH was instead combined with a weak acid?

3 **Evidence Notebook** Explain why the concentration of HOCl in pool water would change if the pool pH was increased or decreased.

© Houghton Mifflin Harcourt Publishing Company

EXPLORATION 5   Analyzing Acid-Base Equilibrium Systems

EXPLORATION 5

Analyzing Acid-Base Equilibrium Systems

When an acid and a base are combined, the products are water and a salt. A salt is formed from the cation of a base and the anion of an acid. The HCl and NaOH reaction you performed as part of your lab was an example of this type of acid-base reaction. The salt solution produced in an acid-base reaction may be acidic, basic, or neutral, depending on the strength of the reactants.

4 **Collaborate** With a partner, identify the salts that will form when nitric acid, HNO_3, and potassium hydroxide, KOH, are combined and when nitric acid and calcium hydroxide, $Ca(OH)_2$, are combined. What combinations of strong and weak acids and bases will produce an acidic, basic, or neutral solution? Which of these solutions will form an equilibrium?

Acids and Bases in Solution

Because not all acids and bases are the same, the equilibrium point of an acid-base reaction is determined by the properties of both the acid and the base. Figure 20 shows how strong acids, such as HCl, ionize in water. All of the HCl ionizes to form H_3O^+ ions and Cl^- ions. In weak acids, such as acetic acid, $HC_2H_3O_2$, hydrogen atoms are bound more tightly, so only some of the $HC_2H_3O_2$ molecules ionize.

FIGURE 20: Strong acids form more hydronium ions in solution than weak acids do.

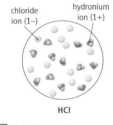

chloride ion (1−)
hydronium ion (1+)

water molecule
acetic acid molecule

hydronium ion (1+)
acetate ion (1−)

$HC_2H_3O_2$

a Hydrochloric acid, a strong acid

b Acetic acid, a weak acid

HCl

5 **EVALUATE** Figure 21 shows solid calcium carbonate, $CaCO_3$, in hydrochloric acid in the left beaker, and in acetic acid, $HC_2H_3O_2$, in the right beaker. Make a claim for whether $CaCO_3$ reacts more vigorously with HCl than with $HC_2H_3O_2$. Use evidence from Figures 20 and 21 to support your claim, and explain your reasoning.

FIGURE 21: Reactions of $CaCO_3$ with HCl and $HC_2H_3O_2$ solutions

3D Learning Objective

Students identify patterns at different scales in acid-base equilibrium systems and **use scientific principles to explain** the reactions between strong and weak acids and bases. Students **explore the number and type of molecules present** in a neutralization reaction and buffered solution.

CCC   Patterns

Have students distinguish between a strong acid and a solution that is highly concentrated. *Ask: What is the difference between a strong acid and a weak acid? How does this concept differ from concentration?* A strong acid completely ionizes when mixed with a solvent, and a weak acid does not. Concentration describes the ratio of solute to solvent in the solution. A solution containing a weak acid could be highly concentrated or diluted. The same is true for a strong acid.

Collaborate

Say Something Pair high-level readers with low-level readers. Have the high-level reader read aloud the section about acids and bases in solution. When that person is done reading, the partner should summarize or expand on what was just read. Have student pairs switch roles and continue until all sections of text have been read and summarized. Rotate among the pairs to provide support as needed.

4 KNO_3 and $Ca(NO_3)_2$ are the salts that will form. A strong base and a weak acid will form a basic solution. A strong acid and a weak base will form an acidic solution. A strong acid and a strong base will form a neutral solution when there are equal amounts of the strong acid and strong base.

5 The reaction with HCl in the left beaker is more vigorous because it is producing more bubbles. This is CO_2, a product of both reactions. Because the HCl reaction is producing more CO_2, it is the reaction that will favor the products the most. Students should explain that the concentration of hydronium ions is higher in hydrochloric acid, increasing the rate of the chemical reaction between calcium carbonate and hydronium ions.

Constructing Explanations and Designing Solutions

Direct students to explore acid-base solutions using online simulations. The University of Colorado at Boulder hosts helpful online simulations on this topic. Some have found these simulations useful, but they are not necessary for this program. HMH neither controls nor endorses these simulations.

Differentiate Instruction

ELL Support Have students develop a labeled diagram that shows the movement of the proton during the forward and reverse reactions for the formation of conjugate acids and bases.

Medical Science Connection

Tell students that household "ammonia" is a dilute aqueous solution of ammonia gas that could be called aqueous ammonium hydroxide. Connect to **everyday phenomena** by pointing out some common uses for ammonia. Students might be interested to learn that ammonia is the final end point of proteins that have been broken down in the liver. Because ammonia is toxic to the body, it must be excreted safely. Have students research the process by which the body converts ammonia into a safe substance that can be excreted.

 a, c

Strong acids ionize completely in water and no reactant molecules remain. Weak acids do not ionize completely. Thus, when a weak acid is combined with water, some amount of reactant is still present, and an equilibrium forms. The behavior of a weak acid can be written in the form of a chemical equilibrium equation. In this equation, HA represents a weak acid, such as acetic acid. The negative ion (A^-) formed in solution is known as that acid's *conjugate base*. In the reverse reaction, the conjugate base can accept a proton, like bases would.

$$HA(aq) + H_2O(l) \rightleftharpoons H_3O^+(aq) + A^-(aq)$$

1 **ANALYZE** How could you make more conjugate base in this equilibrium system? Select all correct answers.

☐ **a.** add more acid

☐ **b.** increase the pressure

☐ **c.** remove hydronium ions

☐ **d.** remove water molecules

Figure 22 shows how a strong base, such as sodium hydroxide, NaOH, dissociates completely in water, producing many hydroxide ions. A weak base, such as ammonia, NH_3, produces few hydroxide ions in solution.

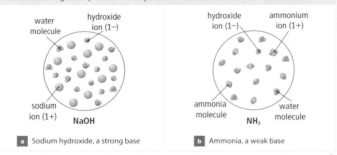

FIGURE 22: Strong bases produce more hydroxide ions in solution than do weak bases do.

a Sodium hydroxide, a strong base   b Ammonia, a weak base

For a weak base in solution, the proton-transfer reaction of some molecules can be written as a chemical equation showing the reactants and products at equilibrium:

$$B(aq) + H_2O(l) \rightleftharpoons BH^+(aq) + OH^-(aq)$$

The positive ion, BH^+, is known as the weak base's *conjugate acid*. In the reverse reaction, the conjugate acid can donate a proton. Each pair of related molecules or ions forms a conjugate acid-base pair. Thus, HA, an acid, forms A^-, its conjugate base, and HA and A^- are a conjugate pair. Likewise, B, a base, forms BH^+, its conjugate acid, and together B and BH^+ are a conjugate pair.

Strong acids and strong bases are highly reactive, but their conjugates are only slightly reactive. In contrast, weak acids and weak bases are only slightly reactive, but their conjugates are more reactive.

Neutralization Reactions and Buffers

You have probably heard different forms of the term *neutralization* used in everyday life, such as neutralizing an odor or a country remaining neutral during a war. In chemistry, a *neutralization reaction* is one in which an acid and a base react to form a salt and water with a neutral pH. The individual properties of the acid and base are neutralized by the reaction between the two solutions.

2 EXPLAIN Select the correct terms to complete the statement.

HCl forms many | few hydronium ions in solution, and NH_3 produces many | few hydroxide ions in solution. When equal amounts of HCl and NH_3 are combined, there will be an excess of hydronium | hydroxide ions. The solution will be slightly acidic | basic. NaOH produces many | few hydroxide ions in solution, and $HC_2H_3O_2$ produces many | few hydronium ions. When equal amounts of NaOH and $HC_2H_3O_2$ are combined, there will be an excess of hydronium | hydroxide ions. The solution will be slightly acidic | basic.

A *buffer* is a solution of a weak acid and one of its salts, or a weak base and one of its salts. Buffers resist changes in pH. For example, a buffered solution can be made by combining equal concentrations of acetic acid and sodium acetate. If a strong base is added, the acetic acid neutralizes it. The equilibrium with the salt shifts, so there is little or no change in pH. If a strong acid is added, the conjugate base neutralizes it, and the equilibrium shifts, again maintaining the pH. Eventually, enough base may be added to completely neutralize the acid, and a large pH change occurs.

3 MODEL With a group, construct a mathematical model or graph that shows how the acid-base equilibrium changes and the hydronium ion concentration changes in a buffered solution as a strong acid or base is added

FIGURE 23: Aspirin is acidic and is buffered to prevent large changes in pH within the body.

Buffer action has many important applications in chemistry and physiology. Human blood is naturally buffered to maintain a pH of between 7.3 and 7.5. This is essential because large changes in pH would lead to serious disturbances of normal body functions. Figure 23 shows an example of one of the many medicines that are buffered to prevent large and potentially damaging changes in pH when medication is taken orally or intravenously.

4 **Evidence Notebook** The ideal equilibrium for pool water is equal concentrations of HOCl and OCl^- ions. This occurs at a pH of 7.5. Explain how you would treat a pool that has a pH of 6.5 and a pool that has a pH of 8.5 in order to restore the ideal equilibrium.

© Houghton Mifflin Harcourt Publishing Company • Image Credits: ©Sergio Purtell/Houghton Mifflin Harcourt

---

Collaborate Have students work in groups of three or four to answer the following questions: *Why is it important for the pH of your blood to stay within a certain range? How do you think your body maintains this pH?* After groups have generated their answers, have them share their responses with the class. If there is enough time, allow students to research these questions and share what they found with the class.

2 many, few, hydronium, acidic, many, few, hydroxide, basic

3 Students may choose to use a chemical equation as their model. $HC_2H_3O_2(aq) + H_2O(l) \rightarrow H_3O^+(aq) + C_2H_3O_2^-(aq)$; The buffer keeps the hydronium ion concentration almost constant when a small amount of strong acid or strong base is added to the solution. For example, when sodium hydroxide is added, the hydroxide ions react with the hydronium ions in the solution, forming water. Acetic acid molecules then ionize, mostly replacing the hydronium ions neutralized by the base.

Evidence Notebook

4 If the pool water is too acidic (the pH is too low), as is the case for the pool with a pH of 6.5, a base should be added to react with excess hydronium ions and raise the pH. If the pool water is too basic (the pH is too high), as is the case for the pool with a pH of 8.5, an acid should be added to react with the excess hydroxide ions and lower the pH.

FORMATIVE ASSESSMENT

Quick Write Write on the board the following question: *How do a strong acid and a weak acid react differently when added to water?* Give students five minutes to write a short essay response to the question using what they have learned in this Exploration.

TAKE IT FURTHER Language Arts

Collaborate

You may choose to assign this activity or direct students to the Interactive Online Student Edition, where they can choose from all available paths. These activities can be assigned individually, to pairs, or to small groups.

 SEP **Constructing Explanations and Designing Solutions**

Assign groups to research systems that produce carbon monoxide in homes and businesses. Have groups research what is being done to reduce the formation of carbon monoxide. This will involve investigating how each device is attempting to avoid incomplete combustion.

 Language Arts Connection

WHST.9-12.7 Conduct short as well as more sustained research projects to answer a question (including a self-generated question) or solve a problem; narrow or broaden the inquiry when appropriate; synthesize multiple sources on the subject, demonstrating understanding of the subject under investigation.

Remind students that to carry out a research project, they need an understanding of the purpose and goals of the project, well-designed and relevant research questions, reliable sources that match the research questions, and a variety of authoritative primary and secondary sources.

Information Literacy Skills Have students ask themselves the following questions when obtaining information: *What upfront research should I do to finalize my research question or hypothesis? What is the best search engine or database for my research? How can I tell the difference between scholarly and popular publications?* Remind students to scan resources to determine what they should read in depth. Use written or verbal responses as needed to assess students' information literacy skills.

 b

Language Arts

Carbon Monoxide Poisoning

Every year, more than 400 people in the U.S. die from carbon monoxide, CO, poisoning, and approximately 50 000 more people require hospital treatment for CO exposure. What causes carbon monoxide's harmful effects on human health and the environment?

Carbon monoxide is a product of the incomplete combustion of carbon-containing fuels, including coal, petroleum products, and natural gas. When these fuels burn in pure oxygen, most carbon atoms are converted to CO_2. However, when O_2 is a limiting factor, CO may form as one of the combustion products.

The majority of CO in the atmosphere comes from automobile emissions. Atmospheric CO reacts with hydroxyl radicals, OH, to form CO_2, a greenhouse gas. This reaction also affects climate change by reducing the concentration of hydroxyl radicals in the atmosphere. These radicals are able to break down methane and other pollutants in the atmosphere.

The negative effects of carbon monoxide extend from the environment to human health. For example, inside homes, fuel-burning furnaces are designed to vent the CO-containing exhaust gases into the atmosphere. During power outages, some people use portable fuel-fired heaters and generators that are not vented. When used incorrectly, these devices can release exhaust into the home, leading to CO poisoning.

1 APPLY How can you minimize exposure to carbon monoxide when burning carbon-containing fuel?

○ **a.** Burn fuel in areas with low oxygen.

○ **b.** Burn fuel in enclosed spaces with ventilation.

○ **c.** Burn fuel in enclosed spaces without ventilation.

In addition to ensuring that fuel-burning devices are operated properly, carbon monoxide detectors may be used in the home to alert people when CO levels become dangerous. Incidents of CO poisoning increase during events that cause disruption of electrical or natural gas service, such as natural disasters.

What is the mechanism of CO poisoning? In the human body, O_2 is absorbed by blood as it passes through the lungs. The O_2 moves through the body bound to hemoglobin molecules in the blood. Each hemoglobin molecule can bind up to four O_2 molecules in a reversible reaction, forming oxyhemoglobin $Hb(O_2)_4$. Hb represents hemoglobin.

$$Hb(aq) + 4O_2(g) \rightleftharpoons Hb(O_2)_4(aq)$$

When carbon monoxide is inhaled, CO molecules bind to hemoglobin in place of O_2 and form carboxyhemoglobin. CO binds to hemoglobin more tightly than O_2 does, and so the product is favored.

$$Hb(aq) + 4CO(g) \rightleftharpoons Hb(CO)_4(aq)$$

FIGURE 24: A hyperbaric oxygen chamber can be used to treat carbon monoxide poisoning.

Because of the binding power of CO, some of the hemoglobin in a person who has been breathing CO cannot bind with oxygen. O_2 is blocked from reaching the cells, and cells cannot carry out vital processes. The most effective way of treating CO poisoning is to replace the CO with O_2 using this equilibrium reaction:

$$Hb(CO)_4(aq) + 4O_2(g) \rightleftharpoons Hb(O_2)_4(aq) + 4CO(g)$$

2 **ANALYZE** In which direction would you force this equilibrium to make a person with CO poisoning better sooner? What conditions would you change to shift the equilibrium? Use evidence to support your claim.

_____

_____

_____

_____

_____

_____

_____

_____

In mild cases of carbon monoxide poisoning, breathing pure oxygen is sufficient treatment to remove CO from the hemoglobin. Periodically, CO is exhaled and leaves the equilibrium system, allowing oxygen to be bound by hemoglobin. In more severe cases, it may be preferable to use a hyperbaric chamber, shown in Figure 24, for treatment. The patient is placed in a chamber where the air pressure is increased by two or three times that of normal air pressure. These conditions increase the concentration of O_2 present in the blood as well as the rate of the reaction in which CO is replaced by O_2, so the patient recovers faster.

> **Language Arts Connection** Create a pamphlet that helps people recognize the risks of carbon monoxide emissions and poisoning. Explain why CO is dangerous in terms that someone who has not studied chemistry could understand. Use multiple sources to research devices that release CO, how the levels of released CO are measured, and how these devices have changed over time to be safer. How could these devices be improved to reduce the amount of CO released? What are the costs and benefits associated with improving these devices?

3 **MODEL** Diagram at the molecular level the equilibrium shift that occurs in the hemoglobin, oxygen gas, and carbon monoxide gas equilibrium system in a person recovering from carbon monoxide poisoning.

| SHIFTING EQUILIBRIUM | EQUILIBRIUM IN THE HUMAN BODY | PRACTICE WITH THE EQUILIBRIUM CONSTANT | Go online to choose one of these other paths. |

2 The forward reaction is favored to treat the patient. To accomplish this, the patient is allowed to breathe concentrated oxygen. When carbon monoxide is released from the hemoglobin, a higher concentration of oxygen is available to react with the hemoglobin.

3 Diagrams should show hemoglobin molecules in the lungs and label that these molecules have four places to bind O_2 or CO molecules. The lungs should have more CO molecules than O_2 molecules and more CO molecules should be bonded to the hemoglobin than O_2 molecules. Next, the lungs should show an increased amount of O_2 as the person receives concentrated oxygen gas as a treatment. Some CO should be exhaled, and more O_2 should be bound to the hemoglobin molecules.

Explore Online

Shifting Equilibrium

Students investigate how changing pressure affects the equilibrium of a system and the numbers and types of molecules present.

Equilibrium in the Human Body

Students research an example of homeostasis and equilibrium in the human body and write a blog post that explains feedback that governs the system and how the system can be changed.

Practice with the Equilibrium Constant

Students use the equilibrium constant to quantify equilibrium in various systems.

EVALUATE Lesson Self-Check

Can You Explain the Phenomenon?

Claims, Evidence, and Reasoning

Have students clearly state their claim—their explanation for the phenomenon they have been investigating throughout this lesson. They should present their reasoning for making this claim, along with evidence such as facts, examples, and statistics that support their claim. You may want to have students present their arguments orally, in writing, or as a debate. Refer students to the **English Language Arts Handbook** for more information on evaluating claims and presenting arguments.

Cultivating Student Questions

Assessing Student Growth Review the list of questions students generated at the beginning of the lesson. Have volunteers select any unanswered questions and suggest how they could be investigated. After approving student plans, have small groups conduct the investigations and report back to the class.

Evidence Notebook

1 Hypochlorous acid, HOCl, is used to treat pool water. When HOCl is added to water, it dissociates into hydrogen and hypochlorite ions. The reverse reaction occurs at the same time, and the following equilibrium is established: $HOCl(aq) \rightleftharpoons H^+(aq) + OCl^-(aq)$. The oxygen in the hypochlorous acid destroys microorganisms. Because HOCl is removed from the system as it reacts with microscopic organisms, the levels need to be monitored to ensure that enough HOCl remains to disinfect the pool. If the pH of the pool is decreased, the extra H^+ ions would react with the OCl^- ions to produce more HOCl, increasing the HOCl concentration. If the pH of the pool is increased, the extra OH^- ions would combine with some of the H^+ ions to produce water. More HOCl would break apart to form H^+, and OCl^- and the HOCl concentration would decrease.

Lesson Self-Check

CAN YOU EXPLAIN THE PHENOMENON?

FIGURE 25: Swimming pool water is treated to protect the health of the swimmers.

Keeping swimming pool water clean and free of harmful bacteria is important for the health of the people swimming in the pool. Large debris is removed from pools by physical filters. Smaller pollutants are commonly treated with chemicals. Hypochlorous acid, HOCl, is used to treat pools because it destroys harmful bacteria and other microscopic contaminants.

 Evidence Notebook Refer to your notes in your Evidence Notebook to make a claim about how a chemical equilibrium system is used to treat pool water. Your explanation should include a discussion of the following points:

Claim How can an equilibrium system in swimming pools be managed to provide safe water for swimmers?

Evidence What evidence supports the idea that reactions at equilibrium produce chemicals that are harmful to bacteria? How does the pH of the swimming pool water affect the equilibrium?

Reasoning How does the evidence you provided support your claim about the chemical equilibrium used to treat pool water?

CHECKPOINTS

Check Your Understanding

1. Select the correct terms to complete the statement about the pH scale.

The pH of a solution is a measure of the concentration of the hydroxide | hydronium ions it contains. The pH can be calculated by finding log[H₃O⁻] | log[OH⁻] | −log[H₃O⁻] | −log[OH⁻]. The pH of milk is about 6.6, so milk is acidic | basic | neutral. The pH of soapy water is about 12, so soapy water is acidic | basic | neutral.

2. Which of the following are true of a chemical reaction at equilibrium? Select all correct answers.

☐ **a.** The forward and reverse reactions proceed at the same rate.

☐ **b.** The concentrations of the reactants and the products are the same.

☐ **c.** The rate of the forward reaction is greater than the rate of the reverse reaction.

☐ **d.** The concentrations of the reactants may differ from those of the products.

3. Which of these shows an acid followed by its conjugate base?

○ **a.** HSO_4^-, H_2SO_4

○ **b.** HCl, NaCl

○ **c.** HCO_3^-, CO_3^{2-}

○ **d.** H_2O, H_3O^+

4. Increasing the concentration of a reactant in an equilibrium system

○ **a.** shifts the equilibrium toward the products.

○ **b.** shifts the equilibrium toward the reactants.

○ **c.** does not shift the equilibrium.

5. Decreasing the temperature of an endothermic equilibrium system

○ **a.** shifts the equilibrium toward the products.

○ **b.** shifts the equilibrium toward the reactants.

○ **c.** does not shift the equilibrium.

Use the following information to answer Question 6.

Historically, sulfur dioxide, SO_2, generated from the burning of coal has been a major precursor to acid precipitation by way of its conversion to sulfur trioxide, SO_3, and its subsequent reaction with water.

Imagine you have a sealed vessel containing the following equilibrium system:

$$2SO_3(g) \rightleftharpoons 2SO_2(g) + O_2(g)$$

6. Select the correct terms to complete the statement about how the equilibrium will shift under the following conditions.

Decreasing the pressure of the container will produce more SO_3 | SO_2 | O_2 | SO_2 and O_2.
Decreasing the volume of the container will produce more SO_3 | SO_2.

7. Under what conditions will increasing the pressure on a gaseous equilibrium system shift the equilibrium? Select all correct answers.

☐ **a.** A shift will further increase the pressure on a system.

☐ **b.** A shift will decrease the pressure on a system.

☐ **c.** A shift will increase the number of molecules in the system.

☐ **d.** A shift will decrease the number of molecules in the system.

☐ **e.** There are an unequal number of moles in the reactants and the products.

☐ **f.** There are an equal number of moles in the reactants and the products.

8. Which of the following examples involve an acid-base equilibrium system? Select all correct answers.

☐ **a.** a weak base reacting with water

☐ **b.** a strong acid reacting with water

☐ **c.** a strong acid reacting with a weak base dissolved in water

☐ **d.** a strong base reacting with a strong acid dissolved in water

Answers

1. hydronium, $-\log[H_3O^+]$, acidic, basic
2. a, d
3. c
4. a
5. b
6. SO_2 and O_2, SO_3
7. b, d, e
8. a, c

Answers

9. To start, the forward reaction is faster because the reactant particles collide and interact more often. The reverse reaction starts off slowly as C and D begin to accumulate from the forward reaction and picks up speed as the forward reaction continues. At equilibrium, the forward and reverse reactions proceed at the same rate. At equilibrium, the concentrations of the reactants and the products stop changing, but they are not necessarily the same. The reactions never stop completely.

10. Increasing the temperature will shift the equilibrium of the reaction toward the reactants because the reaction is exothermic. Decreasing the temperature will shift it toward the products. Increasing pressure will shift the equilibrium toward the products because there are fewer product molecules. Decreasing pressure will shift the equilibrium toward the reactants.

11. The strength of an acid depends on the degree of ionization. HCl is a strong acid that ionizes completely. H_3PO_4 is a weak acid that ionizes only slightly. HCl forms more hydronium ions and is likely to react more vigorously with other substances than phosphoric acid does.

Make Your Own Study Guide

Have students create a study guide that helps them organize and visualize the important information from this lesson. Their study guide should focus on the main ideas from this lesson and tie multiple ideas together. Students can create an outline, a concept map, a graphic organizer, or another representation.

EVALUATE

CHECKPOINTS (continued)

9. Consider the generic reaction: $A + B \rightleftharpoons C + D$. If you start with only A and B, how do the rates of the forward and reverse reactions change as the reaction progresses? What can be predicted about the concentrations once the reaction reaches equilibrium? Does the reaction ever stop completely?

_____

_____

_____

_____

10. According to Le Châtelier's principle, how will changes in temperature and changes in pressure affect the equilibrium of the following reaction?

$$CO(g) + 3H_2(g) \rightleftharpoons CH_4(g) + H_2O(g) + energy$$

_____

_____

_____

_____

11. Phosphoric acid, H_3PO_4, is a weak acid and is found in many soft drinks. Hydrochloric acid, HCl, is a strong acid that is toxic if ingested. Explain how the degree of ionization differs for these two acids and how this difference affects their properties at the larger scale.

_____

_____

_____

_____

MAKE YOUR OWN STUDY GUIDE

 In your Evidence Notebook, design a study guide that supports the main ideas from this lesson:

Reversible reaction systems form a state of equilibrium when the forward and reverse reactions occur at the same rate.

Le Châtelier's principle states that an equilibrium system responds to a stress, such as changing pressure, temperature, or concentration of reactants or products, by shifting the equilibrium in order to relieve that stress.

Remember to include the following information in your study guide:
- Use examples that model main ideas.
- Record explanations for the phenomena you investigated.
- Use evidence to support your explanations. Your support can include drawings, data, graphs, laboratory conclusions, and other evidence recorded throughout the lesson.

Consider how the microscale models for macroscale equilibrium you have developed in this lesson can be used to analyze the stability and change of many different types of systems.

Analyzing Chemical Systems

Building to the Performance Expectations

The learning experiences in this lesson prepare students for mastery of

HS-PS1-6 Refine the design of a chemical system by specifying a change in conditions that would produce increased amounts of products at equilibrium.

HS-ETS1-3 Evaluate a solution to a complex real-world problem based on prioritized criteria and trade-offs that account for a range of constraints, including cost, safety, reliability, and aesthetics, as well as possible social, cultural, and environmental impacts.

 Trace Tool to the NGSS

Go online to view the complete coverage of standards across lessons, units, and grade levels.

 SEP **Science & Engineering Practices**

Constructing Explanations and Designing Solutions
Evaluate a solution to a complex real-world problem, based on scientific knowledge, student-generated sources of evidence, prioritized criteria, and tradeoff considerations.

Constructing Explanations and Designing Solutions
Refine a solution to a complex real-world problem, based on scientific knowledge, student-generated sources of evidence, prioritized criteria, and tradeoff considerations.

 **VIDEO** Constructing Scientific Explanations

---

 **DCI** **Disciplinary Core Ideas**

PS1.B Chemical Reactions
In many situations, a dynamic and condition-dependent balance between a reaction and the reverse reaction determines the numbers of all types of molecules present. (HS-PS1-6)

 **VIDEO** Equilibrium

ETS1.A Defining and Delimiting Engineering Problems
Humanity faces major global challenges today, such as the need for supplies of clean water and food or for energy sources that minimize pollution, which can be addressed through engineering. These global challenges also may have manifestations in local communities. (HS-ETS1-1)

ETS1.B Developing Possible Solutions
When evaluating solutions, it is important to take into account a range of constraints, including cost, safety, reliability, and aesthetics, and to consider social, cultural, and environmental impacts (HS-ETS1-3)

 **VIDEO** Engineering: Chemistry

---

 **CCC** **Crosscutting Concepts**

Stability and Change
Much of science deals with constructing explanations of how things change and how they remain stable.

 **VIDEO** Stability and Change

Systems and System Models
Models (e.g., physical, mathematical, computer models) can be used to simulate systems and interactions—including energy, matter, and information flows—within and between systems at different scales.

Systems and System Models
When investigating or describing a system, the boundaries and initial conditions of the system need to be defined and their inputs and outputs analyzed and described using models.

ELA STANDARDS

RST.11-12.7 Integrate and evaluate multiple sources of information presented in diverse formats and media (e.g., quantitative data, video, multimedia) in order to address a question or solve a problem.

RST.11-12.8 Evaluate the hypotheses, data, analysis, and conclusions in a science or technical text, verifying the data when possible and corroborating or challenging conclusions with other sources of information.

WHST.9-12.7 Conduct short as well as more sustained research projects to answer a question (including a self-generated question) or solve a problem; narrow or broaden the inquiry when appropriate; synthesize multiple sources on the subject, demonstrating understanding of the subject under investigation.

Supporting All Students, All Standards

Integrating the Three Dimensions

In this lesson, students use models to describe and analyze systems in the natural and designed worlds (**SEP Constructing Explanations and Designing Solutions DCI ETS1.B, CCC Systems and System Models**). They prioritize criteria and take into account a range of constraints as they design and evaluate an electrochemical cell (**DCI ETS1.B, CCC Systems and System Models**). Students explore the chemical reactions involved in the Haber-Bosch process and recognize the impacts of the process on society and the environment (**DCI PS1.B, DCI ETS1.B, CCC Influence of Engineering, Technology, and Science on Society and the Natural World**). They investigate and model the processes that link fossil fuel combustion, ocean pH, and the integrity of marine organisms' carbonate shells (**SEP Constructing Explanations and Designing Solutions, DCI PS1.B, CCC Stability and Change**). Students explore equilibrium reactions in the carbon dioxide–carbonate system in seawater and evaluate proposed solutions to the global challenge of ocean acidification (**SEP Constructing Explanations and Designing Solutions, DCI ETS1.B, DCI PS1.A, DCI PS1.B, CCC Influence of Engineering, Technology, and Science on Society and the Natural World**).

Preassessment

Have students complete the unit pretest or see the Assessment Guide.

Build on Prior Knowledge

In this lesson, students build on the concept of chemical equilibrium to understand ocean equilibrium systems. Have students work in pairs to summarize what they know about chemical equilibrium, such as:

- At chemical equilibrium, the concentrations of reactants and products are constant because the reaction is proceeding in both directions at the same rate.
- The concentrations of reactants and products are not necessarily the same at equilibrium, but there is no net change in their concentrations.
- Weak acids and weak bases form equilibrium systems in which the concentrations of acids and bases can change.

 **Professional Development** Go online to view **Professional Development videos** with strategies to integrate CCCs and SEPs, including the ones used in this lesson.

Content Background

The set of equilibrium reactions that involves carbon dioxide gas, various ions, and solid calcium carbonate in shells and coral skeletons is important for many ocean organisms. It might seem as if an increase in the concentration of carbon dioxide in the ocean would provide more carbonate for organisms that build shells or skeletons from calcium carbonate. However, an increase in carbon dioxide leads to a decrease in pH and an increase in bicarbonate ions at the expense of carbonate ions. Marine organisms need carbonate ions, not bicarbonate ions, to build calcium carbonate body parts. So, an increase in the concentration of carbon dioxide means that it becomes more difficult for organisms to build shells or skeletons, and can even cause some existing calcium carbonate body structures to dissolve.

Other effects of a higher carbon dioxide concentration and ocean acidification for marine organisms include possible increases in rates of photosynthesis, changes to metabolic processes that work best in a specific pH range, and other effects of changes in seawater chemistry. For example, changes in seawater chemistry could make it harder for organisms to absorb nutrients such as iron from ocean water. Researchers have also observed that some organisms exhibited behavior that indicated that their sense of smell was impaired in more acidic water.

Differentiate Instruction

LESSON VOCABULARY

- ocean acidification

ELL SUPPORT

Write the word *acidification* on the board. Circle the root word *acid* and the suffix *-ification*. Explain that the suffix generally means "to become." *Ocean acidification* means the ocean is becoming acidic. Write these words on the board, and have students use the same thought process to define them:
- simplification (to become simple)
- beautification (to become beautiful)
- qualification (to become qualified)

ENGAGE: Investigative Phenomenon

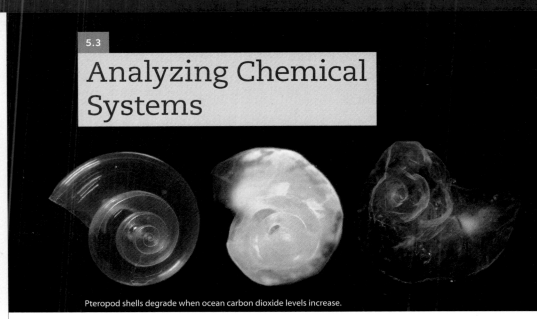

5.3

Analyzing Chemical Systems

Pteropod shells degrade when ocean carbon dioxide levels increase.

CAN YOU EXPLAIN THE PHENOMENON?

Scientists and engineers must find ways to understand complex questions and problems in order to reach conclusions and develop solutions. In this lesson, you will investigate ways to explain the complex relationship between carbon dioxide, which is a product of respiration and of fossil fuel combustion, and the ability of some marine organisms to grow shells. These seemingly unrelated processes are linked by a series of equilibrium reactions, which in turn are linked to the cycling of matter and energy in the Earth system.

Some pteropods, also known as sea snails, and other marine organisms have shells and skeletons made of calcium carbonate, $CaCO_3$. These structures are built from calcium and carbonate ions in ocean water. The concentration of carbonate ions in the water depends on the amount of carbon dioxide, CO_2, dissolved in the ocean. Human activity has dramatically increased the concentration of atmospheric CO_2 over the past 50–100 years. This means that the amount of CO_2 dissolved in the ocean has also increased. The calcium carbonate structures of some marine organisms are degrading in response to this shift.

1 **ANALYZE** How might Le Châtelier's principle be related to the degradation of calcium carbonate structures in marine animals?

_____

_____

2 **Evidence Notebook** As you explore the lesson, gather evidence to help you explain the link between carbon dioxide emissions and shell degradation. How can you develop and use models to explain shell degradation at the atomic scale and at the macroscopic scale?

© Houghton Mifflin Harcourt Publishing Company • Image Credits: (t) ©DAVID LIITTSCHWAGER/National Geographic Stock

Lesson 3 Analyzing Chemical Systems **359**

Build on Prior Lessons

In Lessons 1 and 2, students were introduced to the concepts of reaction rates, collision theory, chemical equilibrium, and acid/base interactions. Lesson 3 builds on these concepts as students explore real-world and designed chemical systems. They explore a case study in which they learn about the chemical reactions involved in ocean acidification and evaluate proposed solutions.

Lesson Objective

Students revisit systems and explore real-world chemical reactions and processes in designed and natural systems.

Cultivating Student Questions

Have students look at the photo of pteropod shells. Prompt them to ask all questions that come to mind about shelled marine organisms. Record the questions on chart paper, and sort the questions based on their focus. With students, narrow the questions down to the ones that directly relate to the learning objective. Have students reflect on this list throughout the lesson and check off questions as they are answered.

Can You Explain the Phenomenon?

The Investigative Phenomenon is the focus of the lesson. Students should record their initial thoughts about the balance between dissolved carbon dioxide and carbonate ions. They will explore the carbon dioxide–carbonate system in the ocean and how it is in equilibrium. Students will collect evidence related to this phenomenon throughout the lesson and revisit the question at the end of the lesson. They will use what they have learned to explain and construct models of the processes that have disrupted this equilibrium in the ocean.

1 Accept all reasonable answers that demonstrate understanding of Le Châtelier's principle, including types of stress factors.

Evidence Notebook
2 The topics of shell degradation and modeling systems will be revisited throughout this lesson.

Lesson 3 Analyzing Chemical Systems   359

EXPLORATION 1 Defining Chemical Systems

3D Learning Objective

Students use models to analyze systems in the natural and designed worlds. They explore how defining systems can help scientists and engineers define problems, develop solutions, and evaluate solutions to complex real-world problems.

Everyday phenomena discussed throughout the Explorations of the lesson can often be used to connect the science content to students' personal experiences.

Differentiate Instruction

ELL Support Write each label in **Figure 1** on the board. Guide students in pronouncing and defining the terms. Have students use words they are familiar with to describe each of the meanings.

Exploring Visuals

Carbon Cycle Ask volunteers to describe the paths in the diagram in **Figure 1** as others follow along. Suggest that they focus on arrows and think in terms of inputs and outputs to each part of the cycle.

Earth Science Connection

A biogeochemical cycle is a pathway along which matter moves through Earth's atmosphere, hydrosphere, biosphere, and lithosphere. Have students research one of the numerous cycles on Earth and draw a diagram similar to the carbon cycle in **Figure 1.** Examples are cycles of hydrogen, calcium, nitrogen, oxygen, water, and rocks.

1 Students should recognize that the reactants and products in a chemical reaction can be viewed as inputs and outputs (or components) of a system. Chemical equations can, but do not always, capture energy inputs and outputs, and they capture mathematical relationships between the quantities of components. They do not capture spatial or physical features, such as molecular shape, or the environment in which the reaction is taking place.

Defining Chemical Systems

As you have seen, chemistry involves the study of matter and its interactions at many different scales. Whether studying a nuclear reaction or optimizing a heat pack, chemists and engineers must first identify the scope and relevant components of the question or problem they are addressing. Often, they do this by defining the system or set of systems involved in the question or problem. How can chemical systems be defined, modeled, and refined to help study phenomena or solve problems?

 1 **Collaborate** Discuss with a partner how a chemical reaction can be viewed as a system. What parts of the system are described when the reaction is modeled with a chemical equation? Are there parts of the system that are not included in this type of model?

A Chemical System in the Natural World

The Earth system is a dynamic, complex set of interacting chemical, physical, and biological components, processes, and cycles, all involving a variety of systems and subsystems. The carbon cycle, shown in Figure 1, is one of the ways Earth's subsystems are interconnected. Some of the most pressing problems facing scientists and engineers—such as energy production and climate change—involve the carbon cycle. Plants, algae, and other photosynthetic organisms require carbon dioxide to produce glucose for energy and release carbon dioxide as a product of respiration. Humans also release large amounts of carbon dioxide into the atmosphere by extracting and burning fossil fuels.

FIGURE 1: The carbon cycle involves interactions among all of Earth's subsystems.

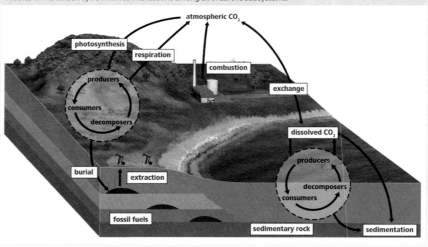

2 APPLY How might a global decrease in use of fossil fuels, such as coal to generate electrical energy, affect the system shown in Figure 1? Select all correct answers.

☐ **a.** Photosynthesis would happen more often.

☐ **b.** Atmospheric carbon dioxide concentrations would decrease.

☐ **c.** Cellular respiration would increase.

☐ **d.** Less carbon dioxide would dissolve in the oceans.

As Figure 1 shows, the matter in fossil fuels does not disappear when extracted and burned for energy. Rather, like all matter in a closed system, the carbon released during the combustion of fossil fuels moves to another part of the system in a different form.

A Chemical System in the Designed World

Reactions and processes occurring in natural systems can be difficult, and sometimes impossible, to control. For example, solar energy may produce an excess of electrical energy on a sunny day, but very little electrical energy on a rainy day. Scientists and engineers use their understanding of chemical systems and of Earth's systems to find ways to capture and store this energy, including by recharging electrochemical batteries.

3 DEFINE What are three criteria for a designed system that stores electrical energy?

_____

_____

Most batteries work by converting chemical energy into electrical energy. This is done via an oxidation-reduction reaction, in which electrons are transferred from one substance to another. In some oxidation-reduction reactions, energy is released as heat. But batteries use this reaction in a system called an electrochemical cell, which generates electrical energy instead of energy as heat.

Consider a strip of zinc metal in a copper(II) sulfate solution. In this reaction, zinc loses electrons and has been oxidized. Copper(II) gains electrons and is said to have been reduced, because its charge has been reduced. When the copper(II) ions are reduced, they fall out of solution as copper atoms. This can be seen as a layer of copper on the zinc bar in the beaker on the right in Figure 2.

Explore Online ▶

YOU SOLVE IT

How Can You Design a Battery? Optimize the voltage and energy storage in an electric vehicle battery by changing the composition of the electrodes.

FIGURE 2: The blue color of the copper sulfate solution is due to the presence of the copper(II) ions. The solution becomes lighter in color as copper ions in the solution are replaced by zinc ions. The copper atoms replace zinc atoms on the zinc bar.

We can model the changes in the zinc and copper species as:

$$Zn(s) + Cu^{2+}(aq) \rightarrow Cu(s) + Zn^{2+}(aq)$$

DCI **ETS1.B Developing Possible Solutions**

Ask students to name an example of an **everyday phenomenon** that includes a chemical system that uses technology. Have them try to identify the type of reaction that occurs and what problems the technology solves.

History of Science

Collaborate Have students work in groups to make a timeline showing the history of the battery. Students should research the work of Alessandro Volta and his "voltaic pile," the Danielle cell, the carbon-zinc battery invented by Georges Leclanché, the Edison battery, the invention of the alkaline battery by Lewis Urry, and the invention and optimization of lithium batteries during the twentieth century. Encourage students to add photos and diagrams to their timeline.

Explore Online ▶

YOU SOLVE IT 👥 Individuals or Small Groups ⏱ 45 minutes

How Can You Design a Battery?

SEP **Asking Questions and Defining Problems**

Students use models to combine materials in electrochemical cells and design a new battery that meets given qualitative and quantitative constraints.

Student worksheet and teacher support available online.

2 b, d

3 **Sample answer:** The device should be smaller than whatever it powers, it should be rechargeable, and it should hold a charge for at least 6 hours.

Differentiate Instruction

MTSS/RTI Help struggling students connect the vocabulary associated with electrochemical cells to the diagram in **Figure 2**. Sketch a similar diagram on the board. Ask students to name each part of the battery as you discuss it, including the anode, the cathode, the wires, the salt bridge, the electrolyte solution in the anode half-cell, and the electrolyte solution in the cathode half-cell.

Extension Ask students how they might build a battery using nickels, pennies, and cardboard disks soaked in salt water. Students should build a repeating column: nickel, disk, penny, disk (repeat). The bottom and top of the column must be different coins, and when the two coins are connected to a sensitive voltmeter, students should measure a small voltage.

CCC Systems and System Models

Show, or have students write, the full equation for the reaction of zinc and copper sulfate: $Zn(s) + CuSO_4(aq) \rightleftharpoons Cu(s) + ZnSO_4(aq)$. Have the class "translate" each part of the equation by writing or saying it without chemical symbols or shorthand. Have them identify ways in which the equation is a clearer or more succinct description of the reaction than the verbal description. Use this activity as a basis for discussing how system models, such as equations, are useful both for studying systems and for describing systems to others.

1 Electrons, loses, gains, Ions, stop flowing

2 Students should recognize that a chemical equation is useful for describing a reaction at the atomic level and for explaining how changes occur, while a diagram is more useful for explaining larger-scale processes, such as the flow of energy or matter though a system.

FORMATIVE ASSESSMENT

3-2-1 Have students write three things they learned in this Exploration about chemical systems, two things they found interesting, and one question they still have about the concepts presented in the Exploration.

If the substance that is being oxidized is separated from the substance that is being reduced, as shown in Figure 3, the electron transfer is accompanied by a transfer of electrical energy instead of energy as heat. This is how an electrochemical cell operates. This name comes from the transformation from chemical energy to electrical energy that occurs in the cell. Inside an electrochemical cell are two electrodes—the negative anode and the positive cathode. Each electrode is in contact with an electrolyte, in what is called a half-cell.

One means of separating oxidation and reduction reactions is by separating them with a porous barrier, or salt bridge. The salt bridge permits the flow of ions, but not metal atoms, between the solutions. Ions in the two solutions can move across the salt bridge, which keeps a precipitate from building up on the electrodes, as you saw in Figure 2. Electrons can be transferred from the anode to the cathode through an external connecting wire.

In the electrochemical cell shown in Figure 3, the half-cell on the left is composed of a zinc anode submerged in a solution of zinc sulfate, $ZnSO_4$. The half-cell on the right is composed of a copper cathode submerged in a solution of copper sulfate, $CuSO_4$.

FIGURE 3: The reactions in this electrochemical cell cause electrons to build up on the zinc electrode (left). When the circuit is completed, electrons flow through the circuit to the copper electrode (right).

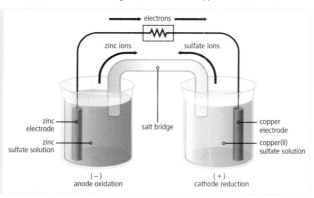

1 **EXPLAIN** Select the correct terms to complete the statement explaining how electrons and ions move in an electrochemical cell.

Electrons | Ions spontaneously flow through the connecting wire from the anode to the cathode. The anode loses | gains electrons, and the cathode loses | gains electrons. Electrons | Ions in the solution move across the salt bridge. If the half-cells were not separated, current would continue to flow | stop flowing.

The electrochemical cell in Figure 3 is called a wet cell battery, because the electrolyte solutions are liquid. However, everyday electronics are usually powered by dry cell batteries, which use a paste electrolyte. Batteries may also have one or more electrochemical cells. The batteries in a flashlight contain only one cell. Other batteries, such as small 9-volt batteries and most 12-volt car batteries, contain several cells in series.

2 **Evidence Notebook** The chemical equation for the Zn and Cu^{2+} reaction and the diagram of an electrochemical cell are both models of electrochemical reactions. How could you use these two types of models to explain the link between carbon dioxide emissions and shell degradation?

EXPLORATION 2 Storing a Charge

EXPLORATION 1 Defining Chemical Systems, continued   EXPLORATION 2 Storing

EXPLORATION 2

Engineering Lab
Storing a Charge

You are probably familiar with the batteries used to power devices such as calculators, watches, and toys. These batteries are most likely zinc-carbon batteries, alkaline batteries, or lithium ion batteries. All of these batteries convert chemical energy to electrical energy. Electrical energy is converted into chemical energy when rechargeable batteries are in a recharge cycle. In this investigation, you will design a system that uses common household items to generate electrical energy to power a small LED bulb. With your classmates, you will investigate how different combinations of these materials affect the design's performance.

The items that you will use for this investigation act as an electrochemical cell. Recall that in an electrochemical cell, electrons are lost during a chemical reaction at the *anode*. Electrons are gained in a chemical reaction at the *cathode*. The flow of electrons from the anode to the cathode makes up the electrical current.

DESIGN CHALLENGE The class has been tasked with figuring out which combination of food item and metals will produce the highest voltage and current. Groups will test either lemons or potatoes with different combinations of metal electrodes. All possible combinations should be tested, no materials other than those listed may be used, and groups must complete their work within the available time frame. Groups will combine their data to determine which design performs best.

POSSIBLE MATERIALS

- indirectly vented chemical splash goggles, nonlatex apron, nonlatex gloves
- aluminum foil
- copper strip, 1 mm × 1 cm × 5 cm

- copper wire
- LED bulb
- lemon
- magnesium strip, 1 mm × 1 cm × 5 cm

- multimeter
- potato
- scalpel
- zinc strip, 1 mm × 1 cm × 5 cm

SAFETY INFORMATION

- Wear indirectly vented chemical splash goggles, a nonlatex apron, and nonlatex gloves during the setup, hands-on, and takedown segments of the activity.
- Never taste any substance or chemical in the lab.
- Use caution when using sharp tools, which can cut or puncture skin.
- Wash your hands with soap and water immediately after completing this activity.

indirectly vented chemical splash goggles

3 **DEFINE THE PROBLEM**

How will you determine which design is best? List at least three criteria and two constraints for the battery system design. Rank the criteria from most to least important.

_____

_____

_____

Lesson 3 Analyzing Chemical Systems   **363**

3D Learning Objective

Students describe and model an electrochemical system in order to develop and evaluate solutions on the basis of scientific knowledge, student-generated evidence, and prioritized criteria.

 Engineering Lab Small Groups   90 minutes
Storing a Charge

SEP **Constructing Explanations and Designing Solutions**

Students combine household items to design a battery and power a small LED. They gather data about different combinations, then draw conclusions about which arrangement results in the best battery.

Collaborate

Jigsaw Form groups of four students. Assign each group a battery type: lithium, lithium ion, alkaline, nickel metal hydride, lead acid, rechargeable alkaline, absorbent glass mat (AGM), zinc-air, or molten salt. Groups will research the battery's basic structure, function, and uses. Afterward, have groups share and compare what they have learned about batteries. Then, ask volunteers to share insights from their conversations in a class discussion.

DCI **ETS1.B Developing Possible Solutions**

Different areas of engineering focus on different types of systems. Engineers who design batteries must become experts in which components an electrochemical system needs in order to function.

Ask: *What do you think this investigation might tell you about more complex batteries?* It might help explain the basic components of a battery system, or the parts that are necessary for a battery to work.

3 Students should recognize (based on the design challenge) that voltage and current are two key criteria and that testing these will determine which design is most successful. Constraints may include the materials provided for the lab, the amount of time available to complete the lab, and safety-related limitations.

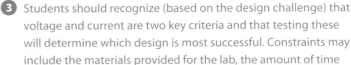
Student Lab Worksheet and complete Teacher Support are available online.

Environmental Science Connection

Help students relate the lab to **everyday phenomena** by guiding a discussion about the advantages of recycling batteries. Have students consider benefits to individuals, industries, and the environment. For example, recycling batteries prevents heavy metals (such as lead, nickel, or mercury) from polluting the environment. Recycling these metals means less mining is required to meet human demand. Less mining means additional environmental benefits and additional energy conservation as well as lower costs for industries that use heavy metals. Ideally, if industries have lower costs, so will the consumers who depend on their products.

CCC Influence of Engineering, Technology, and Science on Society and the Natural World

Engineering Connection Discuss how new technologies create opportunities for additional innovation. Solar backpacks that combine solar energy technology with rechargeable battery technology are a good example. **Ask:** *Think about the advantages that lithium ion batteries provide. Why are they a good choice for a solar backpack?* Lithium ion batteries store a lot of energy for their size and may be charged many times. They can be small enough to be incorporated into a backpack without adding too much weight yet still be useful as a charging tool for a long time. They also hold their charge well, which means that the backpack can be carried indoors, away from the sun, and used at a later time.

Analyze

1. Students should provide evidence from the investigation and explanations for their claims. **Sample answer:** The combination of a lemon with a magnesium anode and a copper cathode performed the best, and the combination of a potato with an aluminum anode and a zinc cathode performed the worst.

2. Most students will find that the best combination of electrodes is a copper cathode and a magnesium anode. Lemons will perform well. Students' responses should summarize class results.

DESIGN SOLUTIONS

1. With your group, write a procedure in your Evidence Notebook to safely determine which combination of materials best meets the criteria and constraints for the design. As you plan the procedure, consider the following questions:
   - How will you conduct tests on each combination?
   - What variables will you measure in each test?
   - What will your control be?
   - How can you divide the work in your group so that it is completed within the allotted time frame?

2. Make a data table in your Evidence Notebook in which to record your measurements.

3. Make sure your teacher approves your procedure and safety plan before proceeding. If necessary, adjust your plans based on your teacher's suggestions.

TEST

1. Obtain your materials and set up any equipment you will need. Take appropriate safety precautions.

2. Perform your tests and record your measurements.

3. Organize the data into tables and graphs. Make sure the tables and graphs are logically constructed and clearly labeled.

4. Compare each design's performance to the criteria you listed and choose the one that best meets the criteria.

5. Make a labeled diagram of the best design, including any measurements and the flow of electric current.

6. Clean all equipment and your lab station. Return equipment to its proper place. Follow your teacher's instructions for discarding materials. Wash your hands thoroughly after all work is finished and before you leave the lab.

ANALYZE

1. Which combination of materials performed best, and which performed the worst? Do you notice any patterns in your data? Explain.

_____

_____

_____

2. Combine all the data gathered by the class into a table. Which system had the highest voltage overall? Which system had the highest current overall? Were any patterns evident in the data? Describe the results.

_____

_____

_____

_____

© Houghton Mifflin Harcourt Publishing Company

OPTIMIZE

Answer the following questions in your Evidence Notebook.

1. Based on the data and observations your class made, what changes might you make to increase the maximum current obtained? What changes might you make to increase the maximum voltage?

2. What additional data or research would be helpful if you were to repeat your experiment?

① DRAW CONCLUSIONS

Write a conclusion that addresses each of the points below.

Claim Which combination of materials resulted in the best battery?

Evidence Cite evidence from the results of your group and your classmates to support your claim.

Reasoning Explain how the evidence you gave supports your claim. Describe, in detail, the connections between the evidence you cited and the argument you are making.

EXTEND

Imagine you are asked to test which design in this experiment has the longest battery life, but you have only one sample of each food with which to conduct your test. In your Evidence Notebook, describe how you would approach the problem.

② **Evidence Notebook** Think about the diagram you made for your battery investigation. Were the scale and type of model useful for your investigation? Why or why not? How can your answer help you construct your models of the effect of carbon dioxide on marine shell degradation?

Claims, Evidence, and Reasoning

Collaborate Be sure everyone in a group gets a chance to state their views about how evidence from the results supports the claim. The group can then agree on how to state their reasoning.

Optimize

1. **Sample answer:** I would try a magnesium strip with a copper strip because another group got high voltage with that combination.

2. **Sample answer:** Research about how metals react with potatoes and lemons would help guide which combinations to try. Our data showing that using the same metal for both electrodes will not produce a current would help reduce the number of trials next time.

① Answers should be based on the criteria established at the beginning of the lab and on the results of the investigation, with clear reasoning to connect the evidence to the claim.

Evidence Notebook

② Student answers should show evidence of thinking about what makes a good model and the different scales they might choose. **Sample answer:** This was a good model of the experiment because we were deciding how to arrange the materials. A model at the atomic scale, such as a chemical equation, would have been helpful for deciding whether a lemon or a potato would be more likely to work well. I can use this answer to choose the scales I want to use to model the effect of carbon dioxide on marine shell degradation.

FORMATIVE ASSESSMENT

Have students answer these questions about designing a battery:

Ask: *What determined the criteria and constraints for this lab?* The criteria were described in the introduction and design challenge. The constraints were determined by the time, space, and materials available.

Ask: *What determined whether the metal you used for your battery's electrodes was the cathode or the anode?* The anode is the metal that more easily gives up electrons.

Lesson 3 Analyzing Chemical Systems   365

EXPLORATION 3 Case Study: Optimizing an Industrial Reaction

3D Learning Objective

Students explore the **balance between a reaction and the reverse reaction** in the Haber-Bosch process and consider its **impacts, including some that were not anticipated, on society and the environment.** They use scientific knowledge and tradeoff considerations to evaluate the Haber-Bosch process in the context of **complex, real-world problems.**

Differentiate Instruction

MTSS/RTI Before beginning the Case Study, identify students who might feel less confident with chemical equilibrium systems. Have these students use online simulations of chemical equilibrium systems to develop more confidence with how changes introduced to an equilibrium system might affect forward and reverse rates of reaction. Avoid simulations that use the Haber-Bosch process.

History of Science

In 1911, Fritz Haber became director of the Institute for Physical and Electrochemistry in Berlin. He resigned in1933 after being ordered under the Nazi regime to fire anyone on his staff who was Jewish. (Haber himself had converted from Judaism to Christianity.) He left Germany, but his work on poison gas weapons and the synthesis of ammonia—which produced a new source of explosives in addition to synthetic fertilizers—enabled Germany to prolong World War I. Have interested students do research to learn more about Haber and his work.

1 a, b

2 Increasing pressure or temperature or adding more reactant would increase the rate of reaction and thus make it possible to obtain more ammonia from it.

EXPLORATION 3

Case Study: Optimizing an Industrial Reaction

Nitrogen compounds are an essential part of fertilizer for agriculture because nitrogen atoms are a key component of plant DNA, proteins, and chlorophyll molecules. Nitrogen is abundant in the atmosphere in the form of nitrogen gas, N_2, but few organisms are able to metabolize it in this form. Nitrogen fixation, the conversion of atmospheric nitrogen into a form that is usable for plants, is therefore crucial for agriculture and plant health.

In the early 1900s, scientists and engineers began looking for ways to fix nitrogen industrially. One process used an electric arc to convert atmospheric nitrogen into nitric oxide. Because of the large amount of electrical energy needed for this process, it was abandoned in favor of a second process. This second method used calcium carbide, CaC_2, which reacts with N_2 at 1000 °C to form calcium cyanamide, $CaCN_2$, and carbon. But this process also required high inputs of electrical energy to produce calcium carbide.

1 **PREDICT** Which criteria or constraints would a new nitrogen-fixation process have to meet in order to be considered an improvement over the two methods discussed above? Select all correct answers.

☐ **a.** a higher amount of product per unit of energy put into the system

☐ **b.** a process that uses lower reaction temperature

☐ **c.** a process that does not cause air pollution

☐ **d.** a process that uses more electrical energy

Harnessing an Equilibrium Reaction

Around 1905, German chemist Fritz Haber began work on a nitrogen-fixation method based on the equilibrium reaction between atmospheric nitrogen and hydrogen:

$$N_2(g) + 3H_2(g) \rightleftharpoons 2NH_3(g)$$

Under normal conditions, this reaction proceeds so slowly that the amount of ammonia it produces is too small to be useful in agriculture. Haber needed to refine the process to maximize the amount of ammonia produced.

FIGURE 4: Chemical plants worldwide produce over 140 million metric tons of ammonia per year.

2 **ANALYZE** What stresses could engineers apply to increase the amount of ammonia obtained from this equilibrium reaction?

_____

_____

_____

_____

_____

_____

© Houghton Mifflin Harcourt Publishing Company • Image Credits: ©saoirse_2010/Getty Images

The mechanism of a reaction can also be altered by adding a *catalyst*, a substance that changes the rate of the reaction without being consumed or changed significantly. The addition of a catalyst speeds up the overall rate of a reaction for both the forward and the reverse reactions in an equilibrium system.

3 **MODEL** Draw two additional lines showing how the equilibrium reaction will proceed when a more efficient catalyst is present.

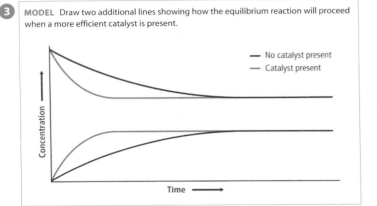

— No catalyst present
— Catalyst present

Concentration

Time

Haber developed a method to produce ammonia from nitrogen and hydrogen using a combination of high temperature, high pressure, and a catalyst. In 1909, another German chemist named Carl Bosch began developing a way to use Haber's method to produce ammonia at an industrial scale. By 1929, the Haber-Bosch process had become the world's main source of nitrogen for synthetic fertilizers.

 Collaborate With a partner, find a simulation that will allow you to test the effects of temperature and the presence of a catalyst on a chemical equilibrium system. Make a claim about how you can change the conditions of the system to produce more product at equilibrium. Run several tests with the simulation and collect data that either support or refute your claim.

 4 **EXPLAIN** Removal of ammonia from the system as the reaction proceeds is another important component of the Haber-Bosch process. How does removing ammonia affect the equilibrium reaction?

_____

_____

_____

_____

5 **Evidence Notebook** In your unit project, you are investigating the Solvay process. Similarly to the Haber-Bosch process, the Solvay process involves manipulating the inputs and outputs of an equilibrium reaction to maximize the amount of product obtained. How is equilibrium controlled in the Haber-Bosch process? How is it controlled in the Solvay process?

Explore Online ▶
YOU SOLVE IT

How Can You Increase Ammonia Production?
Adjust reaction conditions to increase the amount of ammonia produced.

DCI **PS1.B Chemical Reactions**

Remind students that Le Châtelier's principle states that changes in pressure, concentration, and temperature are stress factors in equilibrium systems. In the hypothetical reaction $A + B \rightleftharpoons C + D$, increasing the concentration of A or B is a stress on the system that shifts the reaction to the right. Decreasing the concentration of C or D has the same effect, so removing product from the system is another way to influence the reaction rate. Ammonia produced in the Haber-Bosch process is removed from the system by condensation, which decreases the partial pressure of gaseous ammonia in the reaction and is the same as lowering the concentration.

Explore Online

YOU SOLVE IT 👥 Small Groups ⏱ 20–45 minutes
How Can You Increase Ammonia Production?

SEP **Constructing Explanations and Designing Solutions**

Students refine the design of a model chemical system by changing conditions to produce increased amounts of ammonia at equilibrium.

Student worksheet and teacher support available online.

3 Students should add lines that begin at the same places as the other lines but that reach the equilibrium position earlier than the blue or red lines.

4 Removing ammonia from the reaction shifts the reaction to the right to favor production of more ammonia.

Evidence Notebook
5 In the Haber-Bosch process, equilibrium is controlled by altering the pressure of the system, adding a catalyst, and removing ammonia as it forms. In the Solvay process, equilibrium is controlled by temperature and by using ammonia as a buffer.

CCC **Influence of Engineering, Technology, and Science on Society and the Natural World**

In addition to the Haber-Bosch process, an important factor in the Green Revolution was the development of high-yield food seeds. The development of these seeds led to a dramatic increase in crop production, but there are additional costs associated with buying and implementing new technologies. Have students research how small- and large-scale farms have been affected by new technologies such as high-yield varieties.

Exploring Visuals

Draw students' attention to **Figure 6** and the dip in the fertilizer graph around the year 1990. Ask for their ideas about why this decrease might have occurred. Explain that an increase in fertilizer prices around this time caused many farmers to seek ways to reduce fertilizer use. Many began to use extensive soil testing to identify specific nutrient needs for farmland and Global Positioning System (GPS) application methods to target specific areas with the needed nutrients.

Language Arts Connection
RST.11-12.8 Evaluate the hypotheses, data, analysis, and conclusions in a science or technical text.
Remind students that they can find tips on evaluating scientific texts in the online **English Language Arts Handbook.**

1 The world population began to grow much more quickly when the production of nitrogen fertilizer became industrialized.

2 Haber's work on the synthesis of ammonia and catalysts for the reaction led to the establishment of an ammonia manufacturing company that enabled Germany to extend their involvement in World War I. Students should provide data, such as the effects of the war or the benefits of the Haber-Bosch process, to support their opinion about whether Haber should have been awarded the Nobel Prize.

 Influence of Engineering, Technology, and Science on the Natural World

The Green Revolution

FIGURE 5: Ammonia is used to make fertilizer for crops.

Beginning around 1945, many areas of the world saw rapid increases in agricultural production. Developing countries such as Mexico, India, and Pakistan underwent massive increases in farm productivity and land use in what is now called the Green Revolution.

The Green Revolution was due to the development of high-yield crop varieties, improved pesticides, and a large increase in the availability of nitrogen fertilizers, driven in large part by the Haber-Bosch process. Figure 6 shows the changes in world population and the changes in the amount of fertilizer used (in kilograms of nitrogen per hectare per year) in the latter half of the 20th century.

Impacts of the Haber-Bosch Process on Population and Fertilizer Use

FIGURE 6: These graphs show world population and estimated population growth without the influence of the Haber-Bosch process (left), and use of nitrogen fertilizers since 1900 (right).

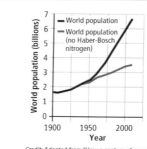 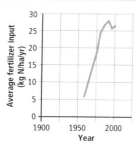

Credit: Adapted from "How a century of ammonia synthesis changed the world" by Jan Willem Erisman et al., from *Nature Geoscience,* September 28, 2008. Copyright © 2008 by Springer Nature. Used with permission of Copyright Clearance Center.

 ANALYZE What conclusion can you draw from Figure 6 about the relationship between nitrogen fertilizer use and population growth?

_____

_____

_____

 Language Arts Connection Fritz Haber received a Nobel Prize in Chemistry for his work on the Haber-Bosch process. The award was controversial because of Haber's role in the development of chemical weapons in World War I. Using multiple sources, including scientific texts, develop an argument for or against awarding the Nobel Prize in Chemistry to Haber. Write a letter to the prize committee explaining your position. Support your argument with data from your research and include a list of sources.

New technologies, such as the Haber-Bosch process, involve tradeoffs. Societies need to weigh the immediate benefits against longer-term ecological and economic costs. For example, the increased use of fertilizer as a result of the Haber-Bosch process led to increased chemical runoff from farms. Excess nitrogen in oceans leads to overgrowth of algae, which leads to oxygen depletion as the algae die and decompose. Figure 7 shows how runoff from farms along the Mississippi River watershed affects the Gulf of Mexico.

Effects of Industrial Fertilizer Use on the Environment

FIGURE 7: The Gulf of Mexico dead zone is an area of about 15 000 square kilometers that is polluted by agricultural runoff. The concentration of oxygen in this area is too low for many fish and marine species to survive there.

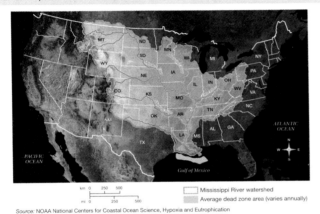

Source: NOAA National Centers for Coastal Ocean Science, Hypoxia and Eutrophication

3 **ARGUE** Do you think the development of industrial fertilizers was an overall positive or negative development? Use evidence from the text to support your argument.

_____

_____

_____

Predicting the impacts of new technologies is difficult, which is one reason the engineering design process includes iterative steps of evaluating and refining solutions. Problems caused by the new technology may be corrected, or other solutions may be developed.

4 **Collaborate** Work with a partner to think of potential solutions to fertilizer pollution in water systems. List and prioritize criteria and constraints, brainstorm solutions, and choose which ideas seem most likely to meet the criteria and constraints.

5 **Evidence Notebook** You have seen several ways to model an equilibrium reaction and the effects of that reaction on the Earth system. What types of graphs or other models could you use to model the series of equilibrium reactions that affect shell degradation? What additional information would you need to develop these models?

DCI **ETS1.B Developing Possible Solutions**

Ask students whether the solution to the dead zone is the responsibility of farmers and homeowners or the government. Have them describe **everyday phenomena** experienced by farmers that may influence the decision to use fertilizer or implement a solution.

Collaborate

Discussion Encourage students to discuss with their partners solutions that could be implemented by individual farmers, as well as solutions that could be implemented by local, state, or national governments.

3 Accept all reasonable and complete answers that are supported by evidence from the text. **Sample answer:** The overall effect was positive because, as the graph suggests, the lives of many people were saved by increased food production.

4 Students should propose a solution to fertilizer pollution and provide a list of prioritized criteria and constraints. **Sample answer:** A pollution removal system can be designed for use in key runoff areas. It should include an effective method of removing harmful chemicals from the water, be easy to install and maintain, be cost-effective, and not harm ecosystems.

 Evidence Notebook

5 Students may suggest a model that shows the effect of increasing the concentration of a reactant on the reaction rate, an equilibrium equation, a diagram, or other models. Additional information needed will vary depending on the models a student mentions.

FORMATIVE ASSESSMENT
3-Minute Pause Have students pause to think of the concepts presented in this Exploration. Then have them respond to the following prompts.

I became more aware of …
I didn't realize that …
I still don't understand …

EXPLORATION 4 Exploring the Effects of Carbon Dioxide and pH

3D Learning Objective

Students **generate evidence to help construct explanations** of how atmospheric carbon dioxide affects the stability of ocean pH and of how ocean pH affects the integrity of marine organisms' carbonate shells. Evidence from the lab will enable students to make predictions about the chemical reactions underlying ocean acidification.

Hands-On Lab 👥 Pairs or Small Groups ⏱ 90 minutes
Exploring the Effects of Carbon Dioxide and pH

SEP **Constructing Explanations and Designing Solutions**

Students show experimentally that increased amounts of CO_2 result in decreased seawater pH. Then, they plan an investigation to determine the effect of decreased pH levels on calcium carbonate, the main component of the shells and skeletons of marine organisms. Students should recognize that equilibrium among carbon dioxide, carbonate ions, and bicarbonate ions is sensitive to changes in concentration.

Part I: Modeling the Effects of Carbon Dioxide on Water pH

Advance Preparation Measure out 50 mL of bromothymol blue indicator solution in a 200 mL beaker for each group.

Safety Information Warn students to be careful only to exhale, not inhale, through the straw.

Materials Alert If not enough beakers are available for individual use, substitute clear plastic cups.

CCC **Stability and Change**

Point out that this lab, like many scientific investigations, provides evidence for how things change or remain stable. *Ask: What are some ways scientists in other disciplines work to explain stability and change?* Geneticists work to understand how mutations arise and persist in DNA. Earth scientists study how Earth has changed over time.

1 Accept all reasonable answers.

EXPLORATION 4

 Hands-On Lab
Exploring the Effects of Carbon Dioxide and pH

The production of industrial fertilizer addressed an important need by helping to boost agricultural production, but its use had unanticipated impacts on the health of aquatic ecosystems. In this lab, you will investigate potential impacts of another technological solution—the burning of fossil fuels to obtain energy. Carbon dioxide, CO_2, is released into the atmosphere when fossil fuels are burned. CO_2 dissolves in ocean water and is part of a system of equilibrium reactions that take place in the ocean. At the macroscopic level, this system appears stable, but the forward and reverse reactions taking place occur constantly and adjust in response when stress, such as an increased input, is added. In this investigation, you will model two parts of this process at the macroscopic scale.

RESEARCH QUESTION What is the relationship between carbon dioxide in water and the integrity of marine animals' shells?

- -

1 **MAKE A CLAIM**

Why do you think structures made of calcium carbonate, $CaCO_3$, deteriorate with increased levels of atmospheric carbon dioxide? What is the role of pH?

_____

_____

_____

Part I: Modeling the Effects of Carbon Dioxide on Water pH

As cells oxidize glucose to release energy, they produce carbon dioxide, which is removed from the body mainly through the circulatory and respiratory systems. So, when you breathe out, you emit carbon dioxide. In Part I of this investigation, you will use your breath and a pH indicator called bromothymol blue to investigate the relationship between carbon dioxide and the pH of water. Bromothymol blue looks blue at pH values higher than 7. When the pH is acidic, the color changes.

- -

MATERIALS

- indirectly vented chemical splash goggles, nonlatex apron, nitrile gloves
- beaker, 200 mL
- bromothymol blue indicator solution (100 mL)
- drinking straw

- -

SAFETY INFORMATION

- Wear indirectly vented chemical splash goggles, a nonlatex apron, and nitrile gloves during the setup, hands-on, and takedown segments of the activity.

- Only exhale through the straw in this investigation. Do not inhale or ingest the bromothymol blue solution. Do not share your straw with anyone else.

- Wash your hands with soap and water when you are finished handling chemicals.

indirectly vented chemical splash goggles

© Houghton Mifflin Harcourt Publishing Company

 Student Lab Worksheet and complete Teacher Support are available online.

CARRY OUT THE INVESTIGATION

1. Pour 50 mL of indicator solution into a beaker. Observe and record the color of the indicator in your Evidence Notebook.
2. Place the end of the straw in the indicator solution and start a timer. Exhale gently through the straw for 8–10 seconds. You should see bubbles. Observe and record the color of the solution as you exhale, and the time it took for the color to change.
3. After the color has changed, stop exhaling into the solution.
4. If you have time, exercise in place for 1 minute, then repeat steps 1–3.

ANALYZE

Answer the following questions in your Evidence Notebook.

1. What did you observe when you exhaled into the water? What do your results tell you about the relationship between carbon dioxide and water pH?

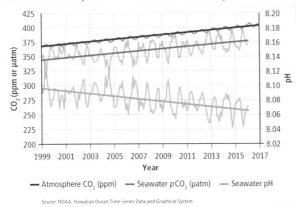

Carbon Dioxide and pH

FIGURE 8: Data collected between 1999 and 2017 show a correlation between carbon dioxide concentrations in the atmosphere and the pH of ocean water.

Key: ▬ Atmosphere CO₂ (ppm)   ▬ Seawater pCO₂ (µatm)   ▬ Seawater pH

Source: NOAA, Hawaiian Ocean Time-Series Data and Graphical System

2. Based on your results, how would the graph in Figure 8 look if carbon dioxide concentrations in the atmosphere began to decrease? Explain your answer using evidence from the investigation.

Part II: Modeling the Effects of pH Changes

In Part II, you will model how the pH of water affects structures made of calcium carbonate, such as chalk and seashells. Because this change is relatively slow, you will use vinegar, which is much more acidic than seawater.

POSSIBLE MATERIALS

- indirectly vented chemical splash goggles, nonlatex apron, nitrile gloves
- beaker, 250 mL (2)
- chalk
- distilled vinegar
- hand lens
- pH indicator or probe
- seashells
- water

Differentiate Instruction

Extension Have students research and produce a graph showing how average atmospheric temperatures have changed between 1999 and 2017, and compare this trend to the CO₂–pH graph. Ask students to describe how higher atmospheric temperatures would affect the dissolved CO₂ in the ocean. Warmer air would warm the water, decreasing the amount of dissolved CO₂ but increasing the amount of CO₂ released back into the atmosphere from the water.

Collaborate

Discussion Have students discuss their observations after Step 4 of Part I. They should explain that the color changes faster because of increased carbon dioxide produced by the body as a result of exercise that burned more glucose. Have students relate this experience to **everyday phenomena.**

Part II: Modeling the Effects of pH Changes

Materials Alert Have students work in small groups for Part II. The liquids can be placed in beakers or in clear plastic cups. If time permits, make a solution of 50% water and 50% vinegar for students to test along with the undiluted vinegar and water.

Analyze

1. **Sample answer:** The solution changed color as I exhaled into it. It changed even faster after I did jumping jacks for one minute. This tells me that carbon dioxide must lower the pH of water, and that the more carbon dioxide there is in water, the faster the pH changes, because the color changed faster after I increased my rate of respiration by exercising, and carbon dioxide is an output of respiration.

2. The trend lines for CO₂ in the ocean and ocean pH would decrease at the same rate as the atmospheric CO₂ concentration. My results showing that CO₂ lowers the pH of water support this answer.

Claims, Evidence, and Reasoning

Have students label the claim, evidence, and reasoning in their Draw Conclusions response to ensure that they address each point.

Collaborate

Discussion Ask students how the effect of exercising on their results is analogous to increasing fossil fuel usage. Both processes increase the CO_2 output as the result of oxidation of a carbon-based fuel.

DCI PS1.B Chemical Reactions

Ask students whether they think shell degradation would be reversed if the pH of seawater were to increase.

1 **Sample answer:** The model is accurate in terms of the effect of acidic solutions on calcium carbonate. The model is inaccurate in terms of the amount of time it takes for a change to become visible and the acidity of the solution.

2 **Sample answer:** When I blew into the water, the change in color indicated that an acid was forming. This shows that carbon dioxide from the air can make water acidic if it dissolves in the water. Vinegar is acidic. The shell began to dissolve in the vinegar, which shows that acid conditions in the ocean can weaken shells.

3 Complete answers will make a claim and provide reasoning for it based on evidence from the students' investigations. Answers may or may not be scientifically complete, depending on students' prior knowledge of the chemistry of ocean acidification.

Evidence Notebook

4 Students should name a way to use their observations to construct each model. **Sample answer:** I could draw or take a photo of the results in Part II to include in a visual model of effects, and I could use data from the pH part of the lab to model the effect of carbon emissions on a global scale.

FORMATIVE ASSESSMENT
One-Sentence Summary Have students write a sentence to answer this question: *How are CO_2 and ocean pH related?*

---

indirectly vented
chemical splash
goggles

SAFETY INFORMATION

· Wear indirectly vented chemical splash goggles, a nonlatex apron, and nitrile gloves during the setup, hands-on, and takedown segments of the activity.

· Immediately wipe up spilled water on the floor so it does not become a slip/fall hazard.

PLAN THE INVESTIGATION

Design your own investigation that safely models the effects of pH change on the shells of marine organisms. Think about what would indicate a change in calcium carbonate. In your Evidence Notebook, write a procedure, develop a data collection plan, write a safety plan, and list the materials you will need. Identify your control, variables, and how you will measure change in your investigation. Make sure your teacher approves your procedure and safety plan before proceeding. Once you have approval, carry out the investigation.

1 **ANALYZE**

In your Evidence Notebook, summarize your results. Do you think your investigation accurately modeled the effects of pH on calcium carbonate? Explain why or why not, citing evidence from your investigation.

2 **CONSTRUCT AN EXPLANATION**

Using evidence from your investigation, explain how atmospheric carbon dioxide, pH, and calcium carbonate are related.

_____

_____

_____

3 **DRAW CONCLUSIONS**

Write a conclusion that addresses each of the points below.

Claim Make a claim explaining why the calcium carbonate shells and skeletons of marine organisms deteriorate with increased levels of atmospheric carbon dioxide.

Evidence Use evidence from the two parts of this investigation to support your claim.

Reasoning Describe how the evidence you gave supports your claim.

_____

_____

_____

_____

_____

_____

_____

4 **Evidence Notebook** What data from this lab would be helpful in constructing your models of how atmospheric carbon dioxide is related to marine organisms' shells?

EXPLORATION 5 Case Study: Ocean Acidification

EXPLORATION 5

Case Study: Ocean Acidification

Since the Industrial Revolution, the increase in the release of sequestered carbon by burning fossil fuels has changed the equilibrium between carbon dioxide in the atmosphere and carbon dioxide in the ocean, as shown in Figure 9. This change in equilibrium results in an increase in H⁺ ions, which corresponds to a decrease in pH, in the world's oceans. This decrease in pH is known as ocean acidification.

Ocean systems cover approximately 71% of Earth's surface and are Earth's single largest reservoir for human-generated carbon dioxide. When carbon dioxide dissolves, it reacts with water to form carbonic acid, H_2CO_3, which ionizes to form hydrogen, H^+, and bicarbonate, HCO_3^-, ions, as shown in the equilibrium equation:

$$CO_2 + H_2O \rightleftharpoons H_2CO_3 \rightleftharpoons H^+ + HCO_3^-$$

Bicarbonate ions then ionize to form hydrogen and carbonate ions:

$$HCO_3^- \rightleftharpoons H^+ + CO_3^{2-}$$

5 **EXPLAIN** Recall that when a stress is applied to an equilibrium reaction, the rate of the reaction shifts. What shift would you expect to see in the above equilibrium reactions if carbon dioxide concentration increases? What would you expect if it decreases?

_____

_____

FIGURE 9: The equilibrium system of carbon dioxide, water, carbonic acid, bicarbonate ions, hydrogen ions, and carbonate ions is affected by changes in the concentration of atmospheric carbon dioxide.

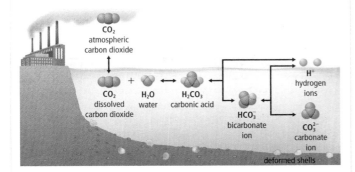

When the CO_2 concentration increases, the first equilibrium reaction shifts in favor of producing more H^+. These these additional H^+ ions shift the second reaction towards producing more bicarbonate ions. This means there are fewer carbonate ions in the water for pteropods and other marine organisms to use to build shells.

Lesson 3 Analyzing Chemical Systems   **373**

3D Learning Objective

Students explore equilibrium reactions in the carbon dioxide–carbonate system in seawater and evaluate proposed solutions to the global challenge of ocean acidification. They consider the influence of technology on the natural world.

Exploring Visuals

Draw students' attention to the molecules illustrated in **Figure 9.** At each step, have them explain what happens to the atoms or ions. For example, in the formation of carbonic acid, two oxygen atoms and one carbon atom from carbon dioxide combine with one oxygen atom and two hydrogen atoms from water to form carbonic acid, which has three oxygen atoms, one carbon atom, and two hydrogen atoms.

Preconception Alert

Draw students' attention to the description of ocean pH change. They may have assumed that ocean acidification meant the ocean's pH is below 7 when, in fact, even after acidification, the ocean is still basic. Explain that even small changes in pH can disturb chemical processes within organisms or harm the shells of some marine organisms.

SEP Constructing Explanations and Designing Solutions

Have students explain the process shown in **Figure 9** in terms of electrostatic forces on the particles. Remind them that water is a polar molecule. Water molecules can therefore attract the ions in carbonic acid and bicarbonate, and the dissolved ions can reform into the original reactants by electrostatic attractions.

5 The rate of the forward reaction will increase if carbon dioxide concentration increases, and it will decrease if carbon dioxide decreases.

Math Connection

A 0.1 difference in pH seems small unless students understand the logarithmic nature of the pH scale. Have students use the formula pH = $-\log[H^+]$ to explicitly calculate the percentage of the ocean pH change from 8.2 to 8.1. $[H^+]_{8.1} = 10^{-8.1} = 7.9433 \times 10^{-9}$; $[H^+]_{8.2} = 10^{-8.2} = 6.3096 \times 10^{-9}$, so percentage change = $(7.9433 \times 10^{-9} - 6.3096 \times 10^{-9})/(6.3096 \times 10^{-9}) \times 100\% \approx 25\%$

Alternatively, have students perform the calculation using only properties of logarithms. $(10^{(8.2-8.1)} - 1) \times 100\% \approx 25\%$ **(MP.2)**

Biology Connection

Another risk of using kelp or eelgrass as a solution to ocean acidification is the danger of introducing invasive species, which are non-native species that outcompete native species for resources. Have students brainstorm possible drawbacks of using the kelp or eelgrass. **Sample answer:** The kelp or eelgrass might spread too much if no natural organisms that use it as a food source are present to control the population.

1 Students should recognize that changes to a population of organisms would have effects on other populations, such as those that rely on it for food. It might also affect humans who rely on ecosystems for income, such as people who work for fisheries.

2 a, b, c

 Evidence Notebook

3 The increase in carbonate ions would shift the equilibrium reaction back to the left, so there would be more bicarbonate ions and carbonic acid in the water and fewer H^+ ions.

Mitigating Ocean Acidification

Ocean acidification occurs because of the increase in atmospheric carbon dioxide, primarily released by the burning of fossil fuels. Acidification does not mean that the world's oceans are acidic. Recall that 7 is neutral on the pH scale. Numbers higher than 7 are basic, and numbers lower than 7 are acidic. Until a few hundred years ago, the pH of the oceans was about 8.2. Today the ocean pH is about 8.1, but because the pH scale is logarithmic rather than linear, that 0.1 difference represents a 25% increase in acidity. This change in pH can have devastating effects on aquatic ecosystems by harming populations of shelled organisms.

1 EXPLAIN What negative impacts might the loss of shelled marine animal populations have on other parts of the marine ecosystems they live in?

_____

_____

_____

FIGURE 10: Kelp can reduce acidification by using carbon dioxide for photosynthesis.

Local Approaches

Solutions to ocean acidification have been proposed on different scales. At the local scale, such as in coastal communities, some proposed solutions rely on technologies. Others rely on organisms, like the kelp shown in Figure 10, that remove carbon dioxide from water and convert it into oxygen and glucose via photosynthesis.

Growing new or reestablishing beds of kelp or eelgrass can have relatively quick, positive effects on ocean acidification and marine ecology. Even though this solution has benefits, it has some limitations, and even risks. Aquatic organisms must be carefully selected to enhance, and not disrupt, the local ecosystems.

Other communities have proposed adding limestone, or calcium carbonate, to ocean water to increase its pH. $CaCO_3$ is a base, and it dissociates in water to form calcium ions, Ca^{2+}, and carbonate ions, CO_3^{2-}. The carbonate ions react with H^+ in the water, raising its pH. Limestone can be mined from underground quarries, but a huge amount would be needed to significantly alter the pH of the more than one billion cubic kilometers of water in the ocean.

2 EVALUATE What are some potential drawbacks to the solution of mining limestone and adding it to the ocean to increase the ocean's pH? Select all correct answers.

☐ **a.** It would take a lot of limestone and a long time to cause a major change in pH.

☐ **b.** Mining limestone would require the use of fossil fuel energy and would add large amounts of carbon dioxide to the atmosphere.

☐ **c.** The constant movement of the ocean's currents means that chemicals added in one location to change pH would quickly disperse over a very large area.

☐ **d.** As limestone reacted to remove carbon dioxide from the water, the change would cause surface water to take in more carbon dioxide from the air.

3 **Evidence Notebook** How would the addition of CO_3^{2-} from limestone affect the equilibrium reactions in the system in Figure 9?

Global Considerations

Ocean acidification is a global, system-level problem that involves the interaction of Earth's systems and human activities. Ocean water around the world is affected because it interacts with the atmosphere and circulates. Although local solutions to acidification play an important role in protecting or restoring specific ecosystems, engineers must consider the greater problem of pH in the entire ocean in order to design a truly effective solution.

FIGURE 11: This model shows current oceanic pH levels and predicted pH levels if people reduce or do not reduce atmospheric CO_2 levels.

Present day   2100, with CO_2 reduction   2100, with no CO_2 reduction

more acidic pH | 7.3 | 7.6 | 7.9 | 8.1 | 8.4 | more basic pH

Source: NOAA Climate.gov, 2010, "Ocean Acidification, Today and in the Future"

Scientists use known and expected levels of carbon dioxide in the atmosphere to make computer models that project these changes over time. From these and other data, they can determine the pH levels of the ocean. Figure 11 shows a projection of how pH in the ocean might change if humans reduce carbon dioxide emissions significantly, and if emissions continue at the current rate. Because the pH scale is logarithmic, the third map indicates a change in acidity to a level that is three times the current level.

4 **INFER** Based on Figure 11, what are some likely constraints on any global solution to ocean acidification?

_____

_____

_____

Reducing carbon dioxide emissions is an important part of mitigating ocean acidification. Societies can greatly reduce carbon dioxide production by conserving energy and relying more on alternative energies such as wind, solar, and geothermal energy. Even so, we will continue to use some fossil fuels for many years. Thus, one method engineers have developed to lower carbon dioxide emissions is through carbon capture and storage (CCS). In this process, carbon dioxide emitted during fossil fuel combustion is captured and moved through a pipeline into rock several kilometers below the ground.

Good locations for carbon dioxide storage include oil and gas fields, where underground pipes already exist; saline formations, where the gas can be absorbed by saltwater; and porous rock formations, such as basalt. Basalt is volcanic rock that includes a number of different minerals. Over time, the carbon dioxide reacts with other molecules in the basalt, forming calcite, dolomite, and other materials. These reactions keep carbon "stored" underground and out of the atmosphere. However, they have only been tested on relatively small scales and short time frames. We do not yet know the long-term economic and ecological costs and benefits of geoengineering solutions such as this one.

© Houghton Mifflin Harcourt Publishing Company

CCC **Influence of Engineering, Technology, and Science on Society and the Natural World**

Engineers work continually to reduce the costs and maximize the benefits associated with technological systems. Ocean acidification and other components of climate change are an example of how technology—in this case, based on the burning of fossil fuels—can lead to new problems while solving old ones. **Ask:** *What are some possible impacts of the proposed solutions mentioned in this Exploration?* Student discussions should include consideration of positive and negative impacts.

Explore Online

Encourage students to go online to view an animated computer model and find more information about how ocean pH has changed in the past and how scientists predict it will continue to change.

Collaborate

Think-Pair-Share Give students the following statements about ocean circulation off the east and west coasts of the United States: "The ocean water along the east coast of the United States is warmer than the ocean water along the west coast. The Atlantic Ocean and the Pacific Ocean both contain circular ocean currents known as *gyres*."

Have students work in pairs to answer the following question. **Ask:** *Do you think these gyres rotate clockwise or counterclockwise along these two coasts? Support your claims with reasoning.* Students can share their answers during a class discussion. They should reach the conclusion that both gyres rotate clockwise because that explains the transport of colder water toward the equator along the west coast and warmer water toward the North Pole along the east coast.

4 **Sample answer:** Any global solution to ocean acidification would have to happen very quickly, given the changes expected by 2100, so time is a constraint. Because a solution would require reduced carbon dioxide emissions, any solution would have to include alternative energy technology. Because of the global nature of the problem, the cost of any solution would be a major constraint, as would cooperation among many different countries.

DCI **ETS1.A Defining and Delimiting Engineering Problems**

Have students work in small groups to research examples of **everyday phenomena** that are indirectly affected by ocean acidification. Provide an opportunity for groups to describe their examples to the class and explain the connections.

Language Arts Connection
WHST.9-12.7 Conduct short as well as more sustained research projects to answer a question or solve a problem.
Remind students that they should be careful to use reliable sources for their information. Caution them that websites about the Kyoto Protocol, the Paris Agreement, and climate change in general may be published by political groups and may misrepresent scientific data or construe opinions as factual.

1 Students should provide a reasonable explanation to support their argument for whether CCS technology is a feasible solution. An argument for feasibility is that the technology has been tested and is currently used at power plants. Arguments against feasibility include the possibility of carbon dioxide release during an earthquake and the high cost of implementation.

2 Reports should focus on either the Kyoto Protocol or the Paris Agreement. They should provide information in addition to details provided in the text, including purpose, efforts at implementation by various countries, methods of monitoring emissions and holding countries accountable, and a history of U.S. participation in the treaties.

Evidence Notebook
3 Students should clearly identify boundaries, inputs, and outputs of each model.

FORMATIVE ASSESSMENT
Quick Write Have students write a few sentences summarizing ocean acidification and the importance of finding a solution.

CCS is one potentially effective way to keep carbon dioxide from being emitted into the atmosphere, and it is already in use in a small number of power plants. There are, however, disadvantages to using CCS. Carbon dioxide is just one of the harmful products of combustion of fossil fuels. Sulfur and nitrogen oxides, heavy metals, and other contaminants are also released into the environment. CCS can be very expensive, which limits its application. Another concern is that carbon dioxide stored underground might cause earthquakes, releasing the stored carbon dioxide.

1 **ARGUE** Based on your list of constraints on a global solution to ocean acidification, do you think that CCS technology might be a feasible solution to problems related to ocean acidification? Why or why not?

_____

_____

_____

Reaching Global Agreements on Climate Change

FIGURE 12: Involved citizens can urge governments to find solutions.

One of the most difficult parts of addressing global challenges, such as climate change or ocean acidification, is reconciling the interests, resources, and cultural values of different countries. Solutions to these problems require nations to work together.

The Kyoto Protocol is an international agreement that sets internationally binding emission reduction targets. During the first commitment period, 2008–2012, a total of 37 countries and what was then called the European Community committed to reduce greenhouse gas emissions by an average of 5% compared to 1990 levels. During the second period, 2013–2020, parties committed to reduce emissions to at least 18% below 1990 levels. The Protocol established a credit trading system that allows countries that exceed these goals to sell credits to countries that do not. The Kyoto Protocol is seen as an important first step towards emission reduction. However, some of the countries responsible for the most greenhouse gas emissions, including the United States, have not agreed to the treaty.

The Paris Agreement is another example of an international agreement that aims to reduce greenhouse gas emissions as a way of strengthening the global response to climate change. The central aim of the treaty is to limit the amount of greenhouse gases emitted by human activity to levels that trees, soil, and oceans can absorb, beginning at some point between 2050 and 2100. The agreement went into effect in 2016. By 2019, 184 parties had ratified the agreement.

2 **Language Arts Connection** Research the Kyoto Protocol and the Paris Agreement. Prepare a report that explains what they are trying to do, and how countries are trying to achieve the goals. How are countries held accountable and how are emission levels monitored? What is the history of the participation of the United States in these treaties?

3 **Evidence Notebook** As you have seen, ocean acidification is a global problem that stems from atomic-level interactions. Now that you have learned more about the process at the macroscopic and atomic scales, define the system boundaries, inputs, outputs, and scale you will use for each model.

TAKE IT FURTHER Careers in Science

Careers in Science

Environmental Chemist

Human activities and resource use are causing changes in Earth's systems. Environmental chemists study the causes and effects of these changes at both the molecular and societal scales, and recommend solutions when those changes are detrimental. They study the effects of human pollution on systems as small as the area around a manufacturing plant and as large as the atmosphere and oceans. Environmental chemists work with other scientists and engineers to identify and solve environmental problems.

FIGURE 13: Environmental chemists help clean up oil spills.

Environmental chemists study the impact of pollution on plants, animals, and ecosystems. They are often called upon during environmental emergencies to test water, air, or soil samples and determine the extent of the damage. This information helps contain emergencies such as a ship leaking oil in the ocean or a spill of industrial or agricultural chemicals. Environmental chemists also help determine the procedure for containing an emergency and neutralizing or minimizing the damage.

Projects involving environmental chemistry extend beyond the response to a single event. Over the last few decades, the air quality in many large cities in the United States has improved significantly. An understanding of the chemistry of the atmosphere and of the interactions between the atmosphere and contaminants from burning fossil fuels led to many laws and technologies that reduced pollution. Environmental chemists played a large role in developing that understanding.

Chemists play a key role in marine environmental studies as well. The complex chemical interactions within and between the atmosphere and the hydrosphere are only partially understood, and there is still much more to learn. Environmental chemists work to understand the natural processes within these environmental systems and they try to determine how to mitigate the effect of human activities on Earth's systems.

While some environmental chemists may spend a lot of time in the field or at sea collecting samples, they also work in laboratories analyzing data and drawing conclusions from their findings. For a given project, problem, or even large-scale environmental disaster, environmental chemists use a scientific approach to find an explanation.

Environmental chemistry focuses not only on responding to existing environmental pollution, but also on preventing future problems. Environmental chemists seek to develop sustainable methods to reduce, reuse, and recycle matter, conserve energy, and reduce pollution by aligning human-engineered systems with natural systems.

 Chemistry in Your Community Research an environmental chemist who studies issues that affect your community. If possible, conduct a personal interview with the chemist. Learn about the chemist's background and what experiences influenced his or her decision to work in environmental chemistry. Make a video or podcast about the chemist and their work.

| CARBON RESERVOIRS | USING SHELLS TO TREAT WATER | MEASURING OCEAN pH | Go online to choose one of these other paths. |

Collaborate

You may choose to assign this activity or direct students to the Interactive Online Student Edition, where they can choose from all available paths.

 Influence of Engineering, Technology, and Science on Society and the Natural World

Have students choose one environmental problem caused by human pollution and write a report on how environmental chemists have solved it or are working to solve it, either with new technologies or with new methods.

Language Arts Connection
WHST.9-12.7 Conduct short as well as more sustained research projects to answer a question or solve a problem.
Have students work in pairs to conduct their research and produce a video or podcast. Remind them to make a list of questions to ask the chemist if they conduct an interview. Before recording the video or podcast, students should prepare a script and ensure that all needed information is included in a reasonable way.

Explore Online ▶

Carbon Reservoirs

Students investigate different carbon reservoirs.

Using Shells to Treat Water

Students research how discarded shells can be used in water treatment and prepare a report on their findings.

Measuring Ocean pH

Students learn how scientists use ocean buoys as self-operating laboratories to collect long-term data from ocean locations.

EVALUATE Lesson Self-Check

Can You Explain the Phenomenon?

Claims, Evidence, and Reasoning

Have students clearly state their claim—their explanation for the phenomenon they have been investigating throughout this lesson. They should present their reasoning for making this claim, along with evidence such as facts, examples, and statistics that support their claim.

You may want to have students present their arguments orally, in writing, or as a debate. Refer students to the **English Language Arts Handbook** for more information on evaluating claims and presenting arguments.

Cultivating Student Questions

Assessing Student Growth Review the list of questions students generated at the beginning of the lesson. Have volunteers select any unanswered questions and suggest how they could be investigated. After approving student plans, have small groups conduct the investigations and report back to the class.

 Evidence Notebook

1 Student answers should demonstrate understanding of the relationship between an increase in carbon dioxide in the atmosphere and ocean acidification. Accept all reasonable answers that show the atomic and macroscopic scales and an accurate representation of the concepts involved at each scale. **Sample answer:** One model could show the chemical reaction of $CaCO_3$ shell material and acid at the atomic level because the equilibrium reactions explain fundamentally why this shell deterioration happens. The other could show the whole Earth system because it is a global problem and is linked to human activity throughout the world.

Lesson Self-Check

CAN YOU EXPLAIN THE PHENOMENON?

FIGURE 14: The shells of some pteropods and other marine organisms deteriorate with increasing atmospheric carbon dioxide levels.

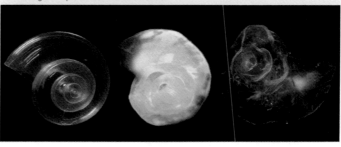

Dramatic changes can occur to marine organisms when they are not able to build or maintain their calcium carbonate shells or skeletons. This phenomenon has been observed in many species of marine organisms around the world. The deterioration of shells has increased dramatically as the concentration of carbon dioxide in the atmosphere has increased over time, and it appears to be accelerating.

There is a strong correlation between the increase in atmospheric carbon dioxide and the damage to coral colonies. Coral reefs are made from thin layers of calcium carbonate, and scientists have established that there is a clear cause-and-effect relationship between the human production of carbon dioxide and the decline of coral reefs around the world. When carbon dioxide levels increase, marine organisms are not able to add to their carbonate shells. These organisms are also losing the carbonate ions that are in their shells, causing the deterioration shown in Figure 14. Such changes have effects that ripple through entire ocean ecosystems.

1 **Evidence Notebook** Refer to the notes in your Evidence Notebook to help you explain the link between carbon dioxide emissions and shell degradation and model the process at the atomic scale and at the macroscopic scale. Be sure to address the following points:

Claim How do your models show the relationship between carbon dioxide in the atmosphere and marine organism shell degradation?

Evidence What evidence supports this claim?

Reasoning How does this evidence support your claim?

Formal Assessment Go online for student self-checks and other assessments.

CHECKPOINTS

Check Your Understanding

1. Why does adding a catalyst to an equilibrium system not change the concentration of reactants or products? Select all correct answers.

☐ **a.** The forward and reverse reaction rates stay the same.

☐ **b.** The forward reaction rate increases.

☐ **c.** The reverse reaction rate increases.

☐ **d.** The forward reaction rate decreases.

☐ **e.** The reverse reaction rate decreases.

2. Which factors made the Haber-Bosch process a good solution for producing synthetic nitrogen fertilizers more efficiently than previous methods? Select all correct answers.

☐ **a.** the use of a catalyst

☐ **b.** the use of high pressure

☐ **c.** the use of electrical energy

☐ **d.** the use of an equilibrium reaction

3. Adding limestone to ocean water has been proposed as a solution to ocean acidification. Which constraint below is not met by this solution?

○ **a.** The solution should be safe.

○ **b.** The solution should have global effects.

○ **c.** The solution should have local effects.

4. What are some possible outcomes of ongoing ocean acidification? Select all correct answers.

☐ **a.** decreases in coral or pteropod populations

☐ **b.** increase in ocean pH

☐ **c.** changes in coral reef ecosystems

☐ **d.** loss of carbon dioxide from the atmosphere

5. Why is the development of a battery system essential for the effective use of wind power?

○ **a.** Windmills require batteries to turn them.

○ **b.** Batteries supply power for transporting electricity from one place to another.

○ **c.** Batteries store excess power for use when the wind does not blow.

6. The reaction between hemoglobin, Hb, and oxygen, O_2, in red blood cells is responsible for transporting O_2 to body tissues. This process can be represented by the equilibrium reaction

$$Hb(aq) + O_2(g) \rightleftharpoons HbO_2(aq)$$

Many people experience shortness of breath at high altitudes, where the pressure of O_2 is lower than it is at sea level. What would help increase a person's blood oxygen levels at high altitudes?

○ **a.** increasing the concentration of O_2 in the air the person inhales

○ **b.** increasing the person's blood pressure

○ **c.** removing CO_2 from the air the person exhales

7. Match each step in designing a battery to the corresponding step in the engineering design process.

evaluating battery designs against established criteria ○	○ optimizing
listing the features of a successful design ○	○ modeling
adjusting design based on test results ○	○ defining the problem
making a sketch that shows the flow of current in the design ○	○ testing

8. Reducing carbon emissions could help mitigate ocean acidification. What are some possible barriers to implementing such a solution? Select all correct answers.

☐ **a.** Governments may be reluctant to spend money on a solution if other countries do not also agree to do so.

☐ **b.** Scientists and engineers do not know how carbon emissions affect oceans.

☐ **c.** Updating facilities to reduce carbon emissions could be costly.

☐ **d.** Employees of fossil-fuel companies might fear that they will lose their jobs.

Answers

1. b, c

2. a, b, d

3. b

4. a, c

5. c

6. b

7. evaluating battery designs against established criteria: testing; listing the features of a successful design: defining the problem; adjusting design based on test results: optimizing; making a sketch that shows the flow of current in the design: modeling

8. a, c, d

Answers

9. **Sample answer:** Strengths are that use of fertilizer makes more food available to feed the world population and increases the productivity per acre of farmland. Weaknesses are that fertilizer use can have environmental impacts such as the Gulf of Mexico dead zone, which is caused by fertilizer runoff.

10. Students should suggest something that will increase the rate of reaction without requiring more energy, such as adding a catalyst or increasing the concentration of A and B. **Sample answer:** I would recommend adding a catalyst, which will increase the rate of reaction without requiring additional energy, and removing C and/or D from the system as efficiently as possible.

11. The idea works at a small scale because calcium carbonate is part of the equilibrium reaction that leads to ocean acidification in response to increasing inputs of carbon dioxide from the atmosphere. However, the amount of calcium carbonate needed to achieve this effect for all of Earth's oceans is prohibitive.

Make Your Own Study Guide

Have students create a study guide that helps them organize and visualize the important information from this lesson. Their study guide should focus on the main ideas from the lesson and tie multiple ideas together. Students can make an outline, a concept map, a graphic organizer, or another representation.

EVALUATE

CHECKPOINTS (continued)

9. What are the strengths and weaknesses of current approaches to using industrial fertilizer? Give examples to support your answer.

10. An industrial facility uses the equilibrium reaction $A + B \rightleftharpoons C + D$ to produce C, an important chemical in manufacturing processes. The facility wants to increase production of C without increasing energy use or adding to the production time. What would you recommend, and why?

11. What is the chemical basis of the idea to add calcium carbonate to the ocean to reverse ocean acidification? Why is this approach unlikely to solve the issue?

MAKE YOUR OWN STUDY GUIDE

 In your Evidence Notebook, design a study guide that supports the main ideas from this lesson:

Scientists and engineers define systems to help study phenomena or solve problems. Chemical systems can be designed or harnessed to meet various needs, including storing electrical energy.

Technologies and innovations, such as the use of fossil fuels for energy and the Haber-Bosch process for nitrogen fixation, can address needs while having unforeseen economic, social, and environmental impacts.

Remember to include the following information in your study guide:
· Use examples that model main ideas.
· Record explanations for the phenomena you investigated.
· Use evidence to support your explanations. Your support can include drawings, data, graphs, laboratory conclusions, and other evidence recorded throughout the lesson.

Consider how the models for equilibrium you developed in this lesson can be used to analyze the stability and change in the systems you modeled.

UNIT 5 Connections

Life Science Connection

Enzymes An enzyme is a biological catalyst that increases the rate of a chemical reaction. Enzymes are critical for maintaining cellular functions in the body. The enzyme glucose oxidase is used in biosensors to monitor blood glucose levels of people with diabetes. Glucose is a reactant in the reaction catalyzed by glucose oxidase and hydrogen peroxide is a product. Although glucose is difficult to measure, hydrogen peroxide is not. A higher glucose level in the blood causes more hydrogen peroxide to be produced, and the hydrogen peroxide can be measured in biosensors.

Make a multimedia presentation that explains how enzymes work and describe the function of several enzymes in the human body. Integrate and evaluate multiple sources in your presentation.

Explore Online ▶

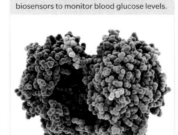

FIGURE 1: Glucose oxidase is used in biosensors to monitor blood glucose levels.

Health Connection

Time Release Pharmacokinetics is the study of interactions between medications and chemicals inside the human body. Understanding how a medication affects a person is important for determining correct dosages. Given the many differences between individuals, scientists are developing medications that are more individualized. Researchers can decide whether to allow a slow, steady release, or immediate exposure to the full dose.

Write a medical pamphlet that explains why different timed releases are important for medical treatment. Also discuss how differences between individuals can affect how medication interacts with body processes. Cite specific text evidence to support your claim.

FIGURE 2: Pharmacokinetics helps scientists develop medications that interact with the body at different rates.

Social Studies Connection

Human Population The human population of an area may change at a predictable rate, or it may be stable for a long time. Many factors can affect this equilibrium state, such as changes in birth or death rates, a large employer moving in or away, or many people moving in or out. These factors may cause shortages or oversupply of some resources. Over time, a new equilibrium is reached.

Build a timeline of the history of your community and label significant events that affected the population. What events caused sudden or long-term changes to its size or makeup? Include text and media comparing the changes to the concept of dynamic chemical equilibrium. How is this a good or poor analogy for chemical equilibrium?

FIGURE 3: Changes in human populations lead to changes in the need for resources.

Support for Unit Connections

Life Science Connection

Enzymes in the body are typically proteins, and the compounds they work on are called substrates. The structure of the enzyme enables it to bind to the substrate, lowering the activation energy of a chemical reaction. The enzyme then separates from the product. Multimedia presentations should include a general description of enzyme function as well as descriptions of several enzymes in the body.

Health Connection

The body absorbs different medications through various routes, including the lungs, stomach, mucous membranes, and intestines. Understanding how the body interacts with a medication allows pharmaceutical scientists to optimize delivery. This optimization could include how the medication is ingested, how it interacts within a particular system, and the time over which the medication is released to the body. One goal of pharmacokinetics is to provide chemical compounds at a site and a rate that make them most effective. Medical pamphlets should include a general explanation of why timed releases are important for some medical treatments as well as specific information about interactions within the body. Suggest that students include diagrams to explain difficult concepts.

Social Studies Connection

In many places, the equilibria may not be obvious, particularly those with rapid changes. Have students look at times of significant change and how changes in resources such as housing and jobs affected the population numbers and characteristics. How did population changes move the overall community system to a more stable state? Timelines should include labels for major changes to the community and ways the populations adjusted to accommodate those changes.

THING EXPLAINER BY RANDALL MUNROE

A BOOK EXPLAINING COMPLEX IDEAS USING ONLY THE 1,000 MOST COMMON WORDS

POWER BOXES

Making power from different metals

You've learned that batteries generate power through electrochemical reactions. Here's a look at their insides.

IDEAS FOR THINKING ABOUT POWER BOXES

A power box has two sides, one holding a carrier wanter and the other holding a carrier maker. Between them is a wall that lets carriers through. The carrier maker would make carriers that cover the carrier wanter. But eating carriers puts pieces of power in the carrier wanter, and you can't have too many pieces of power together, because they push each other away. This stops the carrier wanter from eating too many carriers.

- ● PIECE OF POWER
- ○ POWER CARRIER
- ◉ POWER
  (in power carrier)

CARRIER MAKER

This metal wants to get rid of carriers. If it gets a piece of power inside it, it will send it away in a carrier made from its surface.

CARRIER WANTER

This metal wants to be covered in carriers. It will grab them if they come near and stick them to its surface, and the power from the carrier will go inside them.

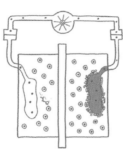

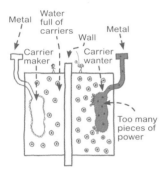

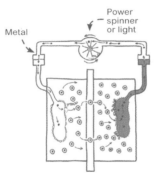

FULL

The two sides of a power box have a wall between them. This wall lets carriers through, but not pieces of power. It also stops the carrier wanter and carrier maker from touching, which would make the carriers all move to the carrier wanter without sending any power anywhere.

Extra pieces of power gather in the carrier wanter, but they can't go anywhere at first.

RUNNING

When you join the two sides with a stick of metal, the pieces of power can get from the carrier wanter to the carrier maker.

If you put a machine in their way—like a light or a power spinner—they can push on it and make it run, just like water pushing on a water wheel.

When the pieces of power get to the carrier maker, it uses them to make new carriers.

EMPTY

After a while, the carrier wanter gets covered in empty carriers, and the carrier maker gets used up. There's nothing left to push the power pieces through the metal path; the power box is dead.

With some power boxes, you can turn the wheel and push power back into the power box. This fills the power box back up.

Teacher Notes

Teacher Notes

_____

_____

_____

_____

_____

_____

_____

_____

_____

_____

_____

_____

_____

_____

POWER BOXES

Carrier maker　　　Carrier wanter　　　　Wall

Metal for power to go out from

Plastic thing to keep water in

If something goes wrong, the power box can start making a kind of air. There's a hole here to let that air out so the box doesn't pop.

Metal for power to go into

SMALL POWER BOX
This kind of power box is used in a lot of places. It powers hand lights, face hair cutters, and things kids play with.

In this kind of power box, the carrier wanter and carrier maker are made from different kinds of metal. The stuff in between is water with a kind of white stuff in it which lets the carriers move across. If the power box breaks, that stuff can come out. Don't worry, it's safe to clean up; it won't hurt your skin.

All power boxes run out of power after a while. With some kinds, you can put power back in and use them again and again, but you can't really do that with the kind shown here.

YOU CAN DROP THESE TO SEE IF THEY'RE DEAD
The carrier wanter in these boxes is made from metal dust. When it gets covered in carriers, it becomes stronger and sticks together, so the dust can't move around. This makes dead power boxes fly back up when you drop them, but full ones just hit the ground and stop.

Power comes in　　Power goes out

CAR POWER BOX
These power boxes are used in cars. They use two kinds of heavy metal as the carrier wanter and the carrier maker, which is why they're so heavy.

The power carrier water in between the two sides can burn your skin.

The carrier maker and the carrier wanter are two different kinds of metal, but there's something strange about this power box: When the carrier wanter gets covered in carriers, and the carrier maker makes them, they both turn into the _same_ kind of metal.

© Houghton Mifflin Harcourt Publishing Company

HAND COMPUTER POWER BOX

These power boxes hold more power for their size than any other. We first made them to power helper machines in people's chests. Those machines need to hold a lot of power, since people don't like it if you take them out too often.

When we started making lots of hand computers, we got better at making these power boxes, since lots of people wanted their computers to work all day without having to get power from the wall.

Of course, people also wanted their hearts to work, but more people have hand computers than heart boxes.

If you cut one of these open, it would look like this—but never cut these open. They can blow up.

LIGHT METAL

In these power boxes, the carrier wanter and carrier maker are both made of very light metals. To make this kind of carrier maker and wanter work together, they're laid down in sheets almost touching each other, like two long sheets of paper laid flat and then rolled up.

TIME COUNTER

POWER BOX

POWER BOX

Teacher Notes

_____

_____

_____

_____

_____

_____

_____

_____

_____

_____

_____

_____

_____

_____

_____

_____

👥 Small Groups ⏱ 90 minutes

Modeling Chemical Equilibrium

SEP **Developing and Using Models**

Students develop a model that demonstrates how an equilibrium reaction can be disrupted and how the reaction can be shifted to produce more product.

Answers

1. A model of equilibrium needs to show that the forward and reverse reactions still occur at equilibrium. There may be more products or more reactants, but the ratio of reactants to products remains the same. Equilibrium does not mean that there are equal amounts of products and reactants.

2. Students should write the chemical equation for the reaction they will model and identify all reactants and products. Models could include physical or computer models.

3. Examples include paper or three-dimensional models using craft supplies, computer models using presentation software, and kinesthetic modeling using groups of students. Each species in the reaction should be easily identified.

4. Have the class takes notes while each group presents their model and give the groups feedback on ways their models worked well and areas where they could improve.

Performance Task Scoring Rubric

Points	Criteria
	Problem statement is clearly defined and identifies supporting questions to be answered.
	Information on the chosen chemical reaction and typical conditions of the reaction is included.
	Includes a model that shows how the forward and reverse reactions still occur at equilibrium.
	Presentation shows an understanding of the process and how equilibrium is maintained.
	A list of references is included.

Modeling Chemical Equilibrium

A reaction at equilibrium has not stopped. Reactants are still forming products, and products are still forming reactants, but at a constant rate. Therefore, the relative concentrations of reactants and products do not change once the reaction reaches equilibrium. How could you model this idea for someone who does not understand how concentrations could stay the same, but the reactions still continue? How could you show them that equilibrium is a dynamic system?

1. DEFINE THE PROBLEM

Describe what types of information a model needs to demonstrate about an equilibrium system. Could you make a model that demonstrates equilibrium when the concentration of reactants is greater than products, as well as when the concentration of products is greater than reactants?

2. CONDUCT RESEARCH

Research a chemical equilibrium reaction that interests you. Are there models and analogies of this chemical equilibrium system? Note what you think these models do well and how you think they could be improved. How can you use these models to influence your own?

3. DEVELOP A MODEL

With your team, decide on the type of model you will make to demonstrate the concept of chemical equilibrium. Determine the materials you will need and any safety considerations. If you are making a physical model, you should consider how many participants you will need to make your model work and whether it requires a lot of space. If you are making a computer simulation or video animation model, consider audience participation in your presentation.

4. COMMUNICATE

Present your model to the class. Without explaining the model to them, have fellow students explain to you how it is showing the dynamic nature of chemical equilibrium. Have them suggest ways in which the model could be improved to either model your reaction more clearly, or to model the concept of equilibrium more clearly.

FIGURE 4: These students are modeling equilibrium using pompoms.

✓ **CHECK YOUR WORK**

Once you have completed this task, you should have the following:

- a clearly defined problem statement with questions that you answer in the presentation
- information on the chemical reaction you chose and typical conditions under which it operates
- a model of the process that shows how a change in the reaction can disrupt the equilibrium and how equilibrium is restored after the change
- a presentation that shows an understanding of the process and how equilibrium is restored
- a list of references cited

UNIT PRACTICE AND REVIEW

Name _____   Date _____

SYNTHESIZE THE UNIT

In your Evidence Notebook, make a concept map, other graphic organizer, or outline using the Study Guides you made for each lesson in this unit. Be sure to use evidence to support your claims.

When synthesizing individual information, remember to follow these general steps:
- Find the central idea of each piece of information.
- Think about the relationships among the central ideas.
- Combine the ideas to come up with a new understanding.

DRIVING QUESTIONS

Look back to the Driving Questions from the opening section of this unit. In your Evidence Notebook, review and revise your previous answers to those questions. Use the evidence you gathered and other observations you made throughout the unit to support your claims.

PRACTICE AND REVIEW

1. According to collision theory, which variables affect the rate of a chemical reaction? Select all correct answers.
   - ☐ **a.** concentration of reactants
   - ☐ **b.** temperature of reaction mixture
   - ☐ **c.** volume of reaction vessel
   - ☐ **d.** chemical structure of the reactants
   - ☐ **e.** surface area of a solid reactant

2. Complete the statement about acids and bases.

   Acids form aqueous solutions containing excess hydronium | hydroxide ions, and bases form solutions containing excess hydronium | hydroxide ions. A neutral solution has a pH that is equal to 0 | 1 | 7 | 10. When crushed limestone is added to a lake that has become acidic, the limestone causes a decrease | an increase in pH as acid is neutralized.

3. Consider the equilibrium reaction:

   $$CO(g) + 3H_2(g) \rightleftharpoons CH_4(g) + H_2O(g) + energy$$

   How will increasing the temperature affect the equilibrium of the reaction?
   - ○ **a.** There is more energy available, so the equilibrium shifts toward the products.
   - ○ **b.** The rate of collisions increases, so the equilibrium shifts toward the products.
   - ○ **c.** There are fewer molecules on the left, so the equilibrium shifts toward the reactants.
   - ○ **d.** The rate of the reverse reaction increases, so the equilibrium shifts toward the reactants.

4. Phosphorus pentachloride decomposes into phosphorus trichloride and chlorine. In a closed system, the reaction reaches equilibrium:

   $$PCl_5(g) \rightleftharpoons PCl_3(g) + Cl_2(g)$$

   Complete the statement about the reaction.

   If a sample of pure PCl_5 could be isolated and placed in a closed container, the forward | reverse reaction would begin immediately. Once the system reaches equilibrium, the amount of chlorine gas in the system would remain constant | steadily increase. At equilibrium, the forward and reverse reactions stop completely | continue to occur. In order to produce more PCl_3, the concentration of PCl_5 | Cl_2 could then be increased.

5. An enzyme is a catalyst that is used by an organism to control the reaction rate of biological reactions. Which of these could be a function of an enzyme in a cell? Select all correct answers.
   - ☐ **a.** to cause a reaction to occur at a lower temperature than outside the cell
   - ☐ **b.** to increase the reaction rate of a reaction that would otherwise be too slow for the cell to function
   - ☐ **c.** to shift a reversible reaction in the direction of the products
   - ☐ **d.** to reduce the concentration of reactants needed to form a given amount of products

Synthesize the Unit

Suggest that students begin by writing the titles of the lessons and the explorations in each unit as well as any associated vocabulary. Encourage students to recognize relationships between concepts introduced in different lessons.

Driving Questions

Encourage students to reflect on how their understanding of each question has changed since the start of the unit. Invite students to share with the class ways their understanding has changed.

Practice and Review

SUMMATIVE ASSESSMENT

Answers
1. **DOK 1** a, b, d, e
2. **DOK 1** hydronium, hydroxide, 7, an increase
3. **DOK 2** d
4. **DOK 2** forward, remain constant, continue to occur, PCl_5
5. **DOK 1** a, b

3D Item Analysis	1	2	3	4	5
SEP Constructing Explanations and Designing Solutions	•	•	•	•	•
DCI PS1.B Chemical Reactions	•	•	•	•	•
CCC Patterns	•	•			•
CCC Stability and Change		•	•	•	•

Answers

6. **DOK 2** The activation energy is the amount of energy that must be added to form the activated complex. Therefore, the activation energy must be greater for the endothermic reaction than for the exothermic reverse reaction because the reactants initially have less energy.

7. **DOK 2** The powdered nature of the dry materials provides large surface areas of contact for oxygen, so a spark could initiate a very rapid reaction that could result in an explosion.

8. **DOK 2** The forward reaction in a reversible reaction does not go to completion because the reactants are constantly replenished by the reverse reaction. This happens because the products of the reverse reaction are the reactants of the forward reaction. Although conditions can drive the equilibrium to strongly favor one direction of reaction, the reverse reaction continues even if it is at a slow rate.

9. **DOK 2 Sample answer:** Even though the catalyst does not favor one direction of the equilibrium system, it does increase the rate of both reactions. Because the product is removed, the effect of the change is to increase the rate of production because the forward reaction is favored by removal of the product.

3D Item Analysis	6	7	8	9
SEP Constructing Explanations and Designing Solutions	•	•	•	•
DCI PS1.B Chemical Reactions	•	•	•	•
DCI ETS1.B Developing Possible Solutions			•	•
CCC Patterns	•	•		
CCC Stability and Change			•	•

UNIT PRACTICE AND REVIEW

6. Explain how the activation energy and the energy of the activated complex of an endothermic reaction compare to the activation energy and the energy of the activated complex of an exothermic reaction.

_____

_____

_____

_____

7. Explain why there is a danger of explosion in places—such as coal mines, sawmills, and grain elevators—where large amounts of dry, powdered, combustible materials are present.

_____

_____

_____

_____

8. In a reversible reaction, the forward and reverse reactions both occur. Why does the forward reaction in an equilibrium system never go to completion? Explain in terms of reactants and products.

_____

_____

_____

_____

9. In a manufacturing process, the product of the forward reaction is continually removed. A catalyst is added, increasing the rates of both the forward and reverse reaction. How will adding a catalyst affect production during the process?

_____

_____

_____

_____

UNIT PROJECT

Return to your unit project. Prepare a presentation using your research and materials, and share it with the class. In your final presentation, evaluate the strength of your original claim, data, analysis, and conclusions.

Remember these tips while presenting:

- Include a clear statement explaining how equilibrium is controlled in the Solvay process.

- Use graphics or multimedia tools to explain how the Solvay process can be optimized to increase the amount of sodium carbonate produced.

- Include criteria and constraints that drive process decisions about optimizing the amount of product produced.

- Incorporate the concepts of stability and change in your explanation of processes.

Resources

Explore Online ▶ Because High School students are accustomed to looking up information online, the Interactive Glossary for *HMH Science Dimensions Chemistry* is provided on *Ed: Your Friend in Learning.*

Integrating Reading and Science Instruction

Integrating reading and science instruction through the use of literature can enhance and enrich students' science experiments. Informational and fictional books can be used to supplement and support science instruction, while reinforcing reading comprehension, skills, and practice.

These resources can help engage students before or after science explorations, as well as help reinforce information students have gained during their explorations, answer any questions they have encountered, and also spark new questions that can be answered through research.

Literature circles are one way to engage students in science-based learning. Visiting the media center in your school is a great way to start. Students can review how to search for books using key terms and search engines.

The following list compiles some trade books that align with the Next Generation Science Standards and the units in **HMH Science Dimensions® Chemistry.**

As with all the materials you share with your class, we suggest that you review the books first to ensure their appropriateness. While titles are available at the time of publication, they may go out of print without notice.

Unit 1 Introduction to Chemistry and Engineering

Invention by Design: How Engineers Get from Thought to Thing by Petroski, Henry (Harvard University Press)

To Explain the World: The Discovery of Modern Science by Weinberg, Steven (Harper Perennial)

Unit 2 Atoms and Elements

The Disappearing Spoon: And Other True Tales of Madness, Love, and the History of the World from the Periodic Table of the Elements by Kean, Sam (Back Bay Books)

Periodic Tales: A Cultural History of the Elements, from Arsenic to Zinc by Aldersley-Williams, Hugh (Ecco)

Linus Pauling: Advancing Science, Advocating Peace by Pasachoff, Naomi (Enslow Publishers)

Marie Curie: The Woman Who Changed the Course of Science by Steele, Phillip (National Geographic Children's Books)

The Periodic Table, Levi, Primo (Everyman's Library Contemporary Classics Series)

The Elements: A Visual Exploration of Every Known Atom in the Universe Gray, Theodore (Running Press Book Publishers)

The Atom: A Visual Tour by Challoner, Jack (MIT Press)

Atom Land: A Guided Tour Through the Strange (and Impossibly Small) World of Particle Physics by Butterworth, Jon (The Experiment)

The Periodic Kingdom: A Journey Into the Land of the Chemical Elements by Atkins, P.W. (Basic Books)

Uncle Tungsten: Memories of a Chemical Boyhood by Sacks, Oliver (Knopf Doubleday)

A Force of Nature: The Frontier Genius of Ernest Rutherford (Great Discoveries) by Reeves, Richard (W. W. Norton)

Unit 3 Compounds and Mixtures

Headstrong: 52 Women Who Changed Science—and the World by Swaby, Rachel (Broadway Books)

Caesar's Last Breath: Decoding the Secrets of the Air Around Us by Kean, Sam (Little, Brown and Company)

Molecules: The Elements and the Architecture of Everything by Gray, Theodore (Running Press Book Publishers)

Napoleon's Buttons: How 17 Molecules Changed History by Le Couteur, Penny and Burreson, Jan (Penguin)

Percy Lavon Julian: Pioneering Chemist by Stille, Darlene Ruth (Capstone Press)

Unit 4 Chemical Reactions

A Universe from Nothing: Why There is Something Rather Than Nothing by Krauss, Lawrence M. (Atria Books)

Rockets by Miller, Ron (Twenty-First Century Books)

Reactions: An Illustrated Exploration of Elements, Molecules, and Change in the Universe Gray, Theodore (Running Press Book Publishers)

That's the Way the Cookie Crumbles: 62 All-New Commentaries on the Fascinating Chemistry of Everyday Life by Schwarcz, Joe (ECW Press)

Dr. Joe and What You Didn't Know: 177 Fascinating Questions about the Chemistry of Everyday Life by Schwarcz, Joe (ECW Press)

Caveman Chemistry by Dunn, Kevin (Universal Publishers)

Unit 5 Reaction Rates and Equilibrium

Culinary Reactions: The Everyday Chemistry of Cooking by Field, Simon Quellen (Chicago Review Press)

What Einstein Told His Cook: Kitchen Science Explained by Wolke, Robert (W. W. Norton & Company)

The Alchemy of Air: A Jewish Genius, A Doomed Tycoon, and the Scientific Discovery that Fed the World but Fueled the Rise of Hitler by Hager, Thomas (Crown/Archetype)

Master Mind: The Rise and Fall of Fritz Haber, the Nobel Laureate Who Launched the Age of Chemical Warfare by Charles, Daniel (HarperCollins)

Rust: The Longest War by Waldman, Jonathan (Simon & Schuster)

Common Core State Standards: English Language Arts and Literacy in History/Social Studies, Science, and Technical Subjects

 A correlation to the Next Generation Science Standards is located in the front of this Teacher Edition. Correlations to the *Common Core State Standards for English Language Arts and Literacy in History/Social Studies, Science, and Technical Subjects* are provided on these pages.

HMH Science Dimensions Chemistry	Page References
SL.11-12.5 Make strategic use of digital media (e.g., textual, graphical, audio, visual, and interactive elements) in presentations to enhance understanding of findings, reasoning, and evidence and to add interest.	**Student Edition** Unit 3 Lesson 1 p. 165 Unit 4 Lesson 3 pp. 287, 295 **Teacher Edition** Unit 3 Lesson 1 p. 165 Unit 4 Lesson 3 p. 287
RST.9-10.7 Translate quantitative or technical information expressed in words in a text into visual form (e.g., a table or chart) and translate information expressed visually or mathematically (e.g., in an equation) into words.	**Student Edition** Unit 1 Lesson 2 p. 33 Unit 2 Lesson 1 p. 67 Unit 2 Lesson 2 p. 87, 91, 93, 96, 98 **Teacher Edition** Unit 2 Lesson 1 p. 67 Unit 2 Lesson 2 p. 98

HMH Science Dimensions Chemistry	Page References
RST.11-12.1 Cite specific textual evidence to support analysis of science and technical texts, attending to important distinctions the author makes and to any gaps or inconsistencies in the account.	**Student Edition** Unit 3 Lesson 2 p. 176 Unit 4 Lesson 2 p. 264 Unit 4 Lesson 3 p. 275 Unit 5 Lesson 1 pp. 323, 327 Unit 5 Lesson 2 p. 341 **Teacher Edition** Unit 3 Lesson 2 p. 189 Unit 3 Lesson 3 p. 210 Unit 4 Lesson 3 p. 275 Unit 5 Project pp. 307J–307K
RST.11-12.7 Integrate and evaluate multiple sources of information presented in diverse formats and media (e.g., quantitative data, video, multimedia) in order to address a question or solve a problem.	**Student Edition** Unit 1 Project pp. 1H–1I Unit 1 Lesson 2 p. 41 Unit 1 Connections p. 45 Unit 2 Lesson 3 p. 125 Unit 2 Connections p. 129 Unit 3 Lesson 2 p. 191 Unit 4 Lesson 3 pp. 292, 294 Unit 5 Lesson 3 p. 377 **Teacher Edition** Unit 1 Lesson 2 pp. 29, 33 Unit 5 Project pp. 307J–307K

HMH Science Dimensions Chemistry	Page References
RST.11-12.8 Evaluate the hypotheses, data, analysis, and conclusions in a science or technical text, verifying the data when possible and corroborating or challenging conclusions with other sources of information.	**Student Edition** Unit 1 Connections p. 45 Unit 1 Performance Task p. 50 Unit 2 Connections p. 129 Unit 3 Performance Task p. 224 Unit 5 Lesson 3 p. 368 **Teacher Edition** Unit 3 Project pp. 141J–141K Unit 4 Project pp. 227I–227J Unit 5 Project pp. 307J–307K Unit 5 Lesson 3 p. 368
RST.11-12.9 Synthesize information from a range of sources (e.g., texts, experiments, simulations) into a coherent understanding of a process, phenomenon, or concept, resolving conflicting information when possible.	**Student Edition** Unit 1 Lesson 2 pp. 33, 41 Unit 1 Connections p. 45 Unit 1 Performance Task p. 50 Unit 2 Connections p. 129 Unit 3 Lesson 3 p. 204 Unit 3 Connections p. 219 Unit 4 Lesson 3 pp. 293, 294 Unit 5 Lesson 1 p. 304 **Teacher Edition** Unit 1 Project pp. 1H–1I Unit 2 Lesson 3 pp. 117, 124 Unit 5 Project pp. 307J–307K

HMH Science Dimensions Chemistry	Page References
WHST.9-12.2 Write informative/explanatory texts, including the narration of historical events, scientific procedures/ experiments, or technical processes.	**Student Edition**
	Unit 1 Project pp. 1H–1I
	Unit 1 Lesson 1 p. 7
	Unit 3 Project pp. 141J–141K
	Unit 3 Lesson 1 p. 153
	Unit 3 Lesson 1 p. 163
	Unit 3 Lesson 3 pp. 202, 219
	Unit 4 Lesson 1 pp. 233, 235
	Unit 4 Lesson 2 p. 269
	Unit 4 Performance Task p. 304
	Unit 5 Lesson 1 pp. 313, 327
	Unit 5 Lesson 2 pp. 335, 349, 350, 355
	Unit 5 Lesson 3 pp. 364, 372, 376
	Unit 5 Connections p. 381
	Unit 5 Performance Task p. 386
	Teacher Edition
	Unit 2 Lesson 2 p. 91
	Unit 3 Lesson 1 pp. 153, 154
	Unit 4 Lesson 1 p. 234
	Unit 4 Lesson 2 pp. 257, 269
	Unit 5 Project pp. 307J–307K
	Unit 5 Lesson 1 p. 320

HMH Science Dimensions Chemistry	Page References
WHST.9-12.5 Develop and strengthen writing as needed by planning, revising, editing, rewriting, or trying a new approach, focusing on addressing what is most significant for a specific purpose and audience.	**Student Edition** Unit 2 Lesson 1 p. 79 Unit 4 Lesson 1 p. 238 **Teacher Edition** Unit 1 Project pp. 1H–1I Unit 2 Lesson 1 p. 79 Unit 4 Project pp. 227I–227J
WHST.9-12.7 Conduct short as well as more sustained research projects to answer a question (including a self-generated question) or solve a problem; narrow or broaden the inquiry when appropriate; synthesize multiple sources on the subject, demonstrating understanding of the subject under investigation.	**Student Edition** Unit 1 Lesson 1 p. 18 Unit 1 Performance Task p. 50 Unit 2 Lesson 2 p. 99 Unit 3 Lesson 2 p. 188 Unit 3 Lesson 3 pp. 201, 215 Unit 3 Performance Task p. 224 Unit 4 Lesson 3 p. 292 Unit 5 Lesson 2 pp. 341, 355 Unit 5 Lesson 3 pp. 376, 377 Unit 5 Performance Task p. 386 **Teacher Edition** Unit 1 Lesson 1 p. 19 Unit 2 Lesson 2 p. 99 Unit 3 Project pp. 141J–141K Unit 3 Lesson 2 pp. 176, 188 Unit 4 Project pp. 227I–227J Unit 5 Project pp. 307J–307K Unit 5 Lesson 2 p. 354 Unit 5 Lesson 3 p. 376

HMH Science Dimensions Chemistry	Page References
WHST.11-12.8 Gather relevant information from multiple authoritative print and digital sources, using advanced searches effectively; assess the strengths and limitations of each source in terms of the specific task, purpose, and audience; integrate information into the text selectively to maintain the flow of ideas, avoiding plagiarism and overreliance on any one source and following a standard format for citation.	**Student Edition** Unit 1 Lesson 1 p. 18 Unit 3 Lesson 1 p. 158 Unit 4 Lesson 3 p. 292 Unit 4 Connections p. 299 **Teacher Edition** Unit 1 Lesson 2 p. 29 Unit 3 Project pp. 141J–141K Unit 3 Lesson 1 p. 158 Unit 4 Project pp. 227I–227J
WHST.9-12.9 Draw evidence from informational texts to support analysis, reflection, and research.	**Student Edition** Unit 1 Lesson 1 p. 18 Unit 1 Performance Task p. 50 Unit 3 Lesson 2 p. 188 Unit 3 Lesson 3 pp. 204, 210, 215 Unit 3 Connections p. 219 Unit 3 Performance Task p. 224 Unit 4 Lesson 2 p. 257 Unit 4 Lesson 3 p. 292 Unit 4 Connections p. 299 **Teacher Edition** Unit 1 Project pp. 1H–1I Unit 1 Lesson 2 p. 41 Unit 2 Lesson 2 p. 99 Unit 3 Project pp. 141J–141K Unit 3 Lesson 3 pp. 208, 215 Unit 4 Lesson 3 p. 291

Common Core State Standards: Mathematics

 A correlation to the Next Generation Science Standards is located in the front of this Teacher Edition. Correlations to the *Common Core State: Mathematics* are provided on these pages.

HMH Science Dimensions Chemistry	Page References
MP.2 Reason abstractly and quantitatively.	**Student Edition**
	Unit 2 Lesson 1 pp. 66, 68
	Unit 2 Lesson 3 pp. 106–110, 115
	Unit 3 Lesson 1 p. 160
	Unit 3 Lesson 2 p. 172
	Unit 3 Performance Task p. 224
	Unit 4 Lesson 1 pp. 233, 236, 238–240, 243, 249
	Unit 4 Lesson 2 pp. 254, 255, 257–261, 263, 264, 267, 268
	Unit 4 Lesson 3 pp. 277–279, 287, 290
	Unit 5 Lesson 1 pp. 314–317, 320
	Unit 5 Lesson 2 pp. 333, 338, 340, 353
	Teacher Edition
	Unit 1 Lesson 1 p. 10
	Unit 1 Lesson 2 pp. 32, 38
	Unit 2 Project pp. 53I–53J
	Unit 2 Lesson 1 p. 68
	Unit 3 Lesson 3 p. 209
	Unit 4 Project pp. 227I–227J
	Unit 4 Lesson 1 pp. 239, 242
	Unit 4 Lesson 2 pp. 255, 257, 260–261
	Unit 4 Lesson 3 p. 275
	Unit 5 Project pp. 307J–307K
	Unit 5 Lesson 1 p. 326
	Unit 5 Lesson 2 p. 334
	Unit 5 Lesson 3 p. 374

HMH Science Dimensions Chemistry	Page References
MP.4 Model with mathematics.	**Student Edition** Unit 2 Lesson 3 pp. 106–110, 114, 115 Unit 3 Lesson 2 p. 172 Unit 4 Lesson 3 pp. 275, 287 Unit 5 Lesson 1 p. 325 Unit 5 Lesson 2 pp. 333, 338, 341, 353 **Teacher Edition** Unit 2 Project pp. 53I–53J Unit 2 Lesson 2 p. 97 Unit 2 Lesson 3 pp. 106–110, 114, 115 Unit 3 Lesson 2 p. 172 Unit 4 Project pp. 227I–227J Unit 4 Lesson 3 pp. 275, 287 Unit 5 Project pp. 307J–307K Unit 5 Lesson 1 p. 325 Unit 5 Lesson 2 pp. 333, 338, 341, 353
HSN-Q.A.1 Use units as a way to understand problems and to guide the solution of multi-step problems; choose and interpret units consistently in formulas; choose and interpret the scale and the origin in graphs and data displays.	**Student Edition** Unit 1 Performance Task p. 50 Unit 2 Lesson 3 pp. 113, 114 Unit 3 Lesson 2 pp. 182, 183 Unit 4 Lesson 2 pp. 254, 255, 257, 258, 260, 264, 267, 268 Unit 4 Lesson 3 pp. 275, 281, 287 Unit 5 Lesson 1 pp. 312, 320, 326 Unit 5 Lesson 2 p. 333 **Teacher Edition** Unit 3 Lesson 2 p. 182 Unit 4 Project pp. 227I–227J Unit 4 Lesson 3 pp. 275, 281, 287 Unit 5 Lesson 1 pp. 312, 320, 326 Unit 5 Lesson 2 p. 348

HMH Science Dimensions Chemistry	**Page References**
HSN-Q.A.2 Define appropriate quantities for the purpose of descriptive modeling.	**Student Edition** Unit 2 Lesson 3 pp. 108–110, 115, 117 Unit 4 Lesson 1 pp. 239, 240 **Teacher Edition** Unit 2 Project pp. 53I–53J Unit 2 Lesson 3 p. 113 Unit 4 Project pp. 227I–227J
HSN-Q.A.3 Choose a level of accuracy appropriate to limitations on measurement when reporting quantities.	**Student Edition** Unit 1 Performance Task p. 50 Unit 3 Lesson 1 p. 147 Unit 3 Lesson 2 pp. 182, 183, 184 Unit 3 Lesson 3 pp. 202, 203 Unit 3 Performance Task p. 224 Unit 4 Lesson 1 pp. 233, 235 Unit 4 Lesson 3 p. 281 Unit 5 Lesson 1 p. 321 **Teacher Edition** Unit 4 Project pp. 227I–227J

Index

Page numbers for definitions are printed in **boldface** type.
Page numbers for illustrations, maps, and charts are printed in *italics*.

Index

Index

Index

Index

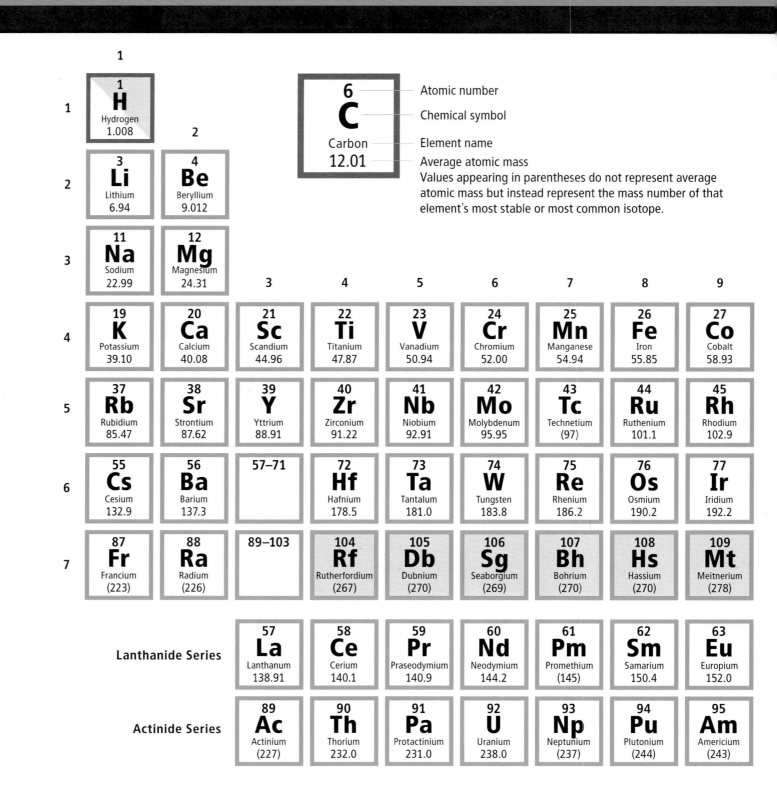

1

1
H
Hydrogen
1.008

2

3
Li
Lithium
6.94

4
Be
Beryllium
9.012

11
Na
Sodium
22.99

12
Mg
Magnesium
24.31

6
C
Carbon
12.01

Atomic number
Chemical symbol
Element name
Average atomic mass
Values appearing in parentheses do not represent average atomic mass but instead represent the mass number of that element's most stable or most common isotope.

3	4	5	6	7	8	9

19 **K** Potassium 39.10
20 **Ca** Calcium 40.08
21 **Sc** Scandium 44.96
22 **Ti** Titanium 47.87
23 **V** Vanadium 50.94
24 **Cr** Chromium 52.00
25 **Mn** Manganese 54.94
26 **Fe** Iron 55.85
27 **Co** Cobalt 58.93

37 **Rb** Rubidium 85.47
38 **Sr** Strontium 87.62
39 **Y** Yttrium 88.91
40 **Zr** Zirconium 91.22
41 **Nb** Niobium 92.91
42 **Mo** Molybdenum 95.95
43 **Tc** Technetium (97)
44 **Ru** Ruthenium 101.1
45 **Rh** Rhodium 102.9

55 **Cs** Cesium 132.9
56 **Ba** Barium 137.3
57–71
72 **Hf** Hafnium 178.5
73 **Ta** Tantalum 181.0
74 **W** Tungsten 183.8
75 **Re** Rhenium 186.2
76 **Os** Osmium 190.2
77 **Ir** Iridium 192.2

87 **Fr** Francium (223)
88 **Ra** Radium (226)
89–103
104 **Rf** Rutherfordium (267)
105 **Db** Dubnium (270)
106 **Sg** Seaborgium (269)
107 **Bh** Bohrium (270)
108 **Hs** Hassium (270)
109 **Mt** Meitnerium (278)

Lanthanide Series
57 **La** Lanthanum 138.91
58 **Ce** Cerium 140.1
59 **Pr** Praseodymium 140.9
60 **Nd** Neodymium 144.2
61 **Pm** Promethium (145)
62 **Sm** Samarium 150.4
63 **Eu** Europium 152.0

Actinide Series
89 **Ac** Actinium (227)
90 **Th** Thorium 232.0
91 **Pa** Protactinium 231.0
92 **U** Uranium 238.0
93 **Np** Neptunium (237)
94 **Pu** Plutonium (244)
95 **Am** Americium (243)

18

| Metals | Metalloids | Nonmetals |

State of Element at STP

☐ Solid ☐ Liquid

☐ Gas ☐ Not yet known

			13	**14**	**15**	**16**	**17**	**18**
								2 **He** Helium 4.003
			5 **B** Boron 10.81	6 **C** Carbon 12.01	7 **N** Nitrogen 14.007	8 **O** Oxygen 15.999	9 **F** Fluorine 19.00	10 **Ne** Neon 20.18
10	**11**	**12**	13 **Al** Aluminum 26.98	14 **Si** Silicon 28.085	15 **P** Phosphorus 30.97	16 **S** Sulfur 32.06	17 **Cl** Chlorine 35.45	18 **Ar** Argon 39.95
28 **Ni** Nickel 58.69	29 **Cu** Copper 63.55	30 **Zn** Zinc 65.38	31 **Ga** Gallium 69.72	32 **Ge** Germanium 72.63	33 **As** Arsenic 74.92	34 **Se** Selenium 79.0	35 **Br** Bromine 79.90	36 **Kr** Krypton 83.80
46 **Pd** Palladium 106.4	47 **Ag** Silver 107.9	48 **Cd** Cadmium 112.4	49 **In** Indium 114.8	50 **Sn** Tin 118.7	51 **Sb** Antimony 121.8	52 **Te** Tellurium 127.6	53 **I** Iodine 126.9	54 **Xe** Xenon 131.3
78 **Pt** Platinum 195.1	79 **Au** Gold 197.0	80 **Hg** Mercury 200.6	81 **Tl** Thallium 204.38	82 **Pb** Lead 207.2	83 **Bi** Bismuth 209.0	84 **Po** Polonium (209)	85 **At** Astatine (210)	86 **Rn** Radon (222)
110 **Ds** Darmstadtium (281)	111 **Rg** Roentgenium (281)	112 **Cn** Copernicium (285)	113 **Nh** Nihonium (286)	114 **Fl** Flerovium (289)	115 **Mc** Moscovium (289)	116 **Lv** Livermorium (293)	117 **Ts** Tennessine (293)	118 **Og** Oganesson (294)

64 **Gd** Gadolinium 157.3	65 **Tb** Terbium 158.9	66 **Dy** Dysprosium 162.5	67 **Ho** Holmium 164.9	68 **Er** Erbium 167.3	69 **Tm** Thulium 168.9	70 **Yb** Ytterbium 173.1	71 **Lu** Lutetium 175.0
96 **Cm** Curium (247)	97 **Bk** Berkelium (247)	98 **Cf** Californium (251)	99 **Es** Einsteinium (252)	100 **Fm** Fermium (257)	101 **Md** Mendelevium (258)	102 **No** Nobelium (259)	103 **Lr** Lawrencium (262)

Elements with atomic numbers of 95 and above are not known to occur naturally, even in trace amounts. They have only been synthesized in the lab. The physical and chemical properties of elements with atomic numbers 100 and above cannot be predicted with certainty.